A Complete Course
in
CALCULUS

SERGE LANG

Columbia University, New York, New York

ADDISON-WESLEY PUBLISHING COMPANY

Reading, Massachusetts · Menlo Park, California · London · Don Mills, Ontario

This book is in the

ADDISON-WESLEY SERIES IN MATHEMATICS

LYNN H. LOOMIS
Consulting Editor

Foreword to the First Course

The purpose of a first course in Calculus is to teach the student the basic notions of derivative and integral, and the basic techniques and applications which accompany them.

At present in the United States, this material is covered during the first year of college. In fact, the material should be taught to students who are approximately fifteen years of age, and belongs properly in the secondary schools. (I have talked with several students of that age, and find them perfectly able to understand what it is all about.)

Irrespective of when it is taught, I believe that the presentation remains more or less invariant. The very talented student, with an obvious aptitude for mathematics, will rapidly require a course in functions of one real variable, more or less as it is understood by professional mathematicians. This book is not primarily addressed to him (although I hope he will be able to acquire from it a good introduction at an early age).

I have not written this course in the style I would use for an advanced monograph, on sophisticated topics. One writes an advanced monograph for oneself, because one wants to give permanent form to one's vision of some beautiful part of mathematics, not otherwise accessible, somewhat in the manner of a composer setting down his symphony in musical notation.

This book is written for the student, to give him an immediate, and pleasant, access to the subject. I hope that I have struck a proper compromise between dwelling too much on special details, and not giving enough technical exercises, necessary to acquire the desired familiarity with the subject. In any case, certain routine habits of sophisticated mathematicians are unsuitable for a first course.

This does not mean that so-called rigor has to be abandoned. The logical development of the mathematics of this course from the most basic axioms proceeds through the following stages:

Set theory   Limits
Integers (whole numbers)   Derivatives
Rational numbers (fractions)   and forward.
Numbers (i.e. real numbers)

iii

No one in his right mind suggests that one should begin a course with set theory. It happens that the most satisfactory place to jump into the subject is between limits and derivatives. In other words, any student is ready to accept as intuitively obvious the notions of numbers and limits and their basic properties. For some reason, it has become fashionable to hold that the best place to enter the subject is between numbers and limits. Experience shows that the students do *not* have the proper psychological background to accept this, and resist it tremendously.

In fact, it turns out that one can have the best of both ideas. The arguments which show how the properties of limits can be reduced to those of numbers form a self-contained whole. Logically, it belongs *before* the subject matter of our course. Nevertheless, we have inserted it as an appendix (p. 293). If any student feels the need for it, he need but read it and visualize it as Chapter 0. In that case, everything that follows is as rigorous as any mathematician would wish it (so far as objects which receive an analytic definition are concerned). Not one word need be changed in any proof. I hope this takes care once and for all of possible controversies concerning so-called rigor.

Some objects receive a geometric definition, and there are applications to physical concepts. In that case, it is of course necessary to insert one step to bridge the physical notion and its mathematical counterpart. The major instances of this are the functions sine and cosine, and the area, as an integral.

For sine and cosine, we rely on the notions of plane geometry. If one accepts standard theorems concerning plane figures then our proofs satisfy the above-mentioned standards. An appendix shows how one can give purely analytic definitions and proofs for the basic properties.

For the integral, we first give a geometric argument. We then show, using the usual Riemann sums, how this geometric argument has a perfect counterpart when we require the rules of the game to reduce all definitions and proofs to numbers. This should satisfy everybody. Furthermore, the theory of the integral is so presented that only its existence depends either on a geometric argument or a slightly involved theoretical investigation (upper and lower sums). According to the level of ability of a class, the teacher may therefore dose the theory according to his judgment.

It is not generally recognized that some of the major difficulties in teaching mathematics are analogous to those in teaching a foreign language. (The secondary schools are responsible for this. Proper training in the secondary schools could entirely eliminate this difficulty.) Consequently, I have made great efforts to carry the student verbally, so to say, in using proper mathematical language. Some proofs are omitted. For instance, they would be of the following type. In the theory of maxima and minima, or increasing and decreasing functions, we carry out in full just one of the cases. The other is left as an exercise. The changes needed in the proof are slight, amounting mainly to the insertion of an occasional minus sign, but they force the student to understand the situation and train him in writing clearly. This is very valuable. Aside from that, such an omission allows the teacher to put greater emphasis on certain topics, if necessary, by carrying out the other proof himself. As in learning languages, repetition is one of the fundamental tools, and a certain amount of mechanical learning, as distinguished from logical thinking, is both healthy and necessary.

I have made no great innovations in the exposition of calculus. Since the subject was discovered some 300 years ago, it was out of the question. Rather, I have omitted some specialized topics which no longer belong in the curriculum. Stirling's formula is included only for reference, and can be skipped, or used to provide exercises. Taylor's formula is proved with the integral form of the remainder, which is then properly estimated. The proof with integration by parts is more natural than the other (differentiating some complicated expression pulled out of nowhere), and is the one which generalizes to the higher dimensional case. I have placed integration after differentiation, because otherwise one has no technique available to evaluate integrals. But on the whole, everything is fairly standard.

I have cut down the amount of analytic geometry to what is both necessary and sufficient for a general first course in this type of mathematics. For some applications, more is required, but these applications are fairly specialized. For instance, if one needs the special properties concerning the focus of a parabola in a course on optics, then that is the place to present them, not in a general course which is to serve mathematicians, physicists, chemists, biologists, and engineers, to mention but a few. I regard the tremendous emphasis on the analytic geometry of conics which has been the fashion for many years as an unfortunate historical accident. What is important is that the basic idea of representing a graph by a figure in the plane should be thoroughly understood, together with basic examples. The more abstruse properties of ellipses, parabolas, and hyperbolas should be skipped.

One other word—of a quite different nature. I disliked calculus and analysis when I was a student. I would have disliked the book I am writing now. It was only later in my life as a mathematician, that I began to appreciate the beauty of calculus. But I found out in the meantime that calculus and analysis are overemphasized at the expense of algebra, mostly through historical accidents. In fact, it is clear that elementary algebra courses (covering groups and vector spaces) should be available much earlier than they are. There are strong indications from physics, biology, and economics that they should receive greater attention at an elementary level than they have up to now. Since algebra is logically independent of calculus (at the early levels), has important applications, and to some minds, has a much greater appeal than calculus (it was like this for me) I would hope that the unbalance of the present programs will soon be changed. There is no reason why a student should be forced to take calculus before he takes an algebra course. This is particularly true at the moment for the more talented students.

An excess in this direction would be as disturbing as in the other. There is no point in replacing old specialized topics by new ones, and the attempts to replace old outdated and musty subjects by new outdated and musty subjects (like boolean algebra) is not to be recommended.

To conclude, if I may be allowed another personal note here, I learned how to teach the present course from Artin, the year I wrote my Doctor's thesis. I could not have had a better introduction to the subject.

SERGE LANG
New York, 1963

Foreword to the Second Course

This volume is a continuation of a *First Course in Calculus,* and deals principally with functions of several variables.

The first chapter (p. 317) deals with vectors in n-space. This chapter covers enough linear algebra to be applied to the next six chapters (up to and including Chapter VII (p. 426)). We then take up more of the basic linear algebra (vector spaces, matrices, linear maps, determinants) to be able to apply this material to functions of several variables, viewing the derivative as a linear map. The applications include the chain rule, and the implicit function theorem, whose proof is based on the inverse mapping theorem. A proof for the latter requires techniques which belong to a more advanced analysis course. We also apply the linear algebra to multiple integrals, discussing the determinant as area (in the 2-dimensional case) and as volume in the higher dimensional case. We then discuss orthogonality, showing how the theory of orthogonality in n-space has the same algebraic foundations as the theory of Fourier series.

We end the book with a first introduction to normed vector spaces, and the (ϵ, δ) language of limits in this context. Such an introduction will be especially useful to students who go on to an advanced calculus course (essentially a first course in analysis), because having seen the (ϵ, δ) previously makes it much easier to assimilate the basic routine of limits, and then go on to more interesting material.

At present, still few students have had linear algebra before the calculus. Hence we developed it systematically, but not exhaustively, to cover what was needed. More complete accounts are easily available. For use in the present book, the reader may omit the treatment of determinants other than in the 2×2- and 3×3- case.

Serge Lang
New York, 1968

vii

To the Second and Complete Editions

The present combined edition of both courses in calculus will provide more flexibility concerning the arrangement of topics. For instance, some instructors may want to cover vectors before series, even though in our arrangement matters dealing with several variables are grouped into the *Second Course*. Combining the two courses in one volume thickens the book, but before the reader complains about this extended size, he should realize that a considerable amount of material has been included, for instance a good introduction to the basic notions of linear algebra (vector spaces, dimension, determinants). With this in mind, I believe one of the original intents of these courses, which was to do away with topics which have hung on through bad habits, has been preserved.

I have added many new exercises and examples because of complaints concerning the lack of them in the first edition. I have also rewritten a few passages to make them clearer, following public requests.

SERGE LANG
New York, 1968

Contents

First Course

CHAPTER I

Numbers and Functions

CHAPTER II

Graphs and Curves

CHAPTER III

The Derivative

Chapter IV

Sine and Cosine

Chapter V

The Mean Value Theorem

Chapter VI

Sketching Curves

Chapter VII

Inverse Functions

Chapter XII

Some Substantial Exercises

Chapter XIII

Applications of Integration

Chapter XIV

Taylor's Formula

Second Course

Chapter I

Vectors

Chapter II

Differentiation of Vectors

Chapter III

Functions of Several Variables

Chapter IV

The Chain Rule and the Gradient

CHAPTER XVII

ϵ and δ

First Course

Chapter I

Numbers and Functions

In starting the study of any sort of mathematics, we cannot prove everything. Every time that we introduce a new concept, we must define it in terms of a concept whose meaning is already known to us, and it is impossible to keep going backwards defining forever. Thus we must choose our starting place, what we assume to be known, and what we are willing to explain and prove in terms of these assumptions.

At the beginning of this chapter, we shall describe most of the things which we assume known for this course. Actually, this involves very little. Roughly speaking, we assume that you know about numbers, addition, subtraction, multiplication, and division (by numbers other than 0). We shall recall the properties of inequalities (when a number is greater than another). On a few occasions we shall take for granted certain properties of numbers which might not have occurred to you before and which will always be made precise. Proofs of these properties will be supplied in the appendix for those of you who are interested.

§1. INTEGERS, RATIONAL NUMBERS, AND REAL NUMBERS

The most common numbers are the numbers 1, 2, 3, . . . which are called *positive integers.*

The numbers $-1, -2, -3, -4, \ldots$ are called *negative integers.* When we want to speak of the positive integers together with the negative integers and 0, we call them simply *integers.* Thus the integers are 0, 1, $-1, 2, -2, 3, -3, \ldots$.

The sum and product of two integers are again integers.

In addition to the integers we have *fractions*, like $\frac{3}{4}$, $\frac{5}{7}$, $-\frac{1}{8}$, $-\frac{101}{27}$, $\frac{8}{16}$, . . . , which may be positive or negative, and which can be written as quotients m/n, where m, n are integers and n is not equal to 0. Such fractions are called *rational numbers.* Every integer m is a rational number, because it can be written as $m/1$, but of course it is not true that every rational number is an integer. We observe that the sum and product of two rational numbers are again rational numbers. If a/b and m/n are two rational numbers (a, b, m, n being integers and b, n unequal to 0), then their sum and product are given by the following formulas, which

1

you know from elementary school:

$$\frac{a}{b}\frac{m}{n} = \frac{am}{bn},$$

$$\frac{a}{b} + \frac{m}{n} = \frac{an + bm}{bn}.$$

In this second formula, we have simply put the two fractions over the common denominator bn.

We can represent the integers and rational numbers geometrically on a straight line. We first select a unit length. The integers are multiples of this unit, and the rational numbers are fractional parts of this unit. We have drawn a few rational numbers on the line below.

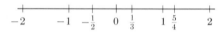

Observe that the negative integers and rational numbers occur to the left of zero.

Finally, we have the numbers which can be represented by infinite decimals, like $\sqrt{2} = 1.414...$ or $\pi = 3.14159...$, and which will be called *real numbers* or simply *numbers*.

Geometrically, the numbers are represented as the collection of all points on the above straight line, not only those which are a rational part of the unit length or a multiple of it.

We note that the sum and product of two numbers are numbers. If a is a number unequal to zero, then there is a unique number b such that $ab = ba = 1$, and we write

$$b = \frac{1}{a} \quad \text{or} \quad b = a^{-1}.$$

We say that b is the *inverse* of a, or "a inverse". We emphasize that the expression

$1/0$ or 0^{-1} is not defined.

In other words, we cannot divide by zero, and we do not attribute any meaning to the symbols $1/0$ or 0^{-1}.

However, if a is a number then the product $0 \cdot a$ is defined and is equal to 0. The product of any number and 0 is 0. Furthermore, if b is any number unequal to 0, then $0/b$ is defined and equal to 0. It can also be written $0 \cdot (1/b)$.

If a is a rational number $\neq 0$, then $1/a$ is also a rational number. Indeed, if we can write $a = m/n$, with integers m, n both different from 0, then

$$\frac{1}{a} = \frac{n}{m}$$

is also a rational number.

Not all numbers are rational numbers. *For instance, $\sqrt{2}$ is not a rational number*, and we shall now prove this fact.

We recall that the *even numbers* are the integers $\pm 2, \pm 4, \pm 6, \pm 8, \ldots$, which can be written in the form $2n$ for some integer n. An *odd* number is an integer like $\pm 1, \pm 3, \pm 5, \pm 7, \ldots$, which can be written in the form $2n + 1$ for some integer n. Thus $6 = 2 \cdot 3$ is even (we select $n = 3$) and

$$11 = 2 \cdot 5 + 1$$

is odd (we select $n = 5$).

We observe that the square of an even number is even. Indeed, if n is an integer and $2n$ is an even number, then

$$(2n)^2 = 4n^2$$

is an even number, which can be written $2(2n^2)$, the product of 2 and the integer $2n^2$.

The square of an odd number is odd. To prove this, let $2n + 1$ be an odd number (n being an integer). Then its square is

$$(2n + 1)^2 = 4n^2 + 4n + 1$$
$$= 2(2n^2 + 2n) + 1.$$

Since $2n^2 + 2n$ is an integer, we have written the square of our odd number in the form $2m + 1$ for some integer m, and thus have shown that our square is odd.

We are now ready to prove that the square root of 2 is not a rational number. Suppose it were. This would mean that we can find a rational number a such that $a^2 = 2$. We can write

$$a = \frac{m}{n},$$

where m, n are integers, and neither m nor n is 0. Furthermore, we can assume that not both m, n are even because we can put the fraction m/n in lowest form and cancel as many powers of 2 dividing both m and n as possible. Thus we can assume that at least one of the integers m or n is odd.

From our assumption that $a^2 = 2$ we get $(m/n)^2 = 2$ or

$$\frac{m^2}{n^2} = 2.$$

Multiplying both sides of this equation by n^2 yields

$$m^2 = 2n^2$$

and the right-hand side is even. By what we saw above, this means that m is even and we can therefore write $m = 2k$ for some integer k. Substituting, we obtain

$$(2k)^2 = 2n^2$$

or $4k^2 = 2n^2$. We cancel 2 and get $2k^2 = n^2$. This means that n^2 is even, and consequently, by what we saw above, that n is even. Thus we have reached the conclusion that both m, n are even, which contradicts the fact that we put our fraction in lowest form. We can therefore conclude that there was no fraction m/n whose square is 2.

It is usually very difficult to determine whether a given number is a rational number or not. For instance, the fact that π is not rational was discovered only at the end of the 18th century.

§2. INEQUALITIES

Aside from addition, multiplication, subtraction and division (by numbers other than 0), we shall now discuss another important feature of the real numbers.

We have the *positive numbers*, represented geometrically on the straight line by those numbers unequal to 0 and lying to the right of 0. If a is a positive number, we write $a > 0$. You have no doubt already worked with positive numbers, and with inequalities. The next two properties are the most basic ones, concerning positivity.

POS 1. *If a, b are positive, so is the product ab and the sum $a + b$.*

POS 2. *If a is a number, then either a is positive, or $a = 0$, or $-a$ is positive, and these possibilities are mutually exclusive.*

If a number is not positive and not 0, then we say that this number is *negative*. By POS 2, if a is negative then $-a$ is positive.

Although you know already that the number 1 is positive, it can in fact be *proved* from our two properties. It may interest you to see the proof, which runs as follows and is very simple. By POS 2, we know that either 1 or -1 is positive. If 1 is not positive, then -1 is positive. By POS 1, it must then follow that $(-1)(-1)$ is positive. But this product is equal to 1. Consequently, it must be 1 which is positive, and not -1. Using property POS 1, we could now conclude that $1 + 1 = 2$ is positive, that $2 + 1 = 3$ is positive, and so forth.

If $a > 0$ we shall also say that a is *greater than* 0. If we wish to say that a is positive or equal to 0, we write

$$a \geqq 0$$

and read this "a greater than or equal to zero".

Given two numbers a, b we shall say that a is *greater than* b and write $a > b$ if $a - b > 0$. We write $a < 0$ if $-a > 0$ and $a < b$ if $b > a$. Thus $3 > 2$ because $3 - 2 > 0$.

We shall write $a \geqq b$ when we want to say that a is *greater than or equal to b*. Thus $3 \geqq 2$ and $3 \geqq 3$ are both true inequalities.

Using only our two properties POS 1 and POS 2 we shall now prove all the usual rules concerning inequalities. You probably know these already, but proving them systematically will both sharpen your wits and etch these rules more profoundly in your mind.

In what follows, let a, b, c be numbers.

Rule 1. If $a > b$ and $b > c$ then $a > c$.

Rule 2. If $a > b$ and $c > 0$ then $ac > bc$.

Rule 3. If $a > b$ and $c < 0$ then $ac < bc$.

Rule 2 expresses the fact that an inequality which is multiplied by a positive number is *preserved*. Rule 3 tells us that if we multiply both sides of an inequality by a negative number, then the inequality gets *reversed*. For instance, we have the inequality

$$1 < 3.$$

Since $2 > 0$ we also have $2 \cdot 1 < 2 \cdot 3$. But -2 is negative, and if we multiply both sides by -2 we get

$$-2 > -6.$$

In the geometric representation of the real numbers on the line, -2 lies to the right of -6. This gives us the geometric representation of the fact that -2 is greater than -6.

To prove Rule 1, suppose that $a > b$ and $b > c$. By definition, this means that $(a - b) > 0$ and $(b - c) > 0$. Using property POS 1, we conclude that

$$a - b + b - c > 0,$$

and canceling b gives us $(a - c) > 0$. By definition, this means $a > c$, as was to be shown.

To prove Rule 2, suppose that $a > b$ and $c > 0$. By definition,

$$a - b > 0.$$

Hence using the property of POS 1 concerning the product of positive numbers, we conclude that

$$(a - b)c > 0.$$

The left-hand side of this inequality is none other than $ac - bc$, which is therefore > 0. Again by definition, this gives us

$$ac > bc.$$

We leave the proof of Rule 3 as an exercise.

If a is a number, then we define the *absolute value* of a to be:

a itself if a is ≥ 0.

$-a$ if a is < 0.

In the second case, when a is negative, then $-a$ is positive. Thus the absolute value of a number is always a positive number, or 0. For instance, the absolute value of 3 is 3 itself. The absolute value of -3 is $-(-3) = 3$. The absolute value of $-\frac{1}{2}$ is $\frac{1}{2}$. The absolute value of $\sqrt{2}$ is $\sqrt{2}$ and the absolute value of $-\sqrt{2}$ is $\sqrt{2}$. We shall denote the absolute value of a number by two bars beside the number. Thus the absolute value of a number a is written $|a|$. For instance, $|3| = 3$ and $|-3| = 3$ also. We have by definition $|0| = 0$. In general, for any number x we have

$$|x| = |-x|.$$

Let a be a number > 0. Then there exists a number whose square is a. This is one of the facts which we take for granted about numbers. If $b^2 = a$ then we observe that

$$(-b)^2 = b^2$$

is also equal to a. Thus either b or $-b$ is positive. We agree to denote by $\sqrt{a}$ the *positive* square root and call it simply *the square root of a*. Thus $\sqrt{4}$ is equal to 2 and not -2, even though $(-2)^2 = 4$. This is the most practical convention about the use of the $\sqrt{}$ sign that we can make. Of course, the square root of 0 is 0 itself. A negative number does *not* have a square root.

Theorem 1. *If a is a number, then $|a|^2 = a^2$ and*

$$|a| = \sqrt{a^2}.$$

Proof. If a is positive then $|a| = a$ and our first assertion is clear. If a is negative, then $|a| = -a$ and

$$(-a)^2 = a^2,$$

so we again get $|a|^2 = a^2$. When $a = 0$ our first assertion simply means $0 = 0$. Finally, taking the (positive) square root, we get

$$|a| = \sqrt{a^2}.$$

Theorem 2. *If a, b are numbers, then*

$$|ab| = |a|\,|b|.$$

Proof. We have:

$$|ab| = \sqrt{(ab)^2} = \sqrt{a^2 b^2} = \sqrt{a^2}\,\sqrt{b^2} = |a|\,|b|.$$

As an example, we see that

$$|-6| = |(-3) \cdot 2| = |-3|\,|2| = 3 \cdot 2 = 6.$$

There is one final inequality which is extremely important.

Theorem 3. *If a, b are two numbers, then*

$$|a + b| \leq |a| + |b|.$$

Proof. We first observe that either ab is positive, or it is negative, or it is 0. In any case, we have

$$ab \leq |ab| = |a|\,|b|.$$

Hence, multiplying both sides by 2, we obtain the inequality

$$2ab \leq 2|a|\,|b|.$$

From this we get

$$\begin{aligned}
(a + b)^2 &= a^2 + 2ab + b^2 \\
&\leq a^2 + 2|a|\,|b| + b^2 \\
&= (|a| + |b|)^2.
\end{aligned}$$

We can take the square root of both sides and use Theorem 1 to conclude that

$$|a + b| \leq |a| + |b|,$$

thereby proving our theorem.

You will find plenty of exercises below to give you practice with inequalities. We shall work out some numerical examples to show you the way.

Example 1. Determine the numbers satisfying the equality

$$|x + 1| = 2.$$

This equality means that either $x + 1 = 2$ or $-(x + 1) = 2$, because the absolute value of $x + 1$ is either $(x + 1)$ itself or $-(x + 1)$. In the first case, solving for x gives us $x = 1$, and in the second case, we get $-x - 1 = 2$ or $x = -3$. Thus the answer is $x = 1$ or $x = -3$.

We shall also give an example showing how to determine numbers satisfying certain inequalities. For this we need some terminology. Let a, b be numbers, and assume $a < b$.

The collection of numbers x such that $a < x < b$ is called the *open interval* between a and b, and is sometimes denoted by (a, b).

The collection of numbers x such that $a \leq x \leq b$ is called the *closed interval* between a and b, and is sometimes denoted by $[a, b]$. A single point will also be called a closed interval.

In both above cases, the numbers a, b are called the *end-points* of the intervals. Sometimes we wish to include only one of them in an interval, and so we define the collection of numbers x such that $a \leq x < b$ to be a *half-closed interval*, and similarly for those numbers x such that $a < x \leq b$.

Finally, if a is a number, we call the collection of numbers $x > a$, or $x \geq a$, or $x < a$, or $x \leq a$ an *infinite interval*. Pictures of intervals are shown below.

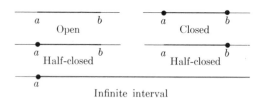

Example 2. Determine all intervals of numbers satisfying

$$|x| \leq 4.$$

We distinguish two cases. The first case is $x \geq 0$. Then $|x| = x$, and in this case, our inequality amounts to

$$0 \leq x \leq 4.$$

The second case is $x < 0$. In this case, $|x| = -x$, and our inequality amounts to $-x \leq 4$, or in other words, $-4 \leq x$. Thus in the second case, the numbers satisfying our inequality are precisely those in the interval

$$-4 \leq x < 0.$$

Considering now both cases together, we see that the interval of numbers satisfying our inequality $|x| \leq 4$ is the interval

$$-4 \leq x \leq 4.$$

Example 3. Determine all intervals of numbers satisfying the inequality

$$|x + 1| > 2.$$

We distinguish cases.

Case 1. $x + 1 \geq 0$. Then $|x + 1| = x + 1$, and in this case, we must find those x such that $x + 1 \geq 0$ and $x + 1 > 2$. The inequality $x + 1 > 2$ implies the inequality $x + 1 \geq 0$. Hence all x such that $x + 1 > 2$ will do, i.e. all x such that $x > 1$.

Case 2. $x + 1 < 0$. Then $|x + 1| = -(x + 1)$, and in this case we must find those numbers x such that $x + 1 < 0$ and $-x - 1 > 2$. These inequalities are equivalent with the inequalities $x < -1$ and $x < -3$.

The set of numbers x satisfying these inequalities is precisely the set of numbers x satisfying $x < -3$.

Putting our two cases together, we find that the required numbers x are those such that $x > 1$ or $x < -3$.

EXERCISES

Determine all intervals of numbers x satisfying the following inequalities.

1. $|x| < 3$ 2. $|2x + 1| \leq 1$
3. $|x^2 - 2| \leq 1$ 4. $|x - 5| < |x + 1|$
5. $(x + 1)(x - 2) < 0$ 6. $(x - 1)(x + 1) > 0$
7. $(x - 5)(x + 5) < 0$ 8. $x(x + 1) \leq 0$
9. $x^2(x - 1) \geq 0$ 10. $(x - 5)^2(x + 10) \leq 0$
11. $(x - 5)^4(x + 10) \leq 0$ 12. $(2x + 1)^6(x - 1) \geq 0$
13. $(4x + 7)^{20}(2x + 8) < 0$ 14. $|x + 4| < 1$
15. $0 < |x + 2| < 1$ 16. $|x| < 2$
17. $|x - 3| < 5$ 18. $|x - 3| < 1$
19. $|x - 3| < 7$

20. Show that if x is a number and $|x| < 3$, then $-3 < x < 3$. Also prove the converse, that if x is a number satisfying this last inequality, then $|x| < 3$.

21. More generally, let a be a positive number. Show that a number x satisfies the inequality $|x| < a$ if and only if

$$-a < x < a.$$

Prove the following inequalities for all numbers x, y.

22. $|x + y| \geq |x| - |y|$ [*Hint:* Write $x = x + y - y$, and apply Theorem 3, together with the fact that $|-y| = |y|$.]

23. $|x - y| \geq |x| - |y|$

24. $|x - y| \leq |x| + |y|$

25. (a) Let a, b be positive numbers such that $a < b$. Show that $a^2 < b^2$.
    (b) If you have read the appendix on induction, prove that $a^n < b^n$ for all positive integers n.

26. Let a, b, c, d be numbers > 0, such that $a/b < c/d$. Show that

$$\frac{a}{b} < \frac{a + c}{b + d} < \frac{c}{d}.$$

27. Let a, b be numbers > 0. Show that

$$\sqrt{ab} \leq \frac{a + b}{2}.$$

§3. FUNCTIONS

A *function, defined for all numbers*, is an association which to any given number associates another number.

It is customary to denote a function by some letter, just as a letter "x" denotes a number. Thus if we denote a given function by f, and x is a number, then we denote by $f(x)$ the number associated with x by the function. This of course does not mean "f times x". There is no multiplication involved here. The symbols $f(x)$ are read "f of x". The association of the number $f(x)$ to the number x is sometimes denoted by a special arrow, namely

$$x \mapsto f(x).$$

For example, consider the function which associates to each number x the number x^2. If f denotes this function, then we have $f(x) = x^2$. In particular, the square of 2 is 4 and hence $f(2) = 4$. The square of 7 is 49 and thus $f(7) = 49$. The square of $\sqrt{2}$ is 2, and hence $f(\sqrt{2}) = 2$. The square of $(x + 1)$ is $x^2 + 2x + 1$ and thus $f(x + 1) = x^2 + 2x + 1$. If h is any number,

$$f(x + h) = x^2 + 2xh + h^2.$$

To take another example, let g be the function which to each number x associates the number $x + 1$. Then we may describe g by the symbols

$$x \mapsto x + 1$$

and write $g(x) = x + 1$. Therefore, $g(1) = 2$. Also $g(2) = 3$, $g(3) = 4$, $g(\sqrt{2}) = \sqrt{2} + 1$, and $g(x + 1) = x + 2$ for any number x.

We can view the *absolute value* as a function,

$$x \mapsto |x|$$

defined by the rule: Given any number a, we associate the number a itself if $a \geqq 0$, and we associate the number $-a$ if $a < 0$. Let F denote the absolute value function. Then $F(x) = |x|$ for any number x. We have in particular $F(2) = 2$, and $F(-2) = 2$ also. The absolute value is not defined by means of a formula like x^2 or $x + 1$. We give you another example of such a function which is not defined by a formula.

We consider the function G described by the following rule:

$$G(x) = 0 \text{ if } x \text{ is a rational number.}$$

$$G(x) = 1 \text{ if } x \text{ is not a rational number.}$$

Then in particular, $G(2) = G(\tfrac{2}{3}) = G(-\tfrac{3}{4}) = 0$ but

$$G(\sqrt{2}) = 1.$$

You must be aware that you can construct a function just by prescribing arbitrarily the rule associating a number to a given one.

If f is a function and x a number, then $f(x)$ is called the *value* of the function at x. Thus if f is the function

$$x \mapsto x^2$$

the value of f at 2 is 4 and the value of f at $\frac{1}{2}$ is $\frac{1}{4}$.

In order to describe a function, we need simply to give its value at any number x. That is the reason why we use the notation $x \mapsto f(x)$. Sometimes, for brevity, we speak of a function $f(x)$, meaning by that the function f whose value at x is $f(x)$. For instance, we would say "Let $f(x)$ be the function $x^3 + 5$" instead of saying "Let f be the function which to each number x associates $x^3 + 5$". Using the special arrow $\mapsto$, we could say also "Let f be the function $x \mapsto x^3 + 5$".

We would also like to be able to define a function for some numbers and leave it undefined for others. For instance we would like to say that $\sqrt{x}$ is a function (the square root function, whose value at a number x is the square root of that number), but we observe that a negative number does not have a square root. Hence it is desirable to make the notion of function somewhat more general by stating explicitly for what numbers it is defined. For instance, the square root function is defined only for numbers $\geqq 0$. This function is denoted by $\sqrt{x}$. The value $\sqrt{x}$ is the unique number $\geqq 0$ whose square is x.

Thus in general, let S be a collection of numbers. By a *function, defined on* S, we mean an association, which to each number x in S associates a number. We call S the *domain of definition* of the function. For example, the domain of definition of the square root function is the collection of all numbers $\geqq 0$.

Let us give another example of a function which is not defined for all numbers. Let S be the collection of all numbers $\neq 0$. The function

$$f(x) = \frac{1}{x}$$

is defined for numbers $x \neq 0$, and is thus defined on the domain S. For this particular function, we have $f(1) = 1, f(2) = \frac{1}{2}, f(\frac{1}{2}) = 2$ and

$$f(\sqrt{2}) = \frac{1}{\sqrt{2}}.$$

One final word before we pass to the exercises: There is no magic reason why we should always use the letter x to describe a function $f(x)$. Thus instead of speaking of the function $f(x) = 1/x$ we could just as well say $f(y) = 1/y$ or $f(q) = 1/q$. Unfortunately, the most neutral way of writing would be $f(\text{blank}) = 1/\text{blank}$, and this is really not convenient.

EXERCISES

1. Let $f(x) = 1/x$. What is $f(\frac{3}{4})$, $f(-\frac{2}{3})$?

2. Let $f(x) = 1/x$ again. What is $f(2x + 1)$ (for any number x such that $x \neq -\frac{1}{2}$)?

3. Let $g(x) = |x| - x$. What is $g(1)$, $g(-1)$, $g(-54)$?

4. Let $f(y) = 2y - y^2$. What is $f(z)$, $f(w)$?

5. For what numbers could you define a function $f(x)$ by the formula

$$f(x) = \frac{1}{x^2 - 2} \, ?$$

   What is the value of this function for $x = 5$?

6. For what numbers could you define a function $f(x)$ by the formula $f(x) = \sqrt[3]{x}$ (cube root of x)? What is $f(27)$?

7. Let $f(x) = x/|x|$, defined for $x \neq 0$. What is:

    (a) $f(1)$ (b) $f(2)$ (c) $f(-3)$ (d) $f(-\frac{4}{3})$

8. Let $f(x) = x + |x|$. What is:

    (a) $f(\frac{1}{2})$ (b) $f(2)$ (c) $f(-4)$ (d) $f(-5)$

9. Let $f(x) = 2x + x^2 - 5$. What is:

    (a) $f(1)$ (b) $f(-1)$ (c) $f(x + 1)$

10. For what numbers could you define a function $f(x)$ by the formula $f(x) = \sqrt[4]{x}$ (fourth root of x)? What is $f(16)$?

11. A function (defined for all numbers) is said to be an *even* function if $f(x) = f(-x)$ for all x. It is said to be an *odd* function if $f(x) = -f(-x)$ for all x. Determine which of the following functions are odd or even.

    (a) $f(x) = x$ (b) $f(x) = x^2$ (c) $f(x) = x^3$
    (d) $f(x) = 1/x$ if $x \neq 0$, and $f(0) = 0$.

12. Let f be any function defined for all numbers. Show that the function $g(x) = f(x) + f(-x)$ is even. What about the function

$$h(x) = f(x) - f(-x),$$

    is it even, odd, or neither?

13. Show that any function defined for all numbers can be written as a sum of an even function and an odd function.

§4. POWERS

In this section we just summarize some elementary arithmetic.

Let n be an integer ≥ 1 and let a be any number. Then a^n is the product of a with itself n times. For example, let $a = 3$. If $n = 2$, then $a^2 = 9$. If $n = 3$, then $a^3 = 27$. Thus we obtain a function which is called the n-th *power*. If f denotes this function, then $f(x) = x^n$.

We recall the rule

$$x^{m+n} = x^m x^n$$

for any number x and integers $m, n \geq 1$.

Again, let n be an integer ≥ 1, and let a be a positive number. We define $a^{1/n}$ to be the unique positive number b such that $b^n = a$. (That there exists such a unique number b is taken for granted as part of the properties of numbers.) We get a function called the n-th *root*. Thus if f is the 4-th root, then $f(16) = 2$ and $f(81) = 3$.

The n-th root function can also be defined at 0, the n-th root of 0 being 0 itself.

Question: If n is an odd integer like 1, 3, 5, 7, . . . , can you define an n-th root function for all numbers?

If a, b are two numbers ≥ 0 and n is an integer ≥ 1 then

$$(ab)^{1/n} = a^{1/n} b^{1/n}.$$

There is another useful and elementary rule. Let m, n be integers ≥ 1 and let a be a number ≥ 0. We define $a^{m/n}$ to be $(a^{1/n})^m$ which is also equal to $(a^m)^{1/n}$. This allows us to define fractional powers, and gives us a function

$$f(x) = x^{m/n}$$

defined for $x \geq 0$.

We now come to powers with negative numbers or 0. We want to define x^a when a is a negative rational number or 0 and $x > 0$. We want the fundamental rule

$$x^{a+b} = x^a x^b$$

to be true. This means that we must define x^0 to be 1. For instance, since

$$2^3 = 2^{3+0} = 2^3 2^0,$$

we see from this example that the only way in which this equation holds is if $2^0 = 1$. Similarly, in general, if the relation

$$x^a = x^{a+0} = x^a x^0$$

is true, then x^0 must be equal to 1.

Suppose finally that a is a positive rational number, and let x be a number > 0. We define x^{-a} to be

$$\frac{1}{x^a} .$$

Thus

$$2^{-3} = \frac{1}{2^3} = \frac{1}{8}, \quad \text{and} \quad 4^{-2/3} = \frac{1}{4^{2/3}} .$$

We observe that in this special case,

$$(4^{-2/3})(4^{2/3}) = 4^0 = 1.$$

In general, $x^a x^{-a} = x^0 = 1$.

We are tempted to define x^a even when a is not a rational number. This is more subtle. For instance, it is absolutely meaningless to say that $2^{\sqrt{2}}$ is the product of 2 square root of 2 times itself. The problem of defining 2^a (or x^a) when a is not rational will be postponed to a later chapter. Until that chapter, when we deal with such a power, we shall assume that there is a function, written x^a, described as we have done above for rational numbers, and satisfying the fundamental relation

$$x^{a+b} = x^a x^b, \qquad x^0 = 1.$$

Example. We have a function $f(x) = x^{\sqrt{2}}$ defined for all $x > 0$. It is actually hard to describe its values for special numbers, like $2^{\sqrt{2}}$. It was unknown for a very long time whether $2^{\sqrt{2}}$ is a rational number or not. The solution (*it is not*) was found only in 1927 by the mathematician Gelfond, who became famous for solving a problem that was known to be very hard.

Warning. Do not confuse a function like x^2 and a function like 2^x. Given a number $c > 0$, we can view c^x as a function defined for all x. (It will be discussed in detail in Chapter VIII.) This function is called an *exponential function*. Thus 2^x and 10^x are exponential functions. We shall select a number

$$e = 2.718...$$

and the exponential function e^x as having special properties which make it better than any other exponential function. The meaning of our use of the word "better" will be explained in Chapter VIII.

EXERCISES

Find a^x and x^a for the following values of x and a.

1. $a = 2$ and $x = 3$
2. $a = 5$ and $x = -1$
3. $a = \frac{1}{2}$ and $x = 4$
4. $a = \frac{1}{3}$ and $x = 2$
5. $a = -\frac{1}{2}$ and $x = 4$
6. $a = 3$ and $x = 2$
7. $a = -3$ and $x = -1$
8. $a = -2$ and $x = -2$
9. $a = -1$ and $x = -4$
10. $a = -\frac{1}{2}$ and $x = 9$
11. Determine whether $2^{\sqrt{2}} + 3^{\sqrt{3}}$ is a rational number. (This is actually a major research problem whose answer is not known today. Later in this course we shall deal with numbers e and π. Although it is known that neither e nor π is rational, it is not known whether $e\pi$ or $e + \pi$ is rational.)

Chapter II

Graphs and Curves

The ideas contained in this chapter allow us to translate certain statements backwards and forwards between the language of numbers and the language of geometry.

It is extremely basic for what follows, because we can use our geometric intuition to help us solve problems concerning numbers and functions, and conversely, we can use theorems concerning numbers and functions to yield results about geometry.

§1. COORDINATES

Once a unit length is selected, we can represent numbers as points on a line. We shall now extend this procedure to the plane, and to pairs of numbers.

We visualize a horizontal line and a vertical line intersecting at an origin O.

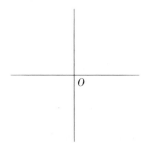

These lines will be called *coordinate axes* or simply *axes*.

We select a unit length and cut the horizontal line into segments of lengths 1, 2, 3, . . . to the left and to the right, and do the same to the vertical line, but up and down, as indicated in the next figure.

On the vertical line we visualize the points going below 0 as corresponding to the negative integers, just as we visualized points on the left of the horizontal line as corresponding to negative integers. We follow the same idea as that used in grading a thermometer, where the numbers below zero are regarded as negative. See figure on page 16.

15

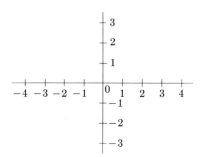

We can now cut the plane into squares whose sides have length 1.

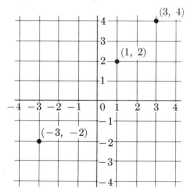

We can describe each point where two lines intersect by a pair of integers. Suppose that we are given a pair of integers like (1, 2). We go to the right of the origin 1 unit and vertically up 2 units to get the point (1, 2) which has been indicated above. We have also indicated the point (3, 4). The diagram is just like a map.

Furthermore, we could also use negative numbers. For instance to describe the point (−3, −2) we go to the left of the origin 3 units and vertically downwards 2 units.

There is actually no reason why we should limit ourselves to points which are described by integers. For instance we can also have the point $(\frac{1}{2}, -1)$ and the point $(-\sqrt{2}, 3)$ as on the figure below.

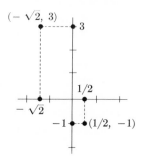

We have not drawn all the squares on the plane. We have drawn only the relevant lines to find our two points.

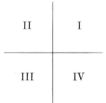

In general, if we take any point P in the plane and draw the perpendicular lines to the horizontal axis and to the vertical axis, we obtain two numbers x, y as in the figure at the right.

The perpendicular line from P to the horizontal axis determines a number x which is negative in the figure because it lies to the left of the origin. The number y determined by the perpendicular from P to the vertical axis is positive because it lies above the origin. The two numbers x, y are called the *coordinates* of the point P, and we can write $P = (x, y)$.

Every pair of numbers (x, y) determines a point of the plane. We find the point by going a distance x from the origin 0 in the horizontal direction and then a distance y in the vertical direction. If x is positive we go to the right of 0. If x is negative, we go to the left of 0. If y is positive we go vertically upwards, and if y is negative we go vertically downwards. The coordinates of the origin are $(0, 0)$. We usually call the horizontal axis the *x-axis* and the vertical axis the *y-axis*. If a point P is described by two numbers, say $(5, -10)$, it is customary to call the first number its x-coordinate and the second number its y-coordinate. Thus 5 is the x-coordinate, and -10 the y-coordinate of our point. Of course, we could use other letters besides x and y, for instance t and s, or u and v.

Our two axes separate the plane into four quadrants which are numbered as indicated in the figure:

II	I
III	IV

If (x, y) is a point in the first quadrant, then both x and y are > 0. If (x, y) is a point in the fourth quadrant, then $x > 0$ but $y < 0$.

EXERCISES

1. Plot the following points: $(-1, 1)$, $(0, 5)$, $(-5, -2)$, $(1, 0)$.

2. Plot the following points: $(\frac{1}{2}, 3)$, $(-\frac{1}{3}, -\frac{1}{2})$, $(\frac{4}{3}, -2)$, $(-\frac{1}{4}, -\frac{1}{2})$.

3. Let (x, y) be the coordinates of a point in the second quadrant. Is x positive or negative? Is y positive or negative?

4. Let (x, y) be the coordinates of a point in the third quadrant. Is x positive or negative? Is y positive or negative?

5. Plot the following points: (1.2, −2.3), (1.7, 3).

6. Plot the following points: (−2.5, $\frac{1}{3}$), (−3.5, $\frac{5}{4}$).

7. Plot the following points: (1.5, −1), (−1.5, −1).

§2. GRAPHS

Let f be a function. We define the *graph* of f to be the collection of all pairs of numbers $(x, f(x))$ whose first coordinate is any number for which f is defined and whose second coordinate is the value of the function at the first coordinate.

For example, the graph of the function $f(x) = x^2$ consists of all pairs (x, y) such that $y = x^2$. In other words, it is the collection of all pairs (x, x^2), like (1, 1), (2, 4), (−1, 1), (−3, 9), etc.

Since each pair of numbers corresponds to a point on the plane (once a system of axes and a unit length have been selected), we can view the graph of f as a collection of points in the plane. The graph of the function $f(x) = x^2$ has been drawn in the figure below, together with the points which we gave above as examples.

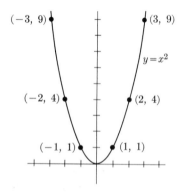

To determine the graph, we plot a lot of points making a table giving the x- and y-coordinates.

x	$f(x)$		x	$f(x)$
1	1		−1	1
2	4		−2	4
3	9		−3	9
$\frac{1}{2}$	$\frac{1}{4}$		$-\frac{1}{2}$	$\frac{1}{4}$

At this stage of the game there is no other way for you to determine the graph of a function other than this trial and error method. Later, we shall develop techniques which give you greater efficiency in doing it.

We shall now give several examples of graphs of functions which occur very frequently in the sequel.

Example 1. Consider the function $f(x) = x$. The points on its graph are of type (x, x). The first coordinate must be equal to the second. Thus $f(1) = 1, f(-\sqrt{2}) = -\sqrt{2}$, etc. The graph looks like this:

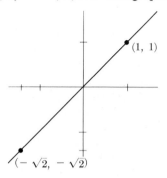

Example 2. Let $f(x) = -x$. Its graph looks like this:

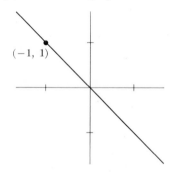

Observe that the graphs of the preceding two functions are straight lines. We shall study the general case of a straight line later.

Example 3. Let $f(x) = |x|$. When $x \geqq 0$, we know that $f(x) = x$. When $x \leqq 0$, we know that $f(x) = -x$. Hence the graph of $|x|$ is obtained by combining the preceding two, and looks like this:

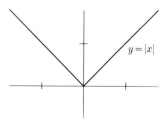

All values of y are $\geqq 0$, whether x is positive or negative.

Example 4. There is an even simpler type of function than the ones we have just looked at, namely the constant functions. For instance, we can define a function f such that $f(x) = 2$ for all numbers x. In other words, we associate the number 2 to any number x. It is a very simple association, and the graph of this function is a horizontal line, intersecting the vertical axis at the point $(0, 2)$.

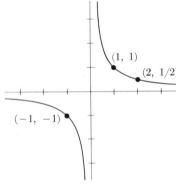

If we took the function $f(x) = -1$, then the graph would be a horizontal line intersecting the vertical axis at the point $(0, -1)$.

In general, let c be a fixed number. The graph of the function $f(x) = c$ is the horizontal line intersecting the vertical axis at the point $(0, c)$. The function $f(x) = c$ is called a *constant* function.

Example 5. The last of our examples is the function $f(x) = 1/x$ (defined for $x \neq 0$). By plotting a few points of the graph, you will see that it looks like this:

For instance, you can plot the following points:

x	$1/x$		x	$1/x$
1	1		1	1
2	$\frac{1}{2}$		-2	$-\frac{1}{2}$
3	$\frac{1}{3}$		-3	$-\frac{1}{3}$
$\frac{1}{2}$	2		$-\frac{1}{2}$	-2
$\frac{1}{3}$	3		$-\frac{1}{3}$	3

As x becomes very large positive, $1/x$ becomes very small. As x approaches 0 from the right, $1/x$ becomes very large. A similar phenomenon occurs when x approaches 0 from the left; then x is negative and $1/x$ is negative also. Hence in that case, $1/x$ is very large negative.

In trying to determine how the graph of a function looks, you can already watch for the following:

> The points at which the graph intersects the two coordinate axes. What happens when x becomes very large positive and very large negative.

On the whole, however, in working out the exercises, your main technique is just to plot a lot of points until it becomes clear to you what the graph looks like.

EXERCISES

Sketch the graphs of the following functions and plot at least three points on each graph. In each case we give the value of the function at x.

1. $x + 1$ 2. $2x$ 3. $3x$

4. $4x$ 5. $2x + 1$ 6. $5x + \frac{1}{2}$

7. $\dfrac{x}{2} + 3$ 8. $-3x + 2$ 9. $2x^2 - 1$

10. $-3x^2 + 1$ 11. x^3 12. x^4

13. $\sqrt{x}$ 14. $x^{-1/2}$ 15. $2x$

16. $x + 1$ 17. $|x| + x$ 18. $|x| + 2x$

19. $-|x|$ 20. $-|x| + x$ 21. $\dfrac{1}{x + 2}$

22. $\dfrac{1}{x - 2}$ 23. $\dfrac{1}{x + 3}$ 24. $\dfrac{1}{x - 3}$

25. $\dfrac{2}{x - 2}$ 26. $\dfrac{2}{x + 2}$ 27. $\dfrac{2}{x}$

28. $\dfrac{-2}{x + 5}$ 29. $\dfrac{3}{x + 1}$ 30. $\dfrac{x}{|x|}$

(In Exercises 13, 14, and 21 through 30, the functions are not defined for all values of x.)

31. Sketch the graph of the function $f(x)$ such that:

     $f(x) = 0$ if $x \leq 0$. $f(x) = 1$ if $x > 0$.

32. Sketch the graph of the function $f(x)$ such that:

     $f(x) = x$ if $x < 0$. $f(0) = 2$. $f(x) = x$ if $x > 0$.

33. Sketch the graph of the function $f(x)$ such that:

    $f(x) = x^2$ if $x < 0.$ $f(x) = x$ if $x \geqq 0.$

34. Sketch the graph of the function $f(x)$ such that:

    $f(x) = |x| + x$ if $-1 \leqq x \leqq 1.$
    $f(x) = 3$ if $x > 1.$ [$f(x)$ is not defined for other values of x.]

35. Sketch the graph of the function $f(x)$ such that:

    $f(x) = x^3$ if $x \leqq 0.$ $f(x) = 1$ if $0 < x < 2.$
    $f(x) = x^2$ if $x \geqq 2.$

36. Sketch the graph of the function $f(x)$ such that:

    $f(x) = x$ if $0 < x \leqq 1.$ $f(x) = x - 1$ if $1 < x \leqq 2.$
    $f(x) = x - 2$ if $2 < x \leqq 3.$ $f(x) = x - 3$ if $3 < x \leqq 4.$

[We leave $f(x)$ undefined for other values of x, but try to define it yourself in such a way as to preserve the symmetry of the graph.]

§3. THE STRAIGHT LINE

One of the most basic types of functions is the type whose graph represents a straight line. We have already seen that the graph of the function $f(x) = x$ is a straight line. If we take $f(x) = 2x$, then the line slants up much more steeply, and even more so for $f(x) = 3x$. The graph of the function $f(x) = 10{,}000x$ would look almost vertical. In general, let a be a positive number $\neq 0$. Then the graph of the function

$$f(x) = ax$$

represents a straight line. The point $(2, 2a)$ lies on the line because $f(2) = 2a$. The point $(\sqrt{2}, \sqrt{2}\, a)$ also lies on the line, and if c is any number, the point (c, ca) lies on the line. The (x, y) coordinates of these points are obtained by making a similarity transformation, starting with the coordinates $(1, a)$ and multiplying them by some number c.

We can visualize this procedure by means of similar triangles. In the figure below, we have a straight line. If we select a point (x, y) on the line and drop the perpendicular from this point to the x-axis, we obtain a right triangle.

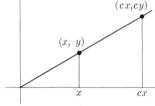

If x is the length of the base of the smaller triangle in the figure, and y its height, and if cx is the length of the base of the bigger triangle, then cy is the height of the bigger triangle: The smaller triangle is similar to the bigger one.

If a is a number < 0, then the graph of the function $f(x) = ax$ is also a straight line, which slants to the left. For instance, the graphs of $f(x) = -x$ or $f(x) = -2x$.

Let a, b be two numbers. The graph of the function $g(x) = ax + b$ is also a straight line, which is parallel to the line determined by the function $f(x) = ax$. In order to convince you of this, we observe the following. When $x = 0$ we see that $g(x) = b$. Let $y' = y - b$. The equation $y' = ax$ is of the type discussed above. If we have a point (x, y') on the straight line $y' = ax$, then we get a point $(x, y' + b)$ on the straight line $y = ax + b$, by simply adding b to the second coordinate. This means that the graph of the function $g(x) = ax + b$ is the straight line parallel to the line determined by the function $f(x) = ax$ and passing through the point $(0, b)$.

Example 1. Let $g(x) = 2x + 1$. When $x = 0$, then $g(x) = 1$. When $g(x) = 0$, then $x = -\frac{1}{2}$. The graph looks like this:

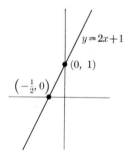

Example 2. Let $g(x) = -2x - 5$. When $x = 0$, then $g(x) = -5$. When $g(x) = 0$, then $x = -\frac{5}{2}$. The graph looks like this:

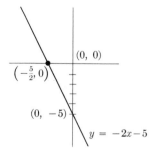

We shall frequently speak of a function $f(x) = ax + b$ as a straight line (although of course, it is its graph which is a straight line).

The number a which is the coefficient of x is called the *slope* of the line. It determines how much the line is slanted. As we have already seen in many examples, when the slope is positive, the line is slanted to the right, and when the slope is negative, the line is slanted to the left. The relationship $y = ax + b$ is also called the *equation* of the line. It gives us the relation between the x- and y-coordinates of a point on the line.

Let $f(x) = ax + b$ be a straight line, and let (x_1, y_1) and (x_2, y_2) be two points of the line. It is easy to find the slope of the line in terms of the coordinates of these two points. By definition, we know that

$$y_1 = ax_1 + b$$

and

$$y_2 = ax_2 + b.$$

Subtracting, we get

$$y_2 - y_1 = ax_2 - ax_1 = a(x_2 - x_1).$$

Consequently, if the two points are distinct, $x_2 \neq x_1$, then we can divide by $x_2 - x_1$ and obtain

$$a = \frac{y_2 - y_1}{x_2 - x_1}.$$

This formula gives us the slope in terms of the coordinates of two distinct points on the line.

Example 3. Look at the line $f(x) = 2x + 5$. Letting $x = 1$, we have $f(x) = 7$ and letting $x = -1$, we get $f(x) = 3$. Thus the points $(1, 7)$ and $(-1, 3)$ are on the line. The slope is 2, and is equal to

$$\frac{7 - 3}{1 - (-1)}$$

as it should be.

Geometrically, our quotient

$$\frac{y_2 - y_1}{x_2 - x_1}$$

is simply the ratio of the vertical side and horizontal side of the triangle in the next diagram:

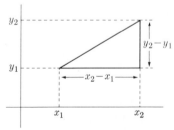

Conversely, given two points in the plane, it is easy to determine the equation of the line passing through them.

Example 4. Let (1, 2) and (2, −1) be the two points. What is the slope of the line between them? What is the equation of the line?

We first find the slope. It must be the quotient

$$\frac{y_2 - y_1}{x_2 - x_1}$$

which is equal to

$$\frac{-1 - 2}{2 - 1} = -3.$$

Thus we know that our line is given by the equation

$$y = -3x + b$$

for some number b. Furthermore, we know also that the line must pass through the point (1, 2). If $f(x) = -3x + b$, then we must have $f(1) = 2$. From this we can solve for b, namely

$$2 = -3 \cdot 1 + b$$

yields $b = 2 + 3 = 5$. Thus the equation of the line is

$$f(x) = -3x + 5.$$

Observe that it does not matter which point we call (x_1, y_1) and which we call (x_2, y_2). We would get the same answer for the slope.

Knowing two points on a line, we first determine the slope and then solve for the constant b, using the coordinates of one of the points.

We can also determine the equation of a line provided we know the slope and one point.

Example 5. Find the equation of the line having slope −7 and passing through the point (−1, 2).

The equation must be of type

$$y = -7x + b$$

for some number b. Furthermore, when $x = -1$, we must have $y = 2$. Thus

$$2 = (-7)(-1) + b$$

and $b = -5$. Hence the equation of the line is

$$y = -7x - 5.$$

Example 6. In general, let a be a number, and (x_1, y_1) some point. *We wish to find the equation of the line having slope equal to a, and passing through the point* (x_1, y_1). The condition that a point (x, y) with $x \neq x_1$ be on this line is equivalent with the condition that

$$\frac{y - y_1}{x - x_1} = a.$$

Thus the equation of the desired line is

$$y - y_1 = a(x - x_1).$$

In Example 5, we could also work it out using the present description, obtaining

$$y - 2 = -7(x - (-1)),$$

from which we also find

$$y = -7x - 5.$$

Example 7. In general, let (x_1, y_1) and (x_2, y_2) be two distinct points with $x_1 \neq x_2$. We wish to find the equation of the line passing through these two points. Its slope must then be equal to

$$\frac{y_2 - y_1}{x_2 - x_1}.$$

From the preceding example, we find that the equation of the line can be expressed by the formula

$$\frac{y - y_1}{x - x_1} = \frac{y_2 - y_1}{x_2 - x_1}$$

for all points (x, y) such that $x \neq x_1$.

Finally, we should mention vertical lines. These cannot be represented by equations of type $y = ax + b$. Suppose that we have a vertical line intersecting the x-axis at the point $(2, 0)$. The y-coordinate of any point on the line can be arbitrary. Thus the equation of the line is simple $x = 2$. In general, the equation of the vertical line intersecting the x-axis at the point $(c, 0)$ is $x = c$.

EXERCISES

Sketch the graphs of the following lines:

1. $y = -2x + 5$

2. $y = 5x - 3$

3. $y = \dfrac{x}{2} + 7$

4. $y = -\dfrac{x}{3} + 1$

What is the equation of the line passing through the following points?

5. $(-1, 1)$ and $(2, -7)$ 6. $(3, \frac{1}{2})$ and $(4, -1)$

7. $(\sqrt{2}, -1)$ and $(\sqrt{2}, 1)$ 8. $(-3, -5)$ and $(\sqrt{3}, 4)$

What is the equation of the line having the given slope and passing through the given point?

9. slope 4 and point $(1, 1)$ 10. slope -2 and point $(\frac{2}{3}, 1)$

11. slope $-\frac{1}{2}$ and point $(\sqrt{2}, 3)$ 12. slope $\sqrt{3}$ and point $(-1, 5)$

Sketch the graphs of the following lines:

13. $x = 5$ 14. $x = -1$ 15. $x = -3$

16. $y = -4$ 17. $y = 2$ 18. $y = 0$.

What is the slope of the line passing through the following points?

19. $(1, \frac{1}{2})$ and $(-1, 1)$ 20. $(\frac{1}{4}, 1)$ and $(\frac{1}{2}, -1)$

21. $(2, 3)$ and $(\sqrt{2}, 1)$ 22. $(\sqrt{3}, 1)$ and $(3, 2)$

What is the equation of the line passing through the following points?

23. $(\pi, 1)$ and $(\sqrt{2}, 3)$ 24. $(\sqrt{2}, 2)$ and $(1, \pi)$

25. $(-1, 2)$ and $(\sqrt{2}, -1)$ 26. $(-1, \sqrt{2})$ and $(-2, -3)$

27. Sketch the graphs of the following lines:

    (a) $y = 2x$ (b) $y = 2x + 1$ (c) $y = 2x + 5$

    (d) $y = 2x - 1$ (e) $y = 2x - 5$

28. Two straight lines are said to be *parallel* if they have the same slope. Let $y = ax + b$ and $y = cx + d$ be the equations of two straight lines with $b \neq d$. (a) If they are parallel, show that they have no point in common. (b) If they are not parallel, show that they have exactly one point in common.

29. Find the common point of the following pairs of lines:

    (a) $y = 3x + 5$ and $y = 2x + 1$ (b) $y = 3x - 2$ and $y = -x + 4$

    (c) $y = 2x + 3$ and $y = -x + 2$ (d) $y = x + 1$ and $y = 2x + 7$

§4. DISTANCE BETWEEN TWO POINTS

Let (x_1, y_1) and (x_2, y_2) be two points in the plane, for instance as in the following diagrams.

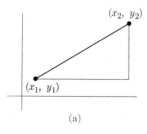

(a)

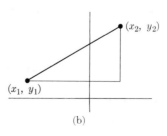

(b)

We can then make up a right triangle. By the Pythagoras theorem, the length of the line segment joining our two points can be determined from the lengths of the two sides. The square of the bottom side is $(x_2 - x_1)^2$, which is also equal to $(x_1 - x_2)^2$. This is clear in part (a) of the figure. It is also true in part (b) (convince yourself by working out an example, as for instance in Example 2 below). The length of the vertical side is $(y_2 - y_1)^2$, which is equal to $(y_1 - y_2)^2$. If L denotes the length of the line segment, then

$$L^2 = (x_1 - x_2)^2 + (y_1 - y_2)^2$$

and consequently,

$$L = \sqrt{(x_2 - x_1)^2 + (y_2 - y_1)^2}.$$

Example 1. Let the two points be $(1, 2)$ and $(1, 3)$. Then the length of the line segment between them is

$$\sqrt{(1 - 1)^2 + (3 - 2)^2} = 1.$$

The length L is also called the *distance* between the two points.

Example 2. Find the distance between the points $(-1, 5)$ and $(4, -3)$.

The distance is

$$\sqrt{(4 - (-1))^2 + (-3 - 5)^2} = \sqrt{89}.$$

(You should plot these points, and convince yourself that the minus signs do not affect the validity of our formula for the length of the line segment between the two points.)

EXERCISES

Find the distance between the following points:

1. The points $(-3, -5)$ and $(1, 4)$
2. The points $(1, 1)$ and $(0, 2)$
3. The points $(-1, 4)$ and $(3, -2)$
4. The points $(1, -1)$ and $(-1, 2)$
5. The points $(\frac{1}{2}, 2)$ and $(1, 1)$
6. Find the coordinates of the fourth corner of a rectangle, three of whose corners are $(-1, 2)$, $(4, 2)$, $(-1, -3)$.
7. What are the lengths of the sides of the rectangle in Exercise 6?
8. Find the coordinates of the fourth corner of a rectangle, three of whose corners are $(-2, -2)$, $(3, -2)$, $(3, 5)$.

9. What are the lengths of the sides of the rectangle in Exercise 8?

10. If x, y are numbers, define the distance between these two numbers to be $|x - y|$. Show that this is the same as the distance between the points $(x, 0)$ and $(y, 0)$ in the plane.

11. Denote by $d(x, y)$ the distance between two numbers x and y. Show that if x, y, z are numbers, then

$$d(x, z) \leq d(x, y) + d(y, z)$$
$$d(x, y) = d(y, x).$$

§5. CURVES AND EQUATIONS

Let $F(x, y)$ be an expression involving a pair of numbers (x, y). Let c be a number. We consider the equation

$$F(x, y) = c.$$

The collection of points (a, b) in the plane satisfying this equation, i.e. such that

$$F(a, b) = c,$$

is called the *graph* of the equation. This graph is also known as a curve, and we will usually not make a distinction between the equation

$$F(x, y) = c$$

and the curve which represents the equation.

For example,

$$x + y = 2$$

is the equation of a straight line, and its graph is the straight line. We shall study below important examples of equations which arise frequently.

If f is a function, then we can form the expression $y - f(x)$, and the graph of the *equation*

$$y - f(x) = 0$$

is none other than the graph of the *function* f as we discussed it in §2. You should observe that there are equations of type

$$F(x, y) = c$$

which are not obtained from a function $y = f(x)$. For instance, the equation $x^2 + y^2 = 1$ is such an equation.

We shall now study important examples of graphs of equations

$$F(x, y) = 0 \qquad \text{or} \qquad F(x, y) = c.$$

§6. THE CIRCLE

The expression $F(x, y) = x^2 + y^2$ has a simple geometric interpretation. It is the square of the distance of the point (x, y) from the origin $(0, 0)$. Thus the points (x, y) satisfying the equation

$$x^2 + y^2 = 1^2 = 1$$

are simply those points whose distance from the origin is 1. It is the circle of radius 1, with center at the origin.

Similarly, the points (x, y) satisfying the equation

$$x^2 + y^2 = 4$$

are those points whose distance from the origin is 2. They constitute the circle of radius 2. In general, if c is any number > 0, then the graph of the equation

$$x^2 + y^2 = c^2$$

is the circle of radius c, with center at the origin.

We have already remarked that the *equation*

$$x^2 + y^2 = 1$$

or $x^2 + y^2 - 1 = 0$ is not of the type $y - f(x) = 0$, i.e. does not come from a function $y = f(x)$. However, we can write our equation in the form

$$y^2 = 1 - x^2.$$

For any value of x between -1 and $+1$, we can solve for y and get

$$y = \sqrt{1 - x^2} \quad \text{or} \quad y = -\sqrt{1 - x^2}.$$

If $x \neq 1$ or $x \neq -1$, then we get two values of y for each value of x. Geometrically, these two values correspond to the points indicated on the following diagram.

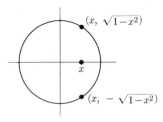

There is a function, defined for $-1 \leq x \leq 1$, such that

$$f(x) = \sqrt{1 - x^2},$$

and the graph of this function is the upper half of our circle. Similarly, there is another function

$$g(x) = -\sqrt{1 - x^2},$$

also defined for $-1 \leq x \leq 1$, whose graph is the lower half of the circle. Neither of these functions is defined for other values of x.

We now ask for the equation of the circle whose center is $(1, 2)$ and whose radius has length 3. It consists of the points (x, y) whose distance from $(1, 2)$ is 3. These are the points satisfying the equation

$$(x - 1)^2 + (y - 2)^2 = 9.$$

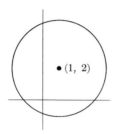

The graph of this equation has been drawn above.

To pick another example, we wish to determine those points at a distance 2 from the point $(-1, -3)$. They are the points (x, y) satisfying the equation

$$(x - (-1))^2 + (y - (-3))^2 = 4$$

or, in other words,

$$(x + 1)^2 + (y + 3)^2 = 4.$$

(Observe carefully the cancellation of minus signs!) Thus the graph of this equation is the circle of radius 2 and center $(-1, -3)$.

In general, let a, b be two numbers and r a number > 0. Then the circle of radius r and center (a, b) is the graph of the equation

$$(x - a)^2 + (y - b)^2 = r^2.$$

In our last example, we have

$$r = 2, \qquad a = -1, \qquad b = -3.$$

Example 1. Suppose that we have a quadratic expression like

$$x^2 + 2x.$$

We can complete the square and write it as

$$x^2 + 2x = (x + 1)^2 - 1.$$

Similarly, given the expression $y^2 - 3y$, we can write it

$$y^2 - 3y = (y - \tfrac{3}{2})^2 - \tfrac{9}{4}.$$

Given an equation

$$x^2 + y^2 + 2x - 3y - 5 = 0,$$

we can use the trick of completing the square to see what its graph looks like. Our equation can be written in the form

$$(x + 1)^2 + (y - \tfrac{3}{2})^2 = 5 + \tfrac{9}{4} + 1 = \tfrac{33}{4}.$$

Thus our equation is a circle of center $(-1, \tfrac{3}{2})$ and radius $\sqrt{33/4}$.

EXERCISES

Sketch the graph of the following equations:

1. (a) $(x - 2)^2 + (y + 1)^2 = 25$ (b) $(x - 2)^2 + (y + 1)^2 = 4$
   (c) $(x - 2)^2 + (y + 1)^2 = 1$ (d) $(x - 2)^2 + (y + 1)^2 = 9$

2. (a) $x^2 + (y - 1)^2 = 9$ (b) $x^2 + (y - 1)^2 = 4$
   (c) $x^2 + (y - 1)^2 = 25$ (d) $x^2 + (y - 1)^2 = 1$

3. (a) $(x + 1)^2 + y^2 = 1$ (b) $(x + 1)^2 + y^2 = 4$
   (c) $(x + 1)^2 + y^2 = 9$ (d) $(x + 1)^2 + y^2 = 25$

4. $\dfrac{x^2}{9} + \dfrac{y^2}{16} = 1$ 5. $\dfrac{x^2}{4} + \dfrac{y^2}{9} = 1$

6. $\dfrac{x^2}{5} + \dfrac{y^2}{16} = 1$ 7. $\dfrac{x^2}{4} + \dfrac{y^2}{25} = 1$

8. $\dfrac{(x - 1)^2}{9} + \dfrac{(y + 2)^2}{16} = 1$ 9. $4x^2 + 25y^2 = 100$

10. $\dfrac{(x + 1)^2}{3} + \dfrac{(y + 2)^2}{4} = 1$ 11. $25x^2 + 16y^2 = 400$

12. $(x - 1)^2 + \dfrac{(y + 3)^2}{4} = 1$

(In Exercises 4 through 12, the graph of the equation is called an *ellipse*. It is a stretched-out circle. Investigate for yourself the effect of changing the coefficients of x^2 and y^2 in these equations.)

§7. THE PARABOLA. CHANGES OF COORDINATES

We have seen what the graph of the equation $y = x^2$ looks like. Suppose that we graph the equation $y = (x - 1)^2$. We shall find that it looks exactly the same, but as if the origin were placed at the point $(1, 0)$.

Similarly, the curve $y - 2 = (x - 4)^2$ looks again like $y = x^2$ except that the whole curve has been moved as if the origin were the point (4, 2). The graphs of these equations have been drawn on the next diagram.

We can formalize these remarks as follows. Suppose that in our given coordinate system we pick a point (a, b) as a new origin. We let new coordinates be $x' = x - a$ and $y' = y - b$. Thus when $x = a$ we have $x' = 0$ and when $y = b$ we have $y' = 0$. If we have a curve

$$y' = x'^2$$

in the new coordinate system whose origin is at the point (a, b), then it gives rise to the equation

$$(y - b) = (x - a)^2$$

in terms of the old coordinate system. This type of curve is known as a *parabola*.

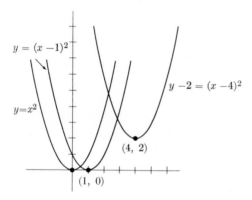

We can apply the same technique of completing the square that we did for the circle.

Example. What is the graph of the equation

$$2y - x^2 - 4x + 6 = 0?$$

Completing the square, we can write

$$x^2 + 4x = (x + 2)^2 - 4.$$

Thus our equation can be rewritten

$$2y = (x + 2)^2 - 10$$

or

$$2(y + 5) = (x + 2)^2.$$

We choose a new coordinate system

$$x' = x + 2 \quad \text{and} \quad y' = y + 5$$

so that our equation becomes

$$2y' = x'^2$$

or $y' = \frac{1}{2}x'^2$. This is a function whose graph you already know, and whose sketch we leave to you.

Finally, we remark that if we have an equation

$$x - y^2 = 0$$

or

$$x = y^2,$$

then we get a parabola which is tilted horizontally.

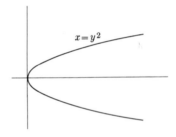

We can then apply the technique of changing the coordinate system to see what the graph of a more general equation is like, for instance the graph of

$$x - y^2 + 2y + 5 = 0.$$

We can write this equation in the form

$$(x + 6) = (y - 1)^2$$

and hence its graph looks like this:

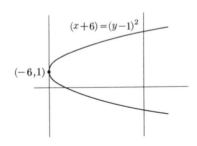

EXERCISES

Sketch the graph of the following equations:

1. $y = -x + 2$ 2. $y = 2x^2 + x - 3$
3. $x - 4y^2 = 0$ 4. $x - y^2 + y + 1 = 0$

Complete the square in the following equations and change the coordinate system to put them into the form

$$x'^2 + y'^2 = r^2 \quad \text{or} \quad y' = cx'^2 \quad \text{or} \quad x' = cy'^2$$

with a suitable constant c.

5. $x^2 + y^2 - 4x + 2y - 20 = 0$ 6. $x^2 + y^2 - 2y - 8 = 0$
7. $x^2 + y^2 + 2x - 2 = 0$ 8. $y - 2x^2 - x + 3 = 0$
9. $y - x^2 - 4x - 5 = 0$ 10. $y - x^2 + 2x + 3 = 0$
11. $x^2 + y^2 + 2x - 4y = -3$ 12. $x^2 + y^2 - 4x - 2y = -3$
13. $x - 2y^2 - y + 3 = 0$ 14. $x - y^2 - 4y = 5$

§8. THE HYPERBOLA

We have already seen what the graph of the equation

$$xy = 1$$

looks like. It is of course the same as the graph of the function $f(x) = 1/x$ (defined for $x \neq 0$). If we pick a coordinate system whose origin is at the point (a, b), the equation

$$y - b = \frac{1}{x - a}$$

is known as a *hyperbola*. In terms of the new coordinate system $x' = x - a$ and $y' = y - b$, our hyperbola has the old type of equation

$$x'y' = 1.$$

If we are given an equation like

$$xy - 2x + 3y + 4 = 5,$$

we can factor the left-hand side and rewrite the equation as

$$(x + 3)(y - 2) + 6 + 4 = 5$$

or

$$(x + 3)(y - 2) = -5.$$

In terms of the coordinate system $x' = x + 3$ and $y' = y - 2$, we get the equation

$$x'y' = -5.$$

The graph of this equation has been drawn on the following diagram.

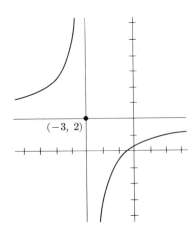

$(-3, 2)$

EXERCISES

Sketch the graphs of the following curves:

1. $(x - 1)(y - 2) = 2$

2. $x(y + 1) = 3$

3. $xy - 4 = 0$

4. $y = \dfrac{2}{1 - x}$

5. $y = \dfrac{1}{x + 1}$

6. $(x + 2)(y - 1) = 1$

7. $(x - 1)(y - 1) = 2$

8. $(x - 1)(y - 1) = 1$

9. $y = \dfrac{1}{x - 2} + 4$

10. $y = \dfrac{1}{x + 1} - 2$

11. $y = \dfrac{4x - 7}{x - 2}$

12. $y = \dfrac{-2x - 1}{x + 1}$

13. $y = \dfrac{x + 1}{x - 1}$

14. $y = \dfrac{x - 1}{x + 1}$

Chapter III

The Derivative

The two fundamental notions of this course are those of the derivative and the integral. We take up the first one in this chapter.

The derivative will give us the slope of a curve at a point. It has also applications to physics, where it can be interpreted as the rate of change.

We shall develop some basic techniques which will allow you to compute the derivative in all the standard situations which you are likely to encounter in practice.

§1. THE SLOPE OF A CURVE

Consider a curve, and take a point P on the curve. We wish to define the notions of slope of the curve at that point, and tangent line to the curve at that point. Sometimes the statement is made that the tangent to the curve at the point is the line which touches the curve only at that point. This is pure nonsense, as the subsequent pictures will convince you.

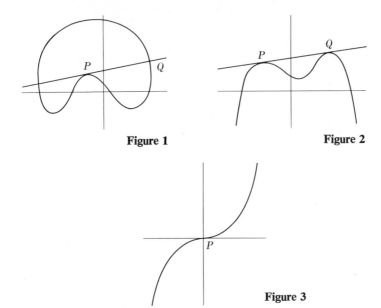

Figure 1 **Figure 2**

Figure 3

In Figs. 1, 2, and 3, we look at the tangent line to the curve at the point P. In Fig. 1 the line cuts the curve at the other point Q. In Fig. 2 the line is also tangent to the curve at the point Q. In Fig. 3 the curve is supposed to be very flat near the point P, and the horizontal line cuts the curve at P, but we would like to say that it is tangent to the curve at P if the curve is very flat. The vertical line cuts the curve only at P, but is not tangent.

Observe also that you cannot get out of the difficulties by trying to distinguish a line "cutting" the curve, or "touching the curve", or by saying that the line should lie on one side of the curve (cf. Fig. 1).

We therefore have to give up the idea of touching the curve only at one point, and look for another idea.

We have to face two problems. One of them is to give the correct geometric idea which allows us to define the tangent to the curve, and the other is to test whether this idea allows us to compute effectively this tangent line when the curve is given by a simple equation with numerical coefficients. It is a remarkable thing that our solution of the first problem will in fact give us a solution to the second.

In the first chapter, we have seen that knowing the slope of a straight line and one point on the straight line allows us to determine the equation of the line. We shall therefore define the slope of a curve at a point and then get its tangent afterward by using the method of Chapter II.

Our examples show us that to define the slope of the curve at P, we should not consider what happens at a point Q which is far removed from P. Rather, it is what happens near P which is important.

Let us therefore take any point Q on the given curve $y = f(x)$, and assume that $Q \neq P$. Then the two points P, Q determine a straight line with a certain slope which depends on P, Q and which we shall write as $S(P, Q)$. Suppose that the point Q approaches the point P on the curve (but stays distinct from P). Then, as Q comes near P, the slope $S(P, Q)$ of the line passing through P and Q should approach the (unknown) slope of the (unknown) tangent line to the curve at P. In the following diagram, we have drawn the tangent line to the curve at P and two lines between P and another point on the curve close to P (Fig. 4). The point Q_2 is closer to P on the curve and so the slope of the line between P and Q_2 is closer to the slope of the tangent line than is the slope of the line between P and Q_1.

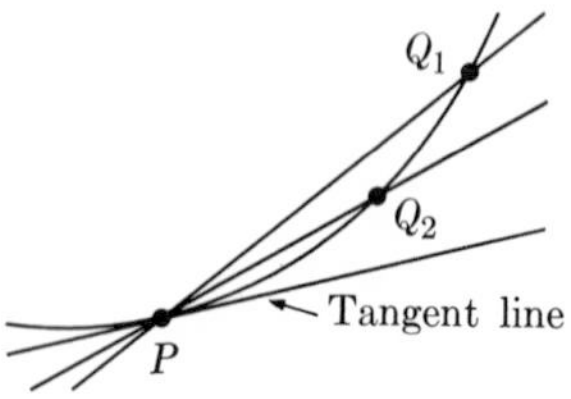

Figure 4

If the limit of the slope $S(P, Q)$ exists as Q approaches P, then it should be regarded as the slope of the curve itself at P. This is the basic idea behind our definition of the slope of the curve at P. We take it as a definition, perhaps the most important definition in this book. To repeat:

Given a curve $y = f(x)$, let P be a point on the curve. The *slope* of the curve at P is the limit of the slope of lines between P and another point Q on the curve, as Q approaches P.

The idea of defining the slope in this manner was discovered in the seventeenth century by Newton and Leibnitz. We shall see that this definition allows us to determine the slope effectively in practice.

First we observe that when $y = ax + b$ is a straight line, then the slope of the line between any two distinct points on the curve is always the same, and is the slope of the line as we defined it in the preceding chapter.

Let us now look at the next simplest example,

$$y = f(x) = x^2.$$

We wish to determine the slope of this curve at the point $(1, 1)$.

We look at a point near $(1, 1)$, for instance a point whose x-coordinate is 1.1. Then $f(1.1) = (1.1)^2 = 1.21$. Thus the point $(1.1, 1.21)$ lies on the curve. The slope of the line between two points (x_1, y_1) and (x_2, y_2) is

$$\frac{y_2 - y_1}{x_2 - x_1}.$$

Therefore the slope of the line between $(1, 1)$ and $(1.1, 1.21)$ is

$$\frac{1.21 - 1}{1.1 - 1} = \frac{0.21}{0.1} = 2.1.$$

In general, the x-coordinate of a point near $(1, 1)$ can be written $1 + h$, where h is some small number, positive or negative, but $h \neq 0$. We have

$$f(1 + h) = (1 + h)^2 = 1 + 2h + h^2.$$

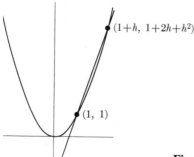

Figure 5

Thus the point $(1 + h, 1 + 2h + h^2)$ lies on the curve. When h is positive, the line between our two points would look like that in Fig. 5.

When h is negative, then $1 + h$ is smaller than 1 and the line would look like this:

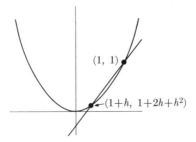

(1, 1)

$(1+h,\ 1+2h+h^2)$

Figure 6

For instance, h could be -0.1 and $1 + h = 0.9$.

The slope of the line between our two points is therefore the quotient

$$\frac{(1 + 2h + h^2) - 1}{(1 + h) - 1},$$

which is equal to

$$\frac{2h + h^2}{h} = 2 + h.$$

When the point whose x-coordinate is $1 + h$ approaches our point $(1, 1)$, the number h approaches 0. As h approaches 0, the slope of the line between our two points approaches 2, which is therefore the slope of the curve at the point $(1, 1)$ by definition.

You will appreciate how simple the computation turns out to be, and how easy it was to get this slope!

Let us take another example. We wish to find the slope of the same curve $(fx) = x^2$ at the point $(-2, 4)$. Again we take a nearby point whose x-coordinate is $-2 + h$ for small $h \neq 0$. The y-coordinate of this nearby point is

$$f(-2 + h) = (-2 + h)^2 = 4 - 4h + h^2.$$

The slope of the line between the two points is therefore

$$\frac{4 - 4h + h^2 - 4}{-2 + h - (-2)} = \frac{-4h + h^2}{h} = -4 + h.$$

As h approaches 0, the nearby point approaches the point $(-2, 4)$ and we see that the slope approaches -4.

EXERCISES

Find the slopes of the following curves at the indicated points:

1. $y = 2x^2$ at the point $(1, 2)$ 2. $y = x^2 + 1$ at the point $(-1, 2)$
3. $y = 2x - 7$ at the point $(2, -3)$ 4. $y = x^3$ at the point $(\frac{1}{2}, \frac{1}{8})$

5. $y = 1/x$ at the point $(2, \frac{1}{2})$ 6. $y = x^2 + 2x$ at the point $(-1, -1)$

7. $y = x^2$ at the point $(2, 4)$ 8. $y = x^2$ at the point $(3, 9)$

9. $y = x^3$ at the point $(1, 1)$ 10. $y = x^3$ at the point $(2, 8)$

11. $y = 2x + 3$ at the point whose x-coordinate is 2.

12. $y = 3x - 5$ at the point whose x-coordinate is 1.

13. $y = ax + b$ at an arbitrary point.

(In Exercises 11, 12, 13 use the h-method, and verify that this method gives the same answer for the slope as that stated in Chapter II, §3.)

§2. THE DERIVATIVE

We continue to consider the function $y = x^2$. Instead of picking a definite numerical value for the x-coordinate of a point, we could work at an arbitrary point on the curve. Its coordinates are then (x, x^2). We write the x-coordinate of a point nearby as $x + h$ for some small number h, positive or negative, but $h \neq 0$. The y-coordinate of this nearby point is

$$(x + h)^2 = x^2 + 2xh + h^2.$$

Hence the slope of the line between them is

$$\frac{(x + h)^2 - x^2}{(x + h) - x} = \frac{x^2 + 2xh + h^2 - x^2}{x + h - x}$$
$$= \frac{2xh + h^2}{h}$$
$$= 2x + h.$$

As h approaches 0, $2x + h$ approaches $2x$. Consequently, the slope of the curve $y = x^2$ at an arbitrary point (x, y) is $2x$. In particular, when $x = 1$ the slope is 2 and when $x = -2$ the slope is -4, as we found out before by the explicit computation using the special x-coordinates 1 and -2.

This time, however, we have found out a general formula giving us the slope for any point on the curve. Thus when $x = 3$ the slope is 6 and when $x = -10$ the slope is -20.

The example we have just worked out gives us the procedure for treating more general functions.

Given a function $f(x)$, we form the quotient

$$\frac{f(x + h) - f(x)}{x + h - x} = \frac{f(x + h) - f(x)}{h}.$$

This quotient is the slope of the line between the points

$$(x, f(x)) \quad \text{and} \quad (x + h, f(x + h)).$$

We shall call it the *Newton quotient*. If it approaches a limit as h approaches 0, then this limit is called the *derivative* of f at x, and we say that f is *differentiable* at x. The limit will be written in an abbreviated fashion,

$$\lim_{h \to 0} \frac{f(x + h) - f(x)}{h}.$$

The derivative will be written $f'(x)$, and we thus have

$$f'(x) = \lim_{h \to 0} \frac{f(x + h) - f(x)}{h}.$$

The derivative may thus be viewed as a function f', which is defined at all numbers x such that the Newton quotient approaches a limit as h tends to 0.

We say that f is *differentiable* if it is differentiable at all points for which it is defined. For instance the function $f(x) = x^2$ is differentiable and its derivative is $2x$.

It will also be convenient to use another notation for the derivative, namely

$$f'(x) = \frac{df}{dx}$$

(or df/dx). Thus the two expressions $f'(x)$ and df/dx mean the same thing. We emphasize however that in the expression df/dx we do not multiply f or x by d or divide df by dx. The expression is to be read *as a whole*. We shall find out later that the expression, under certain circumstances, behaves *as if* we were dividing, and it is for this reason that we adopt this classical way of writing the derivative.

We work out some examples before giving you exercises on this section.

Example 1. Let $f(x) = 2x + 1$. Find the derivative $f'(x)$.

We form the Newton quotient. We have $f(x + h) = 2(x + h) + 1$. Thus

$$\frac{f(x + h) - f(x)}{h} = \frac{2x + 2h + 1 - (2x + 1)}{h} = \frac{2h}{h} = 2.$$

As h approaches 0 (which we write also $h \to 0$), this number is equal to 2 and hence the limit is 2. Thus

$$f'(x) = 2$$

for all values of x. The derivative is constant.

Example 2. Find the slope of the graph of the function $f(x) = 2x^2$ at the point whose x-coordinate is 3.

We may just as well find the slope at an arbitrary point on the graph. It is the derivative $f'(x)$. We have

$$f(x + h) = 2(x + h)^2 = 2(x^2 + 2xh + h^2).$$

The Newton quotient is

$$\frac{f(x + h) - f(x)}{h} = \frac{2(x^2 + 2xh + h^2) - 2x^2}{h}$$

$$= \frac{4xh + 2h^2}{h}$$

$$= 4x + 2h.$$

As $h \to 0$ the limit is $4x$. Hence $f'(x) = 4x$. At the point $x = 3$ we get $f'(3) = 12$, which is the desired slope.

Example 3. Find the equation of the tangent line to the curve $y = 2x^2$ at the point whose x-coordinate is -2.

In the preceding example we have computed the general formula for the slope of the tangent line. It is

$$f'(x) = 4x.$$

At the point $x = -2$ the slope is therefore -8. The tangent line has an equation

$$y = -8x + b$$

for some number b. The y-coordinate of our point is $2(-2)^2 = 8$. Hence we must have

$$8 = -8(-2) + b$$

and solving for b yields

$$b = -8.$$

Thus the equation of the tangent line is

$$y = -8x - 8.$$

In defining the Newton quotient, we can take h positive or negative. It is sometimes convenient when taking the limit to look only at values of h which are positive. In this manner we get what is called the *right derivative*. If in taking the limit of the Newton quotient we took only negative values for h, we would get the *left derivative*.

Example 4. Let $f(x) = |x|$. Find its right derivative and its left derivative when $x = 0$.

The right derivative is the limit

$$\lim_{\substack{h \to 0 \\ h > 0}} \frac{f(0 + h) - f(0)}{h}.$$

When $h > 0$, we have $f(0 + h) = f(h) = h$, and $f(0) = 0$. Thus

$$\frac{f(0 + h) - f(0)}{h} = \frac{h}{h} = 1.$$

The limit as $h \to 0$ and $h > 0$ is therefore 1.

The left derivative is the limit

$$\lim_{\substack{h \to 0 \\ h < 0}} \frac{f(0 + h) - f(0)}{h}.$$

When $h < 0$ we have

$$f(0 + h) = f(h) = -h.$$

Hence

$$\frac{f(0 + h) - f(0)}{h} = \frac{-h}{h} = -1.$$

The limit as $h \to 0$ and $h < 0$ is therefore -1.

We see that the right derivative at 0 is 1 and the left derivative is -1. They are not equal. We would of course expect this from the graph of our function $f(x) = |x|$, which looks like that in Fig. 7.

Figure 7

Both the right derivative of f and the left derivative of f exist but they are not equal.

We would rephrase our definition of the derivative and say that the derivative of a function $f(x)$ is defined when the right derivative and the left derivative exist and they are equal, in which case this common value is simply called the *derivative*.

Example 5. Let $f(x)$ be equal to x if $0 < x \leq 1$ and $x - 1$ if $1 < x \leq 2$. We do not define f for other values of x. Then the graph of f looks like this:

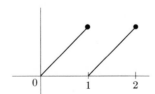

Figure 8

The left derivative of f at 1 exists and is equal to 1, but the right derivative of f at 1 does not exist. We leave the verification of the first assertion to you. To verify the second assertion, we must see whether the limit

$$\lim_{\substack{h \to 0 \\ h > 0}} \frac{f(1 + h) - f(1)}{h}$$

exists. Since $1 + h > 1$ we have

$$f(1 + h) = 1 + h - 1 = h.$$

Also $f(1) = 1$. Thus the Newton quotient is

$$\frac{f(1 + h) - f(1)}{h} = \frac{h - 1}{h} = 1 - \frac{1}{h}.$$

As h approaches 0 the quotient $1/h$ has no limit since it becomes arbitrarily large. Thus the Newton quotient has no limit for $h > 0$ and the function does not have a right derivative when $x = 1$.

EXERCISES

Find the derivatives of the following functions:

1. $x^2 + 1$ 2. x^3

3. $2x^3$ 4. $3x^2$

5. $x^2 - 5$ 6. $2x^2 + x$

7. $2x^2 - 3x$ 8. $\frac{1}{2}x^3 + 2x$

9. $\dfrac{1}{x + 1}$ 10. $\dfrac{2}{x + 1}$

11. In Exercises 1 through 10, find the slope of the graph at the point whose x-coordinate is 2, and find the equation of the tangent line at that point.

12. Let $f(x)$ be defined as follows:

$$f(x) = -x \quad \text{if} \quad x \leq 0 \qquad f(x) = 2 \quad \text{if} \quad x > 0.$$

Find $f'(x)$ when $x = -1$. Find the right and left derivatives of f at $x = 0$, if they exist.

13. Let $f(x) = |x| + x$. Does $f'(0)$ exist? Does $f'(x)$ exist for values of x other than 0?

14. Let $f(x) = 0$ if $x \leq 1$ and $f(x) = x$ if $x > 1$. Sketch the graph. Find the right and left derivatives of f when $x = 1$. Find $f'(x)$ for all other values of x.

15. Determine whether the following functions have a derivative at 0, and if so, what is the derivative.

(a) $f(x) = x|x|$ (b) $f(x) = x^2|x|$ (c) $f(x) = x^3|x|$

§3. LIMITS

In defining the slope of a curve at a point, or the derivative, we used the notion of limit, which we regarded as intuitively clear. It is indeed. You can see in the Appendix how one may define limits using only properties of numbers, but we do not worry about this here. However, we shall make a list of the properties of limits which will be used in the sequel, just to be sure of what we assume about them, and also to give you a technique for computing limits.

First, we note that if F is a constant function, $F(x) = c$ for all x, then

$$\lim_{h \to 0} F(h) = c$$

is the constant itself.

If $F(h) = h$, then

$$\lim_{h \to 0} F(h) = 0.$$

The next properties relate limits with addition, subtraction, multiplication, division, and inequalities.

Suppose that we have two functions $F(x)$ and $G(x)$ which are defined for the same numbers. Then we can form the sum of the two functions $F + G$, whose value at a point x is $F(x) + G(x)$. Thus when $F(x) = x^4$ and $G(x) = 5x^{3/2}$ we have

$$F(x) + G(x) = x^4 + 5x^{3/2}.$$

The value $F(x) + G(x)$ is also written $(F + G)(x)$. The first property of limits concerns the sum of two functions.

Property 1. Suppose that we have two functions F and G defined for small values of h, and assume that the limits

$$\lim_{h \to 0} F(h) \qquad \text{and} \qquad \lim_{h \to 0} G(h)$$

exist. Then

$$\lim_{h \to 0} [F(h) + G(h)]$$

exists and

$$\lim_{h \to 0} (F + G)(h) = \lim_{h \to 0} F(h) + \lim_{h \to 0} G(h).$$

In other words the limit of a sum is equal to the sum of the limits.

A similar statement holds for the difference $F - G$, namely

$$\lim_{h \to 0} (F(h) - G(h)) = \lim_{h \to 0} F(h) - \lim_{h \to 0} G(h)$$

After the sum we discuss the product. Suppose we have two functions F and G defined for the same numbers. Then we can form their product

FG whose value at a number x is

$$(FG)(x) = F(x)G(x).$$

For instance if $F(x) = 2x^2 - 2^x$ and $G(x) = x^2 + 5x$, then the product is

$$(FG)(x) = (2x^2 - 2^x)(x^2 + 5x).$$

Property 2. Let F, G be two functions defined for small values of h, and assume that

$$\lim_{h \to 0} F(h) \quad \text{and} \quad \lim_{h \to 0} G(h)$$

exist. Then the limit of the product exists and we have

$$\lim_{h \to 0} (FG)(h) = \lim_{h \to 0} [F(h)G(h)]$$

$$= \lim_{h \to 0} F(h) \cdot \lim_{h \to 0} G(h).$$

In words, we can say that the product of the limits is equal to the limit of the product.

As a special case, suppose that $F(x)$ is the constant function $F(x) = c$. Then we can form the function cG, product of the constant by G, and we have

$$\lim_{h \to 0} cG(h) = c \cdot \lim_{h \to 0} G(h).$$

Thirdly, we come to quotients. Let F, G be as before, but assume that $G(x) \neq 0$ for any x. Then we can form the quotient function F/G whose value at x is

$$\frac{F}{G}(x) = \frac{F(x)}{G(x)}.$$

Property 3. Assume that the limits

$$\lim_{h \to 0} F(h) \quad \text{and} \quad \lim_{h \to 0} G(h)$$

exist, and that

$$\lim_{h \to 0} G(h) \neq 0.$$

Then the limit of the quotient exists and we have

$$\lim_{h \to 0} \frac{F(h)}{G(h)} = \frac{\lim F(h)}{\lim G(h)}.$$

In words, the quotient of the limits is equal to the limit of the quotient.

As we have done above, we shall sometimes omit writing $h \to 0$ for the sake of simplicity.

Property 4. Let F, G be two functions defined for small values of h, and assume that $G(h) \leqq F(h)$. Assume also that

$$\lim_{h \to 0} F(h) \quad \text{and} \quad \lim_{h \to 0} G(h)$$

exist. Then

$$\lim_{h \to 0} G(h) \leqq \lim_{h \to 0} F(h).$$

Property 5. Let the assumptions be as in Property 4, and in addition, assume that

$$\lim_{h \to 0} G(h) = \lim_{h \to 0} F(h).$$

Let E be another function defined for the same numbers as F, G such that

$$G(h) \leqq E(h) \leqq F(h)$$

for all small values of h. Then

$$\lim_{h \to 0} E(h)$$

exists and is equal to the limits of F and G.

Property 5 is known as the squeezing process. You will find many applications of it in the sequel.

Example 1. Find the limit

$$\lim_{h \to 0} \frac{2xh + 3}{x^2 - 4h}$$

when $x \neq 0$.

The numerator of our quotient approaches 3 when $h \to 0$ and the denominator approaches x^2. Thus the quotient approaches $3/x^2$. We can justify these steps more formally by applying our three properties. For instance:

$$\begin{aligned}
\lim_{h \to 0} (2xh + 3) &= \lim_{h \to 0} (2xh) + \lim_{h \to 0} 3 \\
&= \lim (2x) \lim (h) + \lim 3 \\
&= 2x \cdot 0 + 3 \\
&= 3.
\end{aligned}$$

For the denominator, we have

$$\begin{aligned}
\lim (x^2 - 4h) &= \lim x^2 + \lim (-4h) \\
&= x^2 + \lim (-4) \lim (h) \\
&= x^2 + (-4) \cdot 0 \\
&= x^2.
\end{aligned}$$

Using the rule for the quotient, we get $3/x^2$.

The properties of limits which we have stated above will allow you to compute limits in determining derivatives.   We illustrate this by an example.

Example 2.   Let $f(x) = 1/x$ (defined for $x \neq 0$).   Find the derivative df/dx.

The Newton quotient is

$$\frac{f(x + h) - f(x)}{h} = \frac{\frac{1}{x + h} - \frac{1}{x}}{h}.$$

We put everything over a common denominator $(x + h)xh$. The Newton quotient is equal to

$$\frac{x - (x + h)}{(x + h)xh} = \frac{-h}{(x + h)xh} = \frac{-1}{(x + h)x}.$$

Thus we have to determine the limit of a quotient as h approaches 0. Using the property of a product, we have

$$\lim (x + h)x = \lim (x + h) \lim x$$
$$= x^2.$$

Using the property of quotients, we see that the Newton quotient for the function $1/x$ approaches $-1/x^2$.   Thus

$$\frac{df}{dx} = \lim_{h \to 0} \frac{f(x + h) - f(x)}{h} = \frac{-1}{x^2}.$$

EXERCISES

Find the derivatives of the following functions, justifying the steps in taking limits by means of the first three properties:

1. $f(x) = 2x^2 + 3x$ 2. $f(x) = \dfrac{1}{2x + 1}$ 3. $f(x) = \dfrac{x}{x + 1}$

4. $f(x) = x(x + 1)$ 5. $f(x) = \dfrac{x}{2x - 1}$ 6. $f(x) = 3x^3$

7. $f(x) = x^4$ 8. $f(x) = x^5$ 9. $f(x) = 2x^3$

10. $f(x) = \frac{1}{2}x^3 + x$

§4. POWERS

We have seen that the derivative of the function x^2 is $2x$.

Let us consider the function $f(x) = x^3$ and find its derivative.   We have

$$f(x + h) = (x + h)^3 = x^3 + 3x^2h + 3xh^2 + h^3.$$

Hence the Newton quotient is

$$\frac{f(x + h) - f(x)}{h} = \frac{x^3 + 3x^2h + 3xh^2 + h^3 - x^3}{h}$$

$$= 3x^2 + 3xh + h^2.$$

Using the properties of limits of sums and products, we see that $3x^2$ remains equal to itself as h approaches 0, that $3xh$ and h^3 both approach 0. Hence

$$f'(x) = \lim_{h \to 0} \frac{f(x + h) - f(x)}{h} = 3x^2.$$

This suggests that in general, whenever $f(x) = x^n$ for some positive integer n, the derivative $f'(x)$ should be nx^{n-1}. This is indeed the case, and we state it as a theorem.

Theorem 1. *Let n be an integer ≥ 1 and let $f(x) = x^n$. Then*

$$\frac{df}{dx} = nx^{n-1}.$$

Proof. We have

$$f(x + h) = (x + h)^n = (x + h)(x + h) \cdots (x + h),$$

the product being taken n times. Selecting x from each factor gives us a term x^n. If we take x from all but one factor and h from the remaining factor, we get hx^{n-1} taken n times. This gives us a term $nx^{n-1}h$. All other terms will involve selecting h from at least two factors, and the corresponding term will be divisible by h^2. Thus we get

$$f(x + h) = (x + h)^n = x^n + nx^{n-1}h + h^2 g(x, h),$$

where $g(x, h)$ is simply some expression involving powers of x and h with numerical coefficients which it is unnecessary for us to determine. However, using the rules for limits of sums and products we can conclude that

$$\lim_{h \to 0} g(x, h)$$

will be some number which it is unnecessary for us to determine.
The Newton quotient is therefore

$$\frac{f(x + h) - f(x)}{h} = \frac{x^n + nx^{n-1}h + h^2 g(x, h) - x^n}{h}.$$

We can cancel x^n and are left with

$$\frac{nx^{n-1}h + h^2 g(x, h)}{h}.$$

We can now divide numerator and denominator by h, thereby giving us

$$nx^{n-1} + hg(x, h).$$

As h approaches 0, the term nx^{n-1} remains unchanged. The limit of h as h tends to 0 is 0, and hence by the product rule, the term $hg(x, h)$ approaches 0 when h tends to 0. Thus finally

$$\lim_{h \to 0} \frac{f(x + h) - f(x)}{h} = nx^{n-1},$$

which proves our theorem.

Theorem 2. *Let a be any number and let* $f(x) = x^a$ *(defined for $x > 0$). Then $f(x)$ has a derivative, which is*

$$f'(x) = ax^{a-1}.$$

It would not be difficult to prove Theorem 2 when a is a negative integer. It is best however to wait until we have a rule giving us the derivative of a quotient before doing it. We could also give a proof when a is a rational number. However, we shall prove the general result in a later chapter, and thus we prefer to wait until then, when we have more techniques available.

Examples. If $f(x) = x^{10}$ then $f'(x) = 10x^9$.

If $f(x) = x^{3/2}$ (for $x > 0$) then $f'(x) = \frac{3}{2}x^{1/2}$.

If $f(x) = x^{-5/4}$ then $f'(x) = -\frac{5}{4}x^{-9/4}$.

If $f(x) = x^{\sqrt{2}}$ then $f'(x) = \sqrt{2}\,x^{\sqrt{2}-1}$.

Note especially the special case when $f(x) = x$. Then $f'(x) = 1$.

EXERCISES

1. Write out the expansion of $(x + h)^4$ in terms of powers of x and h.

2. Find the derivative of the function x^4 directly, using the Newton quotient.

3. What are the derivatives of the following functions?

    (a) $x^{2/3}$ (b) $x^{-3/2}$ (c) $x^{7/6}$

4. What is the equation of the tangent line to the curve $y = x^9$ at the point $(1, 1)$?

5. What is the slope of the curve $y = x^{2/3}$ at the point $(8, 4)$? What is the equation of the tangent line at that point?

6. Give the slope and equation of the tangent line to the curve $y = x^{-3/4}$ at the point whose x-coordinate is 16.

7. Give the slope and equation of the tangent line to the curve $y = \sqrt{x}$ at the point whose x-coordinate is 3.

8. Give the derivatives of the following functions at the indicated points:

(a) $f(x) = x^{1/4}$ at $x = 5$ (b) $f(x) = x^{-1/4}$ at $x = 7$

(c) $f(x) = x^{\sqrt{2}}$ at $x = 10$ (d) $f(x) = x^{\pi}$ at $x = 7$

§5. SUMS, PRODUCTS, AND QUOTIENTS

In this section we shall derive several rules which allow you to find the derivatives for sums, products, and quotients of functions when you know the derivative of each factor.

Before stating and proving these rules, we make one remark concerning the derivative.

Let $f(x)$ be a function having a derivative $f'(x)$. Since the quotient

$$\frac{f(x + h) - f(x)}{h}$$

approaches a limit as h approaches 0, and since

$$f(x + h) = f(x) + h \frac{f(x + h) - f(x)}{h},$$

using the rules for sums and products of limits, we conclude that

$$\lim_{h \to 0} f(x + h) = f(x),$$

and that $f(x + h) - f(x)$ approaches 0 as h approaches 0.

Of course, we can never substitute $h = 0$ in our quotient, because then it becomes $0/0$, which is meaningless. Geometrically, letting $h = 0$ amounts to taking the two points on the curve equal to each other. It is then impossible to have a unique straight line through one point. Our procedure of taking the limit of the Newton quotient is meaningful only if $h \neq 0$.

Let c be a number and $f(x)$ a function which has a derivative $f'(x)$ for all values of x for which it is defined. We can multiply f by the constant c to get another function cf whose value at x is $cf(x)$.

The derivative of cf is then given by the formula

$$(cf)'(x) = c \cdot f'(x);$$

in other words, the derivative of a constant times a function is the constant times the derivative of the function.

To prove this rule, we use the definition of derivative. The Newton quotient for the function cf is

$$\frac{(cf)(x + h) - (cf)(x)}{h} = \frac{cf(x + h) - cf(x)}{h} = c \frac{f(x + h) - f(x)}{h}.$$

Let us take the limit as h approaches 0. Then c remains fixed, and

$$\frac{f(x + h) - f(x)}{h}$$

approaches $f'(x)$. According to the rule for the product of limits, we see that our Newton quotient approaches $cf'(x)$, as was to be proved.

For example, let $f(x) = 3x^2$. Then $f'(x) = 6x$. If $f(x) = 17x^{1/2}$, then $f'(x) = \frac{17}{2}x^{-1/2}$. If $f(x) = 10x^a$, then $f'(x) = 10ax^{a-1}$.

Next we look at the sum of two functions.

Let $f(x)$ and $g(x)$ be two functions which have derivatives $f'(x)$ and $g'(x)$, respectively. Then the sum $f(x) + g(x)$ has a derivative, and

$$(f + g)'(x) = f'(x) + g'(x).$$

The derivative of a sum is equal to the sum of the derivatives.

To prove this, we have by definition

$$(f + g)(x + h) = f(x + h) + g(x + h)$$
$$(f + g)(x) = f(x) + g(x).$$

Therefore the Newton quotient for $f + g$ is

$$\frac{(f + g)(x + h) - (f + g)(x)}{h} = \frac{f(x + h) + g(x + h) - f(x) - g(x)}{h}.$$

Collecting terms and separating the fraction, we see that this expression is equal to

$$\frac{f(x + h) - f(x) + g(x + h) - g(x)}{h}$$
$$= \frac{f(x + h) - f(x)}{h} + \frac{g(x + h) - g(x)}{h}.$$

Taking the limit as h approaches 0 and using the rule for the limit of a sum, we see that this last sum approaches $f'(x) + g'(x)$ as h approaches 0. This proves what we wanted.

For example, the derivative of the function $x^3 + x^2$ is $3x^2 + 2x$. The derivative of the function $4x^{1/2} + 5x^{-10}$ is

$$2x^{-1/2} - 50x^{-11}.$$

Carried away by our enthusiasm at determining so easily the derivative of functions built up from others by means of constants and sums, we might now be tempted to state the rule that the derivative of a product is the product of the derivatives. Unfortunately, this is false. To see that the rule is false, we look at an example.

Let $f(x) = x$ and $g(x) = x^2$. Then $f'(x) = 1$ and $g'(x) = 2x$. Therefore $f'(x)g'(x) = 2x$. However, the derivative of the product $(fg)(x) = x^3$ is $3x^2$, which is certainly not equal to $2x$. Thus the product of the derivatives is not equal to the derivative of the product.

Through trial and error the correct rule was discovered. It can be stated as follows:

Let $f(x)$ and $g(x)$ be two functions having derivatives $f'(x)$ and $g'(x)$. Then the product function $f(x)g(x)$ has a derivative, which is given by the formula

$$(fg)'(x) = f'(x)g(x) + f(x)g'(x).$$

In words, the derivative of the product is equal to the derivative of the first times the second, plus the first times the derivative of the second.

The proof is not very much more difficult than the proofs we have already encountered. By definition, we have

$$(fg)(x + h) = f(x + h)g(x + h)$$
$$(fg)(x) = f(x)g(x).$$

Consequently the Newton quotient for the product function fg is

$$\frac{(fg)(x + h) - (fg)(x)}{h} = \frac{f(x + h)g(x + h) - f(x)g(x)}{h}.$$

At this point, it looks a little hopeless to transform this quotient in such a way that we see easily what limit it approaches as h tends to 0. But we rewrite our quotient by inserting

$$-f(x)g(x + h) + f(x)g(x + h)$$

in the numerator. This certainly does not change the value of our quotient, which now looks like

$$\frac{f(x + h)g(x + h) - f(x)g(x + h) + f(x)g(x + h) - f(x)g(x)}{h}.$$

We can split this fraction into a sum of two fractions:

$$\frac{f(x + h)g(x + h) - f(x)g(x + h)}{h} + \frac{f(x)g(x + h) - f(x)g(x)}{h}.$$

We can factor $g(x + h)$ in the first term, and $f(x)$ in the second term, to obtain

$$\frac{f(x + h) - f(x)}{h}g(x + h) + f(x)\frac{g(x + h) - g(x)}{h}.$$

The situation is now well under control. As h tends to 0, $g(x + h)$ tends to $g(x)$, and the two quotients in the expression we have just written tend to $f'(x)$ and $g'(x)$ respectively. Thus the Newton quotient for fg tends to

$$f'(x)g(x) + f(x)g'(x),$$

thereby proving our assertion.

To illustrate the rules for products, let us find the derivative of

$$(x + 1)(3x^2).$$

Applying the rule, we see that it is equal to

$$1 \cdot (3x^2) + (x + 1)6x.$$

Similarly, let $f(x) = 2x^5 + 5x^4$ and $g(x) = 2x^{1/2} + x^{-1}$. Then the derivative of $f(x)g(x)$ is

$$(10x^4 + 20x^3)(2x^{1/2} + x^{-1}) + (2x^5 + 5x^4)\left(x^{-1/2} - \frac{1}{x^2}\right),$$

which you may and should leave just like that without attempting to simplify the expression.

The last rule of this section concerns the derivative of a quotient. We begin with a special case.

Let $g(x)$ be a function having a derivative $g'(x)$, and such that $g(x) \neq 0$. Then the derivative of the quotient $1/g(x)$ exists, and is equal to

$$\frac{-1}{g(x)^2} g'(x).$$

To prove this, we look at the Newton quotient

$$\frac{\dfrac{1}{g(x + h)} - \dfrac{1}{g(x)}}{h}$$

which is equal to

$$\frac{g(x) - g(x + h)}{g(x + h)g(x)h} = -\frac{1}{g(x + h)g(x)} \frac{g(x + h) - g(x)}{h}.$$

Letting h approach 0 we see immediately that our expression approaches

$$\frac{-1}{g(x)^2} g'(x)$$

as desired.

The general case of the rule for quotients can now be easily stated and proved.

Let $f(x)$ and $g(x)$ be two functions having derivatives $f'(x)$ and $g'(x)$ respectively, and such that $g(x) \neq 0$. Then the derivative of the quotient

$f(x)/g(x)$ exists, *and is equal to*

$$\frac{g(x)f'(x) - f(x)g'(x)}{g(x)^2}.$$

Putting this into words yields: *The bottom times the derivative of the top, minus the top times the derivative of the bottom, over the bottom squared* (which you can memorize like a poem).

To prove this rule, we write our quotient in the form

$$\frac{f(x)}{g(x)} = f(x)\frac{1}{g(x)}$$

and use the rule for the derivative of a product, together with the special case we have just proved. We obtain

$$f'(x)\frac{1}{g(x)} + f(x)\frac{-1}{g(x)^2}g'(x).$$

Putting this expression over the common denominator $g(x)^2$ yields

$$\frac{g(x)f'(x) - f(x)g'(x)}{g(x)^2},$$

which is the desired derivative.

We work out some examples.

Let $f(x) = x^2 + 1$ and $g(x) = 3x^4 - 2x$. Then the derivative of $f(x)/g(x)$ is

$$\frac{(3x^4 - 2x)2x - (x^2 + 1)(12x^3 - 2)}{(3x^4 - 2x)^2}.$$

Still another: The derivative of $2x/(x + 4)$ is

$$\frac{(x + 4) \cdot 2 - 2x \cdot 1}{(x + 4)^2}.$$

For future reference, we write the various rules which we have proved into the df/dx notation. The first one:

$$\frac{d(cf)}{dx} = c \cdot \frac{df}{dx}.$$

The sum: $$\frac{d(f + g)}{dx} = \frac{df}{dx} + \frac{dg}{dx}.$$

The product: $$\frac{d(fg)}{dx} = \frac{df}{dx}g(x) + f(x)\frac{dg}{dx}.$$

The quotient: $$\frac{d(f/g)}{dx} = \frac{g\dfrac{df}{dx} - f\dfrac{dg}{dx}}{g(x)^2}.$$

EXERCISES

Find the derivatives of the following functions:

1. $2x^{1/3}$

2. $5x^{11}$

3. $\frac{1}{2}x^{-3/4}$

4. $7x^3 + 4x^2$

5. $25x^{-1} + 12x^{1/2}$

6. $\frac{3}{5}x^2 - 2x^8$

7. $(x^3 + x)(x - 1)$

8. $(2x^2 - 1)(x^4 + 1)$

9. $(x + 1)(x^2 + 5x^{3/2})$

10. $(2x - 5)(3x^4 + 5x + 2)$

11. $(x^{-2/3} + x^2)\left(x^3 + \dfrac{1}{x}\right)$

12. $(2x + 3)\left(\dfrac{1}{x^2} + \dfrac{1}{x}\right)$

13. $\dfrac{2x + 1}{x + 5}$

14. $\dfrac{2x}{x^2 + 3x + 1}$

To break the monotony of the letter x, let us use another.

15. $f(t) = \dfrac{t^2 + 2t - 1}{(t + 1)(t - 1)}$

16. $\dfrac{t^{-5/4}}{t^2 + t - 1}$

17. What is the slope of the curve

$$y = \frac{t}{t + 5}$$

at the point $t = 2$? What is the equation of the tangent line at this point?

18. What is the slope of the curve

$$y = \frac{t^2}{t^2 + 1}$$

at $t = 1$? What is the equation of the tangent line?

§6. THE CHAIN RULE

We know how to build up new functions from old ones by means of sums, products, and quotients. There is one other important way of building up new functions. We shall first give examples of this new way.

Consider the function $(x + 2)^{10}$. We can say that this function is made up of the 10-th power function, and the function $x + 2$. Namely, given a number x, we first add 2 to it, and then take the 10-th power. Let

$$g(x) = x + 2$$

and let f be the 10-th power function. Then we can take the value of f at $x + 2$, namely

$$f(x + 2) = (x + 2)^{10}$$

and we can also write it as

$$f(x + 2) = f(g(x)).$$

Another example: Consider the function $(3x^4 - 1)^{1/2}$. If we let $g(x) = 3x^4 - 1$ and f be the square root function, then

$$f(g(x)) = \sqrt{3x^4 - 1} = (3x^4 - 1)^{1/2}.$$

In order not to get confused by the letter x, which cannot serve us any more in all contexts, we use another letter to denote the values of g. Thus we may write $f(u) = u^{1/2}$.

Similarly, let $f(u)$ be the function $u + 5$ and $g(x) = 2x$. Then

$$f(g(x)) = f(2x) = 2x + 5.$$

One more example of the same type: Let

$$f(u) = \frac{1}{u + 2}$$

and

$$g(x) = x^{10}.$$

Then

$$f(g(x)) = \frac{1}{x^{10} + 2}.$$

In order to give you sufficient practice with many types of functions, we now mention several of them whose definitions will be given later. These will be sin and cos (which we read sine and cosine), log (which we read logarithm or simply log), and the exponential function exp. We shall select a special number e (whose value is approximately 2.718...), such that the function exp is given by

$$\exp(x) = e^x.$$

We now see how we make new functions out of these.

Let $f(u) = \sin u$ and $g(x) = x^2$. Then

$$f(g(x)) = \sin(x^2).$$

Let $f(u) = e^u$ and $g(x) = \cos x$. Then

$$f(g(x)) = e^{\cos x}.$$

Let $f(v) = \log v$ and $g(t) = t^3 - 1$. Then

$$f(g(t)) = \log(t^3 - 1).$$

Let $g(w) = w^{10}$ and $f(z) = \log z + \sin z$. Then

$$g(f(z)) = (\log z + \sin z)^{10}.$$

You should practice with part (a) of the exercises, in order to assimilate properly the terminology and mechanisms of these combined functions.

Whenever we have two functions f and g such that f is defined for all numbers which are values of g, then we can build a new function denoted by $f \circ g$ whose value at a number x is

$$(f \circ g)(x) = f\big(g(x)\big).$$

The rule defining this new function is: Take the number x, find the number $g(x)$, and then take the value of f at $g(x)$. This is the value of $f \circ g$ at x. The function $f \circ g$ is called the *composite function* of f and g. We say that g is the *inner* function and that f is the *outer* function.

It is important to keep in mind that we can compose two functions only when the outer function is defined at all values of the inner function. For instance, let $f(u) = u^{1/2}$ and $g(x) = -x^2$. Then we cannot form the composite function $f \circ g$ because f is defined only for positive numbers (or 0) and the values of g are all negative, or 0. Thus $(-x^2)^{1/2}$ does not make sense.

However, for the moment you are asked to learn the mechanism of composite functions just the way you learned the multiplication table, in order to acquire efficient conditioned reflexes when you meet composite functions. Hence for the drills given by the exercises at the end of the section, you should forget for a while the meaning of the symbols and operate with them formally, just to learn the formal rules properly.

We come to the problem of taking the derivative of a composite function.

We start with an example. Suppose we want to find the derivative of the function $(x + 1)^{10}$. The Newton quotient would be a very long expression, which it would be essentially hopeless to disentangle by brute force, the way we have up to now. It is therefore a pleasant surprise that there will be an easy way of finding the derivative. We tell you the answer right away: The derivative of this function is $10(x + 1)^9$. This looks very much related to the derivative of powers.

Before proving and stating the general theorem, we give you other examples. The derivative of $(x^2 + 2x)^{3/2}$ is $\frac{3}{2}(x^2 + 2x)^{1/2}(2x + 2)$. Observe carefully the extra term $2x + 2$, which is the derivative of the expression $x^2 + 2x$.

The derivative of $(x^2 + x)^{10}$ is $10(x^2 + x)^9(2x + 1)$. Observe again the presence of the term $2x + 1$, which is the derivative of $x^2 + x$.

Can you guess the general rule from the preceding assertions? The general rule was also discovered by trial and error, but we profit from three centuries of experience, and thus we are able to state it and prove it very simply, as follows.

Let f and g be two functions having derivatives, and such that f is defined at all numbers which are values of g. Then the composite function $f \circ g$ has *a derivative, given by the formula*

$$(f \circ g)'(x) = f'(g(x))g'(x).$$

This can be expressed in words by saying that we take the *derivative of the outer function times the derivative of the inner function (or the derivative of what's inside).*

The preceding assertion is known as the *chain rule*, and we shall now prove it. We shall use a property of composite limits proved in the Appendix 1.

We must consider the Newton quotient of the composite function $f \circ g$. By definition, it is

$$\frac{f((gx + h)) - f(g(x))}{h}.$$

Put $u = g(x)$, and let

$$k = g(x + h) - g(x).$$

Then k depends on h, and tends to 0 as h approaches 0. Our Newton quotient is equal to

$$\frac{f(u + k) - f(u)}{h}.$$

Suppose that k is unequal to 0 for all small values of h. Then we can multiply and divide this quotient by k, and obtain

$$\frac{f(u + k) - f(u)}{k} \frac{k}{h} = \frac{f(u + k) - f(u)}{k} \frac{g(x + h) - g(x)}{h}.$$

If we let h approach 0 and use the rule for the limit of a product, we see that our Newton quotient approaches

$$f'(u)g'(x),$$

and this would prove our chain rule, under the assumption that k is not 0.

It does not happen very often that $k = 0$ for arbitrarily small values of h, but when it does happen, the preceding argument breaks down. For those of you who are interested, we shall show you how the argument can be slightly modified so as to be valid in all cases. The uninterested reader can just skip it.

We go back to the definition of the derivative of f. Given a number u such that $f(u)$ is defined, we know that

$$\lim_{k \to 0} \frac{f(u + k) - f(u)}{k} = f'(u).$$

Therefore, the limit of the expression

$$\varphi(k) = \frac{f(u + k) - f(u)}{k} - f'(u)$$

as k approaches 0 is equal to 0. In symbols:

$$\lim_{k \to 0} \varphi(k) = 0.$$

Multiplying by k we obtain

$$k\varphi(k) = f(u + k) - f(u) - kf'(u)$$

or

$$f(u + k) - f(u) = k \cdot f'(u) + k \cdot \varphi(k).$$

So far, this is valid only when k is not 0. But if we define $\varphi(0)$ to be 0, then we note that the relationship we have just derived is still valid when $k = 0$ because k does not appear in the denominator. Substituting $k = 0$ just yields

$$f(u) - f(u) = 0,$$

which is certainly true.

Now let $u = g(x)$ and let $k = g(x + h) - g(x)$. As h approaches zero, so does k.

The Newton quotient for the composite function $f \circ g$ is

$$\frac{f\big(g(x + h)\big) - f\big(g(x)\big)}{h} = \frac{f(u + k) - f(u)}{h},$$

which, by the expression we have just derived, is equal to

$$\frac{k \cdot f'(u) + k \cdot \varphi(k)}{h},$$

or substituting the value for k, is equal to

$$\frac{g(x + h) - g(x)}{h} f'(u) + \frac{g(x + h) - g(x)}{h} \varphi(k).$$

Taking the limit as h approaches 0, we see that the first term approaches $g'(x)f'(u)$. So far as the second term is concerned, taking the limit, we get

$$\lim_{h \to 0} \frac{g(x + h) - g(x)}{h} \varphi(k) = g'(x) \cdot 0 = 0$$

because the limit of $\varphi(k)$ as h or k goes to 0 is 0. This proves that the Newton quotient of $f \circ g$ approaches

$$f'(u)g'(x)$$

and concludes the proof of the chain rule in general.

We are in a position to see the reason for the notation dg/dx. The chain rule in this notation can be expressed by the formula

$$\frac{d(f \circ g)}{dx} = \frac{df}{du}\frac{du}{dx}$$

if $u = g(x)$ is a function of x. Thus the derivative behaves *as if* we could cancel the *du*. As long as we have proved this result, there is nothing wrong with working like a machine in computing derivatives of composite functions, and we shall give you several examples before the exercises.

Let $f(u) = u^{10}$ and $u = g(x) = x^2 + 1$. Then $f'(u) = 10u^9$ and $g'(x) = 2x$. Thus

$$\frac{d(f \circ g)}{dx} = 10u^9 \cdot 2x = 10(x^2 + 1)^9 2x.$$

Let $f(u) = 2u^{1/2}$ and $g(x) = 5x + 1$. Then $f'(u) = u^{-1/2}$ and $g'(x) = 5$. Thus

$$\frac{d(f \circ g)}{dx} = (5x + 1)^{-1/2} \cdot 5.$$

(Pay attention to the constant 5, which is the derivative of $5x + 1$. You are very likely to forget it.)

In order to give you more extensive drilling than would be afforded by the functions we have considered, like powers, we summarize the derivatives of the elementary functions which are to be considered later.

$$\frac{d(\sin x)}{dx} = \cos x. \qquad \frac{d(\cos x)}{dx} = -\sin x.$$

$$\frac{d(e^x)}{dx} = e^x \text{ (yes, } e^x, \text{ the same as the function!)}.$$

$$\frac{d(\log x)}{dx} = \frac{1}{x}.$$

In view of these, and the chain rule, we see that the derivative of $(\sin x)^7$ is $7(\sin x)^6(\cos x)$. (Here again we emphasize the appearance of $\cos x$, which is the derivative of what's inside our composite function.)

The derivative of $(\log x)^{1/2}$ is $\frac{1}{2}(\log x)^{-1/2} \cdot \frac{1}{x}$.

The derivative of $e^{\sin x}$ is $e^{\sin x}(\cos x)$.

The derivative of $\cos(2x^2)$ is $-\sin(2x^2) \cdot 4x$. (The $4x$ is the derivative of $2x^2$.)

EXERCISES

(a) In each case, find two functions $f(u)$ and $g(x)$ such that the indicated function is of type $f(g(x))$.

(b) Find the derivative of the indicated function. Do not attempt to simplify your answers.

1. $(x + 1)^8$

2. $(2x - 5)^{1/2}$

3. $(\sin x)^3$

4. $(\log x)^5$

5. $\sin 2x$

6. $\log (x^2 + 1)$

7. $e^{\cos x}$

8. $\log (e^x + \sin x)$

9. $\sin \left(\log x + \dfrac{1}{x}\right)$

10. $\dfrac{x + 1}{\sin 2x}$

11. $(2x^2 + 3)^3$

12. $\cos (\sin 5x)$

13. $\log (\cos 2x)$

14. $\sin [(2x + 5)^2]$

15. $\sin [\cos (x + 1)]$

16. $\sin (e^x)$

17. $\dfrac{1}{(3x - 1)^4}$

18. $\dfrac{1}{(4x)^3}$

19. $\dfrac{1}{(\sin 2x)^2}$

20. $\dfrac{1}{(\cos 2x)^2}$

21. $\dfrac{1}{\sin 3x}$

22. $(\sin x)(\cos x)$

23. $(x^2 + 1)e^x$

24. $(x^3 + 2x)(\sin 3x)$

25. $\dfrac{1}{\sin x + \cos x}$

26. $\dfrac{\sin 2x}{e^x}$

27. $\dfrac{\log x}{x^2 + 3}$

28. $\dfrac{x + 1}{\cos 2x}$

29. $(2x - 3)(e^x + x)$

30. $(x^3 - 1)(e^{3x} + 5x)$

31. $\dfrac{x^3 + 1}{x - 1}$

32. $\dfrac{x^2 - 1}{2x + 3}$

33. $(x^{4/3} - e^x)(2x + 1)$

34. $(\sin 3x)(x^{1/4} - 1)$

35. $\sin (x^2 + 5x)$

36. e^{3x^2+8}

37. $\dfrac{1}{\log (x^4 + 1)}$

38. $\dfrac{1}{\log (x^{1/2} + 2x)}$

39. $\dfrac{2x}{e^x}$

40. Relax.

§7. HIGHER DERIVATIVES

Given a differentiable function f defined on an interval, its derivative f' is also a function on this interval. If it turns out to be also differentiable (this being usually the case), then its derivative is called the *second derivative* of f and is denoted by $f''(x)$. For instance, the first derivative of $(x^2 + 1)^2$ is $2(x^2 + 1)2x = 4x^3 + 4x$, and the second derivative $f''(x)$ is $12x^2 + 4$.

There is no reason to stop at the second derivative, and one can of course continue with the third, fourth, etc. provided they exist.

Example. The third derivative of the function $f(x) = x^3$ is the constant function 6.

Since it is notationally inconvenient to pile up primes after f to denote successive derivatives, one writes

$$f^{(n)}$$

for the n-th derivative of f. Thus f'' is also written $f^{(2)}$.

EXERCISES

Find the second derivatives of the following functions:

1. $3x^3 + 5x + 1$ 　　　　　　　　　　2. $(x^2 + 1)^5$
3. Find the 80-th derivative of $x^7 + 5x - 1$.
4. Find the 7-th derivative of $x^7 + 5x - 1$.
5. Find the third derivative of $x^2 + 1$.
6. Find the third derivative of $x^3 + 2x - 5$.
7. Find the third derivative of the function $f(x) = \sin x$.
8. Find the fourth derivative of the function $g(x) = \cos x$.
9. Find the 10th derivative of $\sin x$. 　　10. Find the 10th derivative of $\cos x$.
11. Find the 100th derivative of $\sin x$.
12. Find the 100th derivative of $\cos x$.

§8. RATE OF CHANGE

The derivative has an interesting physical interpretation, which was very closely connected with it in its historical development, and is worth mentioning.

Suppose that a particle moves along some straight line a certain distance depending on time t. Then the distance s is a function of t, which we write $s = f(t)$.

For two values of the time, t_1 and t_2, the quotient

$$\frac{f(t_2) - f(t_1)}{t_2 - t_1}$$

can be regarded as a sort of average velocity of the particle. At a given time t_0, it is therefore reasonable to regard the limit

$$\lim_{t \to t_0} \frac{f(t) - f(t_0)}{t - t_0}$$

as the rate of change of s with respect to t. This is none other than the derivative $f'(t)$.

For instance if the particle is an object dropping under the influence of gravity, then experimental data show that

$$s = \tfrac{1}{2}gt^2,$$

where g is the gravitational constant. In that case,

$$\frac{ds}{dt} = gt$$

is its velocity.

The rate of change of the velocity is the acceleration. In the case of gravity, we take the derivative of the speed and we get simply the constant g.

In general, given a function $y = f(x)$, the derivative $f'(x)$ is interpreted as the rate of change of y with respect to x. Thus f' is also a function. If x is given as some function of time, say, $x = g(t)$, then we can determine both the rate of change of y with respect to x, namely dy/dx, but also the rate of change of y with respect to t, namely

$$\frac{dy}{dt} = \frac{dy}{dx}\frac{dx}{dt}$$

by the chain rule.

Example 1. A particle is moving so that at time t the distance traveled is given by the function

$$s(t) = t^2 + 1.$$

The derivative $s'(t)$ is equal to $2t$. Thus the velocity of the particle is equal to 0 at time $t = 0$. Its velocity is equal to 4 at time $t = 2$.

Example 2. A square is expanding in such a way that its edge is changing at a rate of 2 in./sec. When its edge is 6 in. long, find the rate of change of its area.

The area of a square as a function of its side is given by the function

$$f(x) = x^2.$$

If the side x is given as a function of time t, say $x = x(t)$, then the rate of change of the area with respect to time is by definition

$$\frac{d(f(x(t)))}{dt}.$$

Thus we use the chain rule, and if we denote the area by A, we find

$$\frac{dA}{dt} = 2x(t)x'(t).$$

We know that $x'(t)$ is the constant 2. Thus when $x(t) = 6$, we find that

$$\frac{dA}{dt} = 2 \cdot 6 \cdot 2 = 24 \text{ in./sec.}$$

Example 3. A point moves along the graph of $y = x^3$ so that its x-coordinate changes at the rate of 2 units per second. What is the rate of change of its y-coordinate when $x = 3$?

We have by the chain rule,

$$\frac{dy}{dt} = 3x^2 \frac{dx}{dt}.$$

Thus when $x = 3$, we have $dy/dt = 3 \cdot 9 \cdot 2 = 54$ units per second.

EXERCISES

1. A particle is moving so that at time t, the distance is given by $s(t) = t^3 - 2t$. At what time is the acceleration equal to
   (a) 1   (b) 0   (c) -5?

2. A particle is moving so that at time t, the distance is given by the function $s(t) = 2t^4 + t^2$. At what time is the velocity equal to 0?

3. An object travels on a straight line with velocity given by the function $v(t) = 4t^5$. Find the acceleration at time $t = 2$.

4. A particle is moving so that at time t, the distance traveled is given by $s(t) = t^3 - 2t + 1$. At what time is the acceleration equal to 0?

5. A cube is expanding in such a way that its edge is changing at a rate of 5 in./sec. When its edge is 4 in. long, find the rate of change of its volume.

6. A sphere is increasing so that its radius increases at the rate of 1 in./sec. How fast is its volume changing when its radius is 3 in.? (The volume of a sphere is $4\pi r^3/3$.)

7. What is the rate of change of the area of a circle with respect to its radius, diameter, circumference? (You may assume that the area of the circle is given by the formula πr^2, where r is the radius, and its circumference is given by the formula $2\pi r$.)

8. A point moves along the graph of $y = 1/(x^2 + 4)$ so that its x-coordinate changes at the rate of 3 units per second. What is the rate of change of its y-coordinate when $x = 2$?

Supplementary Exercises

SUMS, PRODUCTS, AND QUOTIENTS

Find the derivatives of the following functions. Do not simplify your answers!

1. $3x^3 - 4x + 5$

2. $x^2 + 2x + 27$

3. $x^2 + x - 1$

4. $x^{1/2} - 8x^4 + x^{-1}$

5. $x^{5/2} + x^{-5/2}$

6. $x^7 + 15x^{-1/5}$

7. $(x^2 - 1)(x + 5)$

8. $\left(x^5 + \dfrac{1}{x}\right)(x^5 + 1)$

9. $(x^{3/2} + x^2)(x^4 - 99)$

10. $(x^2 + x + 1)(x^5 - x - 25)$

11. $(2x^2 + 1)\left(\dfrac{1}{x^2} + 4x + 8\right)$

12. $(x^4 - x^2)(x^2 - 1)$

13. $(x + 1)(x + 2)(x + 3)$

14. $5(x - 1)(x + 2)(x^2 + 1)$

15. $x^3(x^2 + 1)(x + 1)$

16. $(x^4 + 1)(x + 5)(2x + 7)$

17. $\dfrac{1}{2x + 3}$

18. $\dfrac{1}{7x + 27}$

19. $\dfrac{-5}{x^3 + 2x^2}$

20. $\dfrac{3}{2x_4 + x^{3/2}}$

21. $\dfrac{-2x}{x + 1}$

22. $\dfrac{x + 1}{x - 5}$

23. $\dfrac{3x^{1/2}}{(x + 1)(x - 1)}$

24. $\dfrac{2x^{1/2} + x^{3/4}}{(x + 1)x^3}$

25. $\dfrac{x^5 + 1}{(x^2 + 1)(x + 7)}$

26. $\dfrac{(x + 1)(x + 5)}{x - 4}$

27. $\dfrac{x^3}{1 - x^2}$

28. $\dfrac{x^5}{x^{3/2} + x}$

29. $\dfrac{x^2 - x}{x^2 + 1}$

30. $\dfrac{x^2 + 2x + 7}{8x}$

31. $\dfrac{2x + 1}{x^2 + x - 4}$

32. $\dfrac{x^5}{x^2 + 3}$

33. $\dfrac{4x - x^3}{x^2 + 2}$

34. $\dfrac{x^3}{x^2 - 5x + 7}$

35. $\dfrac{1 - 5x}{x}$

36. $\dfrac{1 + 6x + x^{3/4}}{7x - 2}$

37. $\dfrac{x^2}{(x + 1)(x - 2)}$

38. $\dfrac{x^{1/2} - x^{-1/2}}{x^{3/4}}$

39. $\dfrac{3x^4 + x^{5/4}}{4x^3 - x^5 + 1}$

40. $\dfrac{x - 1}{(x - 2)(x - 3)}$

Find the equations of the tangent lines to the following curves at the given point.

41. $y = x^{1/4} + 2x^{3/4}$ at $x = 16$

42. $y = 2x^3 + 3$ at $x = \frac{1}{2}$

43. $y = (x - 1)(x - 3)(x - 4)$ at $x = 0$

44. $y = 2x^2 + 5x - 1$ at $x = 2$

45. $y = (x^2 + 1)(2x + 3)$ at $x = 1$

46. $y = \dfrac{x-1}{x+5}$ at $x = 2$ 47. $y = \dfrac{x^2}{x^3+1}$ at $x = 2$

48. $y = \dfrac{x^2+1}{x^3+1}$ at $x = 2$ 49. $y = \dfrac{x^2}{x^2-1}$ at $x = 2$

50. $y = \dfrac{x-1}{x^2+1}$ at $x = 1$

51. Show that the line $y = -x$ is tangent to the curve given by the equation $y = x^3 - 6x^2 + 8x$. Find the point of tangency.

52. Show that the line $y = 9x - 15$ is tangent to the curve $y = x^3 - 3x + 1$. Find the point of tangency.

53. Show that the graphs of the equations

$$y = 3x^2 \quad \text{and} \quad y = 2x^3 + 1$$

have a common tangent line at the point (1, 3). Sketch the graphs.

54. Show that there are exactly two tangent lines to the graph of $y = (x+1)^2$ which pass through the origin, and find their equations.

55. Find all the points (x_0, y_0) on the curve

$$y = 4x^4 - 8x^2 + 16x + 7$$

such that the tangent line to the curve at (x_0, y_0) is parallel to the line

$$16x - y + 5 = 0.$$

Find the tangent line to the curve at each of these points.

CHAIN RULE

Find the derivatives of the following functions.

1. $(2x+1)^2$ 2. $(2x+5)^3$

3. $(5x+3)^7$ 4. $(7x-2)^{81}$

5. $(2x^2+x-5)^3$ 6. $(2x^3-3x)^4$

7. $(3x+1)^{1/2}$ 8. $(2x-5)^{5/4}$

9. $(x^2+x-1)^{-2}$ 10. $(x^4+5x+6)^{-1}$

11. $(x+5)^{-5/3}$ 12. $(x^3+2x+1)^3$

13. $(x-1)(x-5)^3$ 14. $(2x^2+1)^2(x^2+3x)$

15. $(x^3+x^2-2x-1)^4$ 16. $(x^2+1)^3(2x+5)^2$

17. $\dfrac{(x+1)^{3/4}}{(x-1)^{1/2}}$ 18. $\dfrac{(2x+1)^{1/2}}{(x+5)^5}$

19. $\dfrac{(2x^2+x-1)^{5/2}}{(3x+2)^9}$ 20. $\dfrac{(x^2+1)(3x-7)^8}{(x^2+5x-4)^3}$

21. $\sqrt{2x+1}$ 22. $\sqrt{x+3}$

23. $\sqrt{x^2 + x + 5}$ 24. $\sqrt{2x^3 - x + 1}$

In the following exercises, we may assume that there are functions sin u, cos u, log u, and e^u whose derivatives are given by the following formulas:

$$\frac{d \sin u}{du} = \cos u, \qquad \frac{d \cos u}{du} = -\sin u,$$

$$\frac{d(e^u)}{du} = e^u, \qquad \frac{d \log u}{du} = \frac{1}{u}.$$

Find the derivative of each function (with respect to x):

25. $\sin (x^3 + 1)$ 26. $\cos (x^3 + 1)$ 27. $e^{x^3 + 1}$

28. $\log (x^3 + 1)$ 29. $\sin (\cos x)$ 30. $\cos (\sin x)$

31. $e^{\sin(x^3 + 1)}$ 32. $\log [\sin (x^3 + 1)]$ 33. $\sin [(x + 1)(x^2 + 2)]$

34. $\log (2x^2 + 3x + 5)$ 35. $e^{(x+1)(x-3)}$ 36. e^{2x+1}

37. $\sin (2x + 5)$ 38. $\cos (7x + 1)$ 39. $\log (2x + 1)$

40. $\log \dfrac{2x + 1}{x + 3}$ 41. $\sin \dfrac{x - 5}{2x + 4}$ 42. $\cos \dfrac{2x - 1}{x + 3}$

43. $e^{2x^2 + 3x + 1}$ 44. $\log (4x^3 - 2x)$ 45. $\sin [\log (2x + 1)]$

46. $\cos (e^{2x})$ 47. $\cos (3x^2 - 2x + 1)$ 48. $\sin \left(\dfrac{x^2 - 1}{2x^3 + 1} \right)$

49. $(2x + 1)^{80}$ 50. $(\sin x)^{50}$ 51. $(\log x)^{49}$

52. $(\sin 2x)^4$ 53. $(e^{2x+1} - x)^5$ 54. $(\log x)^{20}$

55. $(3 \log (x^2 + 1) - x^3)^{1/2}$ 56. $(\log (2x + 3))^{4/3}$

57. $\dfrac{\sin 2x}{\cos 3x}$ 58. $\dfrac{\sin (2x + 5)}{\cos (x^2 - 1)}$ 59. $\dfrac{\log 2x^2}{\sin x^3}$

60. $\dfrac{e^{x^3}}{x^2 - 1}$ 61. $\dfrac{x^4 + 4}{\cos 2x}$ 62. $\dfrac{\sin (x^3 - 2)}{\sin 2x}$

63. $\dfrac{(2x^2 + 1)^4}{(\cos x^3)}$ 64. $\dfrac{e^{-x}}{\cos 2x}$ 65. e^{-3x}

66. e^{-x^2} 67. $e^{-4x^2 + x}$ 68. $\sqrt{e^x + 1}$

69. $\dfrac{\log (x^2 + 2)}{e^{-x}}$ 70. $\dfrac{\log (2x + 1)}{\sin (4x + 5)}$

RATE OF CHANGE

1. A particle moves differentiably on the parabola $y = x^2$. At what point on the curve are its x- and y-coordinates moving at the same rate? Find these rates at time $t = 1$ in the case $x = t^3$; in the case $y = 4t$.

2. One side of a right triangle decreases 1 in./min and the other side increases 2 in./min. At some time the first side is 8 in. and the second side is 6 in. long. At what rate is the area increasing after 2 min?

3. The length of the side of a square is increasing at the rate of 3 in. per second. Find the rate at which the area is increasing when the side is 15 in. long.

4. A ladder 17 ft long leans against a vertical wall. If the lower end of the ladder is being moved away from the foot of the wall at the rate of 3 ft/sec, how fast is the top descending when the lower end is 8 ft from the wall?

5. A swimming pool is 25 ft wide, 40 ft long, 3 ft deep at one end and 9 ft deep at the other, the bottom being an inclined plane. If water is pumped into the pool at the rate of 10 ft^3/min, how fast is the water level rising when it is 4 ft deep at the deep end?

6. A reservoir has the shape of a cone, vertex down, 10 ft high. The radius of the top is 4 ft. Water is poured into the reservoir at the rate of 5 ft^3/min. How fast is the water rising when the depth of the water is 5 ft? (The volume of a cone whose base has radius r and of height h is $\pi r^2 h/3$.)

7. A particle is moving so that at time t the distance traveled is given by $s(t) = 2t^2 - t$. At what time is the velocity equal to 0? What is the acceleration of the particle?

8. A point moves on the parabola with equation $y = x^2 - 6x$. Find the point on the curve at which the rate of change of the y-coordinate is four times the rate of change of the x-coordinate.

9. Water is flowing into a tank in the form of a hemisphere of radius 10 ft with flat side up at the rate of 4 ft^3/min. Let h be the depth of the water, r the radius of the surface of the water, and V the volume of the water in the tank. Assume that $dV/dt = \pi r^2\, dh/dt$. Find how fast the water level is rising when $h = 5$ ft.

10. A train leaves a station at a certain time and travels north at the rate of 50 mi/hr. A second train leaves the same station 2 hr after the first train leaves, and goes east at the rate of 60 mi/hr. Find the rate at which the two trains are separating 1.5 hr after the second train leaves the station.

11. Sand is falling on a pile, always having the shape of a cone, at the rate of 3 ft^3/min. Assume that the diameter at the base of the pile is always three times the altitude. At what rate is the altitude increasing when the altitude is 4 ft?

Chapter IV

Sine and Cosine

From the sine of an angle and the cosine of an angle, we shall define functions of numbers, and determine their derivatives.

It is convenient to recall all the facts about trigonometry which we need in the sequel, especially the formula giving us the sine and cosine of the sum of two angles. Thus our treatment of the trigonometric functions is self-contained—you do not need to know anything about sine and cosine before starting to read this chapter. However, most of the proofs of statements in §1 come from plane geometry and will be left to you.

§1. THE SINE AND COSINE FUNCTIONS

Suppose that we have given coordinate axes, and a certain angle, as shown on the figure.

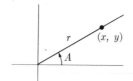

We select a point (x, y) (not the origin) on the line determining our angle A. We let $r = \sqrt{x^2 + y^2}$. Then r is the distance from $(0, 0)$ to the point (x, y). We define

$$\text{sine } A = \frac{y}{r} = \frac{y}{\sqrt{x^2 + y^2}}$$

$$\text{cosine } A = \frac{x}{r} = \frac{x}{\sqrt{x^2 + y^2}} \cdot$$

If we select another point (x_1, y_1) on the line determining our angle A and use its coordinates to get the sine and cosine, then we shall obtain the same values as with (x, y). Indeed, there is a positive number c such that

$$x_1 = cx \quad \text{and} \quad y_1 = cy.$$

Thus

$$\frac{y_1}{\sqrt{x_1^2 + x_1^2}} = \frac{cy}{\sqrt{c^2x^2 + c^2y^2}} \cdot$$

We can factor c from the denominator, and then cancel c in both the numerator and denominator to get

$$\frac{y}{\sqrt{x^2 + y^2}}\,.$$

In this way we see that sine A does not depend on the choice of coordinates (x, y).

The geometric interpretation of the above argument simply states that the triangles in the following diagram are similar.

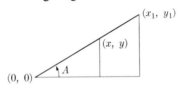

The angle A can go all the way around. For instance, we could have an angle determined by a point (x, y) in the second or third quadrant.

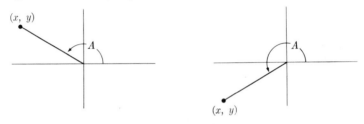

When the angle A is in the first quadrant, then its sine and cosine are positive because both coordinates x, y are positive. When the angle A is in the second quadrant, its sine is positive because y is positive, but its cosine is negative because x is negative.

When A is in the third quadrant, sine A is negative and cosine A is negative also.

In order to define the sine of a *number*, we select a unit for measuring angles. We let π be the area of the circle of radius 1. We then choose a unit angle such that the flat angle is equal to π times the unit angle. (See the following figures.) The right angle has measure $\pi/2$. The full angle going once around is then 2π.

The unit of measurement for which the flat angle is π is called the *radian*. Thus the right angle has $\pi/2$ radians.

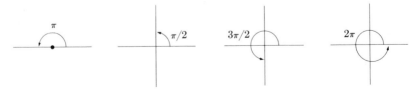

There is another current unit of measurement for which the flat angle is 180. This unit is called the *degree*. Thus the flat angle has 180 degrees, and the right angle has 90 degrees. We also have

$$360 \text{ degrees} = 2\pi \text{ radians}$$
$$60 \text{ degrees} = \pi/3 \text{ radians}$$
$$45 \text{ degrees} = \pi/4 \text{ radians}$$
$$30 \text{ degrees} = \pi/6 \text{ radians.}$$

We make a table of the sines and cosines of these angles.

Angle	Sine	Cosine
$\pi/6$	$1/2$	$\sqrt{3}/2$
$\pi/4$	$1/\sqrt{2}$	$1/\sqrt{2}$
$\pi/3$	$\sqrt{3}/2$	$1/2$
$\pi/2$	1	0
π	0	-1
2π	0	1

Unless otherwise specified, we *always use the radian measure*, and our table is given for this measure.

The values of this table are easily determined, using properties of similar triangles and plane geometry. For instance, we get the sine of the angle $\pi/4$ radians from a right triangle with two equal sides:

We can determine the sine of $\pi/4$ by means of the point $(1, 1)$. Then $r = \sqrt{2}$ and sine $\pi/4$ radians is $1/\sqrt{2}$. Similarly for the cosine.

The following is an important rule relating the sine and cosine.

Theorem 1. *For any angle A we have*

$$\text{cosine } A = \text{sine}\left(A + \frac{\pi}{2}\right) \quad \text{or} \quad \text{sine } A = \text{cosine}\left(A - \frac{\pi}{2}\right).$$

Proof. You can use theorems of plane geometry to prove our theorem. We leave this to you.

We define a function of numbers, which will also be called the *sine*, by the association:

For any number x we associate to it the number which is the sine of x radians.

This function is denoted by $\sin x$ and is defined for all x. Thus $\sin \pi = 0$, $\sin \pi/2 = 1$, $\sin 2\pi = 0$, $\sin 0 = 0$.

Similarly, we have the *cosine function*, which is defined for all numbers x by the rule:

$\cos x$ is the number which is the cosine of the angle x radians.

Thus $\cos 0 = 1$ and $\cos \pi = -1$.

We can also define the tangent function, $\tan x$, which is the quotient

$$\tan x = \frac{\sin x}{\cos x}$$

and is defined for all numbers x such that $\cos x \neq 0$. These are the numbers x which are unequal to

$$\frac{\pi}{2}, \frac{3\pi}{2}, \frac{5\pi}{2}, \cdots ;$$

in general $x \neq (2n + 1)\pi/2$ for some integer n.

If we had used the measure of angles in degrees we would obtain *another* sine function which is not equal to the sine function which we defined in terms of radians. Suppose we call this other sine function sin*. Then

$$\sin^* (180) = \sin \pi,$$

and in general

$$\sin^* (180x) = \sin \pi x$$

for any number x. Thus

$$\sin^* x = \sin \left(\frac{\pi}{180} x\right)$$

is the formula relating our two sine functions. It will become clear later why we always pick the radian measure instead of any other.

At present we have no means of computing values for the sine and cosine other than the very special cases listed above (and similar ones, based on simple symmetries of right triangles). It will be only in Chapter XIV that we shall develop a method which will allow us to find $\sin x$ and $\cos x$ for any value of x, up to any degree of accuracy that you wish.

EXERCISES

Find the following values of the sin function and cos function:

1. $\sin 3\pi/4$ 2. $\sin 2\pi/6$ 3. $\sin \dfrac{2\pi}{3}$ 4. $\sin \left(\pi - \dfrac{\pi}{6}\right)$

5. $\cos \left(\pi + \dfrac{\pi}{6}\right)$ 6. $\cos \left(\pi + \dfrac{2\pi}{6}\right)$ 7. $\cos \left(2\pi - \dfrac{\pi}{6}\right)$ 8. $\cos \dfrac{5\pi}{4}$

Find the following values:

9. $\tan \dfrac{\pi}{4}$ 10. $\tan \dfrac{2\pi}{6}$ 11. $\tan \dfrac{5\pi}{4}$ 12. $\tan \left(2\pi - \dfrac{\pi}{4} \right)$

13. Prove by plane geometry that $\sin (\pi - x) = \sin x$.
14. Prove by plane geometry that $\cos (\pi - x) = -\cos x$.
15. Prove by plane geometry that $\sin (2\pi - x) = -\sin x$.
16. Prove by plane geometry that $\sin (-x) = -\sin x$.
17. Prove by plane geometry that $\cos (-x) = \cos x$.
18. Let a be a given number. Determine all numbers x such that $\sin x = \sin a$. (You may suppose that $0 \leq a < 2\pi$, and distinguish the cases $a = \pi/2$, $a = -\pi/2$ and $a \neq \pm\pi/2$.)

§2. THE GRAPHS

We wish to sketch the graph of the sine function.

We know that $\sin 0 = 0$. As x goes from 0 to $\pi/2$, the sine of x increases until x reaches $\pi/2$, at which point the sine is equal to 1.

As x ranges from $\pi/2$ to π, the sine decreases until it becomes $\sin \pi = 0$.

As x ranges from π to $3\pi/2$ the sine becomes negative, but otherwise behaves in a similar way to the first quadrant, until it reaches

$$\sin 3\pi/2 = -1.$$

Finally, as x goes from $3\pi/2$ to 2π, the sine of x goes from -1 to 0, and we are ready to start all over again.

The graph looks like this:

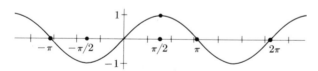

The graph of the cosine will look like that of the sine, but it starts with $\cos 0 = 1$. In the next picture the scale used on the vertical axis is different from that on the horizontal axis so that we will have more room for the arches of the graph.

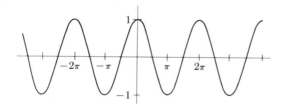

If we go once around by 2π, both the sine and cosine take on the same values, in other words

$$\sin (x + 2\pi) = \sin x$$
$$\cos (x + 2\pi) = \cos x$$

for all x. This holds whether x is positive or negative, and the same would be true if we took $x - 2\pi$ instead of $x + 2\pi$.

You might legitimately ask why one arch of the sine (or cosine) curve looks the way we have drawn it, and not the following way:

In the next section, we shall find the slope of the curve $y = \sin x$. It is equal to $\cos x$. Thus when $x = 0$, the slope is $\cos 0 = 1$. Furthermore, when $x = \pi/2$, we have $\cos \pi/2 = 0$ and hence the slope is 0. This means that the curve becomes horizontal, and cannot have a peak the way we have drawn it above.

At present we have no means for computing more values of $\sin x$ and $\cos x$. However, using the few that we know and the derivative, we can convince ourselves that the graphs look as we have drawn them.

Example. Sketch the graph of $y = \sin (x - \pi)$.

Let $x' = x - \pi$, $y' = y$. We know how to draw the graph of $y = x'$ relative to (x', y)-axes. When $x = 0$, we have $x' = -\pi$. Thus the graph of $y = \sin (x - \pi)$ looks like this.

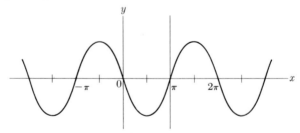

The values $-\pi$, 0, π, 2π indicated are those corresponding to the x-coordinate.

EXERCISES

1. Draw the graph of $\tan x$.

2. Let $\sec x = 1/\cos x$ be defined when $\cos x \neq 0$. Draw the graph of $\sec x$.

3. Let $\cot x = 1/\tan x$. Draw the graph of $\cot x$.
   (Sec and cot are abbreviations for the secant and cotangent.)

4. Draw the graph of the function $\sin (1/x)$ for $0 < x \leqq \pi$.

5. Draw the graph of the function $x \sin (1/x)$ for $0 < x \leqq \pi$.

6. Draw the graph of the function $x^2 \sin (1/x)$ for $0 < x \leqq \pi$.
   (In Exercises 4, 5, 6 the function is not defined for $x = 0$.)

7. Let $f(x) = x^2 \sin (1/x)$ when $x \neq 0$ and let $f(0) = 0$. Using the Newton quotient, show that f has a derivative at 0 and that $f'(0) = 0$.

8. Let $f(x) = x \sin (1/x)$ when $x \neq 0$ and let $f(0) = 0$. Show that f does not have a derivative at 0. Look at small values of x like

$$h = \frac{2}{n\pi},$$

n being a large integer. Try $n = 1, 2, 3, 4$, etc. and see what happens to the values of $f(x)$ and the Newton quotient

$$\frac{f(h) - f(0)}{h}.$$

9. Sketch the graphs of the following functions:

   (a) $y = \sin 2x$ (b) $y = \sin 3x$

   (c) $y = \cos 2x$ (d) $y = \cos 3x$

   (e) $y = \tan 2x$ (f) $y = \sin \left(x + \dfrac{\pi}{4} \right)$

   (g) $y = \tan \left(x + \dfrac{\pi}{6} \right)$ (h) $y = \tan \left(x - \dfrac{\pi}{6} \right)$

   (i) $y = \sin \tfrac{1}{2}x$ (j) $y = \cos \tfrac{1}{2}x$

10. Sketch the graphs of the following functions:

   (a) $y = 1 + \sin x$ (b) $y = 1 + \sin 2x$

   (c) $y = -2 + \cos (x - 1)$ (d) $y = -\cos \tfrac{2}{3}\pi x$

   (e) $y = \sin \left(2x - \dfrac{\pi}{3} \right)$ (f) $y = 5 \sin \tfrac{1}{2}\pi x$

   (g) $y = 4 \cos \tfrac{1}{2}\pi x$ (h) $y = -\cos 2x$

§3. ADDITION FORMULA

In this section we shall state and prove the most important formulas about sine and cosine.

To begin with, using the Pythagoras theorem, we observe that

$$(\sin x)^2 + (\cos x)^2 = 1$$

for all x. Indeed, if we have an angle A and we determine its sine and cosine from the right triangle, as in the following figure,

then we have

$$a^2 + b^2 = r^2.$$

Dividing by r^2 yields

$$\left(\frac{a}{r}\right)^2 + \left(\frac{b}{r}\right)^2 = 1.$$

The same argument works when A is greater than $\pi/2$, by means of a triangle like this one:

In both cases, we have sine $A = a/r$ and cosine $A = b/r$, so that we have the relation

$$(\text{sine } A)^2 + (\text{cosine } A)^2 = 1.$$

It is customary to write the square of the sine and cosine as $\sin^2 A$ and $\cos^2 A$.

Our main result is the *addition formula*.

Theorem 2. *For any angles A and B, we have*

$$\sin (A + B) = \sin A \cos B + \cos A \sin B$$
$$\cos (A + B) = \cos A \cos B - \sin A \sin B.$$

Proof. We shall prove the second formula first.

We consider two angles A, B and their sum:

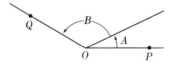

We take two points P, Q as indicated, at a distance 1 from the origin O. We shall now compute the distance from P to Q, using two different coordinate systems.

First, we take a coordinate system as usual:

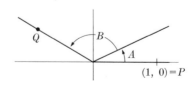

Then the coordinates of P are $(1, 0)$ and those of Q are

$$\big(\cos (A + B), \sin (A + B)\big).$$

The square of the distance between P and Q is

$$\sin^2 (A + B) + \big(\cos (A + B) - 1\big)^2,$$

which is equal to

$$-2 \cos (A + B) + 2.$$

Next we place the coordinate system as shown in the figure below.

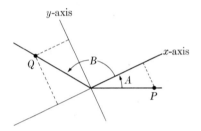

Then the coordinates of P become

$$\big(\cos A, \sin (-A)\big) = (\cos A, -\sin A).$$

Those of Q are simply $(\cos B, \sin B)$. The square of the distance between P and Q is

$$(\sin B + \sin A)^2 + (\cos B - \cos A)^2,$$

which is equal to

$$\sin^2 B + 2 \sin B \sin A + \sin^2 A + \cos^2 B - 2 \cos B \cos A + \cos^2 A$$
$$= 2 + 2 \sin A \sin B - 2 \cos A \cos B.$$

If we set the squares of the two distances equal to each other, we get our formula.

The addition formula for the sine can be obtained by the following device:

$$\sin (A + B) = \cos \left(A + B - \frac{\pi}{2}\right)$$
$$= \cos A \cos \left(B - \frac{\pi}{2}\right) - \sin A \sin \left(B - \frac{\pi}{2}\right)$$
$$= \cos A \sin B + \sin A \sin \left(\frac{\pi}{2} - B\right)$$
$$= \cos A \sin B + \sin A \cos B,$$

thereby proving our formula.

Example. Find sin $(\pi/12)$.
We write

$$\frac{\pi}{12} = \frac{\pi}{3} - \frac{\pi}{4}.$$

Then sin $(\pi/12)$ = sin $(\pi/3)$ cos $(\pi/4)$ − cos $(\pi/3)$ sin $(\pi/4)$, and substituting the known values we find

$$\sin (\pi/12) = \frac{\sqrt{3} - 1}{2\sqrt{2}}.$$

EXERCISES

1. Find sin $7\pi/12$. [*Hint:* Write $7\pi/12 = 4\pi/12 + 3\pi/12$.]

2. Find cos $7\pi/12$.

3. Find the following values:
   (a) sin $\pi/12$ (b) cos $\pi/12$
   (c) sin $5\pi/12$ (d) cos $5\pi/12$
   (e) sin $11\pi/12$ (f) cos $11\pi/12$
   (g) sin $10\pi/12$ (h) cos $10\pi/12$

4. Prove the following formulas.
   (a) sin $2x = 2 \sin x \cos x$ (b) cos $2x = \cos^2 x - \sin^2 x$
   (c) $\cos^2 x = \dfrac{1 + \cos 2x}{2}$ (d) $\sin^2 x = \dfrac{1 - \cos 2x}{2}$

5. Find a formula for sin $3x$ in terms of sin x and cos x. Similarly for sin $4x$, and sin $5x$.

6. Prove by induction that for any positive integer n, sin nx can be expressed as a sum of terms

$$\sum a_{ij}(\sin x)^i(\cos x)^j$$

where a_{ij} are integers.

7. Express $\sin^3 x$ as a sum of terms $a_n \cos nx$ and $b_n \sin nx$ where a_n, b_n are numbers. Prove the formulas

$$\sin mx \sin nx = \tfrac{1}{2}[\cos (m - n)x - \cos (m + n)x],$$

$$\sin mx \cos nx = \tfrac{1}{2}[\sin (m + n)x + \sin (m - n)x],$$

$$\cos mx \cos nx = \tfrac{1}{2}[\cos (m + n)x + \cos (m - n)x].$$

8. Show that for any positive integer k you can express $\sin^k x$ as a sum of terms $a_n \cos nx + b_n \sin nx$ where a_n, b_n are numbers. (In fact, rational numbers.) Prove the same thing for $\cos^k x$. Use induction.

§4. THE DERIVATIVES

We shall prove:

Theorem 3. *The functions* sin *x and* cos *x have derivatives and*

$$\frac{d(\sin x)}{dx} = \cos x$$

$$\frac{d(\cos x)}{dx} = -\sin x.$$

Proof. We shall first determine the derivative of sin x. We have to look at the Newton quotient of sin x. It is

$$\frac{\sin (x + h) - \sin x}{h}.$$

Using the addition formula to expand sin $(x + h)$, we see that the Newton quotient is equal to

$$\frac{\sin x \cos h + \cos x \sin h - \sin x}{h}.$$

We put together the two terms involving sin x:

$$\frac{\cos x \sin h + \sin x(\cos h - 1)}{h}$$

and separate our quotient into a sum of two terms:

$$\cos x \frac{\sin h}{h} + \sin x \frac{\cos h - 1}{h}.$$

We now face the problem of finding the limit of

$$\frac{\sin h}{h} \text{ and } \frac{\cos h - 1}{h} \quad \text{as } h \text{ approaches } 0.$$

This is a somewhat more difficult problem than those we encountered previously. We cannot tell right away what these limits will be. In the next section, we shall prove that

$$\lim_{h \to 0} \frac{\sin h}{h} = 1 \quad \text{and} \quad \lim_{h \to 0} \frac{\cos h - 1}{h} = 0.$$

Once we know these limits, then we see immediately that the first term approaches cos x and the second term approaches

$$(\sin x) \cdot 0 = 0.$$

Hence

$$\lim_{h \to 0} \frac{\sin (x + h) - \sin x}{h} = \cos x.$$

This proves that

$$\frac{d(\sin x)}{dx} = \cos x.$$

To find the derivative of cos x, we could proceed in the same way, and we would encounter the same limits. However, there is a trick which avoids this.

We know that $\cos x = \sin\left(x + \frac{\pi}{2}\right)$. Let $u = x + \frac{\pi}{2}$ and use the chain rule. We get

$$\frac{d(\cos x)}{dx} = \frac{d(\sin u)}{du}\frac{du}{dx}.$$

However, $du/dx = 1$. Hence

$$\frac{d(\cos x)}{dx} = \cos u = \cos\left(x + \frac{\pi}{2}\right) = -\sin x,$$

thereby proving our theorem.

Remark. It is not true that the derivative of the function sin* x is cos* x. Using the chain rule, find out what its derivative is. The reason for using the radian measure of angles is to get a function sin x whose derivative is cos x.

EXERCISES

1. What is the derivative of tan x?

Find the derivative of the following functions:

2. sin (3x)   3. cos (5x)

4. sin ($4x^2 + x$)   5. tan ($x^3 - 5$)

6. tan ($x^4 - x^3$)   7. tan (sin x)

8. sin (tan x)   9. cos (tan x)

10. What is the slope of the curve $y = \sin x$ at the point whose x-coordinate is π? Find the slope of the following curves at the indicated point (we just give the x-coordinate of the point):

11. $y = \cos (3x)$ at $x = \pi/3$ 12. $y = \sin x$ at $x = \pi/6$

13. $y = \sin x + \cos x$ at $x = 3\pi/4$ 14. $y = \tan x$ at $x = -\pi/4$

15. $y = \dfrac{1}{\sin x}$ at $x = -\pi/6$

16. Give the equation of the tangent line to the following curves at the indicated point.

    (a) $y = \sin x$ at $x = \pi/2$ (b) $y = \cos x$ at $x = \pi/6$

(c) $y = \sin 2x$ at $x = \pi/4$

(d) $y = \tan 3x$ at $x = \pi/4$

(e) $y = 1/\sin x$ at $x = \pi/2$

(f) $y = 1/\cos x$ at $x = \pi/4$

(g) $y = 1/\tan x$ at $x = \pi/4$

(h) $y = \tan \dfrac{x}{2}$ at $x = 3\pi$

(i) $y = \sin \dfrac{x}{2}$ at $x = \pi/3$

(j) $y = \cos \dfrac{\pi x}{3}$ at $x = 1$

(k) $y = \sin \pi x$ at $x = \frac{1}{2}$

(l) $y = \tan \pi x$ at $x = \frac{1}{6}$

17. In the following right triangle, suppose that θ is decreasing at the rate of $\frac{1}{30}$ rad/sec. Find each one of the indicated derivatives:

(a) dy/dt, when $\theta = \pi/3$ and x is constant, $x = 12$.

(b) dz/dt, when $\theta = \pi/4$ if y is constant, $y = 10\sqrt{2}$.

(c) dx/dt, when $x = 1$ and $z = 2$, if x and y are both changing.

18. A Ferris wheel 50 ft in diameter makes 1 revolution every 2 min. If the center of the wheel is 30 ft above the ground, how fast is a passenger in the wheel moving vertically when he is 42.5 ft above the ground?

§5. TWO BASIC LIMITS

We shall first prove that

$$\lim_{h \to 0} \frac{\sin h}{h} = 1.$$

Both the numerator and the denominator approach 0 as h approaches 0, and we get no information by trying some cancellation procedure, the way we did it for powers.

Let us assume first that h is positive, and look at the following diagram.

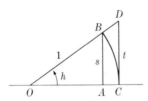

We take a circle of radius 1 and an angle of h radians. Let s be the altitude of the small triangle, and t that of the big triangle. Then

$$\sin h = \frac{s}{1} = s$$

and

$$\tan h = \frac{t}{1} = t = \frac{\sin h}{\cos h}.$$

We see that:

  area of triangle OAB < area of sector OCB < area of triangle OCD.

The base OA of the small triangle is equal to cos h and its altitude is sin h.

The base OC of the big triangle is equal to 1. Its altitude is

$$t = \frac{\sin h}{\cos h}.$$

The area of each triangle is $\frac{1}{2}$ the base times the altitude.

The area of the sector is the fraction $h/2\pi$ of the area of the circle, which is π. Hence the area of the sector is $h/2$. Thus we obtain:

$$\frac{1}{2}\cos h \sin h < \frac{1}{2}h < \frac{1}{2}\frac{\sin h}{\cos h}.$$

We multiply everywhere by 2 and get

$$\cos h \sin h < h < \frac{\sin h}{\cos h}.$$

There are really two inequalities here. The first one is

$$\cos h \sin h < h.$$

Since h is positive, we can divide it by h and then divide by cos h, which is also positive. This yields

$$\frac{\sin h}{h} < \frac{1}{\cos h}.$$

The second inequality is

$$h < \frac{\sin h}{\cos h}.$$

We multiply it by cos h and divide it by h to get

$$\cos h < \frac{\sin h}{h}.$$

Putting our two inequalities together, we get

$$\cos h < \frac{\sin h}{h} < \frac{1}{\cos h}.$$

The game is almost won. Letting h approach 0, we see that $(\sin h)/h$ is squeezed between two quantities which approach 1. Hence it must approach 1 also, and our proof is complete.

We still have to consider the limit

$$\lim_{h \to 0} \frac{\cos h - 1}{h}$$

and show that it is 0. We have

$$\frac{\cos h - 1}{h} = \frac{(\cos h - 1)(\cos h + 1)}{h(\cos h + 1)}$$

$$= \frac{\cos^2 h - 1}{h(\cos h + 1)}$$

$$= \frac{-\sin^2 h}{h(\cos h + 1)}.$$

We can write this last expression in the form

$$-\frac{\sin h}{h} (\sin h) \frac{1}{\cos h + 1}.$$

Using the property concerning the product of limits, we have a product of three factors. The first is

$$-\frac{\sin h}{h}$$

and approaches -1 as h approaches 0.

The second is $\sin h$ and approaches 0 as h approaches 0.

The third is

$$\frac{1}{\cos h + 1}$$

and its limit is $\frac{1}{2}$ as h approaches 0.

Therefore the limit of the product is 0, and everything is proved!

We still have one thing to take care of. We computed our limit when $h > 0$. Suppose that $h < 0$. We can write

$$h = -k$$

with $k > 0$. Then

$$\frac{\sin (-k)}{-k} = \frac{-\sin k}{-k} = \frac{\sin k}{k}.$$

As h tends to 0, so does k. Hence we are reduced to our previous limit because $k > 0$. A similar remark applies to our other limit involving $\cos h$.

EXERCISES

Find the following limits, as h approaches 0.

1. $\dfrac{\sin 2h}{h}$ $\left[\textit{Hint:} \text{ Put } k = 2h. \text{ Then } \dfrac{\sin 2h}{h} = 2\dfrac{\sin k}{k}.\right]$

2. $\dfrac{\sin 3h}{h}$

3. $\dfrac{\sin h}{3h}$

4. $\dfrac{\tan h}{\sin h}$

5. $\dfrac{\cos 2h}{1 + \sin h}$

6. $\dfrac{\sin h^2}{h}$

7. $\dfrac{\sin 2h^2}{3h}$

8. $\dfrac{\sin h^3}{h^3}$

9. $\dfrac{\sin 2h^3}{h^3}$

10. $\dfrac{h \sin h}{\sin 2h^2}$

11. $\dfrac{(\sin h)(\sin 2h)}{(\sin 3h)h}$

Chapter V

The Mean Value Theorem

Given a curve, $y = f(x)$, we shall use the derivative to give us information about the curve. For instance, we shall find the maximum and minimum of the graph, and regions where the curve is increasing or decreasing. We shall use the mean value theorem, which is basic in the theory of derivatives.

§1. THE MAXIMUM AND MINIMUM THEOREM

Let f be a differentiable function. A point c such that $f'(c) = 0$ is called a *critical point* of the function. The derivative being zero means that the slope of the tangent line is 0 and thus that the tangent line itself is horizontal. We have drawn three examples of this phenomenon.

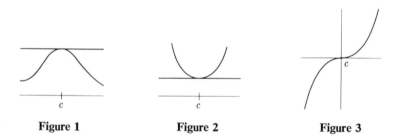

| Figure 1 | Figure 2 | Figure 3 |

The third example is that of a function like $f(x) = x^3$. We have $f'(x) = 3x^2$ and hence when $x = 0, f'(0) = 0$.

The other two examples are those of a maximum and a minimum, respectively, if we look at the graph of the function only near our point c. We shall now formalize these notions.

Let a, b be two numbers with $a < b$. We shall repeatedly deal with the interval of numbers between a and b. Sometimes we want to include the end points a and b, and sometimes we do not. We recall the standard terminology.

The collection of numbers x such that $a < x < b$ is called the *open interval* between a and b.

The collection of numbers x such that $a \leq x \leq b$ is called the *closed interval* between a and b. We denote this closed interval by the symbols $[a, b]$. (A single point will also be called a closed interval.)

If we wish to include only one end point, we shall say that the interval is *half closed*. We have of course two half-closed intervals, namely the one consisting of the numbers x with $a \leqq x < b$, and the other one consisting of the numbers x with $a < x \leqq b$.

Sometimes, if a is a number, we call the collection of numbers $x > a$ (or $x < a$) an open interval. The context will always make this clear.

Let f be a function, and c a number at which f is defined. We shall say that c is a *maximum* of the function if

$$f(c) \geqq f(x)$$

for all numbers x at which f is defined. If we have only $f(c) \geqq f(x)$ for all numbers x in some interval, then we say that c is a maximum of the function *in that interval*.

Example 1. Let $f(x) = \sin x$. Then $\pi/2$ is a maximum for f because $f(\pi/2) = 1$ and $\sin x \leqq 1$ for all values of x. Note that $-3\pi/2$ is also a maximum for $\sin x$.

Example 2. Let $f(x) = 2x$, and view f as a function defined only on the interval

$$0 \leqq x \leqq 2.$$

Then 2 is a maximum for the function in this interval because $f(2) = 4$ and $f(x) \leqq 4$ for all x in the interval.

Example 3. Let $f(x) = 1/x$. We know that f is not defined for $x = 0$. This function has no maximum. It becomes arbitrarily large when x comes close to 0 and $x > 0$.

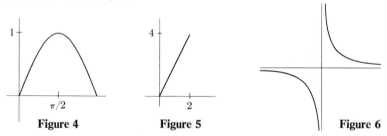

| Figure 4 | Figure 5 | Figure 6 |

We have illustrated our three examples in Figs. 4, 5, and 6.

In the next theorem, we shall prove that under certain circumstances, the derivative of a function at a maximum is 0.

Theorem 1. *Let f be a function which is defined and differentiable on the open interval $a < x < b$. Let c be a number in the interval which is a maximum for the function. (In other words, $f(c) \geqq f(x)$ for all x in the interval.) Then*

$$f'(c) = 0.$$

Proof. If we take small values of h (positive or negative), the number $c + h$ will lie in the interval.

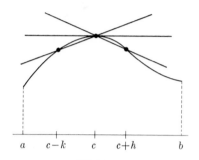

Figure 7

Let us first take h positive (see Fig. 7). We must have

$$f(c) \geq f(c + h)$$

no matter what h is (provided h is small). Therefore $f(c + h) - f(c) \leq 0$. Since $h > 0$, the Newton quotient

$$\frac{f(c + h) - f(c)}{h}$$

is ≤ 0. Hence the limit is ≤ 0, or in symbols:

$$\lim_{\substack{h \to 0 \\ h > 0}} \frac{f(c + h) - f(c)}{h} \leq 0.$$

Now take h negative, say $h = -k$ with $k > 0$. Then

$$f(c - k) - f(c) \leq 0, \qquad f(c) - f(c - k) \geq 0$$

and the quotient is

$$\frac{f(c - k) - f(c)}{-k} = \frac{f(c) - f(c - k)}{k}.$$

Thus the Newton quotient is ≥ 0. Taking the limit as h (or k) approaches 0, we see that

$$\lim_{\substack{h \to 0 \\ h < 0}} \frac{f(c + h) - f(c)}{h} \geq 0.$$

The only way in which our two limits can be equal is that they should both be 0. Therefore $f'(c) = 0$.

We can interpret our arguments geometrically by saying that the line between our two points slants to the left when we take $h > 0$ and slants to the right when we take $h < 0$. As h approaches 0, both lines must approach the tangent line to the curve. The only way this is possible is for the tangent line at the point whose x-coordinate is c to be horizontal. This means that its slope is 0, i.e. $f'(c) = 0$.

Everything we have done with a maximum could have been done with a minimum.

Let f be a function. We say that a number c is a *minimum* for f if $f(c) \leq f(x)$ for all x at which the function is defined.

Theorem 1 remains true when we replace the word "maximum" by the word "minimum". It will be a good exercise for you to prove Theorem 1 for the minimum. When we refer to Theorem 1 we shall use it in both cases.

We illustrate various minima with the graphs of certain functions.

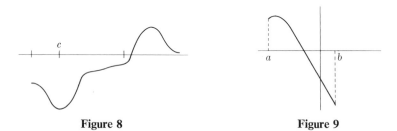

Figure 8   **Figure 9**

In Fig. 8 the function has a minimum. In Fig. 9 the minimum is at the end point of the interval. In Figs. 3 and 6 the function has no minimum.

In the following picture, the point c_1 looks like a maximum and the point c_2 looks like a minimum, provided we stay close to these points, and don't look at what happens to the curve farther away.

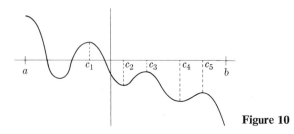

Figure 10

There is a name for such points. We shall say that a point c is a *local minimum* of the function f if there exists an interval

$$a_1 < c < b_1$$

such that $f(c) \leq f(x)$ for all numbers x with $a_1 \leq x \leq b_1$.

Similarly, we define the notion of *local maximum*. (Do it yourself.) In Fig. 10, the point c_3 is a local maximum, c_4 is a local minimum, and c_5 is a local maximum.

The actual maximum and minimum occur at the end points.

In practice, a function usually has only a finite number of critical points, and it is easy to find all points c such that $f'(c) = 0$. One can then determine by inspection which of these are maxima, which are minima, and which are neither.

Example 1. Find the critical points of the function $f(x) = x^3 - 1$.

We have $f'(x) = 3x^2$. Hence there is only one critical point, namely $x = 0$.

Example 2. Find the critical points of the function

$$y = x^3 - 2x + 1.$$

The derivative is $3x^2 - 2$. It is equal to 0 precisely when

$$x^2 = \tfrac{2}{3},$$

which means $x = \sqrt{2/3}$ or $-\sqrt{2/3}$. These are the critical points.

Example 3. Find the local maximum and minimum of the function $f(x) = x^3 - 2x + 1$.

The local maximum and minimum must be a critical point, hence we have only two possibilities, which we found in Example 2. These are $x = \sqrt{2/3}$ and $x = -\sqrt{2/3}$. We make a small table of values of our function:

x	y
0	1
−1	2
−2	−3
1	0
2	5

The number $\sqrt{2/3}$ is between 0 and 1. Since $f(1) = 0$ and $f(0) = 1$, it follows that $\sqrt{2/3}$ must be a local minimum.

Similarly, $-\sqrt{2/3}$ is between 0 and −1. But $f(0) = 1$ and $f(-1) = 2$. Hence $-\sqrt{2/3}$ is a local maximum. The sketch of the graph looks like this:

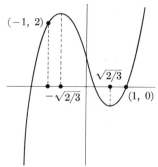

Figure 11

EXERCISES

Find the critical points of the following functions:

1. $x^2 - 2x + 5$ 2. $2x^2 - 3x - 1$

3. $3x^2 - x + 1$ 4. $-x^2 + 2x + 2$

5. $-2x^2 + 3x - 1$ 6. $x^3 + 2$

7. $x^3 - 3x$ 8. $\sin x + \cos x$

9. $\cos x$ 10. $\sin x$

11. A box with open top is to be made with a square base and a constant surface C. Determine the sides of the box if the volume is to be a maximum.

12. A container in the shape of a cylinder with open top is to have a fixed surface area C. Find the radius of its base and its height if it is to have maximum volume.

13. Do the above two problems when box and container are closed at the top.

(The area of a circle of radius x is πx^2 and its length is $2\pi x$. The volume of a cylinder whose base has radius x and of height y is $\pi x^2 y$.)

§2. EXISTENCE OF MAXIMA AND MINIMA

It is important to know when a function has a maximum and a minimum. We shall describe a condition under which it does.

Up to now we have defined derivatives by means of a Newton quotient taken with h positive and negative. However, in Chapter II, we also described the right derivative and the left derivative.

Let $f(x)$ be a function defined on an interval

$$a \leq x \leq b.$$

(*We assume throughout that $a < b$.*) We shall say that it is *differentiable* in this interval if it is differentiable in the interval

$$a < x < b,$$

and if, in addition, it has a right derivative at a, and a left derivative at b. Thus we assume that the limits

$$\lim_{\substack{h \to 0 \\ h > 0}} \frac{f(a + h) - f(a)}{h}$$

and

$$\lim_{\substack{h \to 0 \\ h < 0}} \frac{f(b + h) - f(b)}{h}$$

exist. These limits will be denoted by $f'(a)$ and $f'(b)$ just as with the ordinary derivative.

If we have a point x in the interval which is not equal to the end points, then $f'(x)$ has the usual meaning.

Since the function may not be defined outside the interval, the quotient

$$\frac{f(a + h) - f(a)}{h}$$

would not be defined when $h < 0$, and similarly the quotient

$$\frac{f(b + h) - f(b)}{h}$$

would not be defined when $h > 0$.

We need some criterion to know when a function has a maximum and a minimum in an interval.

A function f is said to be *continuous* if for every x such that f is defined, we have

$$\lim_{h \to 0} f(x + h) = f(x).$$

If f is differentiable, then it must be continuous.

In this chapter, we shall deal mostly with functions defined on an interval with end points a, b such that $a < b$, and these functions will be differentiable in the open interval, and continuous at the end points.

Theorem 2. *Let $f(x)$ be a function which is continuous on the closed interval $a \leqq x \leqq b$. Then f has a maximum and also has a minimum in this interval.*

This means that there is a point c_1 in the interval such that $f(c_1) \geqq f(x)$ for all x in the interval, and there is a point c_2 such that $f(c_2) \leqq f(x)$ for all x in the interval.

If you look back to Fig. 3 and Fig. 6 of §1, you will see graphs of functions which have no maximum or minimum. The reason for this is that the functions are not defined over closed intervals. In the case of a hyperbola, as in Fig. 6, we could define the function at 0 in an arbitrary way, for instance let $f(0) = 997$. We still would not get a maximum or a minimum.

We shall take Theorem 2 for granted, without proof. If you are interested in seeing a proof, you can look in the appendix. The proof must be carried out by using special properties of numbers.

Combining Theorems 1 and 2, we obtain:

Theorem 3. *Let a, b be two numbers, $a < b$. Let f be a function which is continuous over the closed interval*

$$a \leqq x \leqq b$$

and differentiable on the open interval a < x < b. Assume that

$$f(a) = f(b) = 0.$$

Then there exists a point c such that

$$a < c < b$$

and such that f'(c) = 0.

Proof. If the function is constant in the interval, then its derivative is 0 and any point in the open interval $a < x < b$ will do.

If the function is not constant, then there exists some point in the interval where the function is not 0, and this point cannot be one of the end points a or b. Suppose that some value of our function is positive. By Theorem 2, the function has a maximum. Let c be this maximum. Then $f(c)$ must be greater than 0, and c cannot be either one of the end points. Consequently

$$a < c < b.$$

By Theorem 1, we must have $f'(c) = 0$. This proves our theorem in case the function is positive somewhere in the interval.

If the function is negative for some number in the interval, then we use Theorem 2 to get a minimum, and we argue in a similar way, using Theorem 1 (applied to a minimum). (Write out the argument in full as an exercise.)

The following picture illustrates our Theorem 3.

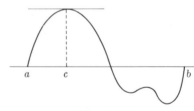

Figure 12

Example 1. Find the maximum of the function $y = 2x + 1$ on the interval $3 \leqq x \leqq 5$.

Let $f(x) = 2x + 1$. Then $f'(x) = 2$, and is constant $\neq 0$. Hence there is no maximum in the open interval $3 < x < 5$. Hence the maximum occurs at the end points, and one verifies by a direct computation that 5 is a maximum.

Example 2. Find a maximum for the function $f(x) = -x^2 + 3x + 5$ on the interval $[-1, 3]$.

Note that $f'(x) = -2x + 3$, and that $f'(x) = 0$ precisely when $x = 3/2$. Thus a maximum for f in the interval occurs either at the end points, or at $x = 3/2$. But $f(-1) = 1$, $f(3/2) = 29/4$ and $f(3) = 5$. Hence $3/2$ is the maximum.

Example 3. Find the maximum value of the function

$$f(x) = \sin 2x + \cos 2x$$

on the interval $0 \leq x \leq \pi/2$.

We have $f'(x) = 2\cos 2x - 2\sin 2x$. The derivative $f'(x)$ is equal to 0 precisely when $\sin 2x = \cos 2x$. For x in the prescribed interval, $0 \leq x \leq \pi/2$, this occurs only when $2x = \pi/4$, or $x = \pi/8$. At that point, we have

$$f(\pi/8) = \frac{2}{\sqrt{2}}.$$

At the end points of the interval, we have $f(0) = 1$ and $f(\pi/2) = -1$. Since $2/\sqrt{2} > 1$ and also > -1, it follows that the point $x = \pi/8$ is the maximum of the function.

EXERCISES

In the following exercises, sketch the graph of the function and find the maximum and minimum values in the given interval.

1. $f(x) = 2x + 1$, $[-1, 2]$
2. $f(x) = 4 - x$, $[-2, 4]$
3. $f(x) = 1/x$, $[-2, -1]$
4. $f(x) = x^2$, $[-2, 1]$
5. $f(x) = \sqrt{x - 2}$, $x \geq 2$
6. $f(x) = \sqrt[3]{x + 1}$, $[-9, 7]$
7. $f(x) = x^3 - 3x + 1$, $[1, 3]$
8. $f(x) = -x^2 + 2$, $[-1, 4]$
9. $f(x) = x^3 - x^2$, $[0, 5]$
10. $f(x) = x^4 - 81x$, $[-2, 2]$

Find the local and absolute maxima and minima of the following functions over the interval $[0, 2\pi]$.

11. $f(x) = \sin x + \cos x$
12. $f(x) = 2\cos x + \cos 2x$
13. $f(x) = \sin^2 x + \cos x$
14. $f(x) = \tan x - 2x$
15. $f(x) = \sin 3x$
16. $f(x) = \dfrac{2}{\cos x} - \tan x$
17. $f(x) = \cos^2 x$
18. $f(x) = \sin^2 x$

Find the absolute maximum of the following functions over the interval $[0, \pi/2]$.

19. $f(x) = \sin^3 x$
20. $f(x) = 1 - \sin^3 x$
21. $f(x) = \sin^2 x + \cos x$
22. $f(x) = \cos^2 x + \sin x$.

§3. THE MEAN VALUE THEOREM

Let $f(x)$ be a function which is differentiable in the closed interval

$$a \leqq x \leqq b.$$

We continue to assume throughout that $a < b$. This time we do not assume as in Theorem 3, that $f(a) = f(b) = 0$. We shall prove that there exists a point c between a and b such that the slope of the tangent line at $(c, f(c))$ is the same as the slope of the line between the end points of our graph. In other words, the tangent line is parallel to the line passing through the end points of our graph.

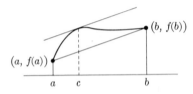

Figure 13

The slope of the line between the two end points is

$$\frac{f(b) - f(a)}{b - a}$$

because the coordinates of the end points are $(a, f(a))$ and $(b, f(b))$ respectively. Thus we have to find a point c such that

$$f'(c) = \frac{f(b) - f(a)}{b - a}.$$

Theorem 4. *Let $a < b$ as before. Let f be a function which is continuous in the closed interval $a \leqq x \leqq b$, and differentiable in the interval $a < x < b$. Then there exists a point c such that $a < c < b$ and*

$$f'(c) = \frac{f(b) - f(a)}{b - a}.$$

Proof. The equation of the line between the two end points is

$$y = \frac{f(b) - f(a)}{b - a}(x - a) + f(a).$$

Indeed, the slope

$$\frac{f(b) - f(a)}{b - a}$$

is the coefficient of x. When $x = a$, $y = f(a)$. Hence we have written down the equation of the line having the given slope and passing through a given point. When $x = b$, we note that $y = f(b)$.

We now consider geometrically the difference between $f(x)$ and the straight line. In other words, we consider the function

$$g(x) = f(x) - \frac{f(b) - f(a)}{b - a}(x - a) - f(a).$$

Then

$$g(a) = f(a) - f(a) = 0$$

and

$$g(b) = f(b) - f(b) = 0$$

also.

We can therefore apply Theorem 3 to the function $g(x)$. We know that there is a point c between a and b, and not equal to a or b, such that

$$g'(c) = 0.$$

But

$$g'(x) = f'(x) - \frac{f(b) - f(a)}{b - a}.$$

Consequently

$$0 = g'(c) = f'(c) - \frac{f(b) - f(a)}{b - a}.$$

This gives us the desired value for $f'(c)$.

The difference between $f(x)$ and the straight line becomes 0 at the end points. This is the geometric idea which allows us to apply our Theorem 3.

Example 1. Let $a = 1$ and $b = 2$. Let $f(x) = x^2$. Find a point c as in Theorem 4.

We have $f'(x) = 2x$, and

$$\frac{f(b) - f(a)}{b - a} = \frac{2^2 - 1^2}{2 - 1} = \frac{3}{1} = 3.$$

We have to solve the equation $2x = 3$. We get $x = 3/2$. Thus $c = 3/2$ is a point such that $f'(c)$ has the required value.

Example 2. Let $f(x) = x^3 + 2x$, and let $a = -1$, $b = 2$. Find a number c as in Theorem 4.

We have $f'(x) = 3x^2 + 2$, and

$$\frac{f(b) - f(a)}{b - a} = \frac{12 - (-3)}{2 - (-1)} = \frac{15}{3} = 5.$$

We must solve $3x^2 + 2 = 5$ and get

$$x = 1 \quad \text{or} \quad x = -1.$$

We take $c = 1$.

EXERCISES

Find a number c as in the mean value theorem for each one of the following functions:

1. $f(x) = x^3$, $1 \leq x \leq 3$
2. $f(x) = (x - 1)^3$, $-1 \leq x \leq 2$
3. $f(x) = x^3$, $-1 \leq x \leq 3$
4. $f(x) = x^2 + 5x$, $0 \leq x \leq 2$

§4. INCREASING AND DECREASING FUNCTIONS

Let f be a function defined on some interval (which may be open or closed). We shall say that f is *increasing* over this interval if

$$f(x_1) \leq f(x_2)$$

whenever x_1 and x_2 are two points of the interval such that $x_1 \leq x_2$.

Thus, if a number lies to the right of another, the value of the function at the larger number must be greater than or equal to the value of the function at the smaller number.

In the next figure, we have drawn the graph of an increasing function.

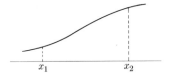

x_1 x_2 **Figure 14**

We say that a function defined on some interval is *decreasing* over this interval if

$$f(x_1) \geq f(x_2)$$

whenever x_1 and x_2 are two points of the interval such that $x_1 \leq x_2$.

Observe that a constant function (whose graph is horizontal) is both increasing and decreasing.

If we want to omit the equality sign in our definitions, we shall use the word *strictly* to qualify decreasing or increasing. Thus a function f is *strictly increasing* if

$$f(x_1) < f(x_2)$$

whenever $x_1 < x_2$, and f is *strictly decreasing* if

$$f(x_1) > f(x_2)$$

whenever $x_1 < x_2$.

The mean value theorem gives us a good test to determine when a function is increasing or decreasing.

Theorem 5. *Let f be a function which is continuous in some interval, and differentiable in the interval (excluding the end points).*

If $f'(x) = 0$ in the interval (excluding the end points), then f is constant.

If $f'(x) > 0$ in the interval (excluding the end points), then f is strictly increasing.

If $f'(x) < 0$ in the interval (excluding the end points), then f is strictly decreasing.

Proof. Let x_1 and x_2 be two points of the interval, and suppose $x_1 < x_2$. By the mean value theorem, there exists a point c such that $x_1 < c < x_2$ and

$$f'(c) = \frac{f(x_2) - f(x_1)}{x_2 - x_1}.$$

The difference $x_2 - x_1$ is positive, and we have

(1) $$f(x_2) - f(x_1) = (x_2 - x_1)f'(c).$$

If the derivative of the function is 0 throughout the interval, excluding the end points, then the right-hand side of (1) is equal to 0, and hence $f(x_1) = f(x_2)$. This means that, given any two points of the interval, the values of the function are equal, and hence the function is constant.

If the derivative $f'(x)$ is >0 for all x in the interval, excluding the end points, then $f'(c) > 0$ (because c is in the interval). Hence the product $(x_2 - x_1)f'(c)$ is positive, and

$$f(x_1) < f(x_2).$$

This proves that the function is increasing.

We leave the proof of the last assertion to you, as an exercise.

Example 1. Determine the regions of increase and decrease for the function $f(x) = x^2 + 5$.

The derivative is $f'(x) = 2x$. It is > 0 when $x > 0$ and hence f is strictly increasing when $x > 0$. The derivative is negative when $x < 0$ and hence f is strictly decreasing when $x < 0$. We leave the sketch of the graph to you.

Example 2. Determine the regions of increase and decrease for the function $f(x) = x^3 - 2x + 1$.

The derivative is $3x^2 - 2$. The condition

$$3x^2 - 2 > 0$$

is equivalent with $3x^2 > 2$ or $x^2 > 2/3$. Thus when $x > \sqrt{2/3}$ or $-x > \sqrt{2/3}$, we have $x^2 > 2/3$. The function is strictly increasing when $x > \sqrt{2/3}$ and when $x < -\sqrt{2/3}$.

The condition

$$f'(x) < 0$$

is equivalent to $3x^2 - 2 < 0$ or $x^2 < 2/3$. Thus the function is decreasing when

$$-\sqrt{2/3} < x < \sqrt{2/3}.$$

Example 3. Prove that $\sin x \le x$ for $x \ge 0$.

We let $f(x) = x - \sin x$. Then $f(0) = 0$. Furthermore,

$$f'(x) = 1 - \cos x.$$

Since $\cos x \le 1$ for all x, it follows that $f'(x) \ge 0$ for all x. Hence $f(x)$ is an increasing function. Hence $f(x) \ge 0$ for all $x \ge 0$ and therefore $\sin x \le x$.

Example 3 illustrates a technique which is useful for proving certain inequalities between functions. In general, *suppose we have two functions f and g over a certain interval* $[a, b]$ *and we assume that f, g are differentiable. Suppose that* $f(a) \le g(a)$, *and that* $f'(x) \le g'(x)$ *throughout the interval. Then* $f(x) \le g(x)$ *in the interval.* We see this just as in Example 3. We let $h(x) = g(x) - f(x)$. Then $h'(x) \ge 0$, so h is increasing throughout the interval, and since $h(a) = g(a) - f(a) \ge 0$, it follows that $h(x) \ge 0$ throughout the interval, whence $g(x) \ge f(x)$.

Example 4. Show that for any integer $n \ge 1$ and any number $x \ge 1$ one has the inequality $x^n - 1 \ge n(x - 1)$.

Let $f(x) = x^n - 1$ and $g(x) = n(x - 1)$. Then $f(1) = g(1) = 0$. On the other hand,

$$f'(x) = nx^{n-1}, \qquad g'(x) = n.$$

If $n = 1$, our inequality is obvious. If $n \ge 1$, then $nx^{n-1} \ge n$ because $x \ge 1$. Hence we conclude that $f(x) \ge g(x)$ for all $x \ge 1$.

The principle just stated can be visualized in the following picture: drawn for the case when $f(a) = g(a)$.

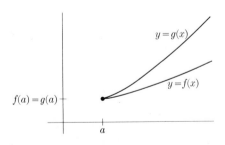

Figure 15

We shall now give a criterion which will allow us to decide when a function is positive or negative throughout an interval. For this, we need what is known as the *intermediate value theorem*.

Theorem 6. *Let x_1 and x_2 be two numbers, with $x_1 \leqq x_2$. Let f be a function which is defined on the interval*

$$x_1 \leqq x \leqq x_2$$

and assume that f is continuous. Let $y_1 = f(x_1)$ and $y_2 = f(x_2)$. Let y_3 be a number between y_1 and y_2. Then there exists a number x_3 between x_1 and x_2 such that $f(x_3) = y_3$.

The proof of Theorem 6 is given in the appendix. It is the type of proof which reduces the theorem to properties of numbers, and which we omit.

As a consequence of Theorem 6, we see that a function which is continuous in an interval, is positive at some point of the interval, and is not equal to 0 at any point of the interval, must be positive throughout the interval. Indeed, if it were negative at some point of the interval, the intermediate value theorem would ensure that there is a point in the interval at which it is equal to 0. For our purposes, we therefore have the following criterion.

Theorem 7. *Let f be a function having a derivative f' at every point of an interval, and assume that f' is continuous. If f' is positive at some point of the interval, and $f'(x) \neq 0$ for any x in the interval except possibly at the end points, then f is strictly increasing in the interval.*

In practice, we can use Theorem 7 by checking that f' is not equal to 0 at any point. This is easier than checking that $f'(x) > 0$ at every point of an interval.

Needless to say, an analogous statement holds when f' is assumed to be negative throughout the interval. State it yourself as an exercise.

Example 5. Determine the intervals on which the function

$$f(x) = x^3 + 5x^2 - 1$$

is increasing and decreasing.

We have $f'(x) = 3x^2 + 10x = x(3x + 10)$. The derivative $f'(x)$ is therefore equal to 0 precisely when $x = 0$ or $x = -10/3$. Thus the sign of the derivative is constant on the intervals

$$x < -10/3, \qquad -10/3 < x < 0, \qquad 0 < x.$$

Since $f'(-5) = 25 > 0$, it follows that the function is strictly increasing for $x < -10/3$. Since $f'(-1) = -7$, it follows that f is strictly decreasing for $-10/3 < x < 0$. Since $f'(1) = 13$, it follows that f is strictly increasing for $x > 0$. This determines what we wanted.

Example 6. Show that among all rectangles of given area, the one with least perimeter is a square.

Let *a* be the given area, and let *x* be the length of one side of the possible rectangle with area *a*. We take $0 < x$. If *y* is the length of the other side, then $xy = a$, so that $y = a/x$ is the length of the other side. Hence

$$f(x) = 2\left(x + \frac{a}{x}\right)$$

is the perimeter. We have $f'(x) = 2(1 - a/x^2)$, so that $f'(x) = 0$ precisely when $x^2 = a$, i.e. $x = \sqrt{a}$ (because we consider only $x > 0$). When $0 < x < \sqrt{a}$ one sees that $f'(x) < 0$ so that *f* is decreasing, and when $x > \sqrt{a}$, one sees that $f'(x) > 0$ so that *f* is increasing. Hence $x = \sqrt{a}$ is a minimum for *f*, and in that case $y = \sqrt{a}$ also, thus proving that the rectangle is a square.

Example 7. A function *f* has a derivative equal to

$$f'(x) = (x - 1)(x - 2)(x + 3).$$

Determine the intervals where the function is increasing.

We consider the intervals $x < -3$, $-3 < x < 1$, $1 < x < 2$ and $x > 2$ successively. In the interval $x < -3$, all three factors $(x - 1)$, $x - 2$, $x + 3$ are negative, and hence $f'(x) < 0$ so that the function is decreasing. In the interval $-3 < x < 1$, both factors $x - 1$ and $x - 2$ are negative, but $x + 3$ is positive. Hence the derivative $f'(x)$ is positive, and the function is increasing. Similarly, the function is decreasing in $1 < x < 2$, and increasing for $x > 2$.

Before closing this chapter, we emphasize the first assertion of Theorem 5. We had already seen that the derivative of a constant is 0. We now have proved the converse. It gives us the following very important result:

Theorem 8. *Let $f(x)$ and $g(x)$ be two functions which are differentiable in some interval and assume that*

$$f'(x) = g'(x)$$

for all x in the interval. Then there is a constant C such that

$$f(x) = g(x) + C$$

for all x in the interval.

Proof. Let $\varphi(x) = f(x) - g(x)$ be the difference of our two functions. Then

$$\varphi'(x) = f'(x) - g'(x) = 0.$$

Hence $\varphi(x)$ is constant, i.e. $\varphi(x) = C$ for some number *C*.

EXERCISES

Determine the intervals on which the following functions are increasing and decreasing.

1. $f(x) = x^3 + 1$

2. $f(x) = (x - 1)(x - 2)(x - 3)$

3. $f(x) = x^2 - x + 5$

4. $f(x) = \sin x + \cos x$

5. $f(x) = \sin 2x \quad (0 \leqq x \leqq 2\pi)$

6. $f(x) = x^4 - 3x^2 + 1$

7. $f(x) = x^3 + x - 2$

8. $f(x) = -x^3 + 2x + 1$

9. $f(x) = 2x^3 + 5$

10. $f(x) = 5x^2 + 1$

11. Consider only values of $x \geqq 0$, and let

$$f_1(x) = x - \sin x \qquad f_2(x) = -1 + \frac{x^2}{2} + \cos x$$

$$f_3(x) = -x + \frac{x^3}{3 \cdot 2} + \sin x \qquad f_4(x) = 1 - \frac{x^2}{2} + \frac{x^4}{4 \cdot 3 \cdot 2} - \cos x$$

$$f_5(x) = x - \frac{x^3}{3 \cdot 2} + \frac{x^5}{5 \cdot 4 \cdot 3 \cdot 2} - \sin x$$

(a) Determine whether $f_1(x)$ is increasing or decreasing. Using the value of $f_1(x)$ at 0, show that $\sin x \leqq x$.

(b) Determine which of the other functions are increasing or decreasing. Using the value of each function at 0, prove the following inequalities:

$$x - \frac{x^3}{3 \cdot 2} \leqq \sin x \leqq x - \frac{x^3}{3 \cdot 2} + \frac{x^5}{5 \cdot 4 \cdot 3 \cdot 2}$$

$$1 - \frac{x^2}{2} \leqq \cos x \leqq 1 - \frac{x^2}{2} + \frac{x^4}{4 \cdot 3 \cdot 2}$$

(c) Show how the above procedure can be continued to get further inequalities for $\sin x$ and $\cos x$. Give the general formula.

12. Assume that there is a function $f(x)$ such that $f(x) \neq 0$ for any x, and $f'(x) = f(x)$. Let $g(x)$ be any function such that $g'(x) = g(x)$. Show that there is a constant C such that $g(x) = Cf(x)$. [*Hint:* Differentiate the quotient g/f.]

For each of the following functions, find the maximum, minimum (a) for all x and (b) in the given interval. Also (c) find where each function is increasing and decreasing.

13. $x^2 - 2x - 8, \quad [0, 4]$

14. $x^2 - 2x + 1, \quad [-1, 4]$

15. $4 - 4x - x^2, \quad [-1, 4]$

16. $x - x^2, \quad [-1, 2]$

17. $3x - x^3, \quad [-2, \sqrt{3}]$

18. $(x - 4)^5, \quad [3, 6]$

19. $x^4 - 2x^2, \quad [-2, 1]$

20. $(x - 1)^{1/3} + \frac{1}{2}(x + 1)^{2/3}, \quad [-2, 7]$

21. $x^{2/5} + 1, \quad [-1, 1]$

22. $\sqrt{x^2 + 1}, \quad [0, \sqrt{8}]$

23. Let f, g be two differential functions on an open interval $a < x < b$. Assume that $f'(x) > g'(x)$ for all x in this interval, and that there exists a number c in this interval such that $f(c) = g(c)$. Show that if x is a point in the interval, then $f(x) > g(x)$ if $x > c$ and $f(x) < g(x)$ if $x < c$.

24. Let f be a function which is infinitely differentiable. Let $c_1 < c_2 < \cdots < c_r$ be numbers such that $f(c_i) = 0$ for all i. Show that f' has at least $r - 1$ zeros [i.e. numbers b such that $f'(b) = 0$].

25. Apply the preceding exercise to a polynomial

$$f(x) = a_n x^n + \cdots + a_0$$

where $a_0, \ldots, a_n$ are numbers, and $a_n \neq 0$. Conclude that such a polynomial has at most n roots. [*Hint:* What is the n-th derivative of f?]

26. Show that among all triangles with given area, the equilateral triangle has the least perimeter.

27. Show that among all triangles with given perimeter, the equilateral triangle has the maximum area.

28. Prove that $\tan x \geq x$ if $0 \leq x \leq \pi/2$.

Supplementary Exercises

1. Find the length of the sides of a rectangle of largest area which can be inscribed in a semicircle, the lower base being on the diameter.

2. A rectangular box has a square base and no top. The combined area of the sides and bottom is 48 ft^2. Find the dimensions of the box of maximum volume meeting these requirements.

3. Prove that, among all rectangles of given area, the square has the least perimeter.

4. A truck is to be driven 300 mi at a constant speed of x mph. Speed laws require $30 \leq x \leq 60$. Assume that gasoline costs 30 cents/gallon and is consumed at the rate of $2 + x^2/600$ gal/hr. If the driver's wages are D dollars per hour, find the most economical speed and the cost of the trip if (a) $D = 0$, (b) $D = 1$, (c) $D = 2$, (d) $D = 3$, (e) $D = 4$.

5. A rectangle is to have an area of 64 in^2. Find its dimensions so that the distance from one corner to the mid-point of a non-adjacent side shall be a minimum.

6. Express the number 4 as the sum of two positive numbers in such a way that the sum of the square of the first and the cube of the second is as small as possible.

7. A wire 24 in. long is cut in two, and one part is bent into the shape of a circle, and the other into the shape of a square. How should it be cut if the sum of the areas of the circle and the square is to be (a) minimum, (b) maximum?

8. Find the point on the graph of the equation $y^2 = 4x$ which is nearest to the point $(2, 1)$.

9. Find the points on the hyperbola $x^2 - y^2 = 1$ nearest to the point $(0, 1)$.

10. Show that $(2, 2)$ is the point on the graph of the equation $y = x^3 - 3x$ that is nearest the point $(11, 1)$.

11. Find the coordinates of the points on the curve $x^2 - y^2 = 16$ which are nearest to the point $(0, 6)$.

12. Find the coordinates of the points on the curve $y^2 = x + 1$ which are nearest to the origin.

13. Find the coordinates of the point on the curve $y^2 = \frac{5}{2}(x + 1)$ which is nearest to the origin.

14. Find the coordinates of the points on the curve $y = 2x^2$ which are closest to the point $(9, 0)$.

15. A circular ring of radius b is uniformly charged with electricity, the total charge being Q. The force exerted by this charge on a particle at a distance x from the center of the ring, in a direction perpendicular to the plane of the ring, is given by $F(x) = Qx(x^2 + b^2)^{-3/2}$. Find the maximum of F for all $x \geq 0$.

16. Let F be the rate of flow of water over a certain spillway. Assume that F is proportional to $y(h - y)^{1/2}$, where y is the depth of the flow, and h is the head, and is constant. What value of y makes F a minimum?

17. Find the point on the x-axis the sum of whose distances from $(2, 0)$ and $(0, 3)$ is a minimum.

18. A piece of wire of length L is cut into two parts, one of which is bent into the shape of an equilateral triangle and the other into the shape of a circle. How should the wire be cut so that the sum of the enclosed areas is (a) a minimum, (b) a maximum?

19. A fence $13\frac{1}{2}$ ft high is 4 ft from the side wall of a house. What is the length of the shortest ladder, one end of which will rest on the level ground outside the fence and the other on the side wall of the house?

20. A tank is to have a given volume V and is to be made in the form of a right circular cylinder with hemispheres attached to each end. The material for the ends costs twice as much per square foot as that for the sides. Find the most economical proportions.

21. Find the length of the longest rod which can be carried horizontally around a corner from a corridor 8 ft wide into one 4 ft wide.

22. Let P, Q be two points in the plane on the same side of the x-axis. Let R be a point on the x-axis (Figure 16). Show that the sum of the distances PR and QR is smallest when the angles θ_1 and θ_2 are equal.

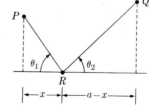

Figure 16

[*Hint:* Let $f(x)$ be the sum of the distances. Show that the condition $f'(x) = 0$ means that $\cos \theta_1 = \cos \theta_2$. Using values of x near 0 and a, and Theorem 7, conclude that $f(x)$ is decreasing for $0 \leq x \leq d$ and increasing for $d \leq x \leq a$ if d is the critical point of f.]

23. Suppose the velocity of light is v_1 in air and v_2 in water. A ray of light traveling from a point P_1 above the surface of water to a point P_2 below the surface will travel by the path which requires the least time. Show that the ray will cross the surface at the point Q in the vertical plane through P_1 and P_2 so placed that

$$\frac{\sin \theta_1}{v_1} = \frac{\sin \theta_2}{v_2},$$

where θ_1 and θ_2 are the angles shown in the following figure:

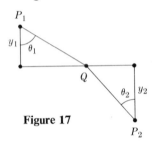

Figure 17

(You may assume that the light will travel in the vertical plane through P_1 and P_2. You may also assume that when the velocity is constant, equal to v, throughout a region, and s is the distance traveled, then the time t is equal to $t = s/v$.)

24. Let p be the probability that a certain event will occur, at any trial. In n trials, suppose that s successes have been observed. The likelihood function L is defined as $L(p) = p^s(1 - p)^{n-s}$. Find the value of p which maximizes the likelihood function. (Take $0 \leq p \leq 1$.)

25. Find an equation for the line through the point $(3, 2)$ making with the coordinate axes a triangle of minimum area in the first quadrant.

26. Let $a_1, \ldots, a_n$ be numbers. Find the number x for which

$$(a_1 - x)^2 + \cdots + (a_n - x)^2$$

is a minimum.

27. When light from a point source strikes a plane surface, the intensity of illumination is proportional to the cosine of the angle of incidence and inversely proportional to the square of the distance from the source. How high should a light be located above the center of a circle of radius 25 cm to give the best illumination along the circumference? (The angle of incidence is measured from the perpendicular to the plane.)

28. A horizontal reservoir has a cross section which is an inverted isosceles triangle, where the length of a leg is 60 ft. Find the angle between the equal legs to give maximum capacity.

29. A reservoir has a horizontal plane bottom and a cross section as shown on the figure. Find the angle of inclination of the sides from the horizontal to give maximum capacity.

100 ft   100 ft

100 ft   **Figure 18**

30. Determine the constant a such that the function

$$f(x) = x^2 + \frac{a}{x}$$

has (a) a local minimum at $x = 2$, (b) a local minimum at $x = -3$. (c) Show that the function cannot have a local maximum for any value of a.

31. The intensity of illumination at any point is proportional to the strength of the light source and varies inversely as the square of the distance from the source. If two sources of strengths a and b respectively are a distance c apart, at what point on the line joining them will the intensity be a minimum?

32. A window is in the shape of a rectangle surmounted by a semicircle. Find the dimensions when the perimeter is 12 ft and the area is as large as possible.

33. Find the radius and angle of the circular sector of maximum area having a perimeter of 16 ft.

34. Two points P and Q are diametrically opposite each other on the shore of a circular pond whose radius is 1 mi. A man wishes to go from P to Q by swimming from P to a point R on the shore and then walking along the shore from R to Q. He can swim 2 mph and walk 4 mph. Find the minimum possible time from P to Q and also the maximum possible time under the stated conditions.

35. A ladder is to reach over a fence 12 ft high to a wall 2 ft behind the fence. What is the length of the shortest ladder that can be used?

36. A cannon, resting on level ground, is aimed upward at an angle of inclination θ. Let r be the range of the cannon, that is, the distance from the cannon to the point of impact of the ball. Then r is given by

$$r = \frac{2v^2}{g} \sin \theta \cos \theta,$$

where v, g are constants. For what angle is the range a maximum?

Chapter VI

Sketching Curves

We have developed enough techniques to be able to sketch curves and graphs of functions much more efficiently than before. We shall investigate systematically the behavior of a curve, and the mean value theorem will play a fundamental role.

We shall especially look for the following aspects of the curve:
1. Intersections with the coordinate axes.
2. Critical points.
3. Regions of increase.
4. Regions of decrease.
5. Maxima and minima (including the local ones).
6. Behavior as x becomes very large positive and very large negative.
7. Values of x near which y becomes very large positive or very large negative.

These seven pieces of information will be quite sufficient to give us a fairly accurate idea of what the graph looks like. We shall devote a section to considering one other aspect, namely:

8. Regions where the curve is convex upwards or downwards. This tells us how the curve is bending.

We shall also introduce a new way of describing points of the plane and functions, namely polar coordinates. These are especially useful in connection with the trigonometric functions.

§1. BEHAVIOR AS x BECOMES VERY LARGE

Suppose we have a function f defined for all sufficiently large numbers. Then we get substantial information concerning our function by investigating how it behaves as x becomes large.

For instance, $\sin x$ oscillates between -1 and $+1$.

However, polynomials don't oscillate. When $f(x) = x^2$, as x becomes large positive, so does x^2. Similarly with the function x^3, or x^4 (etc.).

Example 1. Consider a polynomial

$$f(x) = x^3 + 2x - 1.$$

108

We can write it in the form

$$x^3 \left(1 + \frac{2}{x^2} - \frac{1}{x^3} \right).$$

When x becomes very large, the expression

$$1 + \frac{2}{x^2} - \frac{1}{x^3}$$

approaches 1. In particular, given a small number $\delta > 0$, we have, for all x sufficiently large, the inequality

$$1 - \delta < 1 + \frac{2}{x^2} - \frac{1}{x^3} < 1 + \delta.$$

Therefore $f(x)$ satisfies the inequality

$$x^3(1 - \delta) < f(x) < x^3(1 + \delta).$$

This tells us that $f(x)$ behaves very much like x^3 when x is very large. A similar argument can be applied to any polynomial.

Example 2. Consider a quotient of polynomials like

$$Q(x) = \frac{x^3 + 2x - 1}{2x^3 - x + 1}.$$

Dividing numerator and denominator by x^3, we get

$$Q(x) = \frac{1 + \dfrac{2}{x^2} - \dfrac{1}{x^3}}{2 - \dfrac{1}{x^2} + \dfrac{1}{x^3}}.$$

As x becomes very large, the numerator approaches 1 and the denominator approaches 2. Thus our fraction approaches $\frac{1}{2}$.

Example 3. Consider the quotient

$$Q(x) = \frac{x^2 - 1}{x^3 - 2x + 1}.$$

Does it approach a limit as x becomes very large?

If we divide numerator and denominator by x^3, then we see that our quotient can be written

$$\frac{\dfrac{1}{x} - \dfrac{1}{x^3}}{1 - \dfrac{2}{x^2} + \dfrac{1}{x^3}}.$$

As x becomes very large, the numerator approaches 0 and the denominator approaches 1. Consequently the quotient approaches 0.

Example 4. Consider the quotient

$$Q(x) = \frac{x^3 - 1}{x^2 + 5}$$

and determine what happens when x becomes very large.

We divide numerator and denominator by x^2. This gives

$$Q(x) = \frac{x - \dfrac{1}{x^2}}{1 + \dfrac{5}{x^2}}.$$

As x becomes very large, the numerator is approximately equal to x and the denominator approaches 1. Thus the quotient is approximately equal to x.

These four examples are typical of what happens when we deal with quotients of polynomials.

Instead of saying "when x becomes very large", we shall also say "as x approaches infinity", or even better, "as x approaches plus infinity".

Thus in Example 2 we would write

$$\lim_{x \to \infty} Q(x) = \tfrac{1}{2}.$$

In Example 3 we would write

$$\lim_{x \to \infty} Q(x) = 0.$$

In Example 4, we would write

$$\lim_{x \to \infty} Q(x) = \infty.$$

We emphasize that this way of writing is an *abbreviation*, a shorthand, for the sentences we wrote in our various examples. There is NO NUMBER WHICH IS CALLED INFINITY. The symbol ∞ will not be used except in the context we have just described.

Of course, we could also investigate what happens when x becomes very large *negative*, or, as we shall also say, when x approaches minus infinity, which we write $-\infty$.

In Example 2, we see that as x becomes very large negative, our quotient $Q(x)$ still approaches $\tfrac{1}{2}$, because a fraction like $1/x^3$ becomes very small. (For instance $1/-10,000 = -1/10,000$ is very small negative.) Thus we would write

$$\lim_{x \to -\infty} Q(x) = \tfrac{1}{2}.$$

EXERCISES

Find the limits of the following quotients $Q(x)$ as x becomes very large positive or negative. In other words, find

$$\lim_{x \to \infty} Q(x) \quad \text{and} \quad \lim_{x \to -\infty} Q(x).$$

1. $\dfrac{2x^3 - x}{x^4 - 1}$

2. $\dfrac{\sin x}{x}$

3. $\dfrac{\cos x}{x}$

4. $\dfrac{x^2 + 1}{\pi x^2 - 1}$

5. $\dfrac{\sin 4x}{x^3}$

6. $\dfrac{5x^4 - x^3 + 3x + 2}{x^3 - 1}$

7. $\dfrac{-x^2 + 1}{x + 5}$

8. $\dfrac{2x^4 - 1}{-4x^4 + x^2}$

9. $\dfrac{2x^4 - 1}{-4x^3 + x^2}$

10. $\dfrac{2x^4 - 1}{-4x^5 + x^2}$

Describe the behavior of the following polynomials as x becomes very large positive and very large negative.

11. $x^3 - x + 1$

12. $-x^3 - x + 1$

13. $x^4 + 3x^3 + 2$

14. $-x^4 + 3x^3 + 2$

15. $2x^5 + x^2 - 100$

16. $-3x^5 + x + 1000$

17. $10x^6 - x^4$

18. $-3x^6 + x^3 + 1$

19. A function $f(x)$ which can be expressed as follows:

$$f(x) = a_n x^n + a_{n-1} x^{n-1} + \cdots + a_0,$$

where n is a positive integer and the $a_n, a_{n-1}, \ldots, a_0$ are numbers, is called a polynomial. If $a_n \neq 0$, then n is called the *degree* of the polynomial. Describe the behavior of $f(x)$ as x becomes very large positive or negative, n is odd or even, and $a_n > 0$ or $a_n < 0$. (You will have eight cases to consider.)

20. Using the intermediate value theorem, show that any polynomial of odd degree has a root.

§2. CURVE SKETCHING

We shall put together all the information we have gathered up to now to get an accurate picture of the graph of a function. We deal systematically with the seven properties stated in the introduction, and our discussion will take the form of working out examples.

Example 1. Sketch the graph of the curve

$$y = f(x) = \frac{x - 1}{x + 1}$$

and determine the seven properties stated in the introduction.

1. When $x = 0$, we have $f(x) = -1$. When $x = 1$, $f(x) = 0$.
2. The derivative is

$$f'(x) = \frac{2}{(x+1)^2} .$$

(You can compute it using the quotient rule.) It is never 0, and therefore the function has no critical points.

3. The denominator is a square and hence is always positive. Thus $f'(x) > 0$ for all x. The function is increasing for all x. Of course, the function is not defined for $x = -1$ and neither is the derivative. Thus it would be more accurate to say that the function is increasing in the region

$$x < -1$$

and is increasing in the region $x > -1$.

4. There is no region of decrease.

5. Since the derivative is never 0, there is no relative maximum or minimum.

6. As x becomes very large positive, our function approaches 1 (using the method of the preceding section). As x becomes very large negative, our function also approaches 1.

Finally, there is one more useful piece of information which we can look into, when $f(x)$ itself becomes very large positive or negative:

7. As x approaches -1, the denominator approaches 0 and the numerator approaches -2. If x approaches -1 from the right, then the denominator is positive, and the numerator is negative. Hence the fraction

$$\frac{x-1}{x+1}$$

is negative, and is very large negative.

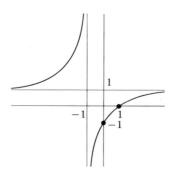

If x approaches -1 from the left, then $x - 1$ is negative, but $x + 1$ is negative also. Hence $f(x)$ is positive and very large, since the denominator is small when x is close to -1. Putting all this information together, we see that the graph looks like that in the preceding figure.

We have drawn the two lines $x = -1$ and $y = 1$, as these play an important role when x approaches -1 and when x becomes very large, positive or negative.

Example 2. Sketch the graph of the curve

$$y = -x^3 + 3x - 5.$$

1. When $x = 0$, we have $y = -5$.
2. The derivative is

$$f'(x) = -3x^2 + 3.$$

It is 0 when $3x^2 = 3$, which is equivalent to saying that

$$x^2 = 1, \quad \text{or} \quad x = \pm 1.$$

These are the critical points.

3. The derivative is positive when $-3x^2 + 3 > 0$, which amounts to saying that

$$3x^2 < 3 \quad \text{or} \quad x^2 < 1.$$

This is equivalent to the condition

$$-1 < x < 1,$$

which is therefore a region of increase.

4. When $-3x^2 + 3 < 0$, the function decreases. This is the region given by the inequality

$$3x^2 > 3$$

or $x^2 > 1$. Thus when

$$x > 1 \quad \text{or} \quad x < -1,$$

the function decreases.

5. Since the function decreases when $x < -1$ and increases when $x > -1$ (and is close to -1), we conclude that the point -1 is a local minimum. Also, $f(-1) = -7$.

Similarly, the point 1 is a relative maximum and $f(1) = -3$.

6. As x becomes very large positive, x^3 is very large positive and $-x^3$ is very large negative. Hence our function becomes very large negative, as we see if we put it in the form

$$f(x) = -x^3 \left(1 - \frac{3}{x^2} + \frac{5}{x^3} \right).$$

Similarly, as x becomes very large negative, our function becomes very large positive.

Putting all this information together, we see that the graph looks like this:

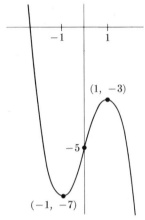

(1, −3)

−1   1

−5

(−1, −7)

EXERCISES

Sketch the following curves, indicating all the information stated in the introduction:

1. $y = \dfrac{x^2 + 2}{x - 3}$

2. $y = \dfrac{x - 3}{x^2 + 1}$

3. $y = \dfrac{x + 1}{x^2 + 1}$

4. $y = \sin^2 x$

5. $y = \cos^2 x$

6. $y = \dfrac{x^2 - 1}{x}$

7. $y = \tan^2 x$

8. $y = \dfrac{x^3 + 1}{x + 1}$

9. $y = x^4 - 2x^3 + 1$

10. $y = \dfrac{2x^2 - 1}{x^2 - 2}$

11. $y = \dfrac{2x - 3}{3x + 1}$

12. $y = x^4 + 4x$

13. $y = x^5 + x$

14. $y = x^6 + 6x$

15. $y = x^7 + x$

16. $y = x^8 + x$

17. Which of the following polynomials have a minimum (for all x)?

    (a) $x^6 - x + 2$ (b) $x^5 - x + 2$
    (c) $-x^6 - x + 2$ (d) $-x^5 - x + 2$
    (e) $x^6 + x + 2$ (f) $x^5 + x + 2$

Sketch the graphs of these polynomials.

18. Which of the polynomials in Exercise 17 have a maximum (for all x)?

19. Sketch the following curves:

    (a) $x^3 + x - 1$ (b) $x^3 - x - 1$ (c) $-x^3 + 2x + 5$

    (d) $-2x^3 + x + 2$ (e) $x^3 - x^2 + 1$ (f) $x^3 + x$

20. Let a, b, c, d be four distinct numbers. What would the following curves look like? You may assume $a < b < c < d$.

    (i) $(x - a)(x - b)$

    (ii) $(x - a)(x - b)(x - c)$

    (iii) $(x - a)(x - b)(x - c)(x - d)$

Sketch the graphs of the following functions and find the regions of increase and decrease, relative maxima and minima, etc.

21. $4x - \frac{1}{3}x^3$ 22. $(x - 1)^{2/3} + 3$ 23. $x^2 + 4x + 2$

24. $\dfrac{4x}{x^2 - 9}$ 25. $x + \dfrac{3}{x}$ 26. $\dfrac{x^2 - 4}{x^3}$

27. $\frac{1}{3}x^3 + x^2 - 2x$ 28. $x^3 - 3x^2 + 6x - 3$ 29. $\dfrac{x^2 - 4}{(x - 2)^2}$

30. $\dfrac{3x - 2}{2x + 3}$ 31. $\dfrac{x}{3x - 5}$ 32. $\dfrac{2x}{x + 4}$

33. $\dfrac{x^2}{\sqrt{x + 1}}$ 34. $\dfrac{x + 1}{x^2 + 5}$ 35. $\dfrac{x + 1}{x^2 - 5}$

36. $\dfrac{x^2 + 1}{x^2 - 1}$ 37. $\dfrac{x^2 - 1}{x^2 - 4}$ 38. $\dfrac{(x + 1)^2}{x^2 - 1}$

39. $x^{2/3}\sqrt{9 - x^2}$ for $-3 \leqq x \leqq 3$.

40. $(x - 4)^{4/3} + 2(x + 4)^{2/3}$

41. $(x - 1)^{1/3} + \frac{1}{2}(x + 1)^{2/3}$ for $-2 \leqq x \leqq 7$

42. $(x - 1)^{1/3} - \frac{1}{2}(x + 1)^{2/3}$ for $2 \leqq x \leqq 3$

43. $\sin x + \cos x$ 44. $x - \sin x$

45. $\sin 2x + \sqrt{3} \cos 2x$ 46. $x + 2 \cos \dfrac{x}{2}$

47. $\sin x + \sin x \cos x$ 48. $\sin 2x - \sin 2x \cos 2x$

49. $\sin x - \sin^3 x$ 50. $\cos x - \cos^3 x$

51. If $a_1, \ldots, a_n$ are numbers $\geqq 0$, show that

$$(a_1 \cdots a_n)^{1/n} \leqq \frac{a_1 + \cdots + a_n}{n}.$$

[*Hint:* By induction. The statement is obvious if $n = 1$. Assume it for some integer $n - 1 \geqq 1$. Taking the n-th power of both sides, it suffices to prove that

$$a_1 \cdots a_n \leqq \left(\frac{a_1 + \cdots + a_n}{n}\right)^n.$$

Let

$$f(x) = \left(\frac{a_1 + \cdots + a_{n-1} + x}{n}\right)^n - a_1 \cdots a_{n-1}x.$$

Compute $f'(x)$. Note that $f(0) \geq 0$. Show that $f'(x) = 0$ for exactly one value of x, say $x = c$. If $c \leq 0$, then the sign of f' is constant for $x > 0$, so that f is either decreasing or increasing for $x \geq 0$. But as x becomes large, $f(x)$ becomes large. Hence f is increasing for $x \geq 0$ and we are done in this case. If on the other hand $c > 0$, compute explicitly the value $f(c)$, and using the induction hypothesis, show that $f(c) \geq 0$. Since c is the only critical point, and since $f(x)$ becomes large when x becomes large, it follows that c must be a minimum, and hence finally that $f(x) \geq 0$ whenever $x \geq 0$.] Another proof for this inequality can be given using the convexity of the log, in a later chapter.

§3. CONVEXITY

Let a, b be numbers, $a < b$. Let f be a continuous function defined on the interval $[a, b]$. Assume that f' and f'' exist on the interval $a < x < b$. We view the second derivative f'' as the rate of change of the slope of the curve $y = f(x)$ over the interval. If the second derivative is positive in the interval $a < x < b$, then the slope of the curve is increasing, and we interpret this as meaning that the curve is bending upward. If the second derivative is negative, we interpret this as meaning that the curve is bending downward. The following two pictures illustrate this.

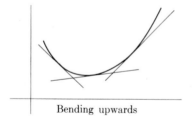
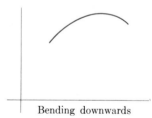

Bending upwards   Bending downwards

One can actually characterize the preceding geometric behavior more analytically. What does it mean to say that a curve is bending upwards? An equivalent condition should be that, given two points P and Q on the curve, the line segment joining P and Q should lie *above* the curve between P and Q, in which case we say that the curve is *convex* upwards. This is illustrated on the picture at the right. We can put this in terms of inequalities. Suppose our curve is given by a function, $y = f(x)$, and the points P and

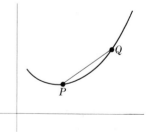

Q are given in terms of their coordinates, $(a, f(a))$ and $(b, f(b))$, for numbers a and b with $a < b$. The equation of the line passing through our two points is

$$y - f(a) = \frac{f(b) - f(a)}{b - a}(x - a),$$

or in other words,

$$y = f(a) + \frac{f(b) - f(a)}{b - a}(x - a).$$

The equation of the given curve is

$$y = f(x).$$

Thus the condition that the line segment between P and Q should lie above the curve between these points can be expressed by the inequality

$$(*) \qquad f(a) + \frac{f(b) - f(a)}{b - a}(x - a) \geq f(x) \qquad \text{for } a < x < b.$$

Thus we define the curve $y = f(x)$ to be *convex upwards* on an interval if for every $a < b$ in that interval, inequality (*) is satisfied. If inequality (*) holds when the sign $\geq$ is replaced by the sign $>$, then we say that the curve is *strictly* convex upwards.

Theorem 1. *Let a, b be numbers, $a < b$. Let f be a continuous function defined over the interval $[a, b]$. Assume that f' and f'' exist on the interval $a < x < b$, and that $f''(x) > 0$ for all x in this interval. Then the curve $y = f(x)$ is strictly convex upwards.*

Proof. Given any numbers c, d with $a \leq c < d \leq b$, all our hypotheses are satisfied for the interval $[c, d]$. Hence it will suffice to prove that the line segment between $(a, f(a))$ and $(b, f(b))$ lies above the curve in the interval $[a, b]$. Let φ be the function giving the difference between the line segment and the curve, i.e.

$$\varphi(x) = f(a) + \frac{f(b) - f(a)}{b - a}(x - a) - f(x).$$

Then

$$\varphi'(x) = \frac{f(b) - f(a)}{b - a} - f'(x),$$

and using the mean value theorem, we conclude that there exists some number c such that $a < c < b$ and

$$\varphi'(x) = f'(c) - f'(x)$$

for all x such that $a < x < b$. Now we may apply the mean value theorem to the function f' itself, with respect to the two numbers x and c. Suppose first that $a < x \leqq c$. Then

$$f'(c) - f'(x) = f''(d)(c - x)$$

for some number d between x and c. Since $f''(d) > 0$, it follows that $\varphi'(x) > 0$ for all x with $a < x < c$. Hence φ is a strictly increasing function in the interval $[a, c]$. Since $\varphi(a) = 0$ (as one verifies at once), it follows that $\varphi(x) > 0$ if $a < x \leqq c$. This proves the desired condition (*) when $a < x \leqq c$.

On the other hand, suppose that $c < x < b$. Then again by the mean value theorem, applied to f', we find

$$f'(x) - f'(c) = f''(e)(x - c)$$

for some number e between c and x. This shows that

$$\varphi'(x) = f'(c) - f'(x) < 0$$

in the present case, and hence that φ is strictly decreasing in the interval $c < x \leqq b$. Since $\varphi(b) = 0$ by a direct computation, we conclude again that $\varphi(x) > 0$, which is the desired condition (*) when $c < x < b$. This proves Theorem 1.

Example 1. Show that the curve $y = x^2$ is convex upwards over all intervals.

This is easily done, since the second derivative is the constant 2, which is certainly >0. We can thus apply Theorem 1.

Example 2. Let $f(x) = \sin x$. Show that the curve $y = \sin x$ is convex upwards in the interval $\pi \leqq x \leqq 2\pi$.

Again, we compute $f''(x) = -\sin x$, and we note that $f''(x) > 0$ in the interval $\pi < x < 2\pi$. Thus we can apply the theorem once more.

Of course, Theorem 1 has an analogue for curves which are convex downwards, i.e. such that the line segment between two points of the curve lies below the curve.

Theorem 2. *Let a, b be numbers, $a < b$. Let f be a continuous function defined over the interval $[a, b]$. Assume that f' and f'' exist on the interval $a < x < b$, and that $f''(x) < 0$ for all x in this interval. Then the curve $y = f(x)$ is strictly convex downwards.*

Proof. The proof is entirely similar to that of Theorem 1, and will be left as an exercise.

Example 3. Determine the intervals where the curve

$$y = -x^3 + 3x - 5$$

is convex upwards and convex downwards.

Let $f(x) = -x^3 + 3x - 5$. Then $f''(x) = -6x$. Thus $f''(x) > 0$ for $x < 0$ and $f''(x) < 0$ for $x > 0$. Hence the curve is convex upwards for $x \leq 0$ and is convex downwards for $x \geq 0$ according to Theorems 1 and 2. The graph of this curve has been discussed in Example 2 of §2, but the present considerations justify theoretically the convexity behaviour which we had already exhibited on this graph.

A point where a curve changes its behaviour from convex upwards to downwards (or vice versa) is called an *inflection point*. If the curve is the graph of a function f whose second derivative exists and is continuous, then we must have $f''(x) = 0$ at that point. The following picture illustrates this:

Inflection point

In Example 3 above, the point $(0, -5)$ is an inflection point. Again the reader can see the illustration given in Example 2 of §2.

The determination of regions of convexity, and inflection points gives us worthwhile pieces of information concerning curves. For instance, knowing that a curve in a region of decrease is actually convex downwards tells us that the decrease occurs essentially as in this example:

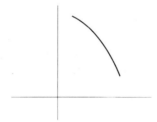

and not as in these examples:

One can give another condition characterizing convex curves. This comes from the fact that an arbitrary point in an interval $[a, b]$ can be written in the form

$$ta + (1 - t)b$$

for some t such that $0 \leq t \leq 1$. To see this, suppose that $a \leq x \leq b$. Then we let

$$t = \frac{b - x}{b - a}.$$

A direct computation shows that $x = ta + (1 - t)b$. Conversely, for any t with $0 \leq t \leq 1$, we have

$$a \leq ta + (1 - t)b \leq b.$$

Indeed, the left and right inequalities follow from these

$$ta + (1 - t)b - a = (1 - t)(b - a) \geq 0$$

and

$$ta + (1 - t)b - b = t(a - b) \leq 0.$$

If we let $u = 1 - t$, then as t goes from 0 to 1, we see that u goes from 1 to 0. Thus the points of the interval $[a, b]$ can also be written in the form

$$(1 - u)a + ub = a + u(b - a).$$

Theorem 3. *Let f be a function defined on the interval $[a, b]$. Then the following two conditions are equivalent.*

CON 1. *The line segment between the points $(a, f(a))$ and $(b, f(b))$ lies above the curve $y = f(x)$ in the interval $[a, b]$.*

CON 2. *For all numbers t with $0 \leq t \leq 1$ we have*

$$f(ta + (1 - t)b) \leq tf(a) + (1 - t)f(b).$$

Proof. Assume CON 1. For any x between a and b, write

$$x = ta + (1 - t)b$$

with $0 \leq t \leq 1$. Then referring to inequality (*), we find

$$f(ta + (1 - t)b) \leq f(a) + \frac{f(b) - f(a)}{b - a}(ta + b - tb - a)$$

$$= f(a) + \frac{f(b) - f(a)}{b - a}(b - a)(1 - t)$$

$$= tf(a) + (1 - t)f(b),$$

thereby proving CON 2. The converse will be left as an exercise.

A function satisfying the hypotheses of Theorem 2 for every pair of points $a \leq b$ in some interval of definition is said to be *convex (upwards)* in that interval.

Instead of writing t and $1 - t$ for the coefficients of a and b, we observe that $t + (1 - t) = 1$, and let $s = 1 - t$. Then CON 2 can be rewritten in the form

$$f(ta + sb) \leq tf(a) + sf(b)$$

for all numbers t, $s \geq 0$ such that $t + s = 1$. Similarly, we define a function g to be *convex downwards* on an interval if

$$g(ta + sb) \geq tg(a) + sg(b)$$

for all numbers t, $s \geq$ such that $t + s = 1$, and all $a < b$ in that interval.

EXERCISES

1. Write out in full the proof of Theorem 2.

2. Determine the intervals of convexity for the curves given in the exercises of §2, thereby justifying the convexity aspects of the sketches which you made previously of these curves.

3. Let the hypotheses be as in Theorem 1. Let x_0 be a number such that $a < x_0 < b$. Show that the tangent line to the curve $y = f(x)$ at $x = x_0$ lies below the graph of f except at $x = x_0$ where it touches the graph.

4. State and prove the analogous statement to Exercise 3, corresponding to Theorem 2.

5. (a) Find the equation for the tangent to the hyperbola $xy = 1$ at the point $(\frac{1}{2}, 2)$.
   (b) Prove that the tangent line is below the hyperbola for all $x > 0$ (except $x = \frac{1}{2}$ where it touches).

6. Let the hypotheses be as in Theorem 1. Show that

$$f\left(\frac{a + b}{2}\right) < \frac{f(a) + f(b)}{2}.$$

$$\left[\text{Hint: Put } x = \frac{a + b}{2} \right].$$

7. Prove that CON 2 implies CON 1 in Theorem 3, i.e. prove the converse of the statement whose proof was given.

8. Determine all inflection points of $\sin x$ and $\cos x$.

9. Determine the inflection points of the curves given in the exercises of §2.

10. Let f, g be functions defined for all numbers, and convex (upwards). Assume that f is an increasing function. Show that $f \circ g$ is convex (upwards).

11. Determine the intervals of convexity for the following curves, and sketch these curves.

(a) $y = x + \dfrac{1}{x}$ (b) $y = \dfrac{x}{x^2 + 1}$ (c) $y = \dfrac{x}{x^2 - 1}$

12. Let f be a function defined for all $x > 0$ and convex downwards. Prove by induction that for all numbers $t_1, \ldots, t_n \geq 0$ such that $t_1 + \cdots + t_n = 1$, and all numbers $x_1, \ldots, x_n > 0$ we have

$$t_1 f(x_1) + \cdots + t_n f(x_n) \leq f(t_1 x_1 + \cdots + t_n x_n).$$

[*Hint:* If $t_n \neq 0$, let $s_i = t_i/(1 - t_n)$ for $i = 1, \ldots, n - 1$. Then by induction, $s_1 f(x_1) + \cdots + s_{n-1} f(x_{n-1}) \leq f(s_1 x_1 + \cdots + s_{n-1} x_{n-1})$. Now add

$$\frac{t_n}{1 - t_n} f(x_n)$$

to both sides, multiply by $(1 - t_n)$, and use the convexity of f to conclude the proof.]

13. Let f be a function which is defined for all $x > 0$ and convex upwards. Prove that for all numbers $x_1, \ldots, x_n > 0$ we have

$$f\left(\frac{x_1 + \cdots + x_n}{n}\right) \leq \frac{1}{n} f(x_1) + \cdots + \frac{1}{n} f(x_n).$$

What is the corresponding inequality if f is assumed to be convex downwards?

§4. POLAR COORDINATES

Instead of describing a point in the plane by its coordinates with respect to two perpendicular axes, we can also describe it as follows. We draw a line between the point and a given origin. The angle which this line makes with the horizontal axis and the distance between the point and the origin determine our point. Thus the point is described by a pair of numbers (r, θ), which are called its *polar coordinates*.

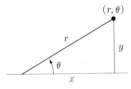

If we have our usual axes and x, y are the ordinary coordinates of our point, then we see that

$$\frac{x}{r} = \cos \theta \quad \text{and} \quad \frac{y}{r} = \sin \theta,$$

whence
$$x = r \cos \theta \quad \text{and} \quad y = r \sin \theta.$$

This allows us to change from polar coordinates to ordinary coordinates.

It is to be understood that r is always supposed to be ≥ 0. In terms of the ordinary coordinates, we have

$$r = \sqrt{x^2 + y^2}.$$

Example 1. Find polar coordinates of the point whose ordinary co-ordinates are $(1, \sqrt{3})$.

We have $x = 1$ and $y = \sqrt{3}$, so that $x = \sqrt{1 + 3} = 2$. Also $\cos \theta = \frac{1}{2}$, $\sin \theta = \sqrt{3}/2$. Hence $\theta = \pi/3$, and the polar coordinates are $(2, \pi/3)$.

We observe that we may have several polar coordinates corresponding to the same point. The point whose polar coordinates are $(r, \theta + 2\pi)$ is the same as the point (r, θ). Thus in our example above, $(2, \pi/6 + 2\pi)$ would also be polar coordinates for our point. In practice, we usually use the value for the angle which lies between 0 and 2π.

Let f be a function whose values are ≥ 0. If we set $r = f(\theta)$, then the set of points $\left(\theta, f(\theta)\right)$ is the graph of the function in polar coordinates. We can also view $r = f(\theta)$ as the equation of a curve.

Example 2. Sketch the graph of the function $r = \sin \theta$ for $0 \leq \theta \leq \pi$. If $\pi < \theta < 2\pi$, the $\sin \theta < 0$ and hence for such θ we don't get a point on the curve.

First we make a table of values, as indicated. As θ ranges from 0 to $\pi/2$, $\sin \theta$ increases until it reaches 1. As θ goes from $\pi/2$ to π, the sine decreases back to 0. Hence the graph looks like this:

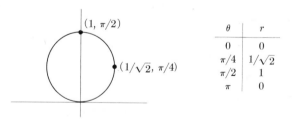

θ	r
0	0
$\pi/4$	$1/\sqrt{2}$
$\pi/2$	1
π	0

Example 3. Change the equation $r = \sin \theta$ of Example 2 to rectangular coordinates.

We substitute the expressions

$$r = x^2 + y^2 \quad \text{and} \quad \sin \theta = y/r = y/\sqrt{x^2 + y^2}$$

in the polar equation, to obtain

$$\sqrt{x^2 + y^2} = \frac{y}{\sqrt{x^2 + y^2}}.$$

Of course, this substitution is valid only when $r \neq 0$, i.e. $r > 0$. We can then simplify the equation we have just obtained, multiplying both sides by $\sqrt{x^2 + y^2}$. We then obtain

$$x^2 + y^2 = y,$$

which after completing the square yields

$$x^2 + (y - \tfrac{1}{2})^2 = \tfrac{1}{4}.$$

Thus we recognize the equation of Example 2 as that of a circle, of center $(0, \tfrac{1}{2})$ and radius $\tfrac{1}{2}$. The point corresponding to the polar coordinate $r = 0$ is the point with rectangular coordinates $x = 0$ and $y = 0$.

Example 4. The equation of the circle of radius 3 and center at the origin in polar coordinates is simply $r = 3$.

Example 5. Consider the equation $\theta = 1$ in polar coordinates. A point whose polar coordinates satisfy this equation can be described as $(r, 1)$ for any value of $r \geq 0$. Thus geometrically, this set of points can be described as a half line, or a ray:

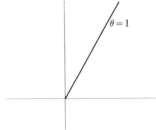

The slope of this ray is equal to $\tan 1$. Thus the equation in rectangular coordinates is

$$y = (\tan 1)x \quad \text{and} \quad x \geq 0.$$

EXERCISES

1. Plot the following points in polar coordinates:
   (a) $(2, \pi/4)$ (b) $(3, \pi/6)$ (c) $(1, -\pi/4)$ (d) $(2, -3\pi/6)$

2. Same directions as in Exercise 1.
   (a) $(1, 1)$ (b) $(4, -3)$
   (These are polar coordinates. Just show approximately the angle represented by the given coordinates.)

3. Find polar coordinates for the following points given in the usual x- and y-coordinates:
   (a) $(1, 1)$ (b) $(-1, -1)$ (c) $(3, 3\sqrt{3})$ (d) $(-1, 0)$

Sketch the graphs of the following curves given in polar coordinates:

4. $r = 5$ 5. $r = \sin 2\theta$ 6. $r = \theta$

7. $r = \sin \theta + \cos \theta$ 8. $r = \dfrac{2}{2 - \cos \theta}$ 9. $r = \sin 3\theta$

10. $r^2 = 2a^2 \cos 2\theta$ $(a > 0)$ 11. $r = 1 + \cos \theta$

12. $r = a \cos \theta$ $(a > 0)$ 13. $r = a \sin \theta$ $(a > 0)$

Sketch the following curves in polar coordinates.

14. $r = 1 + 2 \sin \theta$ 15. $r = 5 + 2 \sin \theta$

16. $r = 6 \cos \theta$ 17. $r = 3/\cos \theta$

18. $r = 2 \tan \theta$ 19. $r = 1 + \sqrt{2} \cos \theta$

20. $r = \sin 2\theta$ 21. $r = \cos 2\theta$

22. $r = 4 \sin^2 \theta$ 23. $r = 2 + \sin 2\theta$

24. $r^2 = \cos \theta$ 25. $r^2 = \sin \theta$

26. $r = 1/\theta$ 27. $r = \sin 4\theta$

28. $r = 1 - \sin \theta$ 29. $r = \dfrac{4}{1 + 2 \cos \theta}$

30. $r = \dfrac{4}{2 - \cos \theta}$ 31. $r = \dfrac{1}{\sin \theta}$

Change the following equations to rectangular coordinates:

32. $\theta = 2$ 33. $r = 4$ 34. $r = 2 \sin \theta$

35. $r = 3 \cos \theta$ 36. $r = 1 - \cos \theta$ 37. $r = 1 - 2 \sin \theta$

38. $r = \dfrac{1}{\cos \theta}$ 39. $r = \dfrac{1}{\sin \theta}$ 40. $r = \dfrac{1}{1 - \cos \theta}$

41. $r = \dfrac{2}{2 - \cos \theta}$ 42. $\theta = \pi$ 43. $\theta = 3$

44. $\theta = 2.5$ 45. $\theta = \pi/2$ 46. $\theta = 0.3$

47. $\theta = 0.5$

§5. PARAMETRIC CURVES

There is one other way in which we can describe a curve. Suppose that we look at a point which moves in the plane. Its coordinates can be given as a function of time t. Thus, when we give two functions of t, say

$$x = f(t), \qquad y = g(t),$$

we may view these as describing a point moving along a curve.

For example, if we let $x = \cos t$ and $y = \sin t$, then our point moves along a circle, counterclockwise, with uniform speed.

When (x, y) is described by two functions of t as above, we say that we have a *parametrization of the curve* in terms of the *parameter t*.

Example 1. Sketch the curve $x = t^2$, $y = t^3$.

We can make a table of values as usual. We also investigate when x and y are increasing or decreasing functions of t. For instance, taking the derivative, we get

$$\frac{dx}{dt} = 2t, \qquad \text{and} \qquad \frac{dy}{dt} = 3t^2.$$

Thus x increases when $t > 0$ and decreases when $t < 0$. The y-coordinate is increasing since $t^2 > 0$ (unless $t = 0$). Furthermore, the x-coordinate is always positive (unless $t = 0$). Thus the graph looks like this:

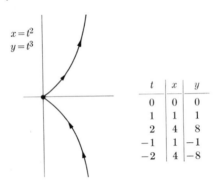

t	x	y
0	0	0
1	1	1
2	4	8
−1	1	−1
−2	4	−8

Example 2. We look at the circle

$$x = \cos \theta, \qquad y = \sin \theta.$$

We shall find another parametrization. Consider the circle of radius 1 and the point (x, y) on it:

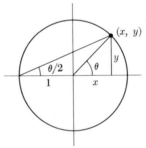

Let

$$t = \frac{y}{x + 1} \qquad (x \neq -1).$$

The equation of the circle is

$$x^2 + y^2 = 1.$$

Then we can interpret t geometrically to be $\tan \dfrac{\theta}{2}$.

From our expression for t we obtain

$$y = (x + 1)t \quad \text{and} \quad y^2 = (x + 1)^2 t^2.$$

On the other hand,

$$y^2 = 1 - x^2 = (x + 1)(1 - x).$$

In the two expressions for y^2, we cancel $(x + 1)(x \neq -1)$ and obtain

$$1 - x = (x + 1)t^2.$$

From this we solve for x, and get

$$x = \frac{1 - t^2}{1 + t^2}.$$

From the formula $y = t(x + 1)$, we get

$$y = \frac{2t}{1 + t^2}.$$

Thus, for $x \neq -1$, we can get t from x and y, but *conversely* we can recover x, y from values of t, which can be given arbitrarily. This allows us to find points on the circle explicitly simply by giving t arbitrary values, which may be selected to be rational numbers. Points (x, y) such that x and y are rational numbers are called *rational points*. The above parametrization shows us how to get all of them (except when $x = -1$).

Example 3. We shall prove that the points on the parametric curve

(*) $x = 2t - 1, \quad y = t + 4$

are precisely the points on a straight line. Eliminating t from these equations, i.e. multiplying the second by 2 and subtracting from the first, we obtain

(**) $x - 2y = -9.$

Thus all points satisfying (*) satisfy (**), which is the equation of a line. Conversely, given a point (x, y) satisfying equation (**), let $t = y - 4$. Then $y = t + 4$, and

$$x = -9 + 2y = 2(t + 4) - 9 = 2t + 8 - 9 = 2t - 1.$$

Hence (x, y) satisfy (*), as was to be shown.

In general, suppose that we have two points (x, y) and (x_1, y_1) in the plane. We define the sum

$$(x, y) + (x_1, y_1) = (x + x_1, y + y_1),$$

and if c is a number, the product

$$c(x, y) = (cx, cy).$$

Thus sum and product are defined componentwise. In Example 3, let $P = (2, 1)$ and $Q = (-1, 4)$. Let $X = (x, y)$. Then the parametric curve of Example 3 can be written in a shorter notation in the form

$$X = Q + tP.$$

When we study vectors in the next course, we shall see that this can be interpreted as the line through Q, in the direction of P.

EXERCISES

Sketch the following curves given in parametric form:

1. $x = t + 1$, $y = 3t + 4$
2. $x = 1 + t^2$, $y = 3 - t$
3. $x = 1 - t^2$, $y = t$ $(-1 \leq t \leq 1)$
4. $x = t - \sin t$, $y = 1 - \cos t$
5. $x = 2(t - \sin t)$, $y = 2(1 - \cos t)$

One can also give a parametrization of curves in polar coordinates. Sketch the following curves in polar coordinates:

6. $r = t^3$, $\theta = \pi t^2$ 7. $r = t$, $\theta = t^2$

8. Find at least five rational points on the circle of radius 1. (It is very difficult in general to find rational points on curves. It is rather remarkable that we did it on the circle.)

9. Using the method above, find an analogous parametrization of the circle

$$x^2 + y^2 = 9.$$

10. Prove that on any curve

$$x^n + y^n = 1$$

(n = positive integer ≥ 3), there is only a finite number of rational points. (If you solve this, you will be instantly world-famous among mathematicians. It is in fact believed that the only rational points are those for which x or $y = 0$. This is Fermat's problem, and has been verified for many values of n. It is also unknown whether there exist infinitely many rational points on a curve of type

$$y^2 = f(x),$$

where f is a polynomial of degree ≥ 5, having distinct roots, for instance

$$y^2 = (x - 1)(x - 2)(x - 3)(x - 4)(x - 5).$$

This is a special case of a more general conjecture made by Mordell some forty years ago, and unproved to this day.)

11. Sketch the following curves given in parametric form.

(a) $x = t, \quad y = t^3$ (b) $x = t, \quad y = t^4$

(c) $x = t^2, \quad y = t^4$ (d) $x = t, \quad y = \sqrt{t}$

12. Show that all points on the parametric curve $x = 2t + 1$, $y = 3t - 1$ lie on a straight line, and determine the ordinary equation of this line. Conversely, show that every point on this line satisfies the parametric equation for some value of t.

13. Show that the points on the parametric curve

$$x = 5t - 1, \qquad y = -2t + 4$$

are precisely the points on a straight line, and determine the equation of this line.

14. Show that the points on the parametric curve

$$x = 2t, \qquad y = 3t^2$$

are precisely the points on a parabola, and determine the ordinary equation of this parabola.

15. Show that the points on the parametric curve

$$x = 2t^2, \qquad y = 3t - 1$$

are precisely the points on a parabola, and determine the ordinary equation of this parabola.

16. Determine the ordinary equation for the following parametrized curves and sketch the graphs.

(a) $x = t, \quad y = 1/2t$ (b) $x = 3t, \quad y = 1/t$

(c) $x = t^2, \quad y = 1/t^2$

(In this case, you may need an inequality in addition to an equation.)

17. Show that the parametric curve given by $x = t^2$, $y = t^4$ is part of a parabola. What is the ordinary equation of this parabola, and which part is parametrized as above?

18. Sketch the parametric curve $x = t^2$, $y = 1/t^4$.

Chapter VII

Inverse Functions

Suppose that we have a function, for instance

$$y = 3x - 5.$$

Then we can solve for x in terms of y, namely

$$x = \tfrac{1}{3}(y + 5).$$

Thus x can be expressed as a function of y.

Although we are able to solve by means of an explicit formula, there are interesting cases where x can be expressed as a function of y, but without such an explicit formula. In this chapter, we shall investigate such cases.

§1. DEFINITION OF INVERSE FUNCTIONS

Let $y = f(x)$ be a function, defined for all x in some interval. If, for each value y_1 of y, there exists exactly *one* value x_1 of x in the interval such that $f(x_1) = y_1$, then we can define an *inverse function*

$$x = g(y)$$

by the rule: Given a number y, we associate with it the unique number x in the interval such that $f(x) = y$.

Our inverse function is defined only at those numbers which are values of f. We have the fundamental relation $f(g(y)) = y$ and $g(f(x)) = x$.

For example, consider the function $y = x^2$, which we view as being defined only for $x \geq 0$. Every positive number (or 0) can be written uniquely as the square of a positive number (or 0). Hence we can define the inverse function, which will also be defined for $y \geq 0$, but not for $y < 0$. It is nothing but the square root function.

The next theorem gives us a good criterion when the inverse function is defined.

Theorem 1. *Let $f(x)$ be a function which is strictly increasing. Then the inverse function exists.*

Proof. This is practically obvious: Given a number y_1 and a number x_1 such that $f(x_1) = y_1$, there cannot be another number x_2 such that

130

$f(x_2) = y_1$ unless $x_2 = x_1$, because if $x_2 \neq x_1$, then either $x_2 > x_1$, in which case $f(x_2) > f(x_1)$, or $x_2 < x_1$, in which case $f(x_2) < f(x_1)$.

Since the positivity of the derivative gives us a good test when a function is strictly increasing, we are able to define inverse functions whenever the function is differentiable and its derivative is positive.

As usual, what we have said above applies as well to functions which are strictly decreasing, and whose derivatives are negative.

Using the intermediate value theorem, we now conclude:

Theorem 2. *Let f be a continuous function on the closed interval*

$$a \leq x \leq b$$

and assume that f is strictly increasing. Let $f(a) = \alpha$ and $f(b) = \beta$. Then the inverse function is defined on the closed interval $[\alpha, \beta]$.

Proof. Given any number γ between α and β, there exists a number c between a and b such that $f(c) = \gamma$, by the intermediate value theorem. Our assertion now follows from Theorem 1.

If we let g be this inverse function, then $g(\alpha) = a$ and $g(\beta) = b$. Furthermore, the inverse function is characterized by the relation

$$f(x) = y \quad \text{if and only if} \quad x = g(y).$$

Example 1. Let $f(x) = x^3 - 2x + 1$, viewed as a function on the interval $x > \sqrt{2/3}$. Can we define the inverse function? For what numbers? If g is the inverse function, what is $g(0)$? What is $g(5)$?

Since $f'(x) = 3x^2 - 2$, the derivative is positive when $x > \sqrt{2/3}$. Hence our function is strictly increasing and the inverse function is defined.

We know (from the techniques of the previous chapter) that $x = \sqrt{2/3}$ is a minimum of f, and $f(\sqrt{2/3}) = (2/3)^{3/2} - 2(2/3)^{1/2} + 1$. The inverse function is defined therefore for $y > f(\sqrt{2/3})$.

Since $f(1) = 0$, we get $g(0) = 1$. Since $f(2) = 5$, we get $g(5) = 2$.

Please note that we do not give an explicit formula for our inverse function.

Example 2. Let $f(x) = x^n$ (n being a positive integer). We view f as defined only for numbers $x > 0$. Since $f'(x)$ is nx^{n-1}, the function is strictly increasing. Hence the inverse function exists. This inverse function g is in fact what we mean by the n-th root. In particular, we have proved that every positive number has an n-th root.

In all the exercises of the previous chapter you determined intervals over which certain functions increase and decrease. You can now define inverse functions for such intervals. In most cases, you cannot write down an explicit formula for such inverse functions.

EXERCISES

For each of the following functions, determine whether there is an inverse
function g, and determine those numbers at which g is defined.

1. $f(x) = 3x + 2$, all x.

2. $f(x) = x^2 + 2x - 3$, $0 \leq x$

3. $f(x) = x^3 + 4x - 5$, all x

4. $f(x) = \dfrac{x}{x + 1}$, $-1 < x$

5. $f(x) = \dfrac{x}{x + 2}$, $-2 < x$

6. $f(x) = \dfrac{x + 1}{x - 1}$, $1 < x$

7. $f(x) = \dfrac{1}{x^2}$, $0 < x \leq 1$

8. $f(x) = \dfrac{x^2}{x^2 + 1}$, $0 \leq x \leq 5$

9. $f(x) = \dfrac{x + 2}{x - 2}$, $0 \leq x < 2$

10. $f(x) = x + \dfrac{1}{x}$, $1 \leq x \leq 10$

11. $f(x) = x + \dfrac{1}{x}$, $0 < x \leq 1$

12. $f(x) = x - \dfrac{1}{x}$, $0 < x \leq 1$

13. $f(x) = \dfrac{2x}{1 + x^2}$, $-1 \leq x \leq 1$

14. $f(x) = \dfrac{2x}{1 + x^2}$, $1 \leq x$

§2. DERIVATIVE OF INVERSE FUNCTIONS

We shall state a theorem which allows us to determine the derivative of
an inverse function when we know the derivative of the given function.

Theorem 3. *Let a, b be two numbers, $a < b$. Let f be a function which
is differentiable on the interval $a < x < b$ and such that its derivative
$f'(x)$ is > 0 for all x in this open interval. Then the inverse function
$x = g(y)$ exists, and we have*

$$g'(y) = \frac{1}{f'(x)} = \frac{1}{f'(g(y))}.$$

Proof. We are supposed to investigate the Newton quotient

$$\frac{g(y + k) - g(y)}{k}.$$

The following picture illustrates the situation:

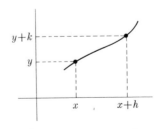

By the intermediate value theorem, every number of the form $y + k$ with small values of k can be written as a value of f. We let $x = g(y)$ and we let $h = g(y + k) - g(y)$. Then

$$x = g(y) \qquad \text{and} \qquad g(y + k) = x + h.$$

Furthermore, $y + k = f(x + h)$ and hence

$$k = f(x + h) - f(x).$$

The Newton quotient for g can therefore be written

$$\frac{h}{f(x + h) - f(x)},$$

and we see that it is the reciprocal of the Newton quotient for f, namely

$$\frac{1}{\dfrac{f(x + h) - f(x)}{h}}.$$

As h approaches 0, we know that k approaches 0. Conversely, as k approaches 0, we know that there exists exactly one value of h such that $f(x + h) = y + k$, because the inverse function is defined. Consequently, the corresponding value of h must also approach 0.

If we now take the limit of the reciprocal of the Newton quotient of f, as h (or k) approaches 0, we get

$$\frac{1}{f'(x)}.$$

By definition, this is the derivative $g'(y)$ and our theorem is proved.

Example 1. Let $f(x) = x^3 - 2x + 1$, viewed as a function on the interval $x > \sqrt{2/3}$. Let g be the inverse function. What is $g'(0)$? What is $g'(5)$?

Since $f'(x) = 3x^2 - 2$ we know that

$$g'(y) = \frac{1}{f'(x)}$$

whenever $y = f(x)$ or $x = g(y)$. But

$$f(1) = 0 \qquad \text{and} \qquad g(0) = 1.$$

Therefore

$$g'(0) = \frac{1}{f'(1)} = 1.$$

Similarly, $f(2) = 5$ and $g(5) = 2$. Hence

$$g'(5) = \frac{1}{f'(2)} = \frac{1}{10},$$

because $f'(2) = 10$.

Please note that the derivative $g'(y)$ is given in terms of $f'(x)$. We don't have a formula in terms of y.

The theorem giving us the derivative of the inverse function could also be expressed by saying that

$$\frac{dx}{dy} = \frac{1}{dy/dx}.$$

Here also, the derivative behaves *as if* we were taking a quotient. Thus the notation is very suggestive and we can use it from now on without thinking, because we proved a theorem justifying it.

Remark. In Theorem 3, we have proved that in fact, the derivative of the inverse function g exists, and is given by $g'(y) = 1/f'(x)$. If one *assumes* that this derivative exists, then one can give a much shorter argument to find its value, using the chain rule. Indeed, we have

$$f(g(y)) = y.$$

Differentiating with respect to y, we find by the chain rule,

$$f'(g(y))g'(y) = 1.$$

Hence

$$g'(y) = \frac{1}{f'(g(y))},$$

as was to be shown.

EXERCISES

In the exercises of Chapter V, §4, restrict f to an interval so that the inverse function is defined in an interval containing the indicated point, and find the derivative of the inverse function at that point. (Let g denote this inverse function in every case.)

1. $g'(2)$ 2. $g'(6)$ 3. $g'(7)$ 4. $g'(-1)$ 5. $g'(\sqrt{3}/2)$

6. $g'(-1)$ 7. $g'(0)$ 8. $g'(2)$ 9. $g'(21)$ 10. $g'(11)$

11. Let f be a continuous function on the interval $[a, b]$. Assume that f is twice differentiable on the open interval $a < x < b$, and that $f'(x) > 0$ and $f''(x) > 0$ on this interval. Let g be the inverse function of f.

    (a) Find an expression for the second derivative of g.
    (b) Show that $g''(y) < 0$ on its interval of definition. Thus g is convex in the opposite direction to f.

§3. THE ARCSINE

It is impossible to define an inverse function for the function $y = \sin x$ because to each value of y there correspond infinitely many values of x (differing by 2π). However, if we restrict our attention to special intervals, we can define the inverse function.

We restrict the sine function to the interval

$$-\frac{\pi}{2} \leqq x \leqq \frac{\pi}{2}.$$

The derivative of $\sin x$ is $\cos x$ and in that interval, we have

$$0 < \cos x$$

except when $x = \pi/2$ or $x = -\pi/2$ in which case the cosine is 0.
Therefore, in the interval

$$-\frac{\pi}{2} \leqq x \leqq \frac{\pi}{2}$$

the function is strictly increasing by Theorem 2 of Chapter V, §4. The inverse function exists, and is called the *arcsine*.

Let $f(x) = \sin x$, and $x = \arcsin y$, the inverse function. Since $f(0) = 0$ we have $\arcsin 0 = 0$. Furthermore, since $\sin(-\pi/2) = -1$ and $\sin(\pi/2) = 1$, we know that the inverse function is defined over the interval going from -1 to $+1$, i.e. for

$$-1 \leqq y \leqq 1.$$

In words, we can say loosely that $\arcsin x$ *is the angle whose sine is x.* (We throw in the word *loosely* because, strictly speaking, $\arcsin x$ is a number, and not an angle, and also because we mean the angle between $-\pi/2$ and $\pi/2$.)

The derivative of $\sin x$ is positive for

$$-\pi/2 < x < \pi/2.$$

Since the derivative of the inverse function $x = g(y)$ is $1/f'(x)$, the derivative of $\arcsin y$ is also positive, in the interval

$$-1 < y < 1.$$

Therefore the inverse function is strictly increasing in that interval. Its graph looks like the figure shown below.

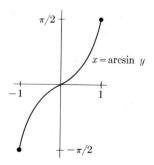

At this point, we cannot call the horizontal axis simultaneously the x- and y-axis. Thus for the moment, the horizontal axis as drawn above is the y-axis and the vertical axis is the x-axis.

According to the general rule for the derivative of inverse functions, we know that when $y = \sin x$ and $x = \arcsin y$ the derivative is

$$\frac{dx}{dy} = \frac{1}{\cos x}.$$

When x is very close to $\pi/2$, we know that $\cos x$ is close to 0. Therefore the derivative is very large. Hence the curve is almost vertical. Similarly, when x is close to $-\pi/2$ and y is close to -1, the curve is almost vertical, as drawn.

Finally, it turns out that we can express our derivative explicitly as a function of y. Indeed, we have the relation

$$\sin^2 x + \cos^2 x = 1,$$

whence

$$\cos^2 x = 1 - \sin^2 x.$$

In the interval between $-\pi/2$ and $\pi/2$, the cosine is $\geqq 0$. Hence we can take the square root, and we get

$$\cos x = \sqrt{1 - \sin^2 x}$$

in that interval. Since $y = \sin x$, we can write our derivative in the form

$$\frac{dx}{dy} = \frac{1}{\sqrt{1 - y^2}}$$

which is expressed entirely in terms of y.

Having now obtained all the information we want concerning the arcsine, we shift back our letters to the usual ones. We state the main properties as a theorem.

Theorem 4. *View the sine function as defined on the interval*

$$[-\pi/2, \pi/2].$$

Then the inverse function is defined on the interval $[-1, 1]$. *Call it*

$$g(x) = \arcsin x.$$

Then g is differentiable in the open interval $-1 < x < 1$, *and*

$$g'(x) = \frac{1}{\sqrt{1 - x^2}}.$$

EXERCISES

1. Define the inverse function arccosine, viewing the cosine only on the interval $[0, \pi]$.

2. What is the derivative of arccosine?

3. Let $g(x) = \arcsin x$. What is $g'(\frac{1}{2})$? What is $g'(1/\sqrt{2})$? What is $g(\frac{1}{2})$? What is $g(1/\sqrt{2})$?

4. Let $g(x) = \arccos x$. What is $g'(\frac{1}{2})$? What is $g'(1/\sqrt{2})$? What is $g(\frac{1}{2})$? What is $g(1/\sqrt{2})$?

5. Let $\sec x = 1/\cos x$. Define the inverse function of the secant over a suitable interval and obtain a formula for the derivative of this inverse function.

Find the following numbers.

6. $\arcsin (\sin 3\pi/2)$ 7. $\arcsin (\sin 2\pi)$ 8. $\arccos (\cos 3\pi/2)$

9. $\arccos (\cos -\pi/2)$ 10. $\arcsin (\sin -3\pi/4)$

Find the derivatives of the following functions:

11. $\arcsin (x^2 - 1)$ 12. $\arccos (2x + 5)$ 13. $\dfrac{1}{\arcsin x}$ 14. $\dfrac{2}{\arccos 2x}$

15. Determine the intervals over which the function arcsin is convex upward, and convex downward.

§4. THE ARCTANGENT

Let $f(x) = \tan x$ and view this function as defined over the interval

$$-\frac{\pi}{2} < x < \frac{\pi}{2}.$$

As x goes from $-\pi/2$ to $\pi/2$, the tangent goes from very large negative values to very large positive values. As x approaches $\pi/2$, the tangent has in fact arbitrarily large positive values, and similarly when x approaches $-\pi/2$, the tangent has arbitrarily large negative values.

We recall that the graph of the tangent looks like that in the figure below.

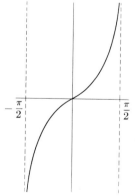

The derivative of tan x is

$$\frac{d(\tan x)}{dx} = 1 + \tan^2 x.$$

Hence the derivative is always positive, and our function is strictly increasing. Therefore the inverse function is defined for all numbers. We call it the *arctangent*. Its derivative is also positive (because it is the reciprocal of the derivative of the tangent) and hence the arctan is strictly increasing also.

The graph looks like this:

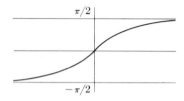

Let $x = g(y) = \arctan y$. Then

$$g'(y) = \frac{1}{1 + \tan^2 x}$$

so that

$$g'(y) = \frac{1}{1 + y^2}.$$

Here again we are able to get an explicit formula for the derivative of the inverse function.

As with the arcsine, when dealing simultaneously with the function and its inverse function, we have to keep our letters x, y separate. However, we now summarize the properties of the arctan in terms of our usual notation.

Theorem 5. *The inverse function of the tangent is defined for all numbers. Call it the arctangent. Then it has a derivative, and that derivative is given by the relation*

$$\frac{d(\arctan x)}{dx} = \frac{1}{1 + x^2}.$$

As x becomes very large positive, arctan x approaches $\pi/2$.
As x becomes very large negative, arctan x approaches $-\pi/2$.
The arctangent is strictly increasing for all x.

In words, we can say that arctan x is the angle whose tangent is x, between $-\pi/2$ and $\pi/2$.

Example. A balloon leaves the ground 100 ft from an observer at the rate of 50 ft/min. How fast is the angle of elevation of the observer's line of sight increasing when the balloon is at an altitude of 1000 ft?
The picture is as follows.

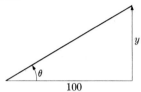

We have to determine $d\theta/dt$. We know that $dy/dt = 50$. We have

$$\frac{y}{100} = \tan \theta,$$

whence

$$\theta = \arctan \left(\frac{y}{100}\right).$$

Hence

$$\frac{d\theta}{dy} = \frac{1}{1 + \left(\frac{y}{100}\right)^2} \cdot \frac{1}{100} \qquad \text{and} \qquad \frac{d\theta}{dt} = \frac{d\theta}{dy}\frac{dy}{dt}.$$

It follows that

$$\frac{d\theta}{dt} \quad \text{when} \quad y = 100 \quad \text{is equal to} \quad \frac{1}{1 + 1^2} \cdot \frac{1}{100} \cdot 50$$

and hence the answer is $\frac{1}{4}$ ft/min.

EXERCISES

1. Let g be the arctan function. What is $g(1)$? What is $g(1/\sqrt{3})$? What is $g(-1)$? What is $g(\sqrt{3})$?

2. Let g be the arctan function. What is $g'(1)$? What is $g'(1/\sqrt{3})$? What is $g'(-1)$? What is $g'(\sqrt{3})$?

3. Suppose you were to define an inverse function for the tangent in the interval $\pi/2 < x < 3\pi/2$. What would be the derivative of this inverse function?

4. What is
   (a) arctan $(\tan 3\pi/4)$?   (b) arctan $(\tan 2\pi)$?
   (c) arctan $(\tan 5\pi/6)$?   (d) arctan $(\tan -5\pi/6)$?

Find the derivatives of the following functions.

5. arctan $3x$ 6. arctan $\sqrt{x}$

7. arcsin x + arccos x 8. x arcsin x

9. arctan (sin 2x)   10. x^2 arctan 2x

11. $\dfrac{\sin x}{\arcsin x}$ 12. arcsin (cos $x - x^2$)

13. arctan $\dfrac{1}{x}$ 14. arctan $\dfrac{1}{2x}$

15. $(1 + \arcsin 3x)^3$ 16. $(\arcsin 2x + \arctan x^2)^{3/2}$

Find the equation of the tangent line at the indicated point for the following curves.

17. $y = \arcsin x, \quad x = 1/\sqrt{2}$ 18. $y = \arccos x, \quad x = 1/\sqrt{2}$

19. $y = \arctan 2x, \quad x = \sqrt{3}/2$ 20. $y = \arctan x, \quad x = -1$

21. $y = \arcsin x, \quad x = -\frac{1}{2}$

22. A balloon leaves the ground 500 ft from an observer at the rate of 200 ft/min. How fast is the angle of elevation of the observer's line of sight increasing when the balloon is at an altitude of 1000 ft?

23. An airplane at an altitude of 4400 ft is flying horizontally directly away from an observer. When the angle of elevation is $\pi/4$, the angle is decreasing at the rate of 0.05 rad/sec. How fast is the airplane flying at that instant?

24. A man is walking along a sidewalk at the rate of 5 ft/sec. A searchlight on the ground 30 ft from the walk is kept trained on him. At what rate is the searchlight revolving when the man is 20 ft from the point on the sidewalk nearest the light?

25. A tower stands at the end of a street. A man drives towards the tower at the rate of 50 ft/sec. The tower is 500 ft tall. How fast is the angle subtended by the tower at the man's eye increasing when the man is 1000 ft from the tower?

26. A police car approaches an intersection at 80 ft/sec. When it is 200 ft from the intersection, a car crosses the intersection traveling at a right angle from the police car at the rate of 60 ft/sec. If the policeman directs his beam of light on this second car, how fast is the light beam turning 2 sec later, assuming that both cars continue at their original rate?

27. A weight is drawn along a level floor by means of a rope which passes over a hook 6 ft above the floor. If the rope is pulled over the hook at the rate of 1 ft/sec find an expression for the rate of change of the angle θ between the rope and the floor as a function of the angle θ.

28. A man standing at a fixed point on a wharf pulls in a small boat. The wharf is 20 ft above the level of the water. If he is pulling the rope at 2 ft/sec, how fast is the angle that the rope makes with the water increasing when the distance from the man to the boat is 50 ft?

29. A helicopter leaves the ground 1000 ft from an observer and rises vertically at 20 ft/sec. At what rate is the observer's angle of elevation of the helicopter changing when the helicopter is 800 ft above the ground?

30. Determine those intervals where arctan is convex upward and convex downward.

Chapter VIII

Exponents and Logarithms

We remember that we had trouble at the very beginning with the function 2^x (or 3^x, or 10^x). It was intuitively very plausible that there should be such functions, satisfying the fundamental equation

$$2^{x+y} = 2^x 2^y$$

for all numbers x, y, and $2^0 = 1$, but we had difficulties in saying what we meant by $2^{\sqrt{2}}$ (or 2^π).

It is the purpose of this chapter to give a systematic treatment of this function, and others like it.

We shall see that its inverse function is defined for positive numbers. It is called the log (or rather the log to the base 2). Thus $y = 2^x$ if and only if $x = \log_2 y$. For instance,

$$3 = \log_2 8 \quad \text{and} \quad 8 = 2^3$$

are two ways of saying the same thing.

Let us assume for the moment that we can make sense of the function 2^x, and let us see how we could find its derivative.

We form the Newton quotient. It is

$$\frac{2^{x+h} - 2^x}{h}.$$

Using the fundamental equation we see that this quotient is equal to

$$\frac{2^x 2^h - 2^x}{h} = 2^x \frac{2^h - 1}{h}.$$

As h approaches 0, 2^x remains fixed, but it is very difficult to see what happens to

$$\frac{2^h - 1}{h}.$$

It is not at all clear that this quotient approaches a limit. Roughly speaking, we meet a difficulty which is analogous to the one we met when we tried to find the derivative of sin x. However, in the present situation, a direct approach would lead to much greater difficulties than those which

141

we met when we discussed

$$\lim_{h\to 0} \frac{\sin h}{h}.$$

It is in fact true that

$$\lim_{h\to 0} \frac{2^h - 1}{h}$$

exists. We see that it does not depend on x. It depends only on 2.

If we tried to take the derivative of 10^x, we would end up with the problem of determining the limit

$$\lim_{h\to 0} \frac{10^h - 1}{h},$$

which is also independent of x.

There seems to be no reason for selecting 2, or 10, or any other number a in investigating the function a^x. However, we shall see that there exists a number called e such that

$$\lim_{h\to 0} \frac{e^h - 1}{h}$$

is equal to 1. This is perfectly marvelous, because if we then form the Newton quotient for e^x, we get

$$\frac{e^{x+h} - e^x}{h} = e^x \cdot \frac{e^h - 1}{h}.$$

Therefore its limit as h approaches 0 is e^x and hence

$$\frac{d(e^x)}{dx} = e^x.$$

We shall find out eventually how to compute e. Its value is 2.718... . In Chapter XIV you will have the technique to compute e to any degree of accuracy you wish.

The sales talk which precedes must now be set aside in your mind. We start from scratch, and in order to develop the theory in the easiest way, it is best to start with the log, and not with the exponential function. We shall then have no difficulties in determining all the limits which arise.

§1. THE LOGARITHM

We define a function $\log x$ to be the area under the curve $1/x$ between 1 and x if $x \geq 1$, and the negative of the area of the curve $1/x$ between 1 and x if $0 < x < 1$. In particular, $\log 1 = 0$.

The shaded portion of our picture at the top of page 143 represents the area under the curve between 1 and x and we have taken an instance where $x > 1$.

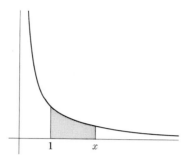

If $x < 1$ and $x > 0$, we would have the picture shown below. If $0 < x < 1$, we have said that $\log x$ is equal to the negative of the area. Thus $\log x < 0$ if $0 < x < 1$ and $\log x > 0$ if $x > 1$.

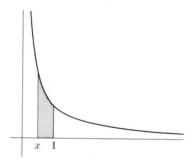

(In defining the log, we have appealed to our geometric intuition of area, just as we did when we defined the sine and cosine. In the next chapter, we shall see how one can avoid this appeal to geometry, and give a purely analytic definition.)

The fundamental fact concerning the logarithm is the following.

Theorem 1. *The function* $\log x$ *is differentiable, and*

$$\frac{d(\log x)}{dx} = \frac{1}{x}.$$

Proof. We form the Newton quotient

$$\frac{\log(x + h) - \log x}{h}$$

and have to prove that it approaches $1/x$ as a limit when h approaches 0.

Let us take $h > 0$ for the moment. Then $\log(x + h) - \log x$ is the area under the curve between x and $x + h$. Since the curve $1/x$ is decreasing, this area satisfies the following inequalities:

$$h\,\frac{1}{x + h} < \log(x + h) - \log x < h\,\frac{1}{x}.$$

Indeed, $1/x$ is the height of the big rectangle as drawn on the next figure, and $1/(x + h)$ is the height of the small rectangle. Since h is the base of the rectangle, and since the area under the curve $1/x$ between x and $x + h$ is in between the two rectangles, we see that it satisfies our inequalities.

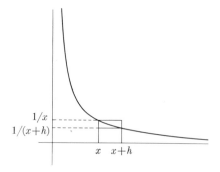

We divide both sides of our inequalities by the positive number h. Then the inequalities are preserved, and we get

$$\frac{1}{x + h} < \frac{\log (x + h) - \log x}{h} < \frac{1}{x}.$$

As h approaches 0, our Newton quotient is squeezed between $1/(x + h)$ and $1/x$ and consequently approaches $1/x$. This proves our theorem in case $h > 0$.

When $h < 0$ we use an entirely similar argument, which we leave as an exercise. (You have to pay attention to the sign of the log. Also when you divide an inequality by h and $h < 0$ then the inequality gets reversed. However, you will again see that the Newton quotient is squeezed between $1/x$ and $1/(x + h)$.)

From now on, we do not need our geometric intuition any more. The notion of area was used only to give us the existence of a function whose derivative is $1/x$, and whose value at 1 is 0. All the arguments which follow depend only on the fact that we have such a function.

Let, therefore, $\log x$ be a function defined for $x > 0$, such that $\log 1 = 0$, and such that

$$\frac{d(\log x)}{dx} = \frac{1}{x}.$$

If $g(x)$ is another such function, then it differs from $\log x$ by a constant C, i.e.

$$g(x) = \log x + C$$

for all $x > 0$. (Use Theorem 8 of Chapter V, §4.) Setting $x = 1$ gives $g(1) = C$. Since we assume that $g(1) = 0$ we see that $g(x) = \log x$. Thus there is only one function having the properties mentioned above.

Theorem 2. *If a, b are two numbers > 0, then*

$$\log(ab) = \log a + \log b.$$

Proof. Consider the function $f(x) = \log(ax)$, defined for all $x > 0$. We can take its derivative by the chain rule, and we obtain

$$\frac{df}{dx} = \frac{1}{ax} \cdot a = \frac{1}{x}.$$

$\left(\text{Put } u = ax \text{ and remember that } \frac{df}{dx} = \frac{df}{du}\frac{du}{dx}.\right)$ Therefore, our functions $f(x)$ and $\log x$ have the same derivative. Consequently, they differ by a constant:

$$\log(ax) = \log x + C.$$

This is true for *all* $x > 0$. In particular, it is true for $x = 1$. This yields

$$\log a = C$$

and determines the constant C as being equal to $\log a$.

But the above relation being true for *all* $x > 0$, it is also true if we set $x = b$. In that case, we obtain

$$\log(ab) = \log b + \log a,$$

thereby proving our theorem.

Please appreciate the elegance and efficiency of the arguments!

Theorem 3. *The function* $\log x$ *is strictly increasing for* $x > 0$. *It takes on arbitrarily large positive and negative values.*

Proof. Since the derivative is $1/x$, which is positive for all $x > 0$, our function is strictly increasing. Since $\log 1 = 0$, we conclude for instance that $\log 2 > 0$.

Using Theorem 2 we now see that

$$\log 4 = \log(2 \cdot 2) = 2\log 2,$$
$$\log 8 = \log(4 \cdot 2) = \log 4 + \log 2 = 3\log 2,$$
$$\log 16 = \log(8 \cdot 2) = \log 8 + \log 2 = 4\log 2,$$

and so on. In general, by induction, assume that $\log 2^{n-1} = (n-1)\log 2$. Then

$$\log 2^n = \log 2 \cdot 2^{n-1} = \log 2 + \log 2^{n-1}$$
$$= \log 2 + (n-1)\log 2 = n\log 2$$

for any positive integer n. As n becomes very large, $n\log 2$ also becomes very large.

Concerning the negative values, observe that

$$0 = \log 1 = \log(2 \cdot \tfrac{1}{2}) = \log 2 + \log(\tfrac{1}{2}).$$

Therefore
$$\log\left(\tfrac{1}{2}\right) = -\log 2,$$

and similarly,
$$\log\left(\frac{1}{2^n}\right) = -n \log 2.$$

For large positive integers n, the number $-n \log 2$ is very large negative. These same arguments can be applied to prove the following theorem.

Theorem 4. *If n is an integer, positive or negative, and a is a number > 0, then*
$$\log(a^n) = n \log a.$$

Proof. We proceed stepwise, assuming first that n is positive. Then
$$\log(a^2) = \log a + \log a = 2 \log a.$$

By induction, assuming $\log(a^{n-1}) = (n-1) \log a$, we have
$$\begin{aligned}
\log(a^n) = \log(a \cdot a^{n-1}) &= \log a + \log(a^{n-1}) \\
&= \log a + (n-1) \log a = n \log a.
\end{aligned}$$

Suppose that n is negative, say $n = -m$ with m positive. Then
$$0 = \log 1 = \log(a^m \cdot a^{-m}) = \log(a^m) + \log(a^{-m}).$$

Therefore
$$\log(a^n) = \log(a^{-m}) = -m \log(a) = n \log a,$$

thereby proving our theorem.

By the intermediate value theorem, the function log takes on *all* values. Its graph looks like that in the next figure. It is convex downwards because the second derivative of $\log x$ is $-1/x^2 < 0$ for all $x > 0$.

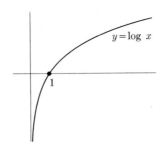

Remark. We shall sometimes consider composite functions of the type $\log(f(x))$. Since the log is not defined for numbers < 0, this expression is defined only for numbers x such that $f(x) > 0$. This is to be understood whenever we write such an expression.

Thus when we write $\log (x - 2)$, this is defined only when $x - 2 > 0$, in other words $x > 2$. When we write $\log (\sin x)$, this is meaningful only when $\sin x > 0$. It is not defined when $\sin x \leq 0$.

EXERCISES

1. What is the tangent line to the curve $y = \log x$ at the point whose x-coordinate is (a) 2, (b) 5, (c) $\frac{1}{2}$?

2. What is the equation of the tangent line of the curve $y = \log (x^2 + 1)$ at the point whose x-coordinate is (a) -1, (b) 2, (c) -3?

3. Find the derivatives of the following functions:

   (a) $\log (\sin x)$ (b) $\sin (\log (2x + 3))$ (c) $\log (x^2 + 5)$ (d) $\dfrac{\log 2x}{\sin x}$

4. What is the equation of the tangent line of the curve $y = \log (x + 1)$ at the point whose x-coordinate is 3?

5. What is the equation of the tangent line of the curve $y = \log (2x - 5)$ at the point whose x-coordinate is 4?

6. (a) Prove that $\log x < x$ for all $x > 1$. [*Hint:* Let $f(x) = x - \log x$, find $f(1)$ and show that f is strictly increasing.]
   (b) Prove that $\log (1 + x) < x$ for all $x > 0$.

7. Let h be a positive number. Compare the area under the curve $1/x$ between 1 and $1 + h$ with the area of suitable rectangles to show that

$$\frac{h}{1 + h} < \log (1 + h) < h.$$

8. Prove that

$$\lim_{h \to 0} \frac{1}{h} \log (1 + h) = 1.$$

9. Prove that for every positive integer n, we have

$$\frac{1}{n + 1} < \log \left(1 + \frac{1}{n} \right) < \frac{1}{n}.$$

10. (a) Let

$$a_n = 1 + \tfrac{1}{2} + \cdots + \frac{1}{n} - \log n$$

   for each integer $n \geq 2$. Show that $a_{n+1} < a_n$.

   (b) Let $b_n = a_n - \dfrac{1}{n}$. Show that $b_{n+1} > b_n$.

   (c) The sequence of positive numbers a_n decreases, and the sequence of positive numbers b_n increases. Since $b_n - a_n$ becomes arbitrarily small as n becomes large, it follows that there is a unique number C such that

$$b_n < C < a_n$$

for all positive integers n. This number is called *Euler's constant*. Prove that this constant is not a rational number. (Undying fame awaits you if you can do this exercise.)

Differentiate the following functions.

11. $\log (2x + 5)$ 12. $\log (x^2 + 3)$ 13. $\log (\arcsin x)$ 14. $\log (\arccos 2x)$

15. $\dfrac{1}{\log x}$ 16. $\dfrac{x}{\log x}$ 17. $x(\log x)^{1/3}$ 18. $\log \sqrt{1 - x^2}$

Sketch the following curves.

19. $y = \log (-x)$, $x < 0$ 20. $y = \log 2x$, $x \neq 0$

21. $y = \log (x + 1)$, $x > -1$ 22. $y = \log (1 - x)$, $x < 1$

23. $y = x - \log x$, $x > 0$

24. Let $a > 0$ and let $b = a^{1/n}$. Show that

$$\log b = \frac{1}{n} \log a.$$

25. Let $a_1, \ldots, a_n$ be numbers > 0. Show that

$$(a_1 \cdots a_n)^{1/n} \leqq \frac{a_1 + \cdots + a_n}{n}.$$

[*Hint:* Take the log, and use the convexity, referring back to Exercises 12 and 13 of Chapter VI, §3.]

§2. THE EXPONENTIAL FUNCTION

We can apply the theory of the inverse function. Since the function log is strictly increasing, the inverse function is defined and we call it exp. Since log takes on *all* values, the inverse function is defined for *all* numbers, positive or negative.

Since $0 = \log 1$, we have by definition

$$1 = \exp (0).$$

Theorem 5. *If z, w are two numbers, then*

$$\exp (z + w) = \exp (z) \cdot \exp (w).$$

Proof. Let $a = \exp z$ and $b = \exp w$. Then $z = \log a$ and $w = \log b$ by definition of the inverse function. By Theorem 2, we know that

$$z + w = \log (ab).$$

By the definition of the inverse function, this means that

$$\exp (z + w) = ab.$$

However, $ab = \exp (z) \cdot \exp (w)$. Our theorem is proved.

We *define* the number e to be exp (1). This is the same as saying that log $e = 1$ or exp (1) $= e$.

(With the geometric interpretation of the log as area under the curve $1/x$, this means that e is the number such that the area between 1 and e is equal to 1.)

Using Theorem 5, we conclude that

$$\exp (2) = \exp (1 + 1) = \exp (1) \exp (1) = e^2.$$

Similarly,

$$\exp (3) = \exp (2 + 1) = \exp (2) \exp (1) = e^2 \cdot e = e^3.$$

Proceeding by induction, we conclude that

$$\exp (n) = e^n$$

for every positive integer n.

If n is a negative integer, write $n = -m$ where m is positive. Then

$$1 = \exp (0) = \exp (m - m) = \exp (m) \exp (-m).$$

Dividing by exp (m), which is e^m, we get

$$\exp (-m) = \frac{1}{e^m}.$$

We see therefore that our exp function gives us the power function for positive and negative integers m.

Theorem 6. *The function* exp *is differentiable, and*

$$\frac{d(\exp x)}{dx} = \exp x.$$

Proof. By the theory of the derivatives of the inverse function, we know that it is differentiable. If $y = \exp x$ and $x = \log y$, then the theory of the derivatives of inverse functions gives us

$$\frac{dy}{dx} = \frac{1}{dx/dy}.$$

But $dx/dy = 1/y$. Hence

$$\frac{dy}{dx} = \frac{1}{1/y} = y = \exp x,$$

thereby proving our theorem.

From now on, we agree to write e^x instead of exp (x). In view of Theorem 5, we have the rule

$$e^{z+w} = e^z e^w$$

for all numbers z, w, and $e^0 = 1$.

The preceding theorem then looks like

$$\frac{d(e^x)}{dx} = e^x.$$

By definition, the derivative of e^x is the limit of the Newton quotient

$$\frac{e^{x+h} - e^x}{h} = e^x \frac{e^h - 1}{h}$$

as h approaches 0. Hence, at the very end of our theory, we now obtain in a very natural way the fact that

$$\lim_{h \to 0} \frac{e^h - 1}{h} = 1.$$

As we said in the introduction, this fact would have been very troublesome to obtain directly.

The function e^x is strictly increasing, and since $e > 1$, e^n becomes very large as n becomes very large. Hence so does e^x for any x.

Actually, e^x increases quite fast. We shall make this more precise in §4.

Finally, the second derivative of e^x is e^x and is > 0 for all x. Hence e^x is convex upwards.

We are now in a position to see that the graph of e^x looks like this:

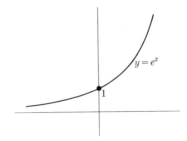

$y = e^x$

EXERCISES

1. What is the equation of the tangent line to the curve $y = e^{2x}$ at the point whose x-coordinate is (a) 1, (b) -2, (c) 0?

2. What is the equation of the tangent line to the curve $y = e^{x/2}$ at the point whose x-coordinate is (a) -4, (b) 1, (c) 0?

3. What is the equation of the tangent line to the curve $y = xe^x$ at the point whose x-coordinate is 2?

4. Find the derivatives of the following functions:

   (a) $e^{\sin 3x}$ (b) $\log(e^x + \sin x)$

   (c) $\sin(e^{x+2})$ (d) $\sin(e^{4x-5})$

5. Find the derivatives of the following functions.

    (a) arctan log x (b) log cos $(3x + 5)$

    (c) $e^{\sin 2x}$ (d) $e^{\arccos x}$

    (e) log e^x (f) x/e^x

    (g) e^{e^x} (h) $e^{-\arcsin x}$

    (i) tan (e^x) (j) $x^{\sqrt{x}}$

    (k) $x^{\sqrt[3]{x}}$ (l) arcsin $(e^x + x)$

    (m) $e^{\tan x}$ (n) tan e^x

6. (a) Show by induction that the n-th derivative of xe^x is $(x + n)e^x$ for all integers $n \geq 1$.

    (b) Show by induction that the n-th derivative of xe^{-x} is $(-1)^n(x - n)e^{-x}$.

    (c) Show that the $(n + 1)$-th derivative of $x^n \log x$ is $n!/x$.

7. (a) Sketch the curve $y = e^{-1/x}$ (defined for $x \neq 0$).

    (b) Sketch the curve $y = e^{-1/x^2}$ (defined for $x \neq 0$).

8. (a) Let $f(x)$ be a differentiable function over some interval satisfying the relation $f'(x) = Kf(x)$ for some constant K. Show that there is a constant C such that $f(x) = Ce^{Kx}$.

    (b) Let f be a differentiable function such that $f'(x) = -2xf(x)$. Show that there is a constant C such that $f(x) = Ce^{-x^2}$.

    (c) In general suppose there is a function h such that $f'(x) = h'(x)f(x)$. Show that $f(x) = Ce^{h(x)}$.

Find the tangent line to the curve at the indicated point.

9. $y = \log x$, $x = e$ 10. $y = x \log x$, $x = e$

11. $y = x \log x$, $x = 2$ 12. $y = \log (x^3)$, $x = e$

13. $y = \dfrac{1}{\log x}$, $x = e$ 14. $y = \dfrac{1}{\log x}$, $x = 2$

15. $y = e^{2x}$, $x = 1$ 16. $y = xe^x$, $x = 2$

17. $y = xe^x$, $x = 5$ 18. $y = xe^{-x}$, $x = 0$

19. $y = e^{-x}$, $x = 0$ 20. $y = x^2e^{-x}$, $x = 1$

21. Show that $1 + x < e^x < \dfrac{1}{1 - x}$ for $0 < x < 1$, and for $-1 < x < 0$.

22. Prove that there is a unique number x such that $e^x + x = 0$.

23. Prove that there is a unique number x such that $\log x + x = 0$.

24. Sketch the graph of the function $\log \dfrac{1 + x}{1 - x}$ for $-1 < x < 1$.

25. Sketch the graph of the function $\log \dfrac{1 + x^2}{1 - x^2}$, $-1 < x < 1$.

26. Does the function of Exercise 24 have an inverse function? If yes, for what values is this inverse function defined?

27. Determine an interval for which the inverse function of Exercise 25 will exist, and determine for what values this inverse is defined.

28. Sketch the graph of the function

$$f(x) = e^{x/2} + e^{-x/2}.$$

29. Sketch the graph of the function

$$f(x) = e^{x/2} - e^{-x/2}.$$

30. Let f be a differentiable function in the open interval $-1 < x < 1$. Assume that

$$f'(x) = \frac{1}{1 - x^2}$$

in this interval. Determine whether f is increasing or decreasing in this interval. Assume that $f(0) = 0$. Sketch the graph of f.

31. Let f be a differentiable function in the open interval $-1 < x < 1$. Assume that

$$f(0) = 0 \quad \text{and} \quad f'(x) = \frac{1}{(1 - x^2)^2}.$$

Determine whether f is increasing or decreasing in this interval. What happens to $f(x)$ as x approaches 1, and as x approaches -1? [*Hint:* Compare the derivative of f with that of the function in the preceding exercise.]

32. *Hyperbolic functions*

(a) Define functions

$$\cosh t = \frac{e^t + e^{-t}}{2} \quad \text{and} \quad \sinh t = \frac{e^t - e^{-t}}{2}.$$

Show that their derivatives are given by

$$\cosh' = \sinh \quad \text{and} \quad \sinh' = \cosh.$$

(b) Show that for all t we have

$$\cosh^2 t - \sinh^2 t = 1.$$

(c) Sketch the graph of the curve $x^2 - y^2 = 1$.
(d) If you let $x = \cosh t$ and $y = \sinh t$, which portion of the curve in (c) is parametrized by these functions?
(e) For a suitable interval of values of t, determine inverse functions for $\cosh t$ and $\sinh t$, and determine their derivatives.

§3. THE GENERAL EXPONENTIAL FUNCTION

Let a be a positive number, and x any number. We *define*

$$a^x = \exp\,(x \log a) = e^{x \log a}.$$

Thus

$$a^{\sqrt{2}} = e^{\sqrt{2} \log a}.$$

Using the properties of the log and exp, it is easy to prove that

$$a^{x+y} = a^x a^y$$

for all numbers x and y and that $a^0 = 1$. Furthermore, $(a^x)^y = a^{xy}$.

We leave the proof as an exercise. However, we observe that when x is a positive integer n, then a^x is indeed the product of a with itself n times. For instance, take $x = 2$. Then

$$e^{2 \log a}$$

is equal to

$$e^{\log a + \log a} = (e^{\log a})^2 = a \cdot a,$$

and similarly,

$$e^{3 \log a}$$

is equal to

$$e^{(\log a) + (\log a) + (\log a)}$$

which is equal to $(e^{\log a})^3$. The general case is proved by induction. Thus our definition of a^x as $e^{x \log a}$ is consistent with our original notation of a^n when x is a positive integer n. This is the justification for the definition in the general case.

The moral of the story is that, by going all the way around the difficulties, and giving up on a frontal attack on the function a^x, we have recovered it at the end, together with all of the desired properties. For instance, we have its derivative:

Theorem 7. *The derivative of a^x is a^x (log a).*

Proof. We use the chain rule. Let $u = (\log a)x$. Then $du/dx = \log a$ and $a^x = e^u$. Hence

$$\frac{d(a^x)}{dx} = a^x (\log a)$$

as desired.

In particular,

$$\frac{d(2^x)}{dx} = 2^x \log 2.$$

This result clarifies the mysterious limit

$$\lim_{h \to 0} \frac{2^h - 1}{h}$$

which we encountered in the introduction. We are now able to see that this limit is log 2, and it arises in a very natural way. We also see that when we take $a = e$ we obtain the only exponential function which is equal to its own derivative. For any other choice of the constant a, we would get an extraneous constant appearing in the derivative.

As an application of our theory of the exponential function, we also can take care of the general power function (which we had left dangling in Chapter III).

Theorem 8. *Let c be any number, and let*

$$f(x) = x^c$$

be defined for $x > 0$. Then $f'(x)$ exists and is equal to

$$f'(x) = cx^{c-1}.$$

Proof. By definition,

$$f(x) = e^{c \log x} = e^u$$

if we put $u = c \log x$. Then

$$\frac{du}{dx} = \frac{c}{x}.$$

Using the chain rule, we see that

$$f'(x) = e^u \cdot \frac{du}{dx} = e^{c \log x} \cdot \frac{c}{x} = x^c \cdot \frac{c}{x} = cx^{c-1}.$$

This proves our theorem.

When x, y are two numbers such that $y = 2^x$, it is customary to say that x is the log of y to the base 2. Similarly, if a is a number > 0, and $y = a^x = e^{x \log a}$, we say that x is the log of y to the base a. When $y = e^x$, we simply say that $x = \log y$.

The log to the base a is sometimes written $\log_a$. It occurs very infrequently, and you might as well forget about it.

We conclude this section by discussing two limits, which are now very easy to handle.

First, we have

$$\lim_{h \to 0} \frac{1}{h} \log (1 + h) = 1.$$

Indeed, the limit on the left is nothing else but the limit of the Newton quotient

$$\lim_{h \to 0} \frac{\log (1 + h) - \log 1}{h} = \log' (1).$$

Since $\log' (x) = 1/x$, it follows that $\log' (1) = 1$, as desired.

Now observe that

$$\log (1 + h)^{1/h} = \frac{1}{h} \log (1 + h),$$

because in general if a, b are numbers, $a > 0$, we have (Exercise 5)

$$\log a^b = b \log a.$$

Taking the exponential function, and using the fact that the exponential is continuous at 1, we find

$$\lim_{h \to 0} \exp \log (1 + h)^{1/h} = \lim_{h \to 0} \exp \frac{1}{h} \log (1 + h)$$

$$= \exp \lim_{h \to 0} \frac{1}{h} \log (1 + h)$$

$$= \exp (1) = e.$$

But $\exp \log (x) = x$ for all $x > 0$ by definition, so that for $x = (1 + h)^{1/h}$ we find

$$\lim_{h \to 0} (1 + h)^{1/h} = e.$$

If we let $h = 1/n$ where n is an integer, then our limit implies

$$\lim_{n \to \infty} \left(1 + \frac{1}{n}\right)^n = e.$$

EXERCISES

1. What is the derivative of 10^x? 7^x?
2. What is the derivative of 3^x? π^x?
3. What is the derivative of the function x^x (defined for $x > 0$)? [*Hint:* $x^x = e^{x \log x}$.]
4. What is the derivative of the function $x^{(x^x)}$?
5. If a, b are numbers, $a > 0$, show that $\log a^b = b \log a$.
6. Sketch the curves $y = 3^x$ and $y = 3^{-x}$.
7. Sketch the curves $y = 2^x$ and $y = 2^{-x}$.
8. Find the equation of the tangent line to the curve $y = x^x$ at the point $x = 1$.
9. Find the equation of the tangent line to each curve of Exercise 1 at $x = 0$.
10. Find the equation of the tangent line to each curve of Exercise 2 at $x = 2$.
11. If a is a number > 1 and $x > 0$, show that

$$x^a - 1 \geq a(x - 1).$$

12. Let p, q be numbers ≥ 1 such that $\dfrac{1}{p} + \dfrac{1}{q} = 1$. If $x \geq 1$, show that

$$x^{1/p} \leq \frac{x}{p} + \frac{1}{q}.$$

13. Let α, β be positive numbers such that $\alpha/\beta \geq 1$, and let p, q be as in Exercise 12. Show that

$$\alpha^{1/p}\beta^{1/q} \leq \frac{\alpha}{p} + \frac{\beta}{q}.$$

14. Let a be a number > 0. Find the minimum and maximum of the function $f(x) = x^2/a^x$.

15. Let a, b be two numbers > 0, and $0 < t < 1$. Show that

$$a^t b^{1-t} \leq ta + (1 - t)b.$$

[*Hint:* Take the log and use convexity.]

§4. ORDER OF MAGNITUDE

The area under the curve $1/x$ between 1 and 2 is at least equal to $\frac{1}{2}$. (Visualize a rectangle like that in the picture below.)

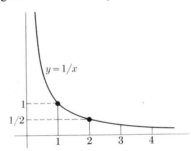

Since $\log e = 1$ and $\log 4 = 2 \log 2 \geq 1$, it follows that $e < 4$. On the other hand, the area under our curve between 1 and 2 is less than 1 because $1/x$ is at most equal to 1 in that interval. Thus we have

$$2 < e < 4.$$

We shall learn how to compute e to any degree of accuracy in a later chapter.

In order to prove Theorem 10, we need an auxiliary statement.

Theorem 9. *Let a be a number > 0. Then*

$$\frac{(1 + a)^n}{n}$$

becomes very large as n becomes very large.

Proof. We can write

$$(1 + a)^n = 1 + na + \frac{n(n - 1)}{2} a^2 + b,$$

where b is some number ≥ 0. This is easily seen by expanding the product of $(1 + a)$ with itself n times. Consequently, dividing by n, we obtain

$$\frac{(1 + a)^n}{n} = \frac{1}{n} + a + \frac{n - 1}{2} a^2 + \frac{b}{n},$$

and b/n is ≥ 0. As n becomes large, we see that the term $\dfrac{n - 1}{2} a^2$ becomes large. All the other terms are ≥ 0. Hence we have proved our theorem.

We apply this to the case of e^n/n. We know that e can be written in the form $1 + a$ with $a > 0$. Hence we see that e^n/n becomes arbitrarily large as n increases indefinitely.

Theorem 10. *The function $f(x) = e^x/x$ is strictly increasing for $x > 1$. As x becomes very large positive, so does $f(x)$.*

Proof. To verify the first assertion, take the derivative

$$f'(x) = \frac{xe^x - e^x}{x^2} = \frac{e^x}{x^2} (x - 1).$$

We know that e^x and x^2 are > 0 for all $x > 0$. Hence our derivative $f'(x)$ is positive when $x > 1$, and so our function is strictly increasing.

When x is an integer n, we know that the values $f(n)$ become arbitrarily large when n becomes large. It follows that it does also for all x when x becomes arbitrarily large. This proves our theorem.

Observe that we can conclude that

$$\frac{x}{e^x} \qquad \text{and} \qquad \frac{n}{e^n}$$

approach 0 as x and n become large. In fact, for any number $a > 0$ we also observe that

$$\frac{n}{(1 + a)^n}$$

approaches 0 as n becomes large.

Corollary 1. *As x becomes arbitrarily large, the function $x - \log x$ also becomes arbitrarily large.*

Proof. The log of e^x/x is $x - \log x$. Our assertion follows from the properties of the log proved previously, namely when y becomes very large, so does $\log y$.

Corollary 2. As x becomes very large, the quotient

$$\frac{x}{\log x}$$

also becomes very large.

Proof. Let $y = \log x$. Then $x = e^y$ and our quotient is of the form

$$\frac{e^y}{y}.$$

We know that $\log x$ becomes large when x becomes large. Thus our assertion follows from the theorem.

Corollary 3. As x becomes very large, $x^{1/x}$ approaches 1 as a limit.

Proof. We have $x^{1/x} = e^{(\log x)/x}$. As x becomes very large, $(\log x)/x$ approaches 0 and hence its exponent approaches 1.

This corollary is used frequently when we look at integers n instead of arbitrary numbers x. Thus

$$n^{1/n}$$

approaches 1 as n becomes very large.

The next theorem is a refinement of some previous ones.

Theorem 11. Let m be a positive integer. Then the function

$$\frac{e^x}{x^m}$$

is strictly increasing for $x > m$ and becomes very large when x becomes very large.

Proof. Let $f(x) = e^x/x^m$. Since

$$x = e^{\log x},$$

we have

$$x^m = e^{m \log x}.$$

Therefore

$$f(x) = e^{x - m \log x}.$$

We have

$$f'(x) = e^{x - m \log x} \left(1 - \frac{m}{x} \right).$$

This is > 0 when $x > m$ and our first assertion is proved.

As to the second, to prove that e^x/x^m becomes very large when x does, it suffices to do it for its log. Taking the log we see that

$$\log f(x) = x - m(\log x),$$

which can also be written

$$(\log x) \left(\frac{x}{\log x} - m \right).$$

As x becomes large, so does $\log x$, and so does $x/\log x$ by Corollary 2 above. Since m is fixed, our expression becomes very large, as desired.

Example. We shall sketch the curve $y = xe^x$. Let $f(x) = xe^x$. Then $f'(x) = xe^x + e^x = e^x(x + 1)$. Thus the only critical point of f is at $x = -1$. When $x < -1$, e^x is > 0 and $x + 1 < 0$. Hence when $x < -1$, $f'(x) < 0$ and f is decreasing. When $x > -1$, we see that $f'(x) > 0$ and f is increasing.

As x becomes very large positive, xe^x also becomes very large. When x is very large negative, say $x = -y$ and y very large positive, then

$$xe^x = -ye^{-y} = -y/e^y$$

approaches 0.

We have $f(-1) = -1/e$ and $f(0) = 0$. Thus the graph looks like this:

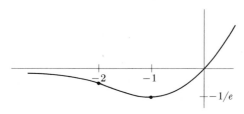

The convexity behavior is as we have drawn it. We test this by taking the second derivative, namely $f''(x) = e^x(x + 2)$. Thus the second derivative is positive when $x > -2$ and negative when $x < -2$. Hence the function is convex downwards when $x < -2$ and convex upwards when $x > -2$.

EXERCISES

1. Sketch the graph of the curve $y = xe^{2x}$. In this and other exercises, you may treat the convexity properties as optional.

Sketch the graphs of the following functions. (In Exercises 6 through 10, $x \neq 0$.)

2. xe^{-x}　　　　　　3. xe^{-x^2}　　　　　　4. $x^2e^{-x^2}$

5. x^2e^{-x}　　　　　　6. e^x/x　　　　　　7. e^x/x^2

8. e^x/x^3　　　　　　9. $e^{1/x}$　　　　　　10. $xe^{1/x}$

11. Show that the equation $e^x = ax$ has at least one solution for any number a except when $0 \leq a < e$.

12. Let $f(x)$ be the function e^{-1/x^2} when $x \neq 0$ and $f(0) = 0$. Show that f has a derivative at 0 and that $f'(0) = 0$.

13. Does f' have a derivative? If yes, what is it?

14. Does f have any further derivatives at 0?

15. Sketch the curve $f(x) = x^x$.

16. Show that the curve

$$y = \frac{\log_a x}{x}$$

has its maximum value at $x = e$ for all numbers $a > 0$.

17. Does $x \log x$ approach a limit as $x \to 0$? What about $x^2 \log x$? [*Hint:* Let $x = 1/t$ and let t become very large.]

18. Sketch the following curves.

(a) $y = x \log x$ (b) $y = x^2 \log x$
(c) $y = x(\log x)^2$ (d) $y = x/\log x$

19. Show that the function $f(x) = x^x$ is strictly increasing for $x > 0$. Let g be its inverse function.

(a) Show that if $y = f(x)$ then

$$\frac{\log \log x}{\log \log y} \to 0 \qquad \text{as} \quad x \to \infty.$$

(b) Show that

$$g(y) = \frac{\log y}{\log \log y} \psi(y)$$

where $\psi(y)$ approaches 1 as $y \to \infty$. [*Hint:* Take the log twice in the expression $y = e^{x \log x}$.]

20. Let $f(x) = 2^x x^x$. Show that f is strictly increasing for $x > 0$. Let g be its inverse function. Show that

$$g(y) = \frac{\log y}{\log \log y} \varphi(y)$$

where $\varphi(y)$ approaches 1 as $y \to \infty$.

21. Sketch the curves (a) $y = x - e^x$ and (b) $y = x + e^x$.

§5. SOME APPLICATIONS

It is worth while to mention briefly some applications of the exponential function to physics and chemistry.

It is known (from experimental data) that when a piece of radium is left to disintegrate, the rate of disintegration is proportional to the amount of radium left.

Suppose that at time $t = 0$ we have 10 grams of radium and let $f(t)$ be the amount of radium left at time t. Then

$$\frac{df}{dt} = kf(t)$$

for some constant k. We take k negative since the physical interpretation is that the amount of substance decreases.

If we take the derivative of the quotient

$$\frac{f(t)}{e^{kt}}$$

and use the rule for the derivative of a quotient, we find

$$\frac{e^{kt}f'(t) - f(t)ke^{kt}}{e^{2kt}},$$

and this is equal to 0 [using our hypothesis concerning $f'(t)$]. Hence there is a constant C such that

$$f(t) = Ce^{kt}.$$

Let $t = 0$. Then $f(0) = C$. Thus $C = 10$, if we assumed that we started with 10 grams. In general, C is interpreted as the amount of initial substance when $t = 0$.

Similarly, consider a chemical reaction. It is frequently the case that the rate of the reaction is proportional to the quantity of reacting substance present. If $f(t)$ denotes the amount of substance left after time t, then

$$\frac{df}{dt} = Kf(t)$$

for some constant K (determined experimentally in each case). We are therefore in a similar situation as before, and

$$f(t) = Ce^{Kt}$$

where C is the amount of substance at $t = 0$.

Example. Suppose $f(t) = 10e^{Kt}$ where K is constant. Assume that $f(3) = 5$. Find K.

We have

$$5 = 10e^{K3}.$$

Taking the log yields

$$\log 5 = \log 10 + 3K$$

whence

$$K = \frac{\log 5 - \log 10}{3}.$$

EXERCISES

1. Let $f(t) = 10e^{Kt}$ for some constant K. Suppose that you know that $f(1/2) = 2$. Find K.

2. Let $f(t) = Ce^{2t}$. Suppose that you know $f(2) = 5$. Determine the constant C.

3. One gram of radium is left to disintegrate. After one million years, there is 0.1 gram left. What is the formula giving the rate of disintegration?

4. A certain chemical substance reacts in such a way that the rate of reaction is equal to the quantity of substance present. After one hour, there are 20 grams of substance left. How much substance was there at the beginning?

5. A radioactive substance disintegrates proportionally to the amount of substance present at a given time, say

$$f(t) = Ce^{Kt}.$$

At what time will there be exactly half the original amount left?

6. Suppose $K = -4$ in the preceding exercise. At what time will there be one-third of the substance left?

7. If bacteria increase in number at a rate proportional to the number present, how long will it take before 1,000,000 bacteria increase to 10,000,000 if it takes 12 minutes to increase to 2,000,000?

8. A substance decomposes at a rate proportional to the amount present. At the end of 3 minutes, 10 percent of the original substance has decomposed. When will half the original amount have decomposed?

9. Let f be a function of a variable t and increasing at the rate $df/dt = kf$ where k is a constant. Let $a_n = f(nt_1)$ where t_1 is a fixed value of t, $t_1 > 0$. Show that $a_0, a_1, a_2, \ldots$ is a geometric progression.

10. In 1900 the population of a city was 50,000. In 1950 it was 100,000. If the rate of increase of the population is proportional to the population, what will be the population in 1984? In what year will it be 200,000?

11. Assume that the rate of change with respect to height of atmospheric pressure at any height is proportional to the pressure there. If the barometer reads 30 at sea level and 24 at 6000 ft above sea level, find the barometric reading 10,000 ft above sea level.

12. Sugar in water decomposes at a rate proportional to the amount still unchanged. If 30 lb of sugar reduces to 10 lb in 4 hr, when will 95% of the sugar be decomposed?

13. A particle moves with speed $s(t)$ satisfying $ds/dt = -ks$, where k is some constant. If the initial speed is 16 units/min and if the speed is halved in 2 min, find the value of t when the speed is 10 units/min.

14. Assume that the difference x between the temperature of a body and that of surrounding air decreases at a rate proportional to this difference. If $x = 100°$ when $t = 0$, and $x = 40°$ when $t = 40$ minutes, find t (a) when $x = 70°$, (b) when $x = 16°$, (c) the value of x when $t = 20$.

15. A moron loses money in gambling at a rate equal to the amount he owns at any given time. At what time t will he have lost half of his initial capital?

Chapter IX

Integration

In this chapter, we solve, more or less simultaneously, the following problems:

(1) Given a function $f(x)$, find a function $F(x)$ such that

$$F'(x) = f(x).$$

This is the inverse of differentiation, and is called integration.

(2) Given a function $f(x)$ which is ≥ 0, give a definition of the area under the curve $y = f(x)$ which does not appeal to geometric intuition.

Actually, in this chapter, we give the ideas behind the solutions of our two problems. The techniques which allow us to compute effectively when specific data are given will be postponed to the next chapter.

In carrying out (2) we shall follow an idea of Archimedes. It is to approximate the function f by horizontal functions, and the area under f by the sum of little rectangles.

The slightly theoretical sections 5 and 6 should be omitted for any class especially allergic to pure theory. The geometric argument involving area should suffice to justify the definite integral, and a mild sales talk on the integral as a limit of sums of small rectangles would be sufficient for the physical applications. Our axiomatization of the fundamental theorem allows the greatest flexibility concerning the extent to which these sections should be carried out in detail.

§1. THE INDEFINITE INTEGRAL

Let $f(x)$ be a function defined over some interval. If $F(x)$ is a function defined over the same interval and such that

$$F'(x) = f(x),$$

then we say that F is an *indefinite integral* of f. If $G(x)$ is another indefinite integral of f, then $G'(x) = f(x)$ also. Hence the derivative of the difference $F - G$ is 0:

$$(F - G)'(x) = F'(x) - G'(x) = f(x) - f(x) = 0.$$

Consequently, by Theorem 3 of Chapter V, §4, there is a constant C such that

$$F(x) = G(x) + C$$

for all x in the interval.

Example 1. An indefinite integral for $\cos x$ would be $\sin x$. But $\sin x + 5$ is also an indefinite integral for $\cos x$.

Example 2. $\log x$ is an indefinite integral for $1/x$. So is $\log x + 10$ or $\log x - \pi$.

In the next chapter, we shall develop techniques for finding indefinite integrals. Here, we merely observe that every time we prove a formula for a derivative, it has an analogue for the integral.

It is customary to denote an indefinite integral of a function f by

$$\int f \qquad \text{or} \qquad \int f(x)\,dx.$$

In this second notation, the dx is meaningless by itself. It is only the full expression $\int f(x)\,dx$ which is meaningful. When we study the method of substitution in the next chapter, we shall get further confirmation for the practicality of our notation.

We shall now make a table of some indefinite integrals, using the information which we have obtained about derivatives.

Let n be an integer, $n \neq -1$. Then we have

$$\int x^n\,dx = \frac{x^{n+1}}{n+1}.$$

If $n = -1$, then

$$\int \frac{1}{x}\,dx = \log x.$$

(This is true only in the interval $x > 0$.)

In the interval $x > 0$ we also have

$$\int x^c\,dx = \frac{x^{c+1}}{c+1}$$

for any number $c \neq -1$.

The following indefinite integrals are valid for all x.

$$\int \cos x\,dx = \sin x \qquad \int \sin x\,dx = -\cos x$$

$$\int e^x\,dx = e^x \qquad \int \frac{1}{1+x^2}\,dx = \arctan x$$

Finally, for $-1 < x < 1$, we have

$$\int \frac{1}{\sqrt{1 - x^2}} \, dx = \arcsin x.$$

In practice, one frequently omits mentioning over what interval the various functions we deal with are defined. However, in any specific problem, one has to keep it in mind. For instance, if we write

$$\int x^{-1/3} \, dx = \tfrac{3}{2} \cdot x^{2/3},$$

this is valid for $x > 0$ and is also valid for $x < 0$. But 0 cannot be in any interval of definition of our functions. Thus we could have

$$\int x^{-1/3} \, dx = \tfrac{3}{2} \cdot x^{2/3} + 5$$

when $x < 0$ and

$$\int x^{-1/3} \, dx = \tfrac{3}{2} \cdot x^{2/3} - 2$$

when $x > 0$.

We agree throughout that indefinite integrals are defined only over intervals. Thus in considering the function $1/x$, we have to consider *separately* the cases $x > 0$ and $x < 0$. For $x > 0$, we have already remarked that $\log x$ is an indefinite integral. It turns out that for the interval $x < 0$ we can also find an indefinite integral, and in fact we have for $x < 0$,

$$\int \frac{1}{x} \, dx = \log(-x).$$

Observe that when $x < 0$, $-x$ is positive, and thus $\log(-x)$ is meaningful. The fact that the derivative of $\log(-x)$ is equal to $1/x$ is true by the chain rule.

For $x < 0$, any other indefinite integral is given by

$$\log(-x) + C,$$

where C is a constant.

It is sometimes stated that in all cases,

$$\int \frac{1}{x} \, dx = \log|x| + C.$$

With our conventions, we do not attribute any meaning to this, because our functions are not defined over intervals (the missing point 0 prevents this). In any case, the formula would be *false*. Indeed, for $x < 0$ we have

$$\int \frac{1}{x} \, dx = \log|x| + C_1,$$

and for $x > 0$ we have

$$\int \frac{1}{x}\, dx = \log |x| + C_2.$$

However, the two constants need not be equal, and hence we cannot write

$$\int \frac{1}{x}\, dx = \log |x| + C$$

in all cases.

We prefer to stick to our convention that integrals are defined only over intervals. When we deal with the log, it is to be understood that we deal only with the case $x > 0$.

EXERCISES

Find indefinite integrals for the following functions:

1. $\sin 2x$ 2. $\cos 3x$ 3. $\dfrac{1}{x+1}$ 4. $\dfrac{1}{x+2}$

(In these last two problems, specify the intervals over which you find an indefinite integral.)

§2. CONTINUOUS FUNCTIONS

Let $f(x)$ be a function. We shall say that f is *continuous* if

$$\lim_{h \to 0} f(x + h) = f(x)$$

for all x at which the function is defined.

It is understood that in taking the limit, only values of h for which $f(x + h)$ is defined are considered. For instance, if f is defined on an interval

$$a \leqq x \leqq b$$

(assuming $a < b$), then we would say that f is continuous at a if

$$\lim_{\substack{h \to 0 \\ h > 0}} f(a + h) = f(a).$$

We cannot take $h < 0$, since the function would not be defined for $a + h$ if $h < 0$.

Geometrically speaking, a function is continuous if there is no break in its graph. All differentiable functions are continuous. We have already remarked this fact, because if a quotient

$$\frac{f(x + h) - f(x)}{h}$$

has a limit, then the numerator $f(x + h) - f(x)$ must approach 0, because

$$\lim_{h \to 0} f(x + h) - f(x) = \lim_{h \to 0} h \frac{f(x + h) - f(x)}{h}$$

$$= \lim_{h \to 0} h \lim_{h \to 0} \frac{f(x + h) - f(x)}{h} = 0.$$

The following are graphs of functions which are not continuous.

In Fig. 1, we have the graph of a function like

$$f(x) = -1 \quad \text{if} \quad x \leq 0$$
$$f(x) = 1 \quad \text{if} \quad x > 0.$$

We see that

$$f(a + h) = f(h) = 1$$

Figure 1

for all $h > 0$. Hence

$$\lim_{\substack{h \to 0 \\ h > 0}} f(a + h) = 1,$$

which is unequal to $f(0)$.

A similar phenomenon occurs in Fig. 2 where there is a break. (Cf. Example 5 of Chapter III, §2.)

Figure 2

§3. AREA

Let $a < b$ be two numbers, and let $f(x)$ be a continuous function defined on the interval $a \leq x \leq b$.

We wish to find a function $F(x)$ which is differentiable in this interval, and such that

$$F'(x) = f(x).$$

In this section, we appeal to our geometric intuition concerning area. We assume that $f(x) \geq 0$ for all x in the interval, and we define geometrically the function $F(x)$ by saying that it is the numerical measure of the area under the curve between a and x.

The following picture illustrates this.

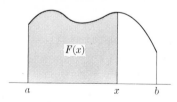

We thus have $F(a) = 0$. The area between a and a is 0.

Theorem 1. *The function $F(x)$ is differentiable, and its derivative is $f(x)$.*

Proof. Since we defined F geometrically, we shall have to argue geometrically.

We have to consider the Newton quotient

$$\frac{F(x + h) - F(x)}{h}.$$

Suppose first that x is unequal to the end point b, and also suppose that we consider only values of $h > 0$.

Then $F(x + h) - F(x)$ is the area between x and $x + h$. A magnified picture may look like this.

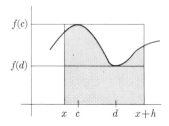

The shaded area represents $F(x + h) - F(x)$.

We let c be a point in the closed interval $[x, x + h]$ which is a maximum for our function f *in that small interval.* We let d be a point in the same closed interval which is a minimum for f in that interval. Thus

$$f(d) \leqq f(t) \leqq f(c)$$

for all t satisfying

$$x \leqq t \leqq x + h.$$

(We are forced to use another letter, t, since x is already being used.)

The area under the curve between x and $x + h$ is bigger than the area of the small rectangle in the figure above, i.e. the rectangle having base h and height $f(d)$.

The area under the curve between x and $x + h$ is smaller than the area of the big rectangle, i.e. the rectangle having base h and height $f(c)$.

This gives us

$$h \cdot f(d) \leqq F(x + h) - F(x) \leqq h \cdot f(c).$$

Dividing by the positive number h yields

$$f(d) \leqq \frac{F(x + h) - F(x)}{h} \leqq f(c).$$

Since c, d are between x and $x + h$, as h approaches 0 both $f(c)$ and $f(d)$

approach $f(x)$. Hence the Newton quotient for F is squeezed between two numbers which approach $f(x)$. It must therefore approach $f(x)$ itself, and we have proved Theorem 1, when $h > 0$.

The proof is essentially the same as the proof which we used to get the derivative of $\log x$. The only difference in the present case is that we pick a maximum and a minimum without being able to give an explicit value for it, the way we could for the function $1/x$. Otherwise, there is no difference in the arguments.

If $x = b$, we look at negative values for h. The argument in that case is entirely similar to the one we have written down in detail, and we find again that the Newton quotient of F is squeezed between $f(c)$ and $f(d)$. We leave it as an exercise.

Suppose that we are able to guess at a function $G(x)$ whose derivative is $f(x)$. Then we know that there is a constant C such that

$$F(x) = G(x) + C.$$

Let $x = a$. We get

$$0 = F(a) = G(a) + C.$$

This shows that $C = -G(a)$. Hence letting $x = b$ yields

$$F(b) = G(b) - G(a).$$

Thus the area under the curve between a and b is $G(b) - G(a)$. This is very useful to know in practice, because we can usually guess the function G.

If we deal with a continuous function f which may be negative in the interval $[a, b]$, then we could still use our notion of area to find the function $F(x)$. However, in those portions where the function is negative, we have to take F to be *minus* the area under the curve. We illustrate this by the following picture. In this case, $F(x)$ would be the area between a_1 and a_2, minus the area between a_2 and x (for the point x indicated in the picture). The argument that $F'(x) = f(x)$ goes through in the same way.

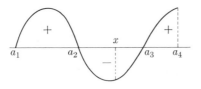

Thus by using our geometric intuition, we have found a function $F(x)$ whose derivative is $f(x)$.

Example 1. Find the area under the curve $y = x^2$ between $x = 1$ and $x = 2$.

Let $f(x) = x^2$. If $G(x) = x^3/3$ then $G'(x) = f(x)$. Hence the area under the curve between 1 and 2 is

$$G(2) - G(1) = \frac{2^3}{3} - \frac{1^3}{3} = \frac{7}{3}.$$

Example 2. Find the area under one arch of the function $\sin x$.

We have to find the area under the curve between 0 and π. Let

$$G(x) = -\cos x.$$

Then $G'(x) = \sin x$. Hence the area is

$$
\begin{aligned}
G(\pi) - G(0) &= -\cos \pi - (-\cos 0) \\
&= -(-1) + 1 \\
&= 2.
\end{aligned}
$$

Note how remarkable this is. The arch of the sine curve going from 0 to π seems to be a very irrational curve, and yet the area turns out to be the integer 2!

EXERCISES

Find the area under the given curves between the given bounds.

1. $y = x^3$ between $x = 1$ and $x = 5$.
2. $y = x$ between $x = 0$ and $x = 2$.   3. $y = \cos x$, one arch.
4. $y = 1/x$ between $x = 1$ and $x = 2$.
5. $y = 1/x$ between $x = 1$ and $x = 3$.
6. $y = x^4$ between $x = -1$ and $x = 1$.
7. $y = e^x$ between $x = 0$ and $x = 1$.

§4. FUNDAMENTAL THEOREM

The argument which we gave in the preceding section, to show that the derivative of the area is equal to the function f, can be made completely general. In fact, if we do this, then we shall be able to apply this argument to many more cases, both for theoretical purposes (in §6, for instance), and in applications, when dealing with lengths of curves or work in Chapter XII. Thus we shall now describe the general framework in which we can carry out the arguments of Theorem 1.

Theorem 2. *Let a, d be two numbers, with $a < d$. Let f be a continuous function on the interval $[a, d]$. Suppose that for each pair of numbers $b \leqq c$ in the interval we are able to associate a number denoted by $I_b^c(f)$ satisfying the following properties:*

Property 1. If M, m are two numbers such that

$$m \leqq f(x) \leqq M$$

for all x in the interval [b, c] then

$$m(c - b) \leqq I_b^c(f) \leqq M(c - b).$$

Property 2. We have

$$I_a^b(f) + I_b^c(f) = I_a^c(f).$$

Then the function $x \mapsto I_a^x(f)$ is differentiable in the interval [a, d] and its derivative at x is f(x). An association as above is uniquely determined.

Proof. We have to form the Newton quotient

$$\frac{I_a^{x+h}(f) - I_a^x(f)}{h}$$

and see if it approaches a limit as $h \to 0$. (If $x = a$ then it is to be understood that $h > 0$, and if $x = b$ then $h < 0$. As usual, we prove that the function $I_a^x(f)$ is right differentiable at a and left differentiable at b.)

Assume for the moment that $h > 0$. By Property 2, applied to the three numbers $a, x, x + h$, we conclude that our Newton quotient is equal to

$$\frac{I_a^x(f) + I_x^{x+h}(f) - I_a^x(f)}{h} = \frac{I_x^{x+h}(f)}{h}.$$

This reduces our investigation of the Newton quotient to the interval between x and $x + h$.

Let s be a point between x and $x + h$ such that f reaches a maximum in this small interval $[x, x + h]$ and let t be a point in this interval such that f reaches a minimum.

We let

$$m = f(t) \qquad \text{and} \qquad M = f(s)$$

and apply Property 1 to the interval $[x, x + h]$. We obtain

$$f(t)(x + h - x) \leqq I_x^{x+h}(f) \leqq f(s)(x + h - x),$$

which we can rewrite as

$$f(t) \cdot h \leqq I_x^{x+h}(f) \leqq f(s) \cdot h.$$

Dividing by the positive number h preserves the inequalities, and yields

$$f(t) \leqq \frac{I_x^{x+h}(f)}{h} \leqq f(s).$$

Since s, t lie between x and $x + h$, we must have (by continuity)

$$\lim_{h \to 0} f(s) = f(x) \qquad \text{and} \qquad \lim_{h \to 0} f(t) = f(x).$$

Thus our Newton quotient is squeezed between two numbers which approach $f(x)$. It must therefore approach $f(x)$, and our theorem is proved when $h > 0$.

The argument when $h < 0$ is entirely similar. We omit it, except for the following remark concerning Property 2.

Suppose that we have two numbers b, c with $c < b$. We define

$$I_b^c(f) = -I_c^b(f),$$

whenever f is a continuous function on the interval $[c, b]$. Then it is easy to verify that Property 2 holds no matter what the numbers b, c are. For instance, suppose $c < b$. We show you how to prove the statement of Property 2 in that case.

By definition

$$I_b^c(f) = -I_c^b(f).$$

We know that

$$I_a^c(f) + I_c^b(f) = I_a^b(f)$$

if we use the ordinary case of Property 2 when the numbers are increasing. Substituting the value for $I_b^c(f)$, we find

$$I_a^c(f) - I_b^c(f) = I_a^b(f),$$

whence

$$I_a^c(f) = I_a^b(f) + I_b^c(f).$$

In the next sections, we shall prove that there exists a way of assigning a number $I_a^b(f)$ satisfying the properties stated in Theorem 2. We shall now prove that any such assignment is *uniquely determined*. Indeed, if $J_a^b(f)$ also satisfies the properties of Theorem 2, then the functions of x given by

$$I_a^x(f) \qquad \text{and} \qquad J_a^x(f)$$

have the same derivative, and consequently there is a constant C such that

$$I_a^x(f) = J_a^x(f) + C$$

for all x in the interval $[a, b]$. But if we let $x = a$, we can use Property 1 to see that $I_a^a(f) = J_a^a(f) = 0$. Hence $C = 0$, whence

$$I_a^x(f) = J_a^x(f)$$

for all x in the interval. In view of this, we define the *definite integral of f* between a and b to be $I_a^b(f)$, provided that it exists. It is usually denoted by $\int_a^b f$.

§5. UPPER AND LOWER SUMS

To show the existence of the integral, we still use the idea of approximating our curves by constant functions.

Let a, b be two numbers, with $a \leq b$. Let f be a continuous function in the interval $a \leq x \leq b$.

By a *partition of the interval* $[a, b]$ we mean a sequence of numbers

$$a = x_0 \leq x_1 \leq x_2 \leq \cdots \leq x_n = b$$

between a and b, such that $x_i \leq x_{i+1}$ ($i = 0, 1, \ldots, n - 1$). For instance, we could take just two numbers,

$$x_0 = a \qquad \text{and} \qquad x_1 = b.$$

This will be called the *trivial partition*.

A partition divides our interval in a lot of smaller intervals $[x_i, x_{i+1}]$.

$$a = x_0 \quad x_1 \qquad x_2 \quad x_3 \quad \cdots \quad x_{n-1} \quad x_n = b$$

Given any number between a and b, in addition to $x_0, \ldots, x_n$, we can add it to the partition to get a new partition having one more small interval. If we add enough intermediate numbers to the partition, then the intervals can be made arbitrarily small.

Let f be a function defined on the interval

$$a \leq x \leq b$$

and continuous. If c_i is a point between x_i and x_{i+1}, then we form the sum

$$f(c_0)(x_1 - x_0) + f(c_1)(x_2 - x_1) + \cdots + f(c_{n-1})(x_n - x_{n-1}).$$

Such a sum will be called a *Riemann sum*. Each value $f(c_i)$ can be viewed as the height of a rectangle, and each $(x_{i+1} - x_i)$ can be viewed as the length of the base.

Let s_i be a point between x_i and x_{i+1} such that f has a maximum in this small interval $[x_i, x_{i+1}]$ at s_i. In other words,

$$f(x) \leq f(s_i)$$

for all x between x_i and x_{i+1}. The rectangles then look like those in the next figure. In the picture, s_0 happens to be equal to $x_1, s_2 = x_2, s_3 = x_4$.

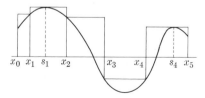

The main idea which we are going to carry out is that, as we make the intervals of our partitions smaller and smaller, the sum of the areas of the rectangles will approach a limit, and this limit can be used to define the area under the curve.

Observe however that when $f(x)$ becomes negative, the value $f(s_i)$ may be negative. Thus the corresponding rectangle gives a negative contribution

$$f(s_i)(x_{i+1} - x_i)$$

to the sum.

If P is the partition given by the numbers

$$x_0 \leqq x_1 \leqq x_2 \leqq \cdots \leqq x_n,$$

then the sum

$$f(s_0)(x_1 - x_0) + f(s_1)(x_2 - x_1) + \cdots + f(s_{n-1})(x_n - x_{n-1})$$

will be called the *upper sum* associated with the function f, and the partition P of the interval $[a, b]$. We shall denote it by the symbols

$$U_a^b(P, f).$$

Also, it is tiresome to write the sum by repeating each term, and so we shall use the abbreviation

$$\sum_{i=0}^{n-1} f(s_i)(x_{i+1} - x_i)$$

to mean the sum from 0 to $n - 1$ of the terms $f(s_i)(x_{i+1} - x_i)$. Thus, by definition,

$$U_a^b(P, f) = \sum_{i=0}^{n-1} f(s_i)(x_{i+1} - x_i).$$

Instead of taking a maximum s_i in the interval $[x_i, x_{i+1}]$ we could have taken a minimum. Let t_i be a point in this interval, such that

$$f(t_i) \leqq f(x)$$

for all x in the small interval $[x_i, x_{i+1}]$. We call the sum

$$f(t_0)(x_1 - x_0) + f(t_1)(x_2 - x_1) + \cdots + f(t_{n-1})(x_n - x_{n-1})$$

the *lower sum* associated with the function f, and the partition P of the interval $[a, b]$. The lower sum will be denoted by

$$L_a^b(P, f).$$

With our convention concerning sums, we can therefore write

$$L_a^b(P, f) = \sum_{i=0}^{n-1} f(t_i)(x_{i+1} - x_i).$$

On the next picture, we have drawn a typical term of the sum.

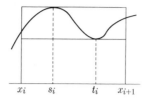

$$x_i \qquad s_i \qquad\qquad t_i \qquad x_{i+1}$$

For all numbers x in the interval $[x_i, x_{i+1}]$ we have

$$f(t_i) \leqq f(x) \leqq f(s_i).$$

Since $x_{i+1} - x_i$ is $\geqq 0$, it follows that each term of the lower sum is less than or equal to each term of the upper sum. Therefore

$$L_a^b(P, f) \leqq U_a^b(P, f).$$

Furthermore, any Riemann sum taken with points c_i (which are not necessarily maxima or minima) is between the lower and upper sum.

What happens to our sums when we add a new point to a partition? We shall see that the lower sum increases and the upper sum decreases.

Theorem 3. *Let f be a continuous function on the interval $[a, b]$. Let $P = (x_0, \ldots, x_n)$ be a partition of $[a, b]$. Let $\bar{x}$ be any number in the interval, and let Q be the partition obtained from P by adding $\bar{x}$ to $(x_0, \ldots, x_n)$. Then*

$$L_a^b(P, f) \leqq L_a^b(Q, f) \leqq U_a^b(Q, f) \leqq U_a^b(P, f).$$

Proof. Let us look at the lower sums, for example. Suppose that our number $\bar{x}$ is between x_j and x_{j+1}:

$$x_j \leqq \bar{x} \leqq x_{j+1}.$$

When we form the lower sum for P, it will be the same as the lower sum for Q except that the term

$$f(t_j)(x_{j+1} - x_j)$$

will now be replaced by two terms. If u is a minimum for f in the interval between x_j and $\bar{x}$, and v is a minimum for f in the interval between $\bar{x}$ and x_{j+1}, then these two terms are

$$f(u)(\bar{x} - x_j) + f(v)(x_{j+1} - \bar{x}).$$

We can write $f(t_j)(x_{j+1} - x_j)$ in the form

$$f(t_j)(x_{j+1} - x_j) = f(t_j)(\bar{x} - x_j) + f(t_j)(x_{j+1} - \bar{x}).$$

Since $f(t_j)$ is less than or equal to $f(u)$ or $f(v)$ (because t_j was a minimum in the whole interval between x_j and x_{j+1}), it follows that

$$f(t_j)(x_{j+1} - x_j) \leq f(u)(\bar{x} - x_j) + f(v)(x_{j+1} - \bar{x}).$$

Thus when we replace the term in the sum for P by the two terms in the sum for Q, the value of the contribution of these two terms increases. Since all other terms are the same, our assertion is proved.

The assertion concerning the fact that the upper sum decreases is left as an exercise. The proof is very similar.

As a consequence of our theorem, we obtain:

Corollary. *Every lower sum is less than or equal to every upper sum.*

Proof. Let P and Q be two partitions. If we add to P all the points of Q and add to Q all the points of P, we obtain a partition R such that every point of P is a point of R and every point of Q is a point of R. Thus R is obtained by adding points to P and to Q. Consequently, we have the inequalities

$$L_a^b(P, f) \leq L_a^b(R, f) \leq U_a^b(R, f) \leq U_a^b(Q, f).$$

This proves our assertion.

It is now a very natural question to ask whether there is a *unique* point between the lower sums and the upper sums. In the next sections, we shall prove:

Theorem 4. *There exists a unique number which is greater or equal to every lower sum and less than or equal to every upper sum.*

This number will be called the *definite integral* of f between a and b, and is denoted by

$$\int_a^b f.$$

Example. Let $f(x) = x^2$ and let the interval be $[0, 1]$. Write out the upper and lower sums for the partition consisting of $(0, \frac{1}{2}, 1)$.

The minimum of the function in the interval $[0, \frac{1}{2}]$ is at 0, and $f(0) = 0$. The minimum of the function in the interval $[\frac{1}{2}, 1]$ is at $\frac{1}{2}$ and $f(\frac{1}{2}) = \frac{1}{4}$. Hence the lower sum is

$$f(0)(\tfrac{1}{2} - 0) + f(\tfrac{1}{2})(1 - \tfrac{1}{2}) = \tfrac{1}{4} \cdot \tfrac{1}{2} = \tfrac{1}{8}.$$

The maximum of the function in the interval $[0, \frac{1}{2}]$ is at $\frac{1}{2}$ and the maximum of the function in the interval $[\frac{1}{2}, 1]$ is at 1. Thus the upper sum is

$$f(\tfrac{1}{2})(\tfrac{1}{2} - 0) + f(1)(1 - \tfrac{1}{2}) = \tfrac{1}{8} + \tfrac{1}{2} = \tfrac{5}{8}.$$

EXERCISES

Write out the lower and upper sums for the following functions and intervals. Use a partition such that the length of each small interval is $\frac{1}{2}$.

1. $f(x) = x^2$ in the interval $[1, 2]$.   2. $f(x) = 1/x$ in the interval $[1, 3]$.

3. $f(x) = x$ in the interval $[0, 2]$.   4. $f(x) = 3$ in the interval $[0, 5]$.

5. Let $f(x) = 1/x$ and let the interval be $[1, 2]$. Let n be a positive integer. Write out the upper and lower sum, using the partition such that the length of each small interval is $1/n$.

6. Prove that

$$\frac{1}{n+1} + \frac{1}{n+2} + \cdots + \frac{1}{n+n} \leq \log 2 \leq \frac{1}{n} + \frac{1}{n+1} + \cdots + \frac{1}{2n-1}.$$

7. Let $f(x) = \log x$. Let n be a positive integer. Write out the upper and lower sums, using the partition of the interval between 1 and n consisting of the integers from 1 to n, i.e. the partition $(1, 2, \ldots, n)$.

§6. THE BASIC PROPERTIES

This section will contain the proof of Theorem 4. We first need to discuss a special property of numbers.

Let S be a collection of numbers, with at least one number in the collection. (We also say that S is not empty.) An *upper bound* for S is a number B such that

$$x \leq B$$

for all x in the collection S. A *least upper bound* for S is an upper bound which is smallest among all upper bounds.

For instance, let S be the collection of numbers whose square is ≤ 4. Then 5 is an upper bound for S and so is 3. However, 2 is the least upper bound.

Another example: Let S be the collection of numbers whose square is < 2. Then $\sqrt{2}$ is the least upper bound. (In this example, the least upper bound does not belong to our collection S.)

The property of numbers which we accept without proof is that *every collection of numbers which is not empty and has an upper bound also has a least upper bound.*

Similarly, we shall say that a number A is a *lower bound* for S if

$$A \leq x$$

for all x in the collection S. A *greatest lower bound* for S is a lower bound which is largest among all lower bounds.

We shall also accept without proof that every non-empty collection of numbers which has a lower bound has a greatest lower bound.

For example, the collection of numbers $1, \frac{1}{2}, \frac{1}{3}, \frac{1}{4}, \ldots$ has a greatest lower bound, which is the number 0. Observe again that this greatest lower bound is not in the collection.

We return to our upper and lower sums.

Let f be as in §5. We consider the collection of numbers consisting of all lower sums

$$L_a^b(P, f)$$

for all partitions P. This collection certainly has an upper bound (any upper sum will be an upper bound). We denote by

$$L_a^b(f)$$

its least upper bound, and call it the *lower integral* of f, over the interval $[a, b]$.

Every upper sum is an upper bound for the collection of lower sums. Therefore

$$L_a^b(f) \leq U_a^b(P, f)$$

for every partition P. Thus $L_a^b(f)$ is a lower bound for the collection of upper sums. We denote by

$$U_a^b(f)$$

the greatest lower bound of the collection of upper sums, and call it the upper integral of f over the interval $[a, b]$. Then

$$L_a^b(f) \leq U_a^b(f).$$

If x is any point in the interval, then we have the numbers

$$L_a^x(f) \qquad \text{and} \qquad U_a^x(f).$$

Thus $L_a^x(f)$ is the value at x of a function defined on the interval. Similarly, $U_a^x(f)$ is the value at x of another function defined on the interval.

Our purpose is to prove that these functions are equal for all x. The way we shall do this is to prove that $L_a^b(f)$ and $U_a^b(f)$ each satisfy the properties stated in Theorem 2. This will both give the existence of the integral, and in view of the remarks at the end of §4, it will also show that $L_a^b(f) = U_a^b(f)$.

Proof of Property 1. Suppose that we have two numbers m, M such that

$$m \leq f(x) \leq M$$

for all x between b and c. Let P be the partition of the interval b, c consisting only of the end points. Then

$$m(c - b) \leq L_b^c(P, f) \leq L_b^c(f).$$

On the other hand,

$$L_b^c(f) \leq U_b^c(f) \leq M(c - b).$$

This proves our property.

Proof of Property 2. Let a, b, c be three numbers with $a \leq b \leq c$. Let f be a continuous function on the interval $[a, c]$. We shall prove:

$$L_a^b(f) + L_b^c(f) = L_a^c(f).$$

A similar statement holds for the upper integrals, namely

$$U_a^b(f) + U_b^c(f) = U_a^c(f).$$

We shall first prove that

$$L_a^b(f) + L_b^c(f) \leq L_a^c(f).$$

Since $L_a^b(f)$ is the *least* upper bound of the lower sums built up with partitions, we can find such a lower sum which comes arbitrarily close to it. Thus, given any small number $\epsilon > 0$, we can find a partition P of the interval $[a, b]$ such that

$$L_a^b(f) - \epsilon \leq L_a^b(P, f).$$

Similarly, we can find a partition Q of the interval $[b, c]$ such that

$$L_b^c(f) - \epsilon \leq L_b^c(Q, f).$$

Adding, we get

$$L_a^b(f) + L_b^c(f) - 2\epsilon \leq L_a^b(P, f) + L_b^c(Q, f).$$

We can view P and Q together as giving a partition of the whole interval $[a, c]$.

We denote this partition simply by (P, Q). The two sums occurring on the right-hand side of our inequality are then equal to the lower sum built up from the partition (P, Q) over the whole interval $[a, c]$. Thus we can write

$$L_a^b(f) + L_b^c(f) - 2\epsilon \leq L_a^c((P, Q), f).$$

But any lower sum made up from a partition is smaller than the lower integral, which is an upper bound (even a least upper bound) of such lower sums. Thus our expression on the right satisfies the inequality

$$L_a^c((P, Q), f) \leqq L_a^c(f).$$

We obtain finally

$$L_a^b(f) + L_b^c(f) - 2\epsilon \leqq L_a^c(f).$$

This is true for every $\epsilon > 0$. Let ϵ approach 0. Then the left-hand side approaches

$$L_a^b(f) + L_b^c(f)$$

and our inequality follows.

We shall now prove the reverse inequality.

Let R be any partition of $[a, c]$. If we add b to R, then we get a partition of $[a, c]$ which splits up into a partition of $[a, b]$ and a partition of $[b, c]$. Call these P and Q. Then

$$L_a^c(R, f) \leqq L_a^c((P, Q), f) = L_a^b(P, f) + L_b^c(Q, f).$$

Since the lower integral is an upper bound for these lower sums, we know that the expression on the right is less than or equal to

$$L_a^b(f) + L_b^c(f),$$

which is therefore an upper bound for $L_a^c(R, f)$. The least upper bound $L_a^c(f)$ is therefore less than or equal to our sum on the right, and the property is proved.

The proof that the upper integral U satisfies the two properties is entirely similar, and will be left as an exercise.

§7. INTEGRABLE FUNCTIONS

In general, let f be a bounded function on $[a, b]$. This means that there exists a number C such that $|f(x)| \leqq C$ for all x in $[a, b]$. Then f may not have a minimum on a closed interval, but we can still form lower sums by replacing the minimum by a greatest lower bound. Thus if P is a partition of $[a, b]$ say

$$a = x_0 \leqq x_1 \leqq \cdots \leqq x_n = b,$$

we let

m_i = greatest lower bound of values $f(x)$ for x in the interval $[x_i, x_{i+1}]$,

M_i = least upper bound of values $f(x)$ for x in the interval $[x_i, x_{i+1}]$.

We then form the sum

$$L_a^b(P, f) = \sum_{i=0}^{n-1} m_i(x_{i+1} - x_i)$$

and similarly for the upper sum,

$$U_a^b(P, f) = \sum_{i=0}^{n-1} M_i(x_{i+1} - x_i).$$

Theorem 3 is still true for any bounded function f, and thus we can define the *lower integral*

$$L_a^b(f) = \text{least upper bound of all } L_a^b(P, f) \text{ for all partitions } P.$$

The upper integral is then defined similarly. The function f is said to be *integrable* if

$$L_a^b(f) = U_a^b(f),$$

that is, if its lower integral is equal to its upper integral, in which case it is called simply the *integral* of f. We proved in the previous section that every continuous function is integrable. It can be shown that a bounded function which is continuous except at a finite number of points is integrable, but we shall leave it as an exercise. However, we prove:

Theorem 5. *Let f be an integrable function on $[a, b]$. Suppose that for each pair of numbers c, d with $a \leq c \leq d \leq b$ we have associated a number denoted by $I_c^d(f)$ satisfying the following properties:*

Property 1. If M, m are two numbers such that

$$m \leq f(x) \leq M$$

for all x in $[c, d]$ then

$$m(d - c) \leq I_c^d(f) \leq M(d - c).$$

Property 2. We have

$$I_a^c(f) + I_c^d(f) = I_a^d(f).$$

Then $I_a^b(f)$ is the integral of f on $[a, b]$.

Proof. Let P be a partition as before. Then

$$L_a^b(P, f) = \sum_{i=0}^{n-1} m_i(x_{i+1} - x_i) \leq \sum_{i=0}^{n-1} I_{x_i}^{x_{i+1}}(f) = I_a^b(f).$$

Similarly,

$$L_a^b(P, f) \leq I_a^b(f) \leq U_a^b(P, f).$$

Since f is integrable, $L_a^b(P, f)$ and $U_a^b(P, f)$ are arbitrarily close together for suitable partitions P, and hence the theorem follows.

EXERCISE

Prove that if f is bounded on $[a, b]$ and continuous except at a finite number of points, then f is integrable. [*Hint:* Let $c_1, \ldots, c_r$ be the points at which f is not continuous. Around each c_i, put an interval of radius δ. Consider partitions of $[a, b]$ which have the points $c_i - \delta$, c_i, $c_i + \delta$. Outside these small intervals, the upper and lower sums are close together because the function is continuous. Inside these intervals, the upper and lower sums are anyhow bounded by an expression of type $2\delta Cr$ where C is a bound for f.]

Chapter X

Properties of the Integral

This is a short chapter. It shows how the integral combines with addition and inequalities. There is no good formula for the integral of a product. The closest thing is integration by parts, which is postponed to the next chapter.

Connecting the integral with the derivative is what allows us to compute integrals. The fact that two functions having the same derivative differ by a constant is again exploited to the hilt.

§1. FURTHER CONNECTION WITH THE DERIVATIVE

Let f be a continuous function on some interval. Let a, b be two points of the interval such that $a < b$, and let F be a function which is differentiable on the interval and whose derivative is f.

$$\vdash\!\!\!\!-\!\!\!-\!\!\!-\!\!\!-\!\!\!-\!\!\!\!\!\!\!+\!\!\!-\!\!\!-\!\!\!-\!\!\!-\!\!\!-\!\!\!\dashv$$
$$a \qquad\quad x \qquad b$$

Then we know that there is a constant C such that

$$\int_a^x f = F(x) + C$$

for all x in the interval. If we put $x = a$, we get

$$0 = \int_a^a f = F(a) + C,$$

whence $C = -F(a)$. We also have

$$\int_a^b f = F(b) + C.$$

From this we obtain

$$\int_a^b f = F(b) - F(a).$$

This is extremely useful in practice, because we can usually guess the function F, and once we have guessed it, we can then compute the integral by means of this relation.

183

Furthermore, it is also practical to use the notation

$$F(x)\Big|_a^b$$

instead of $F(b) - F(a)$. Thus the integral

$$\int_0^\pi \sin x \, dx$$

is equal to

$$-\cos x\Big|_0^\pi,$$

which is $-\cos \pi - (-\cos 0) = 2$.

As another example, suppose we want to find

$$\int_1^3 x^2 \, dx.$$

Let $F(x) = x^3/3$. Then $F'(x) = x^2$. Hence our integral is equal to

$$\frac{x^3}{3}\Big|_1^3 = \frac{27}{3} - \frac{1}{3} = \frac{26}{3}.$$

Finally, we shall usually call the *indefinite integral* simply an *integral*, since the context makes clear what is meant. When we deal with a definite integral $\int_a^b$, the numbers a and b are sometimes called the *lower limit* and *upper limit*, respectively.

EXERCISES

Find the following integrals:

1. $\int_1^2 x^5 \, dx$ 2. $\int_{-1}^1 x^{1/3} \, dx$ 3. $\int_{-\pi}^\pi \sin x \, dx$ 4. $\int_0^\pi \cos x \, dx$

§2. SUMS

Let $f(x)$ and $g(x)$ be two functions defined over some interval, and let $F(x)$ and $G(x)$ be (indefinite) integrals for f and g, respectively. Since the derivative of a sum is the sum of the derivatives, we see that $F + G$ is an integral for $f + g$; in other words,

$$\int [f(x) + g(x)] \, dx = \int f(x) \, dx + \int g(x) \, dx.$$

Similarly, let c be a number. The derivative of $cF(x)$ is $cf(x)$. Hence

$$\int cf(x) \, dx = c \int f(x) \, dx.$$

A constant can be taken in and out of an integral.

Example 1. Find the integral of $\sin x + 3x^4$.

We have

$$\int (\sin x + 3x^4)\, dx = \int \sin x\, dx + \int 3x^4\, dx$$

$$= -\cos x + 3x^5/5.$$

Any formula involving the indefinite integral yields a formula for the definite integral. Using the same notation as above, suppose we have to find

$$\int_a^b [f(x) + g(x)]\, dx.$$

We know that it is

$$[F(x) + G(x)]\Big|_a^b,$$

which is equal to

$$F(b) + G(b) - F(a) - G(a).$$

Thus we get the formula

$$\int_a^b [f(x) + g(x)]\, dx = \int_a^b f(x)\, dx + \int_a^b g(x)\, dx.$$

Similarly, for any constant c,

$$\int_a^b cf(x)\, dx = c\int_a^b f(x)\, dx.$$

Example 2. Find the integral

$$\int_0^\pi [\sin x + 3x^4]\, dx.$$

This (definite) integral is equal to

$$-\cos x + 3x^5/5\Big|_0^\pi = -\cos \pi + 3\pi^5/5 - (-\cos 0 + 0)$$

$$= 1 + 3\pi^5/5 + 1$$

$$= 2 + 3\pi^5/5.$$

In some applications, one meets a slightly wider class of functions than continuous ones. Let f be a function defined on an interval $[a, b]$. We shall say that f is *piecewise continuous* on $[a, b]$ if there exist numbers

$$a = a_0 < a_1 < \cdots < a_n = b$$

and on each interval $[a_{i-1}, a_i]$ there is a continuous function f_i such that $f(x) = f_i(x)$ for $a_{i-1} < x < a_i$. If this is the case, then we define the integral of f from a to b to be the sum

$$\int_a^b f = \int_{a_0}^{a_1} f_1 + \int_{a_1}^{a_2} f_2 + \cdots + \int_{a_{n-1}}^{a_n} f_n.$$

A piecewise continuous function may look like this:

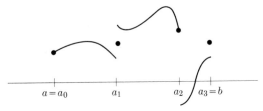

Example 3. Let f be the function defined on the interval $[0, 2]$ by the conditions:

$$f(x) = x \qquad \text{if} \ \ 0 \leq x \leq 1$$
$$f(x) = 2 \qquad \text{if} \ \ 1 < x \leq 2.$$

The graph of f looks like this:

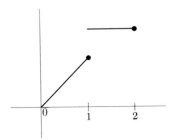

To find the integral of f between 0 and 2, we have

$$\int_0^2 f = \int_0^1 x \, dx + \int_1^2 2 \, dx = \frac{x^2}{2}\Big|_0^1 + 2x\Big|_1^2$$
$$= \tfrac{1}{2} + (4 - 2) = \tfrac{5}{2}.$$

We can also find $\int_0^x f(t) \, dt$ for $0 \leq x \leq 2$. If $0 \leq x \leq 1$:

$$\int_0^x f(t) \, dt = \int_0^x t \, dt = \frac{x^2}{2}.$$

If $1 \leq x \leq 2$:

$$\int_0^x f(t) \, dt = \int_0^1 f(t) \, dt + \int_1^x f(t) \, dt$$
$$= \tfrac{1}{2} + \int_1^x 2 \, dt = \tfrac{1}{2} + 2x - 2.$$

Example 4. Let $f(x)$ be defined for $0 \leq x \leq \pi$ by the formulas:

$$f(x) = \sin x \quad \text{if} \ 0 \leq x < \pi/2$$
$$f(x) = \cos x \quad \text{if} \ \pi/2 \leq x \leq \pi.$$

Then the integral of f from 0 to π is given by:

$$\int_0^\pi f = \int_0^{\pi/2} \sin x \, dx + \int_{\pi/2}^\pi \cos x \, dx$$

$$= -\cos x \Big|_0^{\pi/2} + \sin x \Big|_{\pi/2}^\pi$$

$$= 0.$$

The graph of f looks like this:

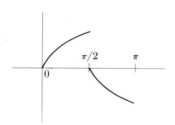

EXERCISES

Find the following integrals:

1. $\int 4x^3 \, dx$

2. $\int (3x^4 - x^5) \, dx$

3. $\int (2 \sin x + 3 \cos x) \, dx$

4. $\int (3x^{2/3} + 5 \cos x) \, dx$

5. $\int \left(5e^x + \frac{1}{x}\right) dx$

6. $\int_{-\pi}^{\pi} (\sin x + \cos x) \, dx$

7. $\int_{-1}^{1} 2x^5 \, dx$

8. $\int_{-1}^{2} e^x \, dx$

9. $\int_{-1}^{3} 4x_2 \, dx$

10. Find the area between the curves $y = x$ and $y = x^2$. [Sketch the curve. If $f(x)$ and $g(x)$ are two continuous functions such that $f(x) \geq g(x)$ on an interval $[a, b]$, then the area between the two curves, from a to b, is

$$\int_a^b \left(f(x) - g(x) \right) dx.$$

In this problem, the curves intersect at $x = 0$ and $x = 1$.]

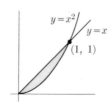

Hence the area is

$$\int_0^1 (x - x^2)\, dx = \left.\frac{x^2}{2} - \frac{x^3}{3}\right|_0^1 = \frac{1}{2} - \frac{1}{3}.$$

11. Find the area between the curves $y = x$ and $y = x^3$.

12. Find the area between the curves $y = x^2$ and $y = x^3$.

13. Find the area between the curve $y = (x - 1)(x - 2)(x - 3)$ and the x-axis. (Sketch the curve.)

14. Find the area between the curve $y = (x + 1)(x - 1)(x + 2)$ and the x-axis.

15. Find the area between the curves $y = \sin x$, $y = \cos x$, the y-axis, and the first point where these curves intersect for $x > 0$.

In each one of the following cases, find the integral of the function on the stated interval, and sketch the graph of the function.

16. On $[-1, 1]$, $f(x) = x$ if $-1 \leq x < 0$ and $f(x) = 5$ if $0 \leq x \leq 1$.

17. On $[-1, 1]$, $f(x) = x^2$ if $-1 \leq x \leq 0$ and $f(x) = -x$ if $0 < x \leq 1$.

18. On $[-1, 1]$, $f(x) = x - 1$ if $-1 \leq x < 0$ and $f(x) = x + 1$ if $0 \leq x \leq 1$.

19. On $[-\pi, \pi]$, $f(x) = \sin x$ if $-\pi \leq x \leq 0$, and $f(x) = x$ if $0 < x \leq \pi$.

20. On $[-\pi, \pi]$, $f(x) = |\sin x|$.   21. On $[-\pi, \pi]$, $f(x) = |\cos x|$.

22. On $[-1, 1]$, $f(x) = |x|$.   23. On $[-\pi, \pi]$, $f(x) = \sin x + |\cos x|$.

24. On $[-\pi, \pi]$, $f(x) = x - |x|$.   25. On $[-\pi, \pi]$, $f(x) = \sin x + |\sin x|$.

§3. INEQUALITIES

Theorem 1. *Let a, b be two numbers, with $a \leq b$. Let f, g be two continuous functions on the interval $[a, b]$ and assume that $f(x) \leq g(x)$ for all x in the interval. Then*

$$\int_a^b f(x)\, dx \leq \int_a^b g(x)\, dx.$$

Proof. Since $g(x) - f(x) \geq 0$, we can use the basic Property 1 of Chapter IX, §4 (with $m = 0$) to conclude that

$$\int_a^b (g - f) \geq 0.$$

But

$$\int_a^b (g - f) = \int_a^b g - \int_a^b f.$$

Transposing the second integral on the right in our inequality, we obtain

$$\int_a^b g \geq \int_a^b f,$$

as desired.

Theorem 1 will be used mostly when $g(x) = |f(x)|$. Since a negative number is always $\leq$ a positive number, we know that

$$f(x) \leq |f(x)|$$

and

$$-f(x) \leq |f(x)|.$$

Theorem 2. *Let a, b be two numbers, with $a \leq b$. Let f be a continuous function on the interval $[a, b]$. Then*

$$\left| \int_a^b f(x)\, dx \right| \leq \int_a^b |f(x)|\, dx.$$

Proof. We simply let $g(x) = |f(x)|$ in the preceding theorem. The absolute value of the integral on the left is equal to

$$\int_a^b f(x)\, dx \qquad \text{or} \qquad -\int_a^b f(x)\, dx.$$

We can apply Theorem 1 either to $f(x)$ or $-f(x)$ to get Theorem 2.

We make one other application of Theorem 2.

Theorem 3. *Let a, b be two numbers and f a continuous function on the closed interval between a and b. (We do not necessarily assume that $a < b$.) Let M be a number such that $|f(x)| \leq M$ for all x in the interval. Then*

$$\left| \int_a^b f(x)\, dx \right| \leq M|b - a|.$$

Proof. If $a \leq b$, we can use Theorem 2 to get

$$\left| \int_a^b f(x)\, dx \right| \leq \int_a^b M\, dx = M \int_a^b dx = M(b - a).$$

If $b < a$, then

$$\int_a^b f = -\int_b^a f.$$

Taking the absolute value gives us the estimate $M(a - b)$. Since $a - b = |b - a|$ in case $b < a$, we have proved our theorem.

Theorem 4. *Let f be a continuous function on the interval $[a, b]$ with $a < b$. Assume that $f(x) \geq 0$ for every x in this interval, and $f(x) > 0$ for some x in this interval. Then*

$$\int_a^b f(x)\, dx > 0.$$

Proof. Let c be a number of the interval such that $f(c) > 0$, and suppose for simplicity that $c \neq b$. Since f is continuous, there exists some number d close to c in the interval, with $c < d \leq b$ such that $f(x)$ is close to $f(c)$ for all x satisfying $c \leq x \leq d$. In particular, we have

$$f(x) \geq \frac{f(c)}{2}, \qquad\qquad c \leq x \leq d.$$

Then

$$\int_a^b f(x)\, dx = \int_a^c f + \int_c^d f + \int_d^b f$$

$$\geq \int_c^d f(x)\, dx \geq \int_c^d \frac{f(c)}{2}\, dx$$

$$= \frac{f(c)}{2}(d - c) > 0.$$

This proves our theorem if $c \neq b$. If $c = b$, we take $d < c$ and argue similarly.

Theorem 4 will not be used in the rest of this book except in a couple of exercises, but it is important in subsequent applications. The geometric idea behind the proof is quite simple, in terms of area. Since the function f is assumed ≥ 0 everywhere, and > 0 at the point c, then it is greater than some fixed positive number [taken to be $f(c)/2$, say] in some interval near c. This means that we can insert a small rectangle of height > 0 between the curve $y = f(x)$ and the x-axis. Then the area under the curve is at least equal to the area of this rectangle, which is > 0.

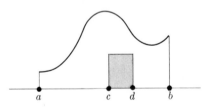

EXERCISES

1. Let a, b be numbers with $a < b$. If f, g are continuous functions on the interval $[a, b]$ let

$$\langle f, g \rangle = \int_a^b f(x)g(x)\, dx.$$

Show that the symbol $\langle f, g \rangle$ satisfies the following properties:
(a) If f_1, f_2, g are continuous on $[a, b]$ then

$$\langle f_1 + f_2, g \rangle = \langle f_1, g \rangle + \langle f_2, g \rangle.$$

If c is a number, then

$$\langle cf, g \rangle = c\langle f, g \rangle.$$

(b) We have $\langle f, g \rangle = \langle g, f \rangle$.

(c) We have $\langle f, f \rangle \geq 0$, and equality holds if and only if $f = 0$.

2. Let the notation be as in Exercise 1. For any number $p \geq 1$ define

$$\|f\|_p = \left[\int_a^b |f(x)|^p \, dx \right]^{1/p}.$$

Let q be such that $\dfrac{1}{p} + \dfrac{1}{q} = 1$. Prove that

$$|\langle f, g \rangle| \leq \|f\|_p \|g\|_q.$$

[*Hint:* If $\|f\|_p$ and $\|g\|_q \neq 0$ let $\alpha = |f|^p / \|f\|_p^p$ and $\beta = |g|^q / \|g\|_q^q$. Then use Exercise 13 of Chapter VIII, §3, and integrate both terms.]

3. Notation being as in the preceding exercise, prove that

$$\|f + g\|_p \leq \|f\|_p + \|g\|_p.$$

[*Hint:* Let I denote the integral. Show that

$$\|f + g\|_p^p \leq I(|f + g|^{p-1}|f|) + I(|f + g|^{p-1}|g|)$$

and apply Exercise 2.]

4. (a) Let f be an increasing continuous function, defined for all $x \geq 1$, such that $f(x) \geq 0$. Show that

$$f(1) + f(2) + \cdots + f(n - 1) \leq \int_1^n f(x) \, dx \leq f(2) + \cdots + f(n).$$

(b) Let $F(x) = \int_1^x f(t) \, dt$. Assume that

$$\lim_{n \to \infty} \frac{f(n)}{F(n)} = 0.$$

Show that

$$\lim_{n \to \infty} \frac{f(1) + f(2) + \cdots + f(n)}{F(n)} = 1.$$

5. Evaluate the following limits, for $n \to \infty$.

(a) $\dfrac{1^{1/3} + 2^{1/3} + \cdots + n^{1/3}}{n^{4/3}}$ (b) $\dfrac{1^{1/4} + 2^{1/4} + \cdots + n^{1/4}}{n^{5/4}}$

(c) $n\left(\dfrac{1}{1^2} + \dfrac{1}{2^2} + \cdots + \dfrac{1}{n^2}\right)$ (d) $\dfrac{1 + 2^4 + \cdots + n^4}{n^5}$

(e) For a fixed integer $k \geq 1$,

$$\frac{1 + 2^k + \cdots + n^k}{n^{k+1}}.$$

6. Let f be a decreasing continuous function, defined for $x \geqq 1$ and such that $f(x) \geqq 0$. Show that

$$f(1) + f(2) + \cdots + f(n - 1) \geqq \int_1^n f(x)\, dx \geqq f(2) + \cdots + f(n).$$

§4. IMPROPER INTEGRALS

We know that the area under the curve $1/x$ between 1 and x is $\log x$. Instead of taking $x > 1$, let us take $0 < x < 1$. As x approaches 0, $\log x$ becomes very large negative. The integral

$$\int_x^1 \frac{1}{t}\, dt = \log t \Big|_x^1 = -\log x$$

is therefore very large positive. We can interpret this by saying that the area becomes very large.

However, it is remarkable that an entirely different situation will occur when we consider the area under the curve $1/x^{1/2} = x^{-1/2}$. We take $x > 0$, of course, and compute the integral

$$\int_x^1 \frac{1}{t^{1/2}}\, dt = \frac{t^{1/2}}{1/2} \Big|_x^1 = 2 - 2x^{1/2}.$$

As x approaches 0, this approaches 2, in spite of the fact that our curve $y = x^{-1/2}$ gives rise to a chimney near the y-axis, and is not even defined for $x = 0$.

When that happens, we shall say that the integral

$$\int_0^1 t^{-1/2}\, dt$$

exists, or *converges* even though the function is not defined at 0 and is not continuous in the *closed* interval $[0, 1]$.

In general, suppose we have two numbers a, b with, say, $a < b$. Let f be a continuous function in the interval $a < x \leqq b$. This means that for every positive number h (such that $a + h < b$), the function f is continuous on the interval

$$a + h \leqq x \leqq b.$$

We can then form our usual integral

$$\int_{a+h}^b f(x)\, dx.$$

If F is an indefinite integral for f over our interval, then the integral is equal to

$$F(b) - F(a + h).$$

If the limit

$$\lim_{h \to 0} F(a + h)$$

exists, then we say that the *improper integral*

$$\int_a^b f(x)\, dx$$

exists, and is equal to $F(b) - \lim_{h \to 0} F(a + h)$.

In our preceding examples, we can say that the improper integral

$$\int_0^1 \frac{1}{x}\, dx$$

does not exist, but that the improper integral

$$\int_0^1 x^{-1/2}\, dx$$

does exist. This second integral is equal to 2.

We make similar definitions when we deal with an interval $a \leqq x < b$ and a function f which is continuous on this interval. If the limit

$$\lim_{\substack{h \to 0 \\ h > 0}} \int_a^{b-h} f(x)\, dx$$

exists, then we say that the improper integral exists, and it is equal to this limit.

Example 1. Show that the improper integral

$$\int_0^1 \frac{1}{x^2}\, dx$$

does not exist.

We consider

$$\int_h^1 x^{-2}\, dx = \frac{x^{-1}}{-1}\bigg|_h^1 = -1 - \left(-\frac{1}{h}\right) = -1 + \frac{1}{h}.$$

This does not approach a limit as h approaches 0 and hence the improper integral does not exist.

There is another type of improper integral, dealing with large values.

Let a be a number and f a continuous function defined for $x \geqq a$. Consider the integral

$$\int_a^B f(x)\, dx$$

for some number $B > a$. If $F(x)$ is any indefinite integral of f, then our integral is equal to $F(B) - F(a)$. If it approaches a limit as B becomes very large, then we *define*

$$\int_a^\infty f(x)\, dx \qquad \text{or} \qquad \int_a^\infty f$$

to be this limit, and say that the *improper integral converges.*

Thus $\int_a^\infty f$ converges if

$$\lim_{B \to \infty} \int_a^B f$$

exists, and is equal to this limit. Otherwise, we say that the improper integral *does not converge.*

Example 2. Determine whether the improper integral $\int_1^\infty \frac{1}{x}\, dx$ converges, and if it does, find its value.

We have, for a large number B,

$$\int_1^B \frac{1}{x}\, dx = \log B - \log 1 = \log B.$$

As B becomes large, so does $\log B$, and hence the improper integral does not converge.

Let us look at the function $1/x^2$. Its graph looks like that in the next figure. At first sight, there seems to be no difference between this function and $1/x$, except that $1/x^2 < 1/x$ when $x > 1$. However, intuitively speaking, we shall find that $1/x^2$ approaches 0 sufficiently faster than $1/x$ to guarantee that the area under the curve between 1 and B approaches a limit as B becomes large.

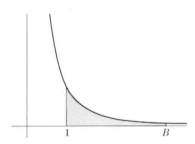

Example 3. Determine whether the improper integral

$$\int_1^\infty \frac{1}{x^2}\, dx$$

converges, and if it does, find its value.

For a large number B, we have

$$\int_1^B \frac{1}{x^2}\, dx = \frac{-1}{x}\Big|_1^B = -\frac{1}{B} + 1.$$

As B becomes large, $1/B$ approaches 0. Hence the limit as B becomes large exists and is equal to 1, which is the value of our integral. We thus have by definition

$$\int_1^\infty \frac{1}{x^2}\, dx = 1.$$

It is frequently possible to determine whether an improper integral converges without computing it, by comparing it with another which is known to converge. We give such a criterion in the following theorem.

Theorem 5. *Let $f(x)$ and $g(x)$ be two continuous functions defined for $x \geq a$ and such that $f(x) \geq 0$ and $g(x) \geq 0$ for all $x \geq a$. Assume that $f(x) \leq g(x)$ and that the improper integral*

$$\int_a^\infty g(x)\, dx$$

converges. Then so does the improper integral

$$\int_a^\infty f(x)\, dx.$$

(*Intuitively speaking, we visualize the theorem as saying that if the area under the graph of g is finite, then the area under the graph of f is also finite because it is smaller.*)

Proof. Let B be a large number. Then according to the inequalities satisfied by the definite integral, we have

$$\int_a^B f \leq \int_a^B g.$$

As B becomes large, and increases, the integral on the right increases. But we know that it approaches a limit; call it L. This limit is a number, which is a bound for the integral of f between a and B, i.e.

$$\int_a^B f \leq L.$$

As B increases, this integral of f also increases (the area under the graph increases because f is ≥ 0) but stays below L for all B. There must be a least upper bound for such integrals of f, and this least upper bound is the desired limit.

Example 4. Determine whether the improper integral

$$\int_1^\infty \frac{x}{x^3 + 1}\, dx$$

converges.

We don't try to evaluate this, but observe that

$$x^3 \leqq x^3 + 1$$

for $x \geqq 1$, whence

$$\frac{x}{x^3 + 1} \leqq \frac{x}{x^3} \leqq \frac{1}{x^2}.$$

All the functions involved are $\geqq 0$ when $x \geqq 1$. Using Example 3, we conclude that our improper integral converges.

Example 5. Note that Theorem 5 also applies to a finite interval. For instance, we wish to prove that the integral

$$\int_0^1 \frac{e^x}{\sqrt{x}}\, dx$$

converges. We use Exercise 8. There is some number $C > 0$ such that $e^x \leqq C$ if $0 \leqq x \leqq 1$ and hence for $0 < x \leqq 1$ we have $e^x/\sqrt{x} \leqq C/\sqrt{x}$. By Exercise 8, the integral

$$\int_0^1 \frac{C}{\sqrt{x}}\, dx$$

converges. Hence by Theorem 5 our given integral $\int_0^1 e^x/\sqrt{x}\, dx$ converges.

EXERCISES

Determine whether the following improper integrals exist or not, and converge or not:

1. $\displaystyle\int_2^\infty \frac{1}{x^{3/2}}\, dx$ 2. $\displaystyle\int_1^\infty \frac{1}{x^{2/3}}\, dx$ 3. $\displaystyle\int_0^\infty \frac{1}{1 + x^2}\, dx$

4. $\displaystyle\int_0^5 \frac{1}{5 - x}\, dx$ 5. $\displaystyle\int_0^2 \frac{1}{x^2 - 2x}\, dx$ 6. $\displaystyle\int_1^\infty e^{-x}\, dx$

7. Let B be a number > 2. Find the area under the curve $y = e^{-2x}$ between 2 and B. Does this area approach a limit when B becomes very large? If so, what limit?

8. Let $0 < a < 1$. Does the integral

$$\int_a^1 \frac{1}{\sqrt{x}}\, dx$$

approach a limit as $a \to 0$? If so what limit?

9. Show that the integral

$$\int_0^1 \frac{1}{\sqrt{\sin x}}\, dx$$

exists. [*Hint:* Get some lower bound for $\sin x$ in terms of cx for some constant c.]

10. Show that the integral

$$\int_0^1 \frac{1}{\sqrt{\tan x}}\, dx$$

exists.

11. Let s be a number < 1. Show that the improper integral

$$\int_0^1 \frac{1}{x^s}\, dx$$

exists.

12. (a) Show that $(\log x)x^{1/4}$ is bounded between 0 and 1.
    (b) Show that

$$\int_0^1 \frac{\log x}{x^{1/2}}\, dx$$

exists.

    (c) For any positive integer n, show that

$$\int_0^1 \frac{(\log x)^n}{\sqrt{x}}\, dx$$

exists.

Chapter XI

Techniques of Integration

The purpose of this chapter is to teach you certain basic tricks to find indefinite integrals. It is of course easier to look up integral tables, but you should have a minimum of training in standard techniques.

§1. SUBSTITUTION

We shall formulate the analogue of the chain rule for integration.

Suppose that we have a function $g(x)$ and another function f such that $f(g(x))$ is defined. (All these functions are supposed to be defined over suitable intervals.) We wish to evaluate an integral

$$\int f(g(x)) \frac{dg(x)}{dx} \, dx.$$

Let $F(u)$ be an indefinite integral for $f(u)$, so that

$$\int f(u) \, du = F(u), \quad \text{i.e.} \quad \frac{dF(u)}{du} = f(u).$$

Then we assert that $F(g(x))$ is an integral for $f(g(x)) \dfrac{dg}{dx}$, or symbolically, that

$$\boxed{\int f(g(x)) \frac{dg}{dx} \, dx = \int f(u) \, du.}$$

This follows at once from the chain rule, because

$$\frac{d(F \circ g)}{dx} = \frac{dF}{du} \frac{du}{dx} = f(u) \frac{du}{dx} = f(g(x)) \frac{dg(x)}{dx} \, .$$

Example 1. Find $\int (x^2 + 1)^3 (2x) \, dx$.

Put $u = x^2 + 1$. Then $du/dx = 2x$ and our integral is in the form

$$\int f(u) \frac{du}{dx} \, dx,$$

the function f being $f(u) = u^3$.

Therefore our integral is equal to

$$\int f(u)\, du = \int u^3\, du = \frac{u^4}{4} = \frac{(x^2 + 1)^4}{4}.$$

We can check this by differentiating the expression on the right, using the chain rule. We get $(x^2 + 1)^3(2x)$, as desired.

Example 2. Find $\int \sin (2x)(2)\, dx$.

Put $u = 2x$. Then $du/dx = 2$. Hence our integral is in the form

$$\int \sin u\, du = -\cos u = -\cos (2x).$$

Observe that

$$\int \sin (2x)\, dx \neq -\cos (2x).$$

If we differentiate $-\cos (2x)$, we get $\sin (2x) \cdot 2$.

The integral in Example 2 could also be written

$$\int 2 \sin (2x)\, dx.$$

It does not matter, of course, where we place the 2.

Example 3. Find $\int \cos (3x)\, dx$.

Let $u = 3x$. Then $du/dx = 3$. There is no extra 3 in our integral. However, we can take a constant in and out of an integral. Our integral is equal to

$$\tfrac{1}{3}\int 3 \cos (3x)\, dx,$$

and this integral is in the form

$$\tfrac{1}{3}\int \cos u\, du.$$

Thus our integral is equal to $\tfrac{1}{3} \sin u = \tfrac{1}{3} \sin (3x)$.

It is convenient to use a purely formal notation which allows us to make a substitution $u = g(x)$, as in the previous examples. Thus instead of writing

$$\frac{du}{dx} = 2x$$

in Example 1, we would write $du = 2x\, dx$. Similarly, in Example 2, we would write $du = 2\, dx$, and in Example 3 we would write $du = 3\, dx$. We do not attribute any meaning to this. It is merely a device of a type used in programming a computing machine. A machine does not think. One simply adjusts certain electric circuits so that the machine performs a certain operation and comes out with the right answer. The fact that writing

$$du = \frac{du}{dx} dx$$

makes us come out with the right answer was *proved* once and for all when we established the relationship

$$\int f(g(x)) \frac{dg}{dx} dx = \int f(u) \, du.$$

The proof consisted in differentiating the answer and checking that it gives us the desired function.

Example 4. Find

$$\int (x^3 + x)^9 (3x^2 + 1) \, dx.$$

Let

$$u = x^3 + x.$$

Then

$$du = (3x^2 + 1) \, dx.$$

Hence our integral is of type $\int f(u) \, du$ and is equal to

$$\int u^9 \, du = \frac{u^{10}}{10} = \frac{(x^3 + x)^{10}}{10}.$$

We should also observe that the formula for integration by substitution applies to the definite integral. We can state this formally as follows.

Let g be a differentiable function on the interval [a, b], whose derivative is continuous. Let f be a continuous function on an interval containing the values of g. Then

$$\int_a^b f(g(x)) \frac{dg}{dx} dx = \int_{g(a)}^{g(b)} f(u) \, du.$$

The proof is immediate. If F is an indefinite integral for f, then $F \circ g$ is an indefinite integral for

$$f(g(x)) \frac{dg}{dx}$$

by the chain rule. Hence the left-hand side of our formula is equal to

$$F(g(b)) - F(g(a)),$$

which is also the value of the right-hand side.

In Example 4, suppose that we consider the integral

$$\int_0^1 (x^3 + x)^9 (3x^2 + 1)\, dx,$$

with $u = x^3 + x$. When $x = 0$, $u = 0$, and when $x = 1$, $u = 2$. Thus our definite integral is equal to

$$\int_0^2 u^9\, du = \frac{2^{10}}{10}.$$

Example 5. Evaluate

$$\int_0^{\sqrt{\pi}} x \sin x^2\, dx.$$

We let $u = x^2$, $du = 2x\, dx$. When $x = 0$, $u = 0$. When $x = \sqrt{\pi}$, $u = \pi$. Thus our integral is equal to

$$\tfrac{1}{2}\int_0^\pi \sin u\, du = \tfrac{1}{2}(-\cos u)\Big|_0^\pi = \tfrac{1}{2}(-\cos \pi + \cos 0) = 1.$$

EXERCISES

Find the following integrals:

1. $\displaystyle\int xe^{x^2}\, dx$

2. $\displaystyle\int x^3 e^{-x^4}\, dx$

3. $\displaystyle\int x^2(1 + x^3)\, dx$

4. $\displaystyle\int \frac{\log x}{x}\, dx$

5. $\displaystyle\int \frac{1}{x(\log x)^n}\, dx$ (n = integer)

6. $\displaystyle\int \frac{2x + 1}{x^2 + x + 1}\, dx$

7. $\displaystyle\int \frac{x}{x + 1}\, dx$

8. $\displaystyle\int \sin x \cos x\, dx$

9. $\displaystyle\int \sin^2 x \cos x\, dx$

10. $\displaystyle\int_0^\pi \sin^5 x \cos x\, dx$

11. $\displaystyle\int_0^\pi \cos^4 x \sin x\, dx$

12. $\displaystyle\int \frac{\sin x}{1 + \cos^2 x}\, dx$

13. $\displaystyle\int \frac{\arctan x}{1 + x^2}\, dx$

14. $\displaystyle\int_0^1 x^3\sqrt{1 - x^2}\, dx$

15. $\displaystyle\int_0^{\pi/2} x \sin (2x^2)\, dx$

16. Find the area under the curve $y = xe^{-x^2}$ between 0 and a number $B > 0$. Does this area approach a limit as B becomes very large? If so, what limit?

17. Find the area under the curve $y = x^2 e^{-x^3}$ between 0 and a number $B > 0$. Does this area approach a limit as B becomes very large? If so, what limit?

In some integrals involving e^x, one can sometimes find the integral by the substitution $u = e^x$, $x = \log u$, and $dx = (1/u)\, du$. You can combine this with the technique of §4 below to deal with the following integrals.

18. $\displaystyle \int \sqrt{1 + e^x}\, dx$

19. $\displaystyle \int \frac{1}{1 + e^x}\, dx$

20. $\displaystyle \int \frac{1}{e^x + e^{-x}}\, dx$

21. $\displaystyle \int \frac{1}{\sqrt{e^x + 1}}\, dx$

§2. INTEGRATION BY PARTS

If f, g are two differentiable functions of x, then

$$\frac{d(fg)}{dx} = f(x)\frac{dg}{dx} + g(x)\frac{df}{dx}.$$

Hence

$$f(x)\frac{dg}{dx} = \frac{d(fg)}{dx} - g(x)\frac{df}{dx}.$$

Using the formula for the integral of a sum, which is the sum of the integrals, we obtain

$$\int f(x)\frac{dg}{dx}\, dx = f(x)g(x) - \int g(x)\frac{df}{dx}\, dx,$$

which is called the formula for integrating by parts.

If we let $u = f(x)$ and $v = g(x)$, then the formula can be abbreviated in our shorthand notation as follows:

$$\boxed{\int u\, dv = uv - \int v\, du.}$$

Example 1. Find the integral $\int \log x\, dx$.

Let $u = \log x$ and $v = x$. Then $du = (1/x)\, dx$ and $dv = dx$. Hence our integral is in the form $\int u\, dv$ and is equal to

$$uv - \int v\, du = x \log x - \int 1\, dx$$
$$= x \log x - x.$$

Example 2. Find $\int e^x \sin x\, dx$.

Let $u = e^x$ and $dv = \sin x\, dx$. Then

$$du = e^x\, dx \qquad \text{and} \qquad v = -\cos x.$$

If we call our integral I, then

$$I = -e^x \cos x - \int -e^x \cos x$$
$$= -e^x \cos x + \int e^x \cos x \, dx.$$

This looks as if we were going around in circles. Don't lose heart. Rather, let $t = e^x$ and $dz = \cos x \, dx$. Then

$$dt = e^x \, dx \quad \text{and} \quad z = \sin x.$$

The second integral becomes

$$\int t \, dz = e^x \sin x - \int e^x \sin x \, dx.$$

We have come back to our integral I but with a minus sign! Thus

$$I = e^x \sin x - e^x \cos x - I.$$

Hence

$$2I = e^x \sin x - e^x \cos x,$$

and dividing by 2 gives us the value of I.

EXERCISES

Find the following integrals:

1. $\int \arcsin x \, dx$

2. $\int \arctan x \, dx$

3. $\int e^{2x} \sin 3x \, dx$

4. $\int e^{-4x} \cos 2x \, dx$

5. $\int (\log x)^2 \, dx$

6. $\int (\log x)^3 \, dx$

7. $\int x^2 e^x \, dx$

8. $\int x^2 e^{-x} \, dx$

9. $\int x \sin x \, dx$

10. $\int x \cos x \, dx$

11. $\int x^2 \sin x \, dx$

12. $\int x^2 \cos x \, dx$

13. $\int x^3 \cos x^2 \, dx$

14. $\int x^5 \sqrt{1 - x^2} \, dx$

15. $\int x^2 \log x \, dx$

16. $\int x^3 \log x \, dx$

17. $\int x^2 (\log x)^2 \, dx$

18. $\int x^3 e^{-x^2} \, dx$

19. $\displaystyle\int \frac{x^7}{(1 - x^4)^2}\, dx$ 20. $\displaystyle\int_{-\pi}^{\pi} x^2 \cos x \, dx$

21. Let B be a number > 0. Find the area under the curve $y = xe^{-x}$ between 0 and B. Does this area approach a limit as B becomes very large?

22. Does the improper integral $\int_1^\infty x^2 e^{-x}\, dx$ converge?

23. Does the improper integral $\int_1^\infty x^3 e^{-x}\, dx$ converge?

24. Let B be a number > 2. Find the area under the curve

$$y = \frac{1}{x(\log x)^2}$$

between 2 and B. Does this area approach a limit as B becomes very large? If so, what limit?

25. Does the improper integral

$$\int_3^\infty \frac{1}{x(\log x)^4}\, dx$$

converge? If yes, to what?

§3. TRIGONOMETRIC INTEGRALS

We shall investigate integrals involving sine and cosine. It will be useful to have the following formulas:

$$\sin^2 x = \frac{1 - \cos 2x}{2} \qquad \cos^2 x = \frac{1 + \cos 2x}{2}.$$

These are easily proved, using

$$\cos 2x = \cos^2 x - \sin^2 x \qquad \text{and} \qquad \sin^2 x + \cos^2 x = 1.$$

We can then integrate $\sin^2 x$, namely

$$\int \sin^2 x \, dx = \int \frac{1}{2}\, dx - \frac{1}{2}\int \cos 2x \, dx = \frac{x}{2} - \frac{1}{4}\sin 2x.$$

There is a general way in which one can integrate $\sin^n x$ for any positive integer n: integrating by parts. Let us take first an example.

Example 1. Find the integral $\int \sin^3 x \, dx$.

We write the integral in the form

$$\int \sin^2 x \sin x \, dx.$$

Let $u = \sin^2 x$ and $dv = \sin x \, dx$. Then

$$du = 2 \sin x \cos x \, dx \qquad \text{and} \qquad v = -\cos x.$$

Thus our integral is equal to

$$-(\sin^2 x)(\cos x) - \int -\cos x(2 \sin x \cos x)\, dx$$
$$= -\sin^2 x \cos x + 2\int \cos^2 x \sin x\, dx.$$

This last integral could then be determined by substitution, for instance $t = \cos x$ and $dt = -\sin x\, dx$. The last integral becomes $-2\int t^2\, dt$, and hence

$$\int \sin^3 x\, dx = -\sin^2 x \cos x - \tfrac{2}{3}\cos^3 x.$$

To deal with an arbitrary positive integer n, we shall show how to reduce the integral $\int \sin^n x\, dx$ to the integral $\int \sin^{n-2} x\, dx$. Proceeding stepwise downwards will give a method for getting the full answer.

Theorem 1. *For any positive integer n, we have*

$$\int \sin^n x\, dx = -\frac{1}{n} \sin^{n-1} x \cos x + \frac{n-1}{n} \int \sin^{n-2} x\, dx.$$

Proof. We write the integral as

$$I_n = \int \sin^n x\, dx = \int \sin^{n-1} x \sin x\, dx.$$

Let $u = \sin^{n-1} x$ and $dv = \sin x\, dx$. Then

$$du = (n-1)\sin^{n-2} x \cos x\, dx \qquad \text{and} \qquad v = -\cos x.$$

Thus

$$I_n = -\sin^{n-1} x \cos x - \int -(n-1)\cos x \sin^{n-2} x \cos x\, dx$$
$$= -\sin^{n-1} x \cos x + (n-1)\int \sin^{n-2} x \cos^2 x\, dx.$$

We replace $\cos^2 x$ by $1 - \sin^2 x$ and get finally

$$I_n = -\sin^{n-1} x \cos x + (n-1)I_{n-2} - (n-1)I_n,$$

whence

$$nI_n = -\sin^{n-1} x \cos x + (n-1)I_{n-2}.$$

Dividing by n gives us our formula.

We leave the proof of the analogous formula for cosine as an exercise.

$$\int \cos^n x\, dx = \frac{1}{n}\cos^{n-1} x \sin x + \frac{n-1}{n}\int \cos^{n-2} x\, dx.$$

Integrals involving tangents can be done by a similar technique, because

$$\frac{d \tan x}{dx} = 1 + \tan^2 x.$$

These functions are less used than sine and cosine, and hence we don't write out the formulas, to lighten this printed page which would otherwise become oppressive.

It is also useful to remember the following trick:

$$\int \frac{1}{\cos x} \, dx = \int \sec x \, dx = \log(\sec x + \tan x).$$

This is done by substitution. We have

$$\frac{1}{\cos x} = \sec x = \frac{(\sec x)(\sec x + \tan x)}{\sec x + \tan x}.$$

Let $u = \sec x + \tan x$. Then the integral is in the form

$$\int \frac{1}{u} \, du.$$

(This is a good opportunity to emphasize that the formula we just obtained is valid on any interval such that $\cos x \neq 0$ and $\sec x + \tan x > 0$. Otherwise the symbols are meaningless. Determine such an interval as an exercise.)

One can integrate mixed powers of sine and cosine by replacing $\sin^2 x$ by $1 - \cos^2 x$, for instance.

Example 2. Find $\int \sin^2 x \cos^2 x \, dx$.

Replacing $\sin^2 x$ by $1 - \cos^2 x$, we see that our integral is equal to

$$\int \cos^2 x \, dx - \int \cos^4 x \, dx$$

and we know how to find each one of these integrals.

When we meet an integral involving a square root, we can frequently get rid of the square root by making a trigonometric substitution.

Example 3. Find the area of a circle of radius 3.

The equation of the circle is

$$x^2 + y^2 = 9,$$

and the portion of the circle in the first quadrant is described by the function

$$y = \sqrt{3^2 - x^2}.$$

One-fourth of the area is therefore given by the integral

$$\int_0^3 \sqrt{3^2 - x^2}\, dx.$$

Let $x = 3 \sin t$. Then $dx = 3 \cos t\, dt$ and our integral becomes

$$\int_0^{\pi/2} \sqrt{3^2 - 3^2 \sin^2 t}\, 3 \cos t\, dt = \int_0^{\pi/2} 9 \cos^2 t\, dt = \frac{9\pi}{4}.$$

(We see that $1 - \sin^2 t = \cos^2 t$ and $\sqrt{1 - \sin^2 t} = \cos t$ in the interval between 0 and $\pi/4$.) The total area of the circle is therefore 9π.

EXERCISES

Find the following integrals.

1. $\int \sin^4 x\, dx$ 2. $\int \cos^3 x\, dx$ 3. $\int \sin^2 x \cos^3 x\, dx$

Find the area of the region enclosed by the following curves:

4. $x^2 + \dfrac{y^2}{9} = 1.$ 5. $\dfrac{x^2}{4} + \dfrac{y^2}{16} = 1.$ 6. $\dfrac{x^2}{a^2} + \dfrac{y^2}{b^2} = 1.$

7. Find the area of a circle of radius $r > 0$.

8. For any two integers m, n prove the formulas:

$$\sin mx \sin nx = \tfrac{1}{2}[\cos (m - n)x - \cos (m + n)x]$$
$$\sin mx \cos nx = \tfrac{1}{2}[\sin (m + n)x + \sin (m - n)x]$$
$$\cos mx \cos nx = \tfrac{1}{2}[\cos (m + n)x + \cos (m - n)x].$$

9. Show that

$$\int_{-\pi}^{\pi} \sin 3x \cos 2x\, dx = 0.$$

10. Show that

$$\int_{-\pi}^{\pi} \cos 5x \cos 2x\, dx = 0.$$

11. Show in general that for any integers m, n we have

$$\int_{-\pi}^{\pi} \sin mx \cos nx\, dx = 0.$$

12. Show in general that

$$\int_{-\pi}^{\pi} \sin mx \sin nx\, dx = \begin{cases} 0 & \text{if } m \neq n, \\ \pi & \text{if } m = n. \end{cases}$$

13. Find $\int \tan x\, dx$.

Find the following integrals:

14. $\displaystyle\int \frac{1}{\sqrt{9 - x^2}}\, dx$ 15. $\displaystyle\int \frac{1}{\sqrt{3 - x^2}}\, dx$

16. $\displaystyle\int \frac{1}{\sqrt{2 - 4x^2}}\, dx$ 17. $\displaystyle\int \frac{1}{\sqrt{a^2 - b^2 x^2}}\, dx$

18. Let f be a continuous function on the interval $[-\pi, \pi]$. Define its *Fourier coefficients*:

$$c_0 = \frac{1}{2\pi} \int_{-\pi}^{\pi} f(x)\, dx,$$

$$a_n = \frac{1}{\pi} \int_{-\pi}^{\pi} f(x) \cos nx\, dx, \qquad b_n = \frac{1}{\pi} \int_{-\pi}^{\pi} f(x) \sin nx\, dx.$$

for n equal to an integer ≥ 1. Compute the Fourier coefficients of the following functions. (If you do 19 first, you might have less work.)

(a) $f(x) = x$ (b) $f(x) = x^2$ (c) $f(x) = |x|$
(d) $f(x) = \cos x$ (e) $f(x) = \sin x$ (f) $f(x) = \sin^2 x$
(g) $f(x) = \cos^2 x$ (h) $f(x) = |\sin x|$ (i) $f(x) = |\cos x|$
(j) $f(x) = 1$

19. (a) Let f be an even function [that is $f(x) = f(-x)$]. Show that its Fourier coefficients b_n are all equal to 0.
   (b) Let f be an odd function [that is $f(x) = -f(-x)$]. What can you say about its Fourier coefficients?

20. Let f be a continuous function, and assume that $f(x + 2\pi) = f(x)$ for all x. Show that for any numbers a, b, c we have

$$\int_{a+2\pi}^{b+2\pi} f(x)\, dx = \int_{a}^{b} f(x)\, dx \qquad \text{and} \qquad \int_{-\pi+c}^{\pi+c} f = \int_{-\pi}^{\pi} f.$$

[*Hint:* For the second integral, take the integral successively from the points $-\pi + c, -\pi, \pi, \pi + c$.]

§4. PARTIAL FRACTIONS

Let $f(x)$ and $g(x)$ be two polynomials. We want to investigate the integral

$$\int \frac{f(x)}{g(x)}\, dx.$$

Using long division, one can reduce the problem to the case when the degree of f is less than the degree of g. The following example illustrates this reduction.

Example 1. Consider the two polynomials $f(x) = x^3 - x + 1$ and $g(x) = x^2 + 1$. Dividing f by g (you should know how from high school) we obtain a quotient of x with remainder $-2x + 1$. Thus

$$x^3 - x + 1 = (x^2 + 1)x + (-2x + 1).$$

Hence

$$\frac{f(x)}{g(x)} = x + \frac{-2x + 1}{x^2 + 1}.$$

To find the integral of $f(x)/g(x)$ we integrate x, and the quotient on the right, which has the property that the degree of the numerator is less than the degree of the denominator.

From now on, *we assume throughout that when we consider a quotient* $f(x)/g(x)$, *the degree of f is less than the degree of g.* Factoring out a constant if necessary, we also assume that $g(x)$ can be written

$$g(x) = x^d + \text{lower terms.}$$

We shall begin by discussing special cases, and then describe afterwards how the general case can be reduced to these.

Case 1. If a is a number, find

$$\int \frac{1}{(x - a)^n} \, dx$$

if n is an integer ≥ 1.

This is an old story. We know how to do it. In fact, we have

$$\int \frac{1}{(x - a)^n} \, dx = \frac{1}{-n + 1} \frac{1}{(x - a)^{n-1}} \qquad \text{if} \quad n \neq 1$$

$$\int \frac{1}{(x - a)} \, dx = \log (x - a).$$

Case 2. If b is a number, find

$$\int \frac{1}{(x^2 + b^2)^n} \, dx.$$

This is new. Using the substitution $x = bz$, $dx = b \, dz$ reduces the integral to

$$\int \frac{1}{(x^2 + 1)^n} \, dx.$$

We shall now discuss how to find this integral. We use integration by parts when $n > 1$. (If $n = 1$, we get the arctangent.) Let the above integral be I_n. We shall start with I_{n-1} because our integration by parts will raise n instead of lowering n. We have

$$I_{n-1} = \int \frac{1}{(x^2 + 1)^{n-1}} \, dx.$$

Let $u = \dfrac{1}{(x^2 + 1)^{n-1}}$ and $dv = dx$. Then

$$du = -(n - 1)\frac{2x}{(x^2 + 1)^n} dx \quad \text{and} \quad v = x.$$

Thus

$$I_{n-1} = \frac{x}{(x^2 + 1)^{n-1}} + 2(n - 1)\int \frac{x^2}{(x^2 + 1)^n} dx.$$

We write $x^2 = x^2 + 1 - 1$. We obtain

$$I_{n-1} = \frac{x}{(x^2 + 1)^{n-1}} + 2(n - 1)\int \frac{1}{(x^2 + 1)^{n-1}} dx$$
$$- 2(n - 1)\int \frac{1}{(x^2 + 1)^n} dx$$

or in other words:

$$I_{n-1} = \frac{x}{(x^2 + 1)^{n-1}} + 2(n - 1)I_{n-1} - 2(n - 1)I_n.$$

Therefore

$$2(n - 1)I_n = \frac{x}{(x^2 + 1)^{n-1}} + (2n - 3)I_{n-1},$$

whence

$$\int \frac{1}{(x^2 + 1)^n} dx = \frac{1}{2(n - 1)} \frac{x}{(x^2 + 1)^{n-1}}$$
$$+ \frac{(2n - 3)}{2(n - 1)} \int \frac{1}{(x^2 + 1)^{n-1}} dx.$$

This gives us a recursion formula which lowers the exponent n in the denominator until we reach $n = 1$. In that case, we know that

$$\int \frac{1}{x^2 + 1} dx = \arctan x.$$

Case 3. Find the integral

$$\int \frac{x}{(x^2 + b^2)^n} dx.$$

This is an old story. We make the substitution

$$u = x^2 + b^2 \quad \text{and} \quad du = 2x \, dx.$$

The integral is then equal to

$$\frac{1}{2} \int \frac{1}{u^n} du,$$

which we know how to evaluate, and thus we find

$$\int \frac{x}{(x^2 + b^2)^n}\, dx = \begin{cases} \frac{1}{2}\log(x^2 + b^2) & \text{if } n = 1 \\ \frac{1}{2(-n+1)}\frac{1}{(x^2 + b^2)^{n-1}} & \text{if } n \neq 1. \end{cases}$$

We shall now investigate a general quotient $f(x)/g(x)$.

If one is given a polynomial of type $x^2 + bx + c$, then one completes the square. The polynomial can thus be written in the form

$$(x - \alpha)(x - \beta) \qquad \text{or} \qquad (x - \alpha)^2 + \beta^2$$

with suitable numbers α, β. For instance,

$$x^2 - x - 6 = (x + 2)(x - 3)$$
$$x^2 - 2x + 5 = (x - 1)^2 + 2^2.$$

It can be shown that a polynomial $g(x)$ can always be written as a product of terms of type

$$(x - \alpha)^n \qquad \text{and} \qquad [(x - \beta)^2 + \gamma^2]^m,$$

n, m being integers ≥ 0. It can also be shown that a quotient $f(x)/g(x)$ can be written as a sum of terms of the following type:

$$\frac{c_1}{x - \alpha} + \frac{c_2}{(x - \alpha)^2} + \cdots + \frac{c_n}{(x - \alpha)^{n-1}}$$

$$+ \frac{d_1 + e_1 x}{(x - \beta)^2 + \gamma^2} + \cdots + \frac{d_m + e_m x}{[(x - \beta)^2 + \gamma^2]^m}$$

with suitable constants $c_1, c_2, \ldots, d_1, d_2, \ldots, e_1, e_2, \ldots$. The way one can determine these constants is to put the right-hand side over the common denominator $g(x)$, equate the numerator $f(x)$ with what is obtained on the right, and solve for the constants. We shall illustrate this by examples, and will not give the proofs of the preceding assertions, which are quite difficult.

Once the quotient $f(x)/g(x)$ is written as above, then Cases 1, 2, and 3 allow us to integrate each term. We then find that the integral involves functions of the following type:

A rational function

Log terms

Arctangent terms.

Example 2. Express the quotient

$$\frac{1}{(x - 2)(x - 3)}$$

as a sum of the previous type, and determine the integral.

This will be

$$\frac{c_1}{x-2} + \frac{c_2}{x-3}.$$

Putting this over the common denominator, we get the numerator

$$c_1(x-3) + c_2(x-2) = (c_1 + c_2)x - 3c_1 - 2c_2,$$

which must be equal to 1. Thus we must have

$$c_1 + c_2 = 0$$
$$-3c_1 - 2c_2 = 1.$$

Solving for c_1 and c_2 gives $c_2 = 1$ and $c_1 = -1$. Hence

$$\int \frac{1}{(x-2)(x-3)}\, dx = \int \frac{-1}{(x-2)}\, dx + \int \frac{1}{(x-3)}\, dx$$
$$= -\log(x-2) + \log(x-3).$$

Example 3. Express the quotient

$$\frac{x+1}{(x-1)^2(x-2)}$$

as a sum of the previous type, and find the integral.

We want to find numbers c_1, c_2, c_3 such that

$$\frac{x+1}{(x-1)^2(x-2)} = \frac{c_1}{x-1} + \frac{c_2}{(x-1)^2} + \frac{c_3}{x-2}.$$

Putting the right-hand side over the common denominator

$$(x-1)^2(x-2),$$

we get a numerator equal to

$$c_1(x-1)(x-2) + c_2(x-2) + c_3(x-1)^2.$$

This can be rewritten as

$$(c_1 + c_3)x^2 + (-3c_1 + c_2 - 2c_3)x + 2c_1 - 2c_2 + c_3,$$

and must be equal to $x + 1$. We equate the coefficients of x^2, x, and the constant terms. We get

$$c_1 \qquad\quad + c_3 = 0$$
$$-3c_1 + c_2 - 2c_3 = 1$$
$$2c_1 - 2c_2 + c_3 = 1.$$

This is a system of three linear equations in three unknowns, which you can solve to determine c_1, c_2, and c_3. One finds $c_1 = -3$, $c_2 = -2$, $c_3 = 3$. Hence

$$\int \frac{x+1}{(x-1)^2(x-2)} dx = \int \frac{-3}{x-1} dx + \int \frac{-2}{(x-1)^2} dx + \int \frac{3}{(x-2)} dx$$

$$= -3 \log(x-1) + \frac{2}{x-1} + 3 \log(x-2).$$

Example 4. Express the quotient

$$\frac{2x+5}{(x^2+1)^2(x-3)}$$

as a sum of the type described above, and find the integral.

We can find numbers c_1, c_2, ... such that the quotient is equal to

$$\frac{c_1 + c_2 x}{x^2+1} + \frac{c_3 + c_4 x}{(x^2+1)^2} + \frac{c_5}{x-3}.$$

We put this over the common denominator $(x^2+1)^2(x-3)$. The numerator is equal to

$$(c_1 + c_2 x)(x^2+1)(x-3) + (c_3 + c_4 x)(x-3) + c_5(x^2+1)^2$$

and must be equal to $2x+5$. If we equate the coefficients of x^4, x^3, x^2, x and the respective constants, we get a system of five linear equations in five unknowns, which can be solved. It is tedious to do it here and we leave it as an exercise. For the integral, we then obtain:

$$\int \frac{2x+5}{(x^2+1)^2(x-3)} dx = c_1 \arctan x + \tfrac{1}{2} c_2 \log(x^2+1)$$

$$+ c_3 \int \frac{1}{(x^2+1)^2} dx + \tfrac{1}{2} c_4 \log(x^2+1) + c_5 \log(x-3).$$

The integral which we left standing is just that of Case 2. Find it explicitly as an exercise.

EXERCISES

1. Find the constants in Example 4.
2. Write out in full the integral

$$\int \frac{1}{(x^2+1)^2} dx.$$

Find the following integrals:

3. (a) $\int \frac{1}{(x-3)(x+2)} dx$ (b) $\int \frac{1}{(x+2)(x+1)} dx$

4. $\displaystyle\int \frac{x}{(x+1)(x+2)(x+3)}\,dx$

5. $\displaystyle\int \frac{x+2}{x^2+x}\,dx$

6. $\displaystyle\int \frac{x}{(x+1)^2}\,dx$

7. $\displaystyle\int \frac{x+1}{(x^2+9)^2}\,dx$

8. $\displaystyle\int \frac{4}{(x^2+16)^2}\,dx$

9. $\displaystyle\int \frac{x}{(x+1)(x+2)^2}\,dx$

10. $\displaystyle\int \frac{1}{(x^2+1)^3}\,dx$

11. $\displaystyle\int \frac{2x-3}{(x-1)(x+7)}\,dx$

12. $\displaystyle\int \frac{1}{x(x^2+x+1)}\,dx$

13. $\displaystyle\int \frac{1}{(x+1)(x^2+1)}\,dx$

14. $\displaystyle\int \frac{1}{(x^2+1)^2}\,dx$

15. $\displaystyle\int \frac{2x-3}{(x-1)(x-2)}\,dx$

16. $\displaystyle\int \frac{x}{x^4-1}\,dx$

17. $\displaystyle\int \frac{1}{x^4-1}\,dx$

18. $\displaystyle\int \frac{x^2-2x-2}{x^3-1}\,dx$

19. $\displaystyle\int \frac{x}{(x^2-3)^2}\,dx$

20. Let $a_1,\dots,a_n$ be distinct numbers. Let

$$\frac{1}{(x-a_1)\cdots(x-a_n)} = \frac{c_1}{x-a_1}+\cdots+\frac{c_n}{x-a_n}.$$

Let $f(x)=(x-a_1)\cdots(x-a_n)$. Show that $c_1=1/f'(a_1)$.

21. If f is a function, define $L(f)=f'/f$. If f, g are functions, show that

$$L(fg)=L(f)+L(g), \quad\text{and}\quad L(cf)=L(f)$$

if c is a number. Compute $L(f)$ for the following functions:

(a) $(x-1)(x-2)$
(b) $(x-1)(x-2)(x-3)$
(c) $(x^2+5)(x^3-1)$
(d) $(x^2-1)/(x^2+1)$

Show that $L(1/f)=-L(f)$.

Supplementary Exercises

SUBSTITUTION

Find the following integrals.

1. $\displaystyle\int \frac{x^3}{x^4+2}\,dx$

2. $\displaystyle\int \sqrt{3x+1}\,dx$

3. $\displaystyle\int \sin^4 x \cos x\,dx$

4. $\displaystyle\int \frac{e^x-e^{-x}}{e^x+e^{-x}}\,dx$

5. $\displaystyle\int \frac{x}{\sqrt{x^2 - 1}}\, dx$

6. $\displaystyle\int x^3 \sqrt{x^4 + 1}\, dx$

7. $\displaystyle\int \frac{x}{(3x^2 + 5)^2}\, dx$

8. $\displaystyle\int (x^2 + 3)^4 x^3\, dx$

9. $\displaystyle\int \frac{\cos x}{\sin^3 x}\, dx$

10. $\displaystyle\int e^x \sqrt{e^x + 1}\, dx$

11. $\displaystyle\int (x^3 + 1)^{7/5} x^5\, dx$

12. $\displaystyle\int \frac{x}{(x^2 - 4)^{3/2}}\, dx$

13. $\displaystyle\int \sin 3x\, dx$

14. $\displaystyle\int \cos 4x\, dx$

15. $\displaystyle\int e^x \sin e^x\, dx$

16. $\displaystyle\int x^2 \sqrt{x^3 + 1}\, dx$

17. $\displaystyle\int \frac{1}{x \log x}\, dx$

18. $\displaystyle\int \frac{\sin x}{1 + \cos^2 x}\, dx$

19. $\displaystyle\int \frac{e^x}{e^x + 1}\, dx$

20. $\displaystyle\int \frac{(\log x)^4}{x}\, dx$

Find the following definite integrals.

21. $\displaystyle\int_0^{\pi/2} \sin^3 x \cos x\, dx$

22. $\displaystyle\int_{-3}^{-1} \frac{1}{(x - 1)^2}\, dx$

23. $\displaystyle\int_0^1 \sqrt{2 - x}\, dx$

24. $\displaystyle\int_0^{\pi} \sin^2 x \cos x\, dx$

25. $\displaystyle\int_0^{\pi/2} \frac{\cos x}{1 + \sin^2 x}\, dx$

26. $\displaystyle\int_0^{2\pi} \frac{\sin x}{1 + \cos^2 x}\, dx$

27. $\displaystyle\int_0^{1/2} \frac{\arcsin x}{\sqrt{1 - x^2}}\, dx$

28. $\displaystyle\int_0^1 \frac{\arctan x}{1 + x^2}\, dx$

29. $\displaystyle\int_0^1 \frac{1 + e^{2x}}{e^x}\, dx$

30. $\displaystyle\int_0^{\pi/2} x \sin x^2\, dx$

31. $\displaystyle\int x e^{-\sqrt{x}}\, dx$

32. $\displaystyle\int \sqrt{x}\, e^{-\sqrt{x}}\, dx$

BY PARTS

Find the following integrals.

1. $\displaystyle\int x \arctan x\, dx$

2. $\displaystyle\int x \arcsin x\, dx$

3. $\displaystyle\int x \arccos x\, dx$

4. $\displaystyle\int x^3 e^{2x}\, dx$

5. $\displaystyle\int_{-1}^{0} \arcsin x\, dx$

6. $\displaystyle\int_{1}^{2} x^3 \log x\, dx$

7. $\displaystyle\int_{0}^{1/2} x \arcsin 2x\, dx$

8. $\displaystyle\int_{1}^{2} \sqrt{x} \log x\, dx$

9. $\displaystyle\int_{-1}^{1} x e^x\, dx$

10. $\displaystyle\int_{0}^{1} x^3 \sqrt{1 - x^2}\, dx$

TRIGONOMETRIC INTEGRALS

Find the following integrals.

1. $\displaystyle\int \frac{\cos^3 x}{\sin x}\, dx$

2. $\displaystyle\int \tan^2 x\, dx$

3. $\displaystyle\int e^x \sin e^x\, dx$

4. $\displaystyle\int \frac{1}{1 - \cos x}\, dx$

5. $\displaystyle\int_{0}^{\pi/2} \cos^2 x\, dx$

6. $\displaystyle\int_{0}^{\pi/3} \sin^6 x\, dx$

7. $\displaystyle\int_{-\pi}^{\pi} \sin^2 x \cos^2 x\, dx$

8. $\displaystyle\int_{0}^{2\pi} \sin^3 2x\, dx$

9. $\displaystyle\int_{0}^{\pi/2} \sin^2 2x \cos^2 2x\, dx$

10. $\displaystyle\int_{0}^{\pi/4} \cos^4 x\, dx$

11. $\displaystyle\int \frac{1}{x\sqrt{x^2 + 9}}\, dx$

12. $\displaystyle\int \frac{1}{(x^2 + 1)^2}\, dx$

13. $\displaystyle\int_{0}^{1} \frac{1}{\sqrt{1 - x^2}}\, dx$

14. $\displaystyle\int \frac{x^2}{\sqrt{x^2 + 4}}\, dx$

15. $\displaystyle\int \frac{x^3}{\sqrt{16 - x^2}}$

16. $\displaystyle\int \frac{x^3}{\sqrt{1 + x^2}}$

17. $\displaystyle\int \frac{1}{x\sqrt{a^2 - x^2}}\, dx$

18. $\displaystyle\int \frac{x^2}{\sqrt{a^2 - x^2}}\, dx$

19. $\displaystyle\int \frac{1}{x\sqrt{a^2 - x^2}}\, dx$

20. $\displaystyle\int \frac{1}{x^2\sqrt{a^2 - x^2}}\, dx$

21. $\displaystyle\int \frac{1}{(1 + x^2)^{3/2}}\, dx$

22. $\displaystyle\int \frac{\sqrt{a^2 - x^2}}{x^2}\, dx$

23. $\displaystyle\int \frac{x^2}{(a^2 - x^2)^{3/2}}\, dx$

24. $\displaystyle\int \frac{\sqrt{a^2 + x^2}}{x}\, dx$

25. $\displaystyle\int_{0}^{4} \frac{1}{(16 + x^2)^2}\, dx$

26. $\displaystyle\int_{0}^{a} x^4 \sqrt{a^2 - x^2}\, dx \quad (a > 0)$

MISCELLANEOUS

1. Show that for positive integers m, n we have

$$\int x^m (\log x)^n \, dx = \frac{x^{m+1}(\log x)^n}{m+1} - \frac{n}{m+1} \int x^m (\log x)^{n-1} \, dx.$$

6. Show by induction that

$$\int x^n e^x \, dx = x^n e^x - n \int x^{n-1} e^x \, dx.$$

3. Show that the improper integral

$$\int_0^1 \log x \, dx$$

exists and find its value.

4. By induction, find the value

$$\int_0^\infty x^n e^{-x} \, dx.$$

5. Evaluate

$$\int_0^\infty x^3 e^{-x^2} \, dx.$$

6. Show by induction that

$$\int_0^1 (1 - x^2)^n \, dx = \frac{2^{2n}(n!)^2}{(2n+1)!}.$$

7. Show that

$$\int_0^1 (1 - x^2)^n \, dx \geq \frac{1}{n+1}.$$

[*Hint:* Note that $1 - x^2 = (1 + x)(1 - x) \geq 1 - x$ if $0 \leq x \leq 1$.]

8. Let f be continuous on $[0, 1]$. Let

$$f_1(x) = \int_0^x f(t) \, dt$$

$$f_2(x) = \int_0^x f_1(t) \, dt$$

and in general,

$$f_n(x) = \int_0^x f_{n-1}(t) \, dt.$$

Show that

$$f_n(x) = \frac{1}{(n-1)!} \int_0^x f(t)(x - t)^{n-1} \, dt.$$

[*Note:* There are two possible choices for $u \, dv$, and one of them won't get you anywhere.]

9. A function f defined for all numbers is said to be *periodic* of period s if $f(x + s) = f(x)$ for all x. Assume that f is continuous and periodic. Show that

$$\int_a^b f = \int_{a+s}^{b+s} f \quad \text{and} \quad \int_a^{a+s} f = \int_0^s f.$$

10. Assume that $f(-x) = -f(x)$. Show that

$$\int_{-a}^a f(x)\, dx = 0.$$

11. Find the value of the integrals (a) $\int_0^{7\pi} |\sin x|\, dx$ (b) $\int_0^{7\pi} |\cos x|\, dx$. (c) For any positive integer n, $\int_0^{n\pi} |\sin x|\, dx$.

Chapter XII

Some Substantial Exercises

We shall not use the contents of this section until the chapter on series, and even then we use only the estimate of $(n!)^{1/n}$. Thus this chapter may be skipped entirely. We include it mostly for reference, and to provide some good exercises for those interested.

§1. AN ESTIMATE FOR $(n!)^{1/n}$

Let n be a positive integer. We define $n!$ (which we read n factorial) to be the product of the first n integers: Thus $1 \cdot 2 \cdot 3 \cdots n$. This is certainly less than n^n (the product of n with itself n times). We shall investigate to what extent it differs from n^n. (Not too much.)

In fact, what we shall prove first is that

$$n! = n^n e^{-n} d_n,$$

where d_n is a number such that $d_n^{1/n}$ approaches 1 as n becomes large. This is a weaker statement than the result stated in the next theorem, whose proof is very simple and very easy to remember. It is a nice application of the lower and upper sum techniques.

Theorem 1. *Let n be a positive integer. Then*

$$(n - 1)! \leqq n^n e^{-n} e \leqq n!$$

Proof. Exercise. Evaluate and compare the integral

$$\int_1^n \log x \, dx$$

with the upper and lower sum associated with the partition $(1, 2, \ldots, n)$ of the interval $[1, n]$. Then exponentiate.

Corollary. *As n becomes very large,*

$$\frac{(n!)^{1/n}}{n} = \left[\frac{n!}{n^n}\right]^{1/n}$$

approaches $1/e$.

Proof. Take the n-th root of the right inequality in our theorem. We get

$$ne^{-1}e^{1/n} \leqq (n!)^{1/n}.$$

Dividing by n yields

$$\frac{1}{e} e^{1/n} \leqq \frac{(n!)^{1/n}}{n}.$$

On the other hand, multiply both sides of the inequality

$$(n-1)! \leqq n^n e^{-n} e$$

by n. We get $n! \leqq n^n e^{-n} en$. Take an n-th root:

$$(n!)^{1/n} \leqq n e^{-1} e^{1/n} n^{1/n}.$$

Dividing by n yields

$$\frac{(n!)^{1/n}}{n} \leqq \frac{1}{e} e^{1/n} n^{1/n}.$$

But we know that both $n^{1/n}$ and $e^{1/n}$ approach 1 as n becomes large. Thus our quotient is squeezed between two numbers approaching $1/e$, and must therefore approach $1/e$.

EXERCISES

1. Use the abbreviation $\lim\limits_{n\to\infty}$ to mean: limit as n becomes very large. Prove that

    (a) $\lim\limits_{n\to\infty} \left[\dfrac{(3n)!}{n^{3n}} \right]^{1/n} = \dfrac{27}{e^3}$ (b) $\lim\limits_{n\to\infty} \left[\dfrac{(3n)!}{n! n^{2n}} \right]^{1/n} = \dfrac{27}{e^2}$

2. Find the limit:

    (a) $\lim\limits_{n\to\infty} \left[\dfrac{(2n)!}{n^{2n}} \right]^{1/n}$ (b) $\lim\limits_{n\to\infty} \left[\dfrac{(2n)!(5n)!}{n^{4n}(3n)!} \right]^{1/n}$

§2. STIRLING'S FORMULA

Using various refinements of the above method, one can prove the following theorem.

Theorem 2. *Let n be a positive integer. Then there is a number* θ *between* 0 *and* 1 *such that*

$$n! = \sqrt{2\pi n}\, n^n e^{-n} e^{\theta/12n}.$$

We shall present another proof giving the main steps, and leave the details to you as exercises.

1. Let $\varphi(x) = \frac{1}{2} \log \dfrac{1+x}{1-x} - x$. Show that

$$\varphi'(x) = \frac{x^2}{1-x^2}.$$

2. Let $\psi(x) = \varphi(x) - \dfrac{x^3}{3(1 - x^2)}$. Show that

$$\psi'(x) = \frac{-2x^4}{3(1 - x^2)^2}.$$

3. For $0 < x < 1$, conclude that $\varphi(x) > 0$ and $\psi(x) < 0$.

4. Deduce that for $0 \leq x < 1$ we have

$$0 \leq \tfrac{1}{2} \log \frac{1 + x}{1 - x} - x \leq \frac{x^3}{3(1 - x^2)}.$$

5. Let $x = \dfrac{1}{2n + 1}$. Then $\dfrac{1 + x}{1 - x} = \dfrac{n + 1}{n}$ and

$$\frac{x^3}{3(1 - x^2)} = \frac{1}{12(2n + 1)(n^2 + n)}.$$

6. Conclude that

$$0 \leq \tfrac{1}{2} \log \frac{n + 1}{n} - \frac{1}{2n + 1} \leq \frac{1}{12(2n + 1)(n^2 + n)}$$

$$0 \leq (n + \tfrac{1}{2}) \log \frac{n + 1}{n} - 1 \leq \frac{1}{12} \left(\frac{1}{n} - \frac{1}{n + 1} \right).$$

7. Let

$$a_n = \frac{n^{n+\frac{1}{2}} e^{-n}}{n!} \qquad \text{and} \qquad b_n = a_n e^{1/12n}.$$

Then $a_n \leq b_n$. Show that

$$\frac{a_{n+1}}{a_n} \geq 1 \qquad \text{and} \qquad \frac{b_{n+1}}{b_n} \leq 1.$$

Thus the a_n are increasing and the b_n are decreasing. Hence there exists a unique number c such that

$$a_n \leq c \leq b_n$$

for all n.

8. Conclude that

$$n! = c^{-1} n^{n+\frac{1}{2}} e^{-n} e^{\theta/12n}$$

for some number θ between 0 and 1.

To get the value of the constant c, one has to use another argument, which will be described in the next section.

§3. WALLIS' PRODUCT

Our first aim is to obtain the following limit, known as the Wallis product.

Theorem 3. *We have*

$$\frac{\pi}{2} = \lim_{n \to \infty} \frac{2}{1} \frac{2}{3} \frac{4}{3} \frac{4}{5} \frac{6}{5} \frac{6}{7} \cdots \frac{2n}{2n-1} \frac{2n}{2n+1}.$$

Proof. The proof will again be presented as an exercise.

1. Using the recurrence formulas for the integrals of powers of the sine, prove that

$$\int_0^{\pi/2} \sin^{2n} x \, dx = \frac{2n-1}{2n} \frac{2n-3}{2n-2} \cdots \frac{1}{2} \frac{\pi}{2}$$

$$\int_0^{\pi/2} \sin^{2n+1} x \, dx = \frac{2n}{2n+1} \frac{2n-2}{2n-1} \cdots \frac{2}{3}.$$

2. Using the fact that powers of the sine are decreasing as $n = 1, 2, 3, \ldots$ and the first integral formula above, conclude that

$$1 \leq \frac{\int_0^{\pi/2} \sin^{2n-1} x \, dx}{\int_0^{\pi/2} \sin^{2n+1} x \, dx} \leq 1 + \frac{1}{2n}.$$

3. Taking the ratio of the integrals of $\sin^{2n} x$ and $\sin^{2n+1} x$ between 0 and $\pi/2$, deduce Wallis' product.

Corollary. *We have*

$$\lim_{n \to \infty} \frac{(n!)^2 2^{2n}}{(2n)! n^{1/2}} = \pi^{1/2}.$$

Proof. Rewrite the Wallis product into the form

$$\frac{\pi}{2} = \lim_{n \to \infty} \frac{2^2 4^2 \cdots (2n-2)^2}{3^2 5^2 \cdots (2n-1)^2} 2n.$$

Take the square root and find the limit stated in the corollary.

Finally, show that the constant c in Stirling's formula is $1/\sqrt{2\pi}$, by arguing as follows. (Justify all the steps.)

$$c = \lim_{n \to \infty} \frac{(2n)^{2n+\frac{1}{2}} e^{-2n}}{(2n)!}$$

$$= \lim_{n \to \infty} \frac{(n!)^2 2^{2n} \sqrt{2}}{(2n)! n^{1/2}} \left[\frac{n^{n+\frac{1}{2}} e^{-n}}{n!} \right]^2$$

$$= \sqrt{2\pi} \cdot c^2.$$

Thus $c = 1/\sqrt{2\pi}$.

Chapter XIII

Applications of Integration

Most of the applications are to physical concepts. The reader should read the appendix on physics and mathematics, to understand the point of view that what we try to find is a mathematical model for a given empirical notion. We shall do this in a number of cases for which the integral can be taken as a model. We shall use both the relation of the integral to Riemann sums, and its axiomatic characterization in Theorem 2 of Chapter IX, §4 to justify the interpretation of the integral in various physical contexts.

§1. LENGTH OF CURVES

Let $y = f(x)$ be a differentiable function over some interval $[a, b]$ (with $a < b$) and assume that its derivative f' is continuous. We wish to find a way to determine the length of the curve described by the graph. The main idea is to approximate the curve by small line segments and add these up.

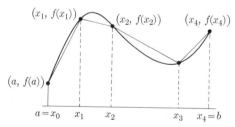

Consequently, we consider a partition of our interval:

$$a = x_0 \leqq x_1 \leqq \cdots \leqq x_n = b.$$

For each x_i we have the point $(x_i, f(x_i))$ on the curve $y = f(x)$. We draw the line segments between two successive points. The length of such a segment is the length of the line between

$$(x_i, f(x_i)) \quad \text{and} \quad (x_{i+1}, f(x_{i+1})),$$

and is equal to

$$\sqrt{(x_{i+1} - x_i)^2 + (f(x_{i+1}) - f(x_i))^2}.$$

223

By the mean value theorem, we conclude that

$$f(x_{i+1}) - f(x_i) = (x_{i+1} - x_i)f'(c_i)$$

for some number c_i between x_i and x_{i+1}. Using this, we see that the length of our line segment is

$$\sqrt{(x_{i+1} - x_i)^2 + (x_{i+1} - x_i)^2 f'(c_i)^2}.$$

We can factor out $(x_{i+1} - x_i)^2$ and we see that the sum of the length of these line segments is

$$\sum_{i=0}^{n-1} \sqrt{1 + f'(c_i)^2}\, (x_{i+1} - x_i).$$

Let $G(x) = \sqrt{1 + f'(x)^2}$. Then $G(x)$ is continuous, and we see that the sum we have just written down is

$$\sum_{i=0}^{n-1} G(c_i)(x_{i+1} - x_i).$$

This is precisely a Riemann sum used to find the integral. It is therefore very reasonable to *define* the length of our curve between a and b to be

$$\int_a^b \sqrt{1 + f'(t)^2}\, dt.$$

Parametric Form

We shall now see what happens when the curve is given in parametric form.

Suppose that our curve is given by

$$x = f(t), \qquad y = g(t),$$

with $a \leqq t \leqq b$, and assume that both f, g have continuous derivatives.

As before, we cut our interval into a partition, say

$$a = t_0 \leqq t_1 \leqq \cdots \leqq t_n = b.$$

We then obtain points $(f(t_i), g(t_i))$ on the curve, and the distance between two successive points is

$$\sqrt{(f(t_{i+1}) - f(t_i))^2 + (g(t_{i+1}) - g(t_i))^2}.$$

We use the mean value theorem for f and g. There are numbers c_i and d_i between t_i and t_{i+1} such that

$$f(t_{i+1}) - f(t_i) = f'(c_i)(t_{i+1} - t_i)$$
$$g(t_{i+1}) - g(t_i) = g'(d_i)(t_{i+1} - t_i).$$

Substituting these values and factoring out $(t_{i+1} - t_i)$, we see that the sum of the lengths of our line segments is equal to

$$\sum_{i=0}^{n-1} \sqrt{f'(c_i)^2 + g'(d_i)^2}\, (t_{i+1} - t_i).$$

Let

$$G(t) = \sqrt{f'(t)^2 + g'(t)^2}.$$

Then our sum is almost equal to

$$\sum_{i=0}^{n-1} G(c_i)(t_{i+1} - t_i),$$

which would be a Riemann sum for G. It is not, because it is not necessarily true that $c_i = d_i$. Nevertheless, what we have done makes it very reasonable to *define* the length of our curve (in parametric form) to be

$$\boxed{\int_a^b \sqrt{f'(t)^2 + g'(t)^2}\, dt.}$$

(A complete justification that this integral is a limit, in a suitable sense, of our sums would require some additional theory, which is irrelevant anyway since we just want to make it reasonable that the above integral should represent what we mean physically by length.)

Observe that when $y = f(x)$ we can let $t = x = g(t)$ and $y = f(t)$. In that case, $g'(t) = 1$ and the formula for the length in parametric form is seen to be the same as the formula we obtained before for a curve $y = f(x)$.

Example. Find the length of the curve

$$x = \cos t, \qquad y = \sin t$$

between $t = 0$ and $t = \pi$.

The length is the integral

$$\int_0^\pi \sqrt{(-\sin t)^2 + (\cos t)^2}\, dt.$$

In view of the relation $(-\sin t)^2 = (\sin t)^2$ and a basic formula relating sine and cosine, we get

$$\int_0^\pi dt = \pi.$$

If we integrated between 0 and 2π we would get 2π. This is the length of the circle of radius 1.

Remark. We can also obtain the length of a curve by the axioms for the integral. If $f(t)$ and $g(t)$ are the coordinate functions of a curve given parametrically, i.e.

$$C(t) = (f(t), g(t)),$$

we view $C(t)$ as a point in the plane. We define the derivative

$$C'(t) = (f'(t), g'(t)),$$

differentiating componentwise. Then $C'(t)$ is interpreted as the velocity of the curve, and

$$v(t) = \sqrt{f'(t)^2 + g'(t)^2}$$

is interpreted as the speed of the curve. The length of a curve depends on its speed, and in fact: If the speed is constant, say M, over an interval of time $[a, b]$, then the length should be $M(b - a)$. Furthermore, if one curve has a greater speed than another, then its length should be greater. In particular, if

$$m \le v(t) \le M$$

for two constants $M, m \ge 0$, and if we denote the length of the curve between a and b by $L_a^b(v)$, then

$$m(b - a) \le L_a^b(v) \le M(b - a).$$

Finally, the length of the curve should satisfy

$$L_a^c(v) = L_a^b(v) + L_b^c(v).$$

Thus, from the axioms for the integral given in Chapter IX, §4, there is only one way to define the length compatible with these properties, and that is

$$\int_a^b \sqrt{f'(t)^2 + g'(t)^2}\, dt$$

as we have done above.

Polar Coordinates

Let us now find a formula for the length of curves given in polar coordinates. Say the curve is

$$r = f(\theta),$$

with $\theta_1 \le \theta \le \theta_2$. We know that

$$x = r \cos \theta = f(\theta) \cos \theta$$

$$y = r \sin \theta = f(\theta) \sin \theta.$$

This puts the curve in parametric form, just as in the preceding considerations. Consequently we can apply the definition as before, and we see that the length is

$$\int_{\theta_1}^{\theta_2} \sqrt{\left(\frac{dx}{d\theta}\right)^2 + \left(\frac{dy}{d\theta}\right)^2}\, d\theta.$$

You can compute $dx/d\theta$ and $dy/d\theta$ using the rule for the derivative of a product. If you do this, you will find that many terms cancel, and that the integral is equal to

$$\int_{\theta_1}^{\theta_2} \sqrt{f(\theta)^2 + f'(\theta)^2}\, d\theta.$$

(The computation is very easy, and is good practice in simple identities involving sine and cosine. We leave it to you as an exercise. Anyhow, working it out will make you remember the formula better.)

EXERCISES

1. Carry out the preceding computation.
2. Find the length of a circle of radius r.
3. Find the length of the curve $x = e^t \cos t$, $y = e^t \sin t$ between $t = 1$ and $t = 2$.
4. Find the length of the curve $x = \cos^3 t$, $y = \sin^3 t$ (a) between $t = 0$ and $t = \pi/4$, and (b) between $t = 0$ and $t = \pi$.

Find the lengths of the following curves:

5. $y = e^x$ between $x = 0$ and $x = 1$.
6. $y = x^{3/2}$ between $x = 1$ and $x = 3$.
7. $y = \frac{1}{2}(e^x + e^{-x})$ between $x = -1$ and $x = 1$.
8. Find the length of one loop of the curve $r = 1 + \cos \theta$ (polar coordinates).
9. Same, with $r = \cos \theta$, between $-\pi/2$ and $\pi/2$.
10. Find the length of the curve $r = 2/\cos \theta$ between $\theta = 0$ and $\theta = \pi/3$.
11. Find the length of the curve $r = |\sin \theta|$ from $\theta = 0$ to $\theta = 2\pi$.
12. Sketch the curve $r = e^\theta$ (in polar coordinates), and also the curve $r = e^{-\theta}$.
13. Find the length of the curve $r = e^\theta$ between $\theta = 1$ and $\theta = 2$.
14. In general, give the length of the curve $r = e^\theta$ between two values θ_1 and θ_2.

§2. AREA IN POLAR COORDINATES

Suppose we are given a continuous function

$$r = f(\theta)$$

which is defined in some interval $a \leq \theta \leq b$. We assume that $f(\theta) \geq 0$ and $b \leq a + 2\pi$.

We wish to find an integral expression for the area encompassed by the curve $r = f(\theta)$ between the two bounds a and b.

Let us take a partition of $[a, b]$, say

$$a = \theta_0 \leqq \theta_1 \leqq \cdots \leqq \theta_n = b.$$

The picture between θ_i and θ_{i+1} might look like this:

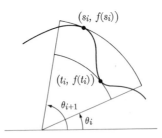

We let s_i be a number between θ_i and θ_{i+1} such that $f(s_i)$ is a maximum in that interval, and we let t_i be a number such that $f(t_i)$ is a minimum in that interval. In the picture, we have drawn the circles (or rather the sectors) of radius $f(s_i)$ and $f(t_i)$, respectively.

Then the area between θ_i, θ_{i+1} and the curve lies between the two sectors. Denote it by A_i. The area of a sector having angle $\theta_{i+1} - \theta_i$ and radius R is equal to the fraction

$$\frac{\theta_{i+1} - \theta_i}{2\pi}$$

of the total area of the circle of radius R, namely πR^2. Hence we get the inequality

$$\frac{\theta_{i+1} - \theta_i}{2\pi} \pi f(t_i)^2 \leqq A_i \leqq \frac{\theta_{i+1} - \theta_i}{2\pi} \pi f(s_i)^2.$$

Let $G(\theta) = \frac{1}{2} f(\theta)^2$. We see that the sum of the small pieces of area A_i satisfies the inequalities

$$\sum_{i=0}^{n-1} G(t_i)(\theta_{i+1} - \theta_i) \leqq \sum_{i=0}^{n-1} A_i \leqq \sum_{i=0}^{n-1} G(s_i)(\theta_{i+1} - \theta_i).$$

Thus the desired area lies between the upper sum and lower sum associated with the partition. Thus it is reasonable to define the *area* to be

$$\int_{\theta_1}^{\theta_2} \tfrac{1}{2} f(\theta)^2 \, d\theta.$$

Example. Find the area bounded by one loop of the curve

$$r^2 = 2a^2 \cos 2\theta \qquad (a > 0).$$

Between $-\dfrac{\pi}{4}$ and $\dfrac{\pi}{4}$ the cosine is ≥ 0. Thus we can write

$$r = \sqrt{2}\, a \sqrt{\cos 2\theta}.$$

The area is therefore

$$\int_{-\pi/4}^{\pi/4} \tfrac{1}{2} 2a^2 \cos 2\theta \, d\theta = a^2.$$

EXERCISES

Find the area enclosed by the following curves:

1. $r = 2(1 + \cos\theta)$
2. $r^2 = a^2 \sin 2\theta$ $(a > 0)$
3. $r = 2a \cos\theta$
4. $r = \cos 3\theta, \; -\pi/6 \leq \theta \leq \pi/6$
5. $r = 1 + \sin\theta$
6. $r = 1 + \sin 2\theta$
7. $r = 2 + \cos\theta$
8. $r = 2 \cos 3\theta, \; -\pi/6 \leq \theta \leq \pi/6$

§3. VOLUMES OF REVOLUTION

Let $y = f(x)$ be a continuous function of x on some interval $a \leq x \leq b$. Assume that $f(x) \geq 0$ in this interval. If we revolve the curve $y = f(x)$ around the x-axis, we obtain a solid, whose volume we wish to compute.

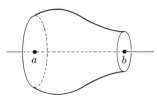

Take a partition of $[a, b]$, say

$$a = x_0 \leq x_1 \leq \cdots \leq x_n = b.$$

Let c_i be a minimum of f in the interval $[x_i, x_{i+1}]$ and let d_i be a maximum of f in that interval. Then the solid of revolution in that small interval lies between a small cylinder and a big cylinder. The width of these cylinders is $x_{i+1} - x_i$ and the radius is $f(c_i)$ for the small cylinder and $f(d_i)$ for the big one. Hence the volume of revolution, denoted by V, satisfies the inequalities

$$\sum_{i=0}^{n-1} \pi f(c_i)^2 (x_{i+1} - x_i) \leq V \leq \sum_{i=0}^{n-1} \pi f(d_i)^2 (x_{i+1} - x_i).$$

It is therefore reasonable to define this volume to be

$$\int_a^b \pi f(x)^2 \, dx.$$

Example. Compute the volume of the sphere of radius 1.

We take the function $y = \sqrt{1 - x^2}$ between 0 and 1. If we rotate this curve around the x-axis, we shall get half the sphere. Its volume is therefore

$$\int_0^1 \pi(1 - x^2)\, dx = \tfrac{2}{3}\pi.$$

The volume of the full sphere is therefore $\tfrac{4}{3}\pi$.

One can also motivate the definition of the volume of revolution by the axioms for the integral given in Chapter IX, §4. One does this by considering the revolution of a rectangle, i.e. considering the case where f is constant, say M. Then one obtains the volume of a cylinder:

and this volume should be equal to $\pi M^2(b - a)$. Using the two properties of the integral which characterize it, we find once again that the volume should be given by the integral

$$\int_a^b \pi f(x)^2\, dx$$

which we wrote previously.

EXERCISES

1. Find the volume of a sphere of radius r.

Find the volumes of revolution of the following:

2. $y = 1/\cos x$ between $x = 0$ and $x = \pi/4$

3. $y = \sin x$ between $x = 0$ and $x = \pi/4$

4. $y = \cos x$ between $x = 0$ and $x = \pi/4$

5. The region between $y = x^2$ and $y = 5x$

6. $y = xe^{x/2}$ between $x = 0$ and $x = 1$

7. $y = x^{1/2}e^{x/2}$ between $x = 1$ and $x = 2$

8. $y = \log x$ between $x = 1$ and $x = 2$

9. $y = \sqrt{1 + x}$ between $x = 1$ and $x = 5$

10. (a) Let B be a number > 1. What is the volume of revolution of the curve $y = e^{-x}$ between 1 and B? Does this volume approach a limit as B becomes large? If so, what limit?
    (b) Same question for the curve $y = e^{-2x}$.
    (c) Same question for the curve $y = xe^{-x^2}$.

11. Find the volume of a cone whose base has radius r, and of height h, by rotating a straight line passing through the origin around the x-axis.

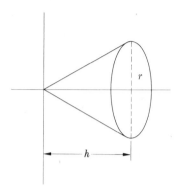

§4. WORK

Suppose a particle moves on a curve, and that the length of the curve is described by a variable u.

Let $f(u)$ be a function. We interpret f as a force acting on the particle, in the direction of the curve. We want to find an integral expression for the work done by the force between two points on the curve.

Whatever our expression will turn out to be, it is reasonable that the work done should satisfy the following properties:

If a, b, c are three numbers, with $a \leqq b \leqq c$, then the work done between a and c is equal to the work done between a and b, plus the work done between b and c. If we denote the work done between a and b by $W_a^b(f)$, then we should have

$$W_a^c(f) = W_a^b(f) + W_b^c(f).$$

Furthermore, if we have a constant force M acting on the particle, it is reasonable to expect that the work done between a and b is

$$M(b - a).$$

Finally, if g is a stronger force than f, say $f(u) \leqq g(u)$, on the interval $[a, b]$, then we shall do more work with g than with f, meaning

$$W_a^b(f) \leqq W_a^b(g).$$

In particular, if there are two constant forces m and M such that

$$m \leqq f(u) \leqq M$$

throughout the interval $[a, b]$, then

$$m(b - a) \leqq W_a^b(f) \leqq M(b - a).$$

But this condition, together with the first one expressed above, determines the integral uniquely! Hence there is only one reasonable way to associate a mathematical formula with work, compatible with physical requirements, and that is: The work done by the force f between a distance a and a distance b is

$$\int_a^b f(u)\, du.$$

If the particle or object happens to move along a straight line, say along the x-axis, then f is given as a function of x, and our integral is simply

$$\int_a^b f(x)\, dx.$$

Furthermore, if the length of the curve u is given as a function of time t (as it is in practice, cf. §1) we see that the force becomes a function of t by the chain rule, namely $f(u(t))$. Thus between time t_1 and t_2 the work done is equal to

$$\int_{t_1}^{t_2} f(u(t)) \frac{du}{dt}\, dt.$$

This is the most practical expression for the work, since curves and forces are most frequently expressed as functions of time.

Example. Find the work done in stretching a spring from its unstretched position to a length of 10 cm. You may assume that the force needed to stretch the spring is proportional to the increase in length.

We visualize the spring as being horizontal, on the x-axis. Thus there is a constant K such that the force is given by

$$f(x) = Kx.$$

The work done is therefore

$$\int_0^{10} Kx\, dx = \tfrac{1}{2}K(100)$$
$$= 50K.$$

§5. DENSITY AND MASS

Consider an interval $[a, b]$ with $0 \leqq a < b$. We think first of this interval as a rod, and let f be a continuous positive function defined on this interval. We interpret f as a density on the rod, so that $f(x)$ is the density at x. Given $a \leqq c \leqq d \leqq b$, we denote by $M_c^d(f)$ the mass of the rod between c and d, corresponding to the given density f. We wish to determine a mathematical notion to represent $M_c^d(f)$. If f is a constant density, with constant value $K \geqq 0$ on $[c, d]$, then the mass $M_c^d(f)$ should be $K(d - c)$. On the other hand, if g is another density such that

$$f(x) \leq g(x),$$

then certainly we should have $M_c^d(f) \leq M_c^d(g)$. In particular, if k, K are constants ≥ 0 such that

$$k \leq f(x) \leq K$$

for x in the interval $[c, d]$, then the mass should satisfy

$$k(d - c) \leq M_c^d(f) \leq K(d - c).$$

Finally, the mass should be additive, that is the mass of two disjoint pieces should be the sum of the mass of the pieces. In particular,

$$M_a^c(f) + M_c^d(f) = M_a^d(f).$$

We know from the basic properties of the integral that there is one and only one way to associate a number $M_c^d(f)$ to the density f compatible with the preceding requirements, and that is the integral, so that the mass is given by the integral:

$$M_a^b(f) = \int_a^b f.$$

§6. PROBABILITY

We have a very similar situation with probability densities. We are given an interval $[a, b]$ and a continuous function f, which we interpret as a probability density on this interval. We consider a function f such that $f(x) \geq 0$ for all x in the interval and in addition assume that

$$\int_a^b f(x)\, dx = 1.$$

Such a function is called a *probability density* over the interval. We have a certain intuitive notion $P_c^d(f)$, which we think of as the probability that certain objects will fall within the interval $[c, d]$, given the probability density f. For instance, we may be shooting some particles along a slit above the interval, and we want a mathematical notion corresponding to the probability that a particle will fall in this interval $[c, d]$.

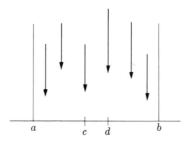

If we have a constant probability density over $[c, d]$, say K, then we want $P_c^d(K)$ to be a constant multiple of $K(d - c)$. In the special case where $K = 1/(b - a)$, we interpret this density as a uniform average density over the interval, and we wish its probability over $[c, d]$ to be the ratio $(d - c)/(b - a)$. From this we see that it is reasonable to require that in fact, $P_c^d(K) = K(d - c)$. Furthermore, if g is another probability density which is smaller than f, that is $g(x) \leq f(x)$ for all x, then we must have $P_c^d(g) \leq P_c^d(f)$. In particular, if k and K are two constants such that $k \leq f(x) \leq K$ for x in $[c, d]$, then

$$k(d - c) \leq P_c^d(f) \leq K(d - c).$$

Finally, the probability should be additive over disjoint intervals, so that in particular,

$$P_a^d(f) = P_a^c(f) + P_c^d(f).$$

We see that P_c^d satisfies the basic properties of the integral, and there is only one way to define probability compatible with these properties, that is

$$P_c^d(f) = \int_c^d f.$$

In particular,

$$P_a^b(f) = \int_a^b f.$$

Furthermore, under the present normalization, in order to have a probabilistic interpretation for $P_a^b(f)$, one must consider only those functions f such that

$$\int_a^b f = 1.$$

As a matter of terminology, we also say that $P_c^d(f)$ is the *probability that x lies within the interval* $[c, d]$.

Example 1. Consider a circle of radius 1 centered at the origin, and a needle which is given an initial push, rotates subject to friction, and comes to rest, pointing to some point of the circle as in the following diagram.

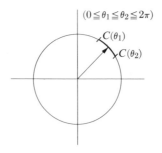

We want to know the probability that the point of the needle will lie in a given circular interval, as shown. We parametrize our circle in the usual way, letting $C(\theta) = (\cos\theta, \sin\theta)$ be a point of the circle, $0 \le \theta \le 2\pi$. The probability will of course depend on the probability density, which may be viewed as a function of θ. Assuming that this function is constant (which means that the needle is being slowed down by friction in a uniform way as it spins and no other force acts on it), let this constant be σ. Then we must have

$$1 = \int_0^{2\pi} \sigma \, d\theta = \sigma \int_0^{2\pi} d\theta = \sigma \cdot 2\pi.$$

Hence $\sigma = 1/2\pi$ is the constant probability density which can be taken as representing the physical situation under consideration. The probability that the needle comes to rest between $C(\theta_1)$ and $C(\theta_2)$ is then equal to $(\theta_2 - \theta_1)/2\pi$. Put another way, this is the probability that θ falls within the interval $[\theta_1, \theta_2]$.

Let us go back to the general case over the interval $[a, b]$. If F is an indefinite integral for f over the interval, then

$$\int_c^d f(x) \, dx = F(d) - F(c) \qquad \text{and} \qquad f(x) = F'(x).$$

The case when f is not constant may correspond empirically to a magnet on the interval, which varies in strength, and thus attracts more particles over certain regions than over others. Experimental data must then be used to determine the density function f, or its associated *probability function*, which we define to be the definite integral

$$F(x) = \int_a^x f(t) \, dt.$$

Example. A probability density on the interval $[-\pi, \pi]$ is given by the following conditions:

$$f(x) = 0 \qquad \text{if} \quad -\pi \le x \le -\pi/2$$
$$f(x) = a \cdot \cos x \qquad \text{if} \quad -\pi/2 \le x \le \pi/2$$
$$f(x) = 0 \qquad \text{if} \quad \pi/2 \le x \le \pi.$$

Here, a is some constant. Since we wish the probability associated with f over the whole interval to be equal to 1, we must have

$$a \int_{-\pi/2}^{\pi/2} \cos x \, dx = 1.$$

Integrating shows that $2a = 1$, so $a = 1/2$. If we let F be the probability function associated with f, so that

$$F(x) = \int_{-\pi/2}^{x} f(t)\, dt,$$

then a direct integration shows that

$$F(x) = \begin{cases} 0 & \text{if } -\pi \leq x \leq -\pi/2 \\ \dfrac{1 + \sin x}{2} & \text{if } -\pi/2 \leq x \leq \pi/2 \\ 2 & \text{if } \pi/2 \leq x \leq \pi. \end{cases}$$

The values between $-\pi/2$ and $\pi/2$ are given as the integral

$$F(x) = \tfrac{1}{2} \int_{-\pi/2}^{x} \cos t\, dt = \tfrac{1}{2} \sin t \Big|_{-\pi/2}^{x} = \tfrac{1}{2}(\sin x + 1).$$

The graphs of f and F look like this:

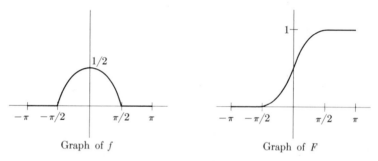

Graph of f Graph of F

In terms of the spinning needle, the probability density means that there is an increasingly vigorous attraction for the needle towards 0, and that the needle never comes to rest on the left side of the circle.

By definition, the probability that $0 \leq x \leq \pi/2$ is simply equal to the value

$$F(\pi/2) - F(0) = 1 - \tfrac{1}{2} = \tfrac{1}{2}.$$

EXERCISES

Each one of the following functions f represents a probability density over the interval $[0, 1]$. Determine the constant c, find the probability function F associated with f, and find the probability that $0 \leq x \leq 1/2$.

1. $f(x) = 1$ 2. $f(x) = cx$ 3. $f(x) = cx^4$
4. $f(x) = c \cdot \sin \pi x$ 5. $f(x) = c \cdot \sin^2 \pi x$
6. $f(x) = 3 - 2x$ 7. $f(x) = e - e^x$

Each one of the following functions f represents a probability density over the interval $[-\pi, \pi]$. In each case determine the constant c, find the probability function F associated with f, and find the probability that $0 \leq x \leq \pi/2$.

8. $f(x) = c|\cos x|$ 9. $f(x) = c|\sin x|$

10. $f(x) = c \cdot \cos^2 x$ 11. $f(x) = c \cdot \sin^2 x$

12. $f(x) = 0$ if $-\pi \leq x \leq 0$ and $f(x) = c(1 - \cos x)$ if $0 \leq x \leq \pi$.

§7. MOMENTS

We wish to describe the notion of "moment" (with respect to the origin), which arises in physics. "Moment" should have the following properties.

Suppose that we have a mass K concentrated at a point b on the x-axis. Then its moment is Kb.

Suppose that we have an interval $[a, b]$, with $a < b$ (which may be interpreted as a rod), and a constant density distribution C over the interval. Then the total mass is $C(b - a)$. The moment of our constant distribution, which we denote by M, should then satisfy the inequalities

$$Ca(b - a) \leq M \leq Cb(b - a).$$

If we think of the total mass $K = C(b - a)$ as being concentrated at the point b, then the right inequality states that the moment of our constant distribution is less than or equal to the moment of a total mass K placed at the point b. The left inequality states that the moment of our constant distribution is greater than or equal to that of a total mass K placed at the point a. If we assume $0 \leq a < b$ then these two inequalities state that the moment should be larger, the farther our total mass is from the origin. We shall assume $0 \leq a < b$ throughout our discussion.

Suppose that we have a variable density distribution over our interval $[a, b]$. This means that our distribution is represented by a function $f(x)$ on the interval. Let us denote its "moment" by $M_a^b(f)$. The following two properties should then be satisfied.

Property 1. If f is continuous on the interval $[a, b]$ and if there are two constants C_1, C_2 both ≥ 0 such that

$$C_1 \leq f(x) \leq C_2$$

for all x in our interval, then the moment of f satisfies the inequalities

$$C_1 a(b - a) \leq M_a^b(f) \leq C_2 b(b - a).$$

(In other words, the moment of f should lie between the moments determined by the constant distributions C_1 and C_2.)

Property 2. If f is continuous on the interval $[a, c]$, with $a \leqq c$ and if b is a point such that $a \leqq b \leqq c$, then

$$M_a^c(f) = M_a^b(f) + M_b^c(f).$$

(In other words, the moment over the big interval is the sum of the moments over the first interval and the second interval.)

We shall now prove that there is one and only one way of obtaining a moment $M_a^b(f)$ satisfying the above two properties, and that is the integral

$$\int_a^b xf(x)\, dx.$$

To begin with, we note that the integral satisfies Property 2. This is an old result.

As to Property 1, assume that f lies between two constants C_1 and C_2 as above. For the interval $a \leqq x \leqq b$, we get

$$C_1 a \leqq xf(x) \leqq C_2 b,$$

and hence by Theorem 1 of Chapter XI, §3 we conclude that

$$C_1 a(b - a) \leqq \int_a^b xf(x)\, dx \leqq C_2 b(b - a).$$

Thus the integral certainly satisfies our two properties.

We shall now prove conversely that any $M_a^b(f)$ satisfying the two properties must be the integral written down above. This is done by our usual technique. We prove that the function $M_a^x(f)$ has a derivative, and that this derivative is $xf(x)$. Such a function must be the integral.

The Newton quotient is

$$\frac{M_a^{x+h}(f) - M_a^x(f)}{h}.$$

Using Property 2, we see that the Newton quotient is equal to

$$\frac{M_x^{x+h}(f)}{h}.$$

Let s be a maximum for f in the small interval between x and $x + h$ and let t be a minimum for f in that small interval. If, say, h is positive, then by Property 1 we conclude that

$$f(t)x(x + h - x) \leqq M_x^{x+h}(f) \leqq f(s)(x + h)(x + h - x),$$

or in other words that

$$f(t)xh \leqq M_x^{x+h}(f) \leqq f(s)(x + h)h.$$

Dividing by h yields

$$xf(t) \le \frac{M_x^{x+h}(f)}{h} \le (x + h)f(s).$$

As h approaches 0, both $f(t)$ and $f(s)$ approach $f(x)$ because s, t lie between x and $x + h$. The usual squeezing argument shows that the Newton quotient approaches $xf(x)$, as was to be shown. If h is negative, a similar argument can be applied as usual.

Consider now a density distribution on the interval $[a, b]$ represented by a continuous function f. We define the *total mass* (or simply *mass*) of this distribution over the interval to be the integral

$$\int_a^b f(x)\, dx.$$

Assume that $f(x) \ge 0$ for all x in the interval, and that $f(x) \ne 0$ for some point in the interval. Then the total mass is positive. We define the *center of gravity* of our distribution over the interval to be that point c such that the moment of our total mass concentrated at the point c is equal to the moment of f over the interval. This can be expressed by the relation

$$c \cdot \int_a^b f(x)\, dx = \int_a^b xf(x)\, dx.$$

In other words,

$$c = \frac{\int_a^b xf(x)\, dx}{\int_a^b f(x)\, dx}.$$

If you study physics, you will recognize this as being the usual formula giving the center of gravity.

Supplementary Exercises

LENGTH OF CURVES

Find the length of the following curves in the indicated interval.

1. $y = x^{3/2}, \quad 0 \le x \le 4$ 2. $y = \log x, \quad \frac{1}{2} \le x \le 2$

3. $y = \log x, \quad 1 \le x \le e^2$ 4. $y = 4 - x^2, \quad -2 \le x \le 2$

5. $x = 2t + 1, \quad y = t^2, \quad 0 \le t \le 2$

6. $x = 4 + 2t, \quad y = \frac{1}{2}t^2 + 3, \quad -2 \le t \le 2$

7. $x = 9t^2, \quad y = 9t^3 - 3t, \quad 0 \le t \le 1/\sqrt{3}$

8. $x = 3t, \quad y = t^3, \quad 0 \le t \le 1$

9. $y = \log (1 - x^2), \quad 0 \leq x \leq \frac{3}{4}$

10. $y = \frac{1}{2}(e^x + e^{-x}), \quad -1 \leq x \leq 0$

11. $y = \log \cos x, \quad 0 \leq x \leq \pi/3$

12. $x = 1 - \cos t, \quad y = t - \sin t, \quad 0 \leq t \leq 2\pi$

13. $x = a(1 - \cos t), \quad y = a(t - \sin t)$, with $a > 0$, and $0 \leq t \leq \pi$.

Find the length of the following curves given in polar coordinates.

14. $r = 3\theta^2$ from $\theta = 1$ to $\theta = 2$

15. $r = e^{-4\theta}$, from $\theta = 1$ to $\theta = 2$

16. $r = 3 \cos \theta$, from $\theta = 0$ to $\theta = \pi/4$

17. $r = 2/\theta$ from $\theta = \frac{1}{2}$ to $\theta = 4$

18. $r = 1 + \cos \theta$ from $\theta = 0$ to $\theta = \pi/4$

19. $r = 1 - \cos \theta$ from $\theta = 0$ to $\theta = \pi$

20. $r = \sin^2 \dfrac{\theta}{2}$ from $\theta = 0$ to $\theta = \pi$

AREA

Find the areas of the following regions, bounded by the curve given in polar coordinates.

1. $r = 10 \cos \theta$ 2. $r = 1 - \cos \theta$

3. $r = \sqrt{1 - \cos \theta}$ 4. $r = 2 + \sin 2\theta$

5. $r = \sin^2 \theta$ 6. $r = 1 - \sin \theta$

7. $r = 1 + 2 \sin \theta$ 8. $r = 1 + \sin 2\theta$

9. $r = \cos 3\theta$ 10. $r = 2 + \cos \theta$

Find the area between the following curves, given in rectangular coordinates.

11. $y = 4 - x^2, y = 0,$ between $x = -2$ and $x = 2$

12. $y = 4 - x^2, y = 8 - 2x^2,$ between $x = -2$ and $x = 2$

13. $y = x^3 + x^2, y = x^3 + 1,$ between $x = -1$ and $x = 1$

14. $y = x - x^2, y = -x,$ between $x = 0$ and $x = 2$

15. $y = x^2, y = x + 1,$ between the two points where the two curves intersect.

16. $y = x^3$ and $y = x + 6$ between $x = 0$ and the value of $x > 0$ where the two curves intersect.

VOLUMES OF REVOLUTION

1. Find the volume of a cone of height h and radius of the circular side r, by rotating a straight line passing through the origin around the x-axis.

Find the volumes of the solid obtained by rotating each region as indicated, around the x-axis.

2. $y = x^2$, between $y = 0$ and $x = 2$

3. $y = \dfrac{4}{x+1}$, $x = -5$, $x = -2$, $y = 0$

4. $y = \sqrt{x}$, the x-axis and $x = 2$

5. $y = 1/x$, $x = 1$, $x = 3$ and the x-axis

6. $y = \sqrt{x}$, $y = x^3$

7. The region bounded by the line $x + y = 1$ and the coordinate axes

8. The ellipse $a^2x^2 + b^2y^2 = a^2b^2$

9. $y = e^{-x}$, between $x = 1$ and $x = 5$

10. $y = \log x$, between $x = 1$ and $x = 2$

11. $y = \tan x$, $x = \pi/3$ and the x-axis

In the next problems, you are asked to find a volume of revolution of a region between certain bounds, and determine whether this volume approaches a limit when the bound B becomes very large. If it does, give this limit.

12. The region bounded by $1/x$, the x-axis, between $x = 1$ and $x = B$ for $B > 1$.

13. The region bounded by $1/x^2$ and the x-axis, between $x = 1$ and $x = B$ for $B > 1$.

14. The region bounded by $y = 1/\sqrt{x}$, the x-axis, between $x = 1$ and $x = B$ for $B > 1$.

In the next problems, find the volume of revolution, determined by bounds involving a number $a > 0$, and find whether this volume approaches a limit as a approaches 0. If it does, state what limit.

15. The region bounded by $y = 1/\sqrt{x}$, the x-axis, between $x = a$ and $x = 1$ for $0 < a < 1$.

16. The region bounded by $y = 1/x$, the x-axis, between $x = a$ and $x = 1$, with $0 < a < 1$.

17. The region bounded by $(\cos x)/\sqrt{\sin x}$, the x-axis, between $x = a$ and $x = \pi/4$, with $0 < a < \pi/4$.

WORK

1. A spring is 18 in. long, and a force of 10 lb is needed to compress it to a length of 16 in. If the force is given as $f(x) = kx$, where k is a constant, and x is the increase in length, what is the constant k? How much work is done in compressing the spring from 16 in. to 12 in.?

2. Assuming that the force is given as $k \sin(\pi x/18)$, in the spring compression problem, answer the two questions of the preceding problem for this force.

3. A particle at the origin attracts another particle with a force inversely proportional to the square of the distance between them. Let C be the proportionality constant. What work is done in moving the second particle along a straight line away from the origin, from a distance r_1 to a distance $r > r_1$ from the origin?

4. In the preceding exercise, determine whether the work approaches a limit as r becomes very large, and find this limit if it exists.

5. Two particles repel each other with a force inversely proportional to the cube of their distance. If one particle is fixed at the origin, what work is done in moving the other along the x-axis from a distance of 10 cm to a distance of 1 cm towards the origin?

6. Assuming that gravity, as usual, is a force inversely proportional to the square of the distance from the center of the earth, what work is done in lifting a weight of 1000 lb from the surface of the earth to a height of 4000 mi above the surface? (Assume the radius of the earth is 4000 mi.)

7. A bag of sand originally weighing 144 lb is lifted at a constant rate of 3 ft/min. The sand leaks out uniformly at such a rate that half of the sand is lost when the bag has been lifted 18 ft. Find the work done in lifting the bag this distance.

8. A metal bar has length L and cross section S. If it is stretched x units, then the force $f(x)$ required is given by

$$f(x) = \frac{ES}{L} x$$

where E is a constant. If a bar 12 in. long of uniform cross section 4 in^2 is stretched 1 in. find the work done (in terms of E).

Chapter XIV

Taylor's Formula

We finally come to the point where we develop a method which allows us to compute the values of the elementary functions like sine, exp, and log. The method is to approximate these functions by polynomials, with an error term which is easily estimated. This error term will be given by an integral, and our first task is to estimate integrals. We then go through the elementary functions systematically, and derive the approximating polynomials.

You should review the estimates of Chapter X, §3, which will be used to estimate our error terms.

§1. TAYLOR'S FORMULA

Let f be a function which is differentiable on some interval. We can then take its derivative f' on that interval. Suppose that this derivative is also differentiable. We need a notation for its derivative. We shall denote it by $f^{(2)}$. Similarly, if the derivative of the function $f^{(2)}$ exists, we denote it by $f^{(3)}$, and so forth. In this system, the first derivative is denoted by $f^{(1)}$. (Of course, we can also write $f^{(2)} = f''$.)

In the d/dx notation, we also write:

$$f^{(2)}(x) = \frac{d^2 f}{dx^2},$$

$$f^{(3)}(x) = \frac{d^3 f}{dx^3},$$

and so forth.

Taylor's formula gives us a polynomial which approximates the function, in terms of the derivatives of the function. Since these derivatives are usually easy to compute, there is no difficulty in computing these polynomials.

For instance, if $f(x) = \sin x$, then $f^{(1)}(x) = \cos x$, $f^{(2)}(x) = -\sin x$, $f^{(3)}(x) = -\cos x$, and $f^{(4)}(x) = \sin x$. From there on, we start all over again.

In the case of e^x, it is even easier, namely $f^{(n)}(x) = e^x$ for all positive integers n.

It is also customary to denote the function f itself by $f^{(0)}$. Thus $f(x) = f^{(0)}(x)$.

We need one more piece of notation before stating Taylor's formula. When we take successive derivatives of functions, the following numbers occur frequently:

$$1, \quad 2 \cdot 1, \quad 3 \cdot 2 \cdot 1, \quad 4 \cdot 3 \cdot 2 \cdot 1, \quad 5 \cdot 4 \cdot 3 \cdot 2 \cdot 1, \quad \text{etc.}$$

These numbers are denoted by

$$1! \quad 2! \quad 3! \quad 4! \quad 5! \quad \text{etc.}$$

Thus

$$1! = 1 \qquad\qquad 4! = 24$$
$$2! = 2 \qquad\qquad 5! = 120$$
$$3! = 6 \qquad\qquad 6! = 720$$

When n is a positive integer, the symbol $n!$ is read n *factorial*. Thus in general,

$$n! = n(n - 1)(n - 2) \cdots 2 \cdot 1$$

is the product of the first n integers from 1 to n.

It is also convenient to agree that $0! = 1$. This is the convention which makes certain formulas easiest to write.

We are now in a position to state Taylor's formula.

Theorem 1. *Let f be a function defined on a closed interval between two numbers a and b. Assume that the function has n derivatives on this interval, and that all of them are continuous functions. Then*

$$f(b) = f(a) + \frac{f^{(1)}(a)}{1!}(b - a) + \frac{f^{(2)}(a)}{2!}(b - a)^2 + \cdots$$
$$+ \frac{f^{(n-1)}(a)}{(n - 1)!}(b - a)^{n-1} + R_n,$$

where R_n (which is called the remainder term) is the integral

$$R_n = \int_a^b \frac{(b - t)^{n-1}}{(n - 1)!} f^{(n)}(t)\, dt.$$

The remainder term looks slightly complicated. In Theorem 2 we shall prove that R_n can be expressed in a form very similar to the other terms, namely

$$R_n = \frac{f^{(n)}(c)}{n!}(b - a)^n$$

for some number c between a and b. Taylor's formula with this form of the remainder is then very easy to memorize.

The most important case of Theorem 1 occurs when $a = 0$. In that case, the formula reads

$$f(b) = f(0) + \frac{f'(0)}{1!} b + \cdots + \frac{f^{(n-1)}(0)}{(n-1)!} b^{n-1} + R_n.$$

Furthermore, if x is any number between a and b, the same formula remains valid for this number x instead of b, simply by considering the interval between a and x instead of the interval between a and b. Thus the formula reads

$$f(x) = f(0) + \frac{f'(0)}{1!} x + \cdots + \frac{f^{(n-1)}(0)}{(n-1)!} x^{n-1} + R_n,$$

where R_n is the integral

$$R_n = \int_0^x \frac{(x-t)^{n-1}}{(n-1)!} f^{(n)}(t)\, dt.$$

Each derivative $f(0), f'(0), \ldots, f^{(n-1)}(0)$ is a number, and we see that the terms preceding R_n make up a polynomial in x. This is the approximating polynomial.

Of course, for the formula to be of any use, we have to estimate the remainder R_n and show that it becomes small when n becomes large, so that the polynomial does indeed approximate the function. We shall do this in the following sections for special functions. You may very well want to look at these sections before reading the proof, so as to familiarize yourselves with the symbols and nature of the theorem.

We shall now prove the theorem, for those of you who are interested in seeing the proof first. It is an application of integration by parts.

We proceed stepwise. We know that a function is the integral of its derivative. Thus when $n = 1$ we have

$$f(b) - f(a) = \int_a^b f'(t)\, dt.$$

Let $u = f'(t)$ and $dv = dt$. Then $du = f''(t)\, dt$. We are tempted to put $v = t$. This is one case where we choose another indefinite integral, namely $v = -(b - t)$, which differs from t by a constant. We still have $dv = dt$ (the minus signs cancel!). Integrating by parts, we get

$$\int_a^b u\, dv = uv \Big|_a^b - \int_a^b v\, du$$

$$= -f'(t)(b - t) \Big|_a^b - \int_a^b -(b - t)f^{(2)}(t)\, dt$$

$$= f'(a)(b - a) + \int_a^b (b - t)f^{(2)}(t)\, dt.$$

This is precisely the Taylor formula when $n = 2$.

We push it one step further, from 2 to 3. We rewrite the integral just obtained as

$$\int_a^b f^{(2)}(t)(b-t)\,dt.$$

Let $u = f^{(2)}(t)$ and $dv = (b-t)\,dt$. Then

$$du = f^{(3)}(t)\,dt \qquad \text{and} \qquad v = \frac{-(b-t)^2}{2}.$$

Thus, integrating by parts, we find that our integral, which is of the form $\int_a^b u\,dv$, is equal to

$$uv\Big|_a^b - \int_a^b v\,du = -f^{(2)}(t)\frac{(b-t)^2}{2}\Big|_a^b - \int_a^b -\frac{(b-t)^2}{2}f^{(3)}(t)\,dt$$

$$= f^{(2)}(a)\frac{(b-a)^2}{2} + R_3.$$

Here, R_3 is the desired remainder, and the term preceding it is just the proper term in the Taylor formula.

If you need it, do the next step yourself, from 3 to 4. We shall now show you how the general step goes, from n to $n+1$.

Suppose that we have already obtained the first $n-1$ terms of the Taylor formula, with a remainder term

$$R_n = \int_a^b \frac{(b-t)^{n-1}}{(n-1)!}f^{(n)}(t)\,dt,$$

which we rewrite

$$R_n = \int_a^b f^{(n)}(t)\frac{(b-t)^{n-1}}{(n-1)!}\,dt.$$

Let $u = f^{(n)}(t)$ and $dv = \dfrac{(b-t)^{n-1}}{(n-1)!}\,dt$. Then

$$du = f^{(n+1)}(t)\,dt \qquad \text{and} \qquad v = \frac{-(b-t)^n}{n!}.$$

(Observe how, when we integrate dv, we get n in the denominator, to climb from $(n-1)!$ to $n!$.)

Integrating by parts, we see that R_n is equal to

$$uv\Big|_a^b - \int_a^b v\,du = -f^{(n)}(t)\frac{(b-t)^n}{n!}\Big|_a^b - \int_a^b -\frac{(b-t)^n}{n!}f^{(n+1)}(t)\,dt$$

$$= f^{(n)}(a)\frac{(b-a)^n}{n!} + \int_a^b \frac{(b-t)^n}{n!}f^{(n+1)}(t)\,dt.$$

Thus we have split off one more term of the Taylor formula, and the new remainder is the desired R_{n+1}. This concludes the proof.

§2. ESTIMATE FOR THE REMAINDER

Theorem 2. *In Taylor's formula of Theorem 1, there exists a number c between a and b such that the remainder R_n is given by*

$$R_n = \frac{f^{(n)}(c)(b-a)^n}{n!}.$$

If M_n is a number such that $|f^{(n)}(x)| \leq M_n$ for all x in the interval, then

$$|R_n| \leq \frac{M_n|b-a|^n}{n!}.$$

Proof. The second assertion follows at once from the first, taking the absolute value of the product of the n-th derivative and the length of the interval.

Let us prove the first assertion. Since $f^{(n)}$ is continuous on the interval, there exists a point u in the interval such that $f^{(n)}(u)$ is a maximum, and a point v such that $f^{(n)}(v)$ is a minimum for all values of $f^{(n)}$ in our interval.

Let us assume that $a < b$. Then for any t in the interval, $b - t$ is ≥ 0, and hence

$$\frac{(b-t)^{n-1}}{(n-1)!} f^{(n)}(v) \leq \frac{(b-t)^{n-1}}{(n-1)!} f^{(n)}(t) \leq \frac{(b-t)^{n-1}}{(n-1)!} f^{(n)}(u).$$

Using Theorem 1 of Chapter X, §3, we conclude that similar inequalities hold when we take the integral. However, $f^{(n)}(v)$ and $f^{(n)}(u)$ are now fixed numbers which can be taken out of the integral sign. Consequently, we obtain

$$f^{(n)}(v) \int_a^b \frac{(b-t)^{n-1}}{(n-1)!} \, dt \leq R_n \leq f^{(n)}(u) \int_a^b \frac{(b-t)^{n-1}}{(n-1)!} \, dt.$$

We now perform the integration, which is very easy, and get

$$f^{(n)}(v) \frac{(b-a)^n}{n!} \leq R_n \leq f^{(n)}(u) \frac{(b-a)^n}{n!}.$$

By the intermediate value theorem, the n-th derivative $f^{(n)}(t)$ takes on all values between its minimum and maximum in the interval. Hence

$$f^{(n)}(t) \frac{(b-a)^n}{n!}$$

takes on all values between *its* minimum and maximum in the interval.

Hence there is some point c in the interval such that

$$R_n = f^{(n)}(c) \frac{(b-a)^n}{n!},$$

which is what we wanted.

The proof in case $b < a$ is similar, except that certain inequalities get reversed. We leave it as an exercise. (*Hint:* Interchange the limits of integration, taking the integral from b to a.)

The estimate of the remainder is particularly useful when b is close to a. In that case, let us rewrite Taylor's formula by setting $b - a = h$. We obtain:

Theorem 3. *Assumptions being as in Theorem 1, we have*

$$f(a+h) = f(a) + f'(a)h + \cdots + f^{(n-1)}(a) \frac{h^{n-1}}{(n-1)!} + R_n$$

with the estimate

$$|R_n| \leq M_n \frac{|h|^n}{n!},$$

where M_n is a bound for the absolute value of the n-th derivative of f between a and $a + h$.

In the following sections, we give several examples. Except in some exercises, we shall always take $a = 0$, so that we have

$$f(x) = f(0) + f'(0)x + \cdots + \frac{f^{(n-1)}(0)}{(n-1)!} x^{n-1} + R_n$$

with the estimate

$$|R_n| \leq M_n \frac{|x|^n}{n!}$$

if M_n is a bound for the n-th derivative of f between 0 and x.

This means that we have expressed $f(x)$ in terms of a polynomial, and a remainder term, the polynomial being called the *Taylor polynomial*

$$P_n(x) = c_0 + c_1 x + \cdots + c_n x^n$$

where

$$c_k = \frac{f^{(k)}(0)}{k!}.$$

We call c_k the k-th *Taylor coefficient* of f.

Uniqueness Theorem. *Let b be a number > 0. Let f be a function having $n + 1$ continuous derivatives in the interval $-b < x < b$. Assume that there are numbers $a_0, \ldots, a_n$ such that we can write*

$$f(x) = a_0 + a_1 x + \cdots + a_n x^n + g(x),$$

where $g(x)$ is a function satisfying

$$|g(x)| \leqq C|x|^{n+1}$$

for some number $C > 0$ and all x in the interval. Then

$$a_k = \frac{f^{(k)}(0)}{k!}$$

is the k-th Taylor coefficient of f.

Proof. If c_k is the k-th Taylor coefficient of f as above, then we have

$$c_0 + c_1 x + \cdots + c_n x^n + R_{n+1}(x) = a_0 + a_1 x + \cdots + a_n x^n + g(x).$$

Letting $b_k = c_k - a_k$ and subtracting the polynomial on the right from that on the left, we obtain

$$b_0 + b_1 x + \cdots + b_n x^n = g(x) - R_{n+1}(x).$$

Letting $x = 0$ shows that $b_0 = 0$. Suppose by induction that we have shown $b_0 = b_1 = \cdots = b_{m-1} = 0$ for $0 \leqq m \leqq n$. Then

$$b_m x^m + \cdots + b_n x^n = g(x) - R_{n+1}(x).$$

Dividing by x^m for $x \neq 0$, we find

$$b_m + b_{m+1} x + \cdots + b_n x^{n-m} = \frac{g(x)}{x^m} - \frac{R_{n+1}(x)}{x^m}.$$

Now let x approach 0. The terms on the right approach 0, and all terms on the left (except possibly b_m) approach 0. Hence $b_m = 0$, thus proving our uniqueness theorem.

In some applications, we are able to construct an approximation to f by a polynomial using some other means than by computing the derivatives for the Taylor coefficients. If we can write f in the form given in the Uniqueness Theorem, then we know that in fact we have found the Taylor polynomial approximation of f to the n-th degree.

The estimate for the remainder being $\leqq C|x|^{n+1}$, it is useful to give an explicit name for such estimates. Thus, let f be a function defined on some open interval containing 0. We say that $f(x)$ is $O(x^n)$ for $x \to 0$ if there is a constant C such that for all x sufficiently small, we have

$$|f(x)| \leqq C|x|^n.$$

Example 1. The function f such that $f(x) = x^3$ is $O(x^2)$ for $x \to 0$. Indeed, for $|x| \leq 1$ we know that

$$|x^3| = |x|\,|x|^2 \leq |x|^2.$$

This can be generalized (cf. Exercise 4b).

Example 2. We have $\sin x = O(x)$ for $x \to 0$. This will come out of the Taylor formula for $\sin x$ in the next section, but we already know from previous work that

$$\sin x \leq x \qquad\qquad \text{for } 0 \leq x \leq 1.$$

Since

$$|\sin(-x)| = |-\sin x| = |\sin x| \leq |x|,$$

we see that $\sin x = O(x)$ for $x \to 0$.

EXERCISES

(The first exercises are to show you how to recover some classical forms of the remainder.)

1. Let $g(t)$ be a continuous function on an interval between two numbers a and b. Show that

$$\int_a^b g(t)\, dt$$

lies between $m(b - a)$ and $M(b - a)$ if m, M are minimum and maximum values of g over the interval.

2. Use the intermediate value theorem to conclude that there is a number c in the interval such that

$$\int_a^b g(t)\, dt = g(c)(b - a).$$

3. Apply this to the remainder term

$$R_n = \int_a^b \frac{(b - t)^{n-1}}{(n - 1)!} f^{(n)}(t)\, dt$$

to conclude that there exists a number c between a and b such that

$$R_n = \frac{(b - c)^{n-1}(b - a)}{(n - 1)!} f^{(n)}(c).$$

4. (a) If f and g are functions which are both $O(x^n)$ for $x \to 0$, show that $f + g$ is $O(x^n)$ for $x \to 0$. If K is a constant, show that Kf is $O(x^n)$ for $x \to 0$.
   (b) If $n \geq m$ show that $x^n = O(x^m)$ for $x \to 0$.
   (c) If $f(x) = O(x^n)$ and $g(x) = O(x^m)$ for $x \to 0$, show that

$$f(x)g(x) = O(x^{n+m}) \qquad\qquad \text{for } x \to 0.$$

(d) Let P, Q be polynomials of degree $\leqq n$, and assume that

$$f(x) = P(x) + O(x^{n+1}), \qquad \text{for} \quad x \to 0,$$
$$g(x) = Q(x) + O(x^{n+1}), \qquad \text{for} \quad x \to 0.$$

Show that $f(x)g(x) = P(x)Q(x) + O(x^{n+1})$, for $x \to 0$.

5. Show that for $x \to 0$,

$$1 + 2x - 5x^2 = 1 + 2x + O(x^2).$$

6. Show that for $x \to 0$,

$$1 + 2x - 5x^2 + 2x^3 = 1 + 2x + O(x^2).$$

7. In general, let $a_0, \ldots, a_n$ be numbers, and let $k < n$. Show that

$$a_0 + a_1 x + \cdots + a_n x^n = a_0 + a_1 x + \cdots + a_k x^k + O(x^{k+1}).$$

Example. Suppose that two functions f and g have Taylor formulas giving

$$f(x) = x - 2x^3 + x^4 + O(x^5),$$
$$g(x) = 1 + x \qquad\quad + O(x^5),$$

for $x \to 0$. Then

$$(x - 2x^3 + x^4)(1 + x) = x + x^2 - x^4 + x^5$$

and hence

$$f(x)g(x) = x + x^2 - x^4 + O(x^5).$$

Thus $x + x^2 - x^4$ is the Taylor polynomial of fg of degree $\leqq 4$.

§3. TRIGONOMETRIC FUNCTIONS

Let $f(x) = \sin x$ and take $a = 0$ in Taylor's formula. We have already mentioned what the derivatives of $\sin x$ and $\cos x$ are. Thus

$$f(0) = 0, \qquad f^{(2)}(0) = 0$$
$$f'(0) = 1, \qquad f^{(3)}(0) = -1.$$

The Taylor formula for $\sin x$ is therefore as follows:

$$\sin x = x - \frac{x^3}{3!} + \frac{x^5}{5!} - \cdots + (-1)^{n-1} \frac{x^{2n-1}}{(2n-1)!} + R_{2n+1}.$$

We see that all the even terms are 0 because $\sin 0 = 0$.

We can estimate $\sin x$ and $\cos x$ very simply, because

$$|\sin x| \leqq 1 \qquad \text{and} \qquad |\cos x| \leqq 1$$

for all x. Thus we take the bound

$$M_n = 1$$

for all n, and

$$|R_n| \leqq \frac{|x|^n}{n!}.$$

Thus if we look at all values of x such that $|x| \leq 1$, we see that R_n approaches 0 when n becomes very large.

Example 1. Compute sin (0.1) to 3 decimals.

Let us estimate R_3. We let $a = 0$, $b = a + 0.1$ in Taylor's formula. We get the estimate

$$|R_3| \leq \frac{(0.1)^3}{3!} = \frac{10^{-3}}{6}.$$

Such an error term would put us within the required range of accuracy. Hence we can just use the first term of Taylor's formula,

$$\sin (0.1) = 0.100,$$

with an error which does not exceed $\pm\frac{1}{6} 10^{-4}$.

We see how efficient this is for computing the sine for small values of x.

Example 2. Compute $\sin\left(\dfrac{\pi}{6} + 0.2\right)$ to an accuracy of 10^{-4}.

In this case, we take $a = \pi/6$. By trial and error, and guessing, we try for the remainder R_4. Thus

$$\sin (a + h) = \sin a + \cos (a)\frac{h}{1} - \sin (a)\frac{h^2}{2!} - \cos (a)\frac{h^3}{3!} + R_4$$

$$= \frac{1}{2} + \frac{\sqrt{3}}{2}(0.2) - \frac{1}{2}\frac{(0.2)^2}{2} - \frac{\sqrt{3}}{2}\frac{(0.2)^3}{6} + R_4.$$

For R_4 we have the estimate

$$|R_4| \leq \frac{(0.2)^4}{4!} = \frac{16 \cdot 10^{-4}}{24} \leq 10^{-4},$$

which is within the required bounds of accuracy. You do not need to carry out the actual decimal expansion of the first four terms, which are given just as an illustration.

Example 3. Find the limit

$$\lim_{x \to 0} \frac{\sin x - x + x^3/3!}{x^4}.$$

We have for $|x| \leq 1$:

$$\sin x - x + \frac{x^3}{3!} = R_5(x) \qquad \text{and} \qquad |R_5(x)| \leq \frac{|x|^5}{5!}.$$

Hence

$$\left|\frac{\sin x - x + x^3/3!}{x^4}\right| \leq \frac{|R_5(x)|}{|x^4|} \leq \frac{|x|}{5!}.$$

The desired limit is therefore equal to 0.

It is still true that the remainder term of the Taylor formula for $\sin x$ approaches 0 when n becomes large, even when x is > 1. For this we need:

Theorem 4. *Let c be any number. Then $c^n/n!$ approaches 0 as n becomes very large.*

Proof. Let n_0 be an integer such that $n_0 > 2c$. Thus $c < n_0/2$, and $c/n_0 < \frac{1}{2}$. We write

$$\frac{c^n}{n!} = \frac{c \cdot c \cdots c}{1 \cdot 2 \cdots n_0} \frac{c}{(n_0 + 1)(n_0 + 2) \cdots n}$$

$$\leq \frac{c^{n_0}}{n_0!} \left(\frac{1}{2}\right) \cdots \left(\frac{1}{2}\right)$$

$$= \frac{c^{n_0}}{n_0!} \left(\frac{1}{2}\right)^{n-n_0}$$

As n becomes large, $(1/2)^{n-n_0}$ becomes small and our fraction approaches 0. Take for instance $c = 10$. We write

$$\frac{10^n}{n!} = \frac{10 \cdots 10}{1 \cdot 2 \cdots 20} \frac{(10) \cdots (10)}{(21) \cdots (n)} = \frac{10^{20}}{20!} \left(\frac{1}{2}\right)^{n-20}$$

and $(1/2)^{n-20}$ approaches 0 as n becomes large.

From this we see that given a number $b > 0$, the remainder in Taylor's formula for $\sin x$ approaches 0, if $|x| \leq b$.

EXERCISES

1. Write down the first 5 terms of the Taylor formula for $\cos x$.

2. Give an estimate for the remainder similar to that for $\sin x$.

3. Compute $\cos (0.1)$ to 3 decimals.

4. Estimate the remainder R_3 in the Taylor formula for $\cos x$, for the value $x = 0.1$.

5. Estimate the remainder R_4 in the Taylor formula for $\sin x$, for the value $x = 0.2$.

6. Write down the terms of order ≤ 4 of the Taylor formula for $\tan x$.

7. Estimate the remainder R_4 in the Taylor formula for $\tan x$, for $0 \leq x \leq 0.2$.

8. Compute sine 31 degrees to 3 places.

Write down the terms of order ≤ 4 of the Taylor formula for the following functions:

9. $\sin^2 x$ 10. $\cos^3 x$

11. $\dfrac{1}{\cos x}$ 12. $\sin^3 x$

§4. EXPONENTIAL FUNCTION

All derivatives of e^x are equal to e^x and $e^0 = 1$. Hence the Taylor series for e^x is

$$e^x = 1 + x + \frac{x^2}{2!} + \cdots + \frac{x^{n-1}}{(n-1)!} + R_n.$$

Case 1. Look at values of x such that $x < 0$; then $e^x < 1$ and of course $e^x > 0$ for all x. Hence by Theorem 2, we get

$$|R_n| \leqq \frac{|x|^n}{n!},$$

which is the same estimate we obtained for $\sin x$.

Case 2. Look at values of $x > 0$, and say $x \leqq b$ for some number b. Since e^x is strictly increasing, we know that

$$e^x \leqq e^b$$

for any value of $x \leqq b$. Hence by Theorem 5, we get

$$|R_n| \leqq e^b \frac{b^n}{n!},$$

and we see again that this tends to 0 as n becomes large.

Example 1. Compute e to 3 decimals.

We have $e = e^1$. From Chapter VIII, §4 we know that $e < 4$. We estimate R_7:

$$|R_7| \leqq e\frac{1}{7!} \leqq 4\frac{1}{5{,}040} \leqq 10^{-3}.$$

Thus

$$e = 1 + 1 + \frac{1}{2} + \cdots + \frac{1}{6!} + R_7$$

$$= 2.718\ldots .$$

Of course, the smaller x is, the fewer terms of the Taylor series do we need to approximate e^x.

Example 2. How many terms of the Taylor series do you need to compute $e^{1/10}$ to an accuracy of 10^{-3}?

We certainly have $e^{1/10} < 2$. Thus

$$|R_3| \leqq 2\frac{(1/10)^3}{3!} < \frac{1}{2}10^{-3}.$$

Hence we need just 3 terms (including the 0-th term).

EXERCISES

1. Write down the terms of order ≤ 4 of the Taylor formula e^{-x^2}.
2. Estimate the remainder R_3 in the Taylor series for e^x for $x = 1/2$.
3. Estimate the remainder R_4 for $x = 10^{-2}$.
4. Estimate the remainder R_3 for $x = 10^{-2}$.
5. Write down the terms of order ≤ 5 of the Taylor series for e^{-x}.
6. Compute $1/e$ to 3 decimals, and show which remainder would give you an accuracy of 10^{-3}.
7. Write down the first four terms of the Taylor series for the function f such that

$$f(x) = e^{-1/x^2}$$

when $x \neq 0$, and $f(0) = 0$. Can you say something about the other terms in the Taylor series?

§5. LOGARITHM

We leave it to you to derive the Taylor series for the logarithm. Take $a = 1$. We shall obtain an analogous result here by another method.

Let t be any number, and n an integer > 1. Then

$$\left(1 - t + t^2 - \cdots + (-1)^{n-1} t^{n-1}\right)(1 + t) = 1 + (-1)^{n-1} t^n.$$

This is trivially proved. We first multiply the big sum on the left by 1 and then by t, getting

$$1 - t + t^2 - \cdots + (-1)^{n-1} t^{n-1}$$
$$+ t - t^2 + \cdots - (-1)^{n-2} t^{n-1} + (-1)^{n-1} t^n,$$

and add, to obtain what we want.

Suppose that $t \neq -1$. Then we can divide by $1 + t$. Thus

$$\frac{1 + (-1)^{n-1} t^n}{1 + t} = \frac{1}{1 + t} + \frac{(-1)^{n-1} t^n}{1 + t}.$$

This yields

$$\boxed{\frac{1}{1 + t} = 1 - t + t^2 - \cdots + (-1)^{n-1} t^{n-1} + \frac{(-1)^n t^n}{1 + t}.}$$

Consider the interval $-1 < x \leq 1$, and take the integral from 0 to x (in this interval). The integrals of the powers of t are well known to you. The integral

$$\int_0^x \frac{1}{1 + t} \, dt = \log (1 + x)$$

is computed by the substitution $u = 1 + t$, $du = dt$. Thus we get:

Theorem 5. *For $-1 < x \leq 1$, we have*

$$\log (1 + x) = x - \frac{x^2}{2} + \frac{x^3}{3} - \cdots + (-1)^{n-1} \frac{x^n}{n} + R_{n+1},$$

where the remainder R_{n+1} is the integral

$$(-1)^n \int_0^x \frac{t^n}{1 + t} \, dt.$$

We shall now estimate the remainder term.

Case 1. Let a be a number with $0 < a \leq 1$, and consider the interval $0 \leq x \leq a$.

In that case, $1 + t \geq 1$. Thus

$$\frac{t^n}{1 + t} \leq t^n,$$

and our integral is bounded by $\int_0^x t^n \, dt$. Thus in that case,

$$|R_{n+1}| \leq \int_0^x t^n \, dt \leq \frac{x^{n+1}}{n + 1} \leq \frac{a^{n+1}}{n + 1}.$$

(We perform the integration and use the fact that $x \leq 1$.) In particular, the remainder approaches 0 as n becomes large.

Case 2. Let a be a number with $-1 < a < 0$ and consider the interval $a \leq x \leq 0$.

In that case, we see that $0 < 1 + a \leq 1 + t$ if t lies between x and 0.

Thus

$$\left| \frac{t^n}{1 + t} \right| = \frac{|t|^n}{1 + t} \leq \frac{(-t)^n}{1 + a}.$$

To estimate the absolute value of the integral, we can invert the limits (we do this because $x \leq 0$) and thus

$$|R_{n+1}| \leq \int_x^0 \frac{(-t)^n}{1 + a} \, dt$$

$$= \frac{(-x)^{n+1}}{(n + 1)(1 + a)} = \frac{|x|^{n+1}}{(n + 1)(1 + a)} \leq \frac{|a|^{n+1}}{(n + 1)(1 + a)}.$$

Therefore the remainder also approaches 0 in that case.

Example. Compute log 1.1 to three decimals.

To do this, i.e. compute log $(1 + 0.1)$, we take $n = 2$, and $a = 0.1$ in Case 1. We find that

$$|R_3| \leq \tfrac{1}{3} \times 10^{-3}.$$

Hence

$$\log (1.1) = 0.1 - 0.005,$$

with an error not exceeding $\tfrac{1}{3} \times 10^{-3}$.

EXERCISES

1. Compute the following values up to an accuracy of 10^{-3}, estimating the remainder each time.

   (a) log 1.2   (b) log 0.9   (c) log 1.05
   (d) log $\tfrac{9}{10}$ (e) log $\tfrac{24}{25}$ (f) log $\tfrac{26}{25}$

2. Show that the expression given in Theorem 5 for the log satisfies the conditions of the Uniqueness Theorem for the Taylor expansion.

§6. THE ARCTANGENT

We proceed as with the logarithm, except that we consider

$$\frac{1}{1 + t^2} = 1 - t^2 + t^4 - \cdots + (-1)^{n-1}t^{2n-2} + (-1)^n \frac{t^{2n}}{1 + t^2}.$$

After integration from 0 to any number x, we obtain:

Theorem 6. *The arctan has an expansion*

$$\arctan x = x - \frac{x^3}{3} + \frac{x^5}{5} - \cdots + (-1)^{n-1} \frac{x^{2n-1}}{2n - 1} + R_{2n},$$

where

$$R_{2n} = (-1)^n \int_0^x \frac{t^{2n}}{1 + t^2}\, dt.$$

If b is a positive number such that $|x| \leq b$ then

$$|R_{2n}| \leq \int_0^b t^{2n}\, dt \leq \frac{b^{2n+1}}{2n + 1}.$$

When $-1 \leq x \leq 1$, the remainder approaches 0 as n becomes large.

From our theorem, we get an expression for $\pi/4$:

$$\frac{\pi}{4} = 1 - \frac{1}{3} + \frac{1}{5} - \cdots$$

from the Taylor formula for arctan 1. However, it takes many terms to get a good approximation to $\pi/4$ by this expression. You will find a more clever approach in the exercises.

EXERCISES

1. Prove the addition formula for the tangent:

$$\tan (x + y) = \frac{\tan x + \tan y}{1 - \tan x \tan y}.$$

2. Prove that $\pi/4 = \arctan \frac{1}{2} + \arctan \frac{1}{3}$.

3. Verify that $\pi = 3.14159...$.

4. You will need even fewer terms if you prove that

$$\frac{\pi}{4} = 4 \arctan \frac{1}{5} - \arctan \frac{1}{239}.$$

Find the following limits as x approaches 0:

5. $\dfrac{e^x - 1}{x}$

6. $\dfrac{\sin (x^2)}{(\sin x)^2}$

7. $\dfrac{\tan x}{\sin x}$

8. $\dfrac{\arctan x}{x}$

9. $\dfrac{\log (1 + x)}{x}$

10. $\dfrac{\log (1 + 2x)}{x}$

11. $\dfrac{e^x - (1 + x)}{x^2}$

12. $\dfrac{\sin x - x}{x^2}$

13. $\dfrac{\cos x - 1}{x^2}$

14. $\dfrac{\log (1 + x^2)}{\sin (x^2)}$

15. $\dfrac{\tan (x^2)}{(\sin x)^2}$

16. $\dfrac{\log (1 + x^2)}{(\sin x)^2}$

17. Show that the polynomial approximation to the arctangent given in Theorem 6 satisfies the conditions of the Uniqueness Theorem. (Perform integrations just as we did for the logarithm.)

§7. THE BINOMIAL EXPANSION

Let us first consider a special case.

Let n be a positive integer, and consider the function

$$f(x) = (1 + x)^n.$$

We have no difficulty computing the derivatives:

$$f'(x) = n(1 + x)^{n-1}$$
$$f''(x) = n(n - 1)(1 + x)^{n-2}$$
$$\vdots$$
$$f^{(n)}(x) = n!$$
$$f^{(n+1)}(x) = 0.$$

Thus the Taylor formula has no remainder after the n-th term, and we get:

Theorem 7. *Let n be a positive integer. For any number x, we have*

$$(1 + x)^n = 1 + nx + \frac{n(n-1)}{2!} x^2$$

$$+ \frac{n(n-1)(n-2)}{3!} x^3 + \cdots + x^n.$$

The coefficient of x^k is sometimes denoted by C_k^n or $\binom{n}{k}$ and is called a *binomial coefficient*. Thus:

$$\binom{n}{k} = \frac{n!}{k!(n-k)!}.$$

If we want an expression for $(a + b)^n$ with numbers a, b, then we let $x = b/a$. Then

$$\left(1 + \frac{b}{a}\right)^n = \frac{1}{a^n}(a + b)^n,$$

and from this we conclude at once that

$$(a + b)^n = \sum_{k=0}^{n} \binom{n}{k} a^k b^{n-k}.$$

We shall now consider the function $(1 + x)^s$ when s is not an integer. We define the *binomial coefficient*

$$\binom{s}{k} = \frac{s(s-1)\cdots(s-k+1)}{k!}.$$

Theorem 8. *Let s be any number and let x lie in the interval $-1 < x < 1$. Then we have*

$$(1 + x)^s = 1 + sx + \frac{s(s-1)}{2!} x^2$$

$$+ \frac{s(s-1)(s-2)}{3!} x^3 + \cdots + \binom{s}{k} x^k + R_{k+1},$$

where the remainder term is equal to the usual integral. The remainder R_k approaches 0 as k becomes large.

Proof. The proof that the remainder approaches 0 is slightly more involved than our previous proofs, and will be omitted. There is of course no difficulty in verifying that when $f(x) = (1 + x)^s$ then

$$\frac{f^{(k)}(0)}{k!} = \binom{s}{k}$$

and you should definitely do this as an exercise.

What we shall do, however, is discuss the remainder R_2. Let

$$f(x) = (1 + x)^s,$$

where s is not an integer. We have

$$f^{(2)}(x) = s(s - 1)(1 + x)^{s-2}.$$

The Taylor formula gives

$$(1 + x)^s = 1 + sx + R_2.$$

For small x, this means that $1 + sx$ should be a good approximation to the s power of $1 + x$, if R_2 can be proved to be small. This we can do easily. We know that

$$|R_2| \leqq \frac{M_2|x|^2}{2!} \leqq \frac{|s(s - 1)|}{2}(1 + c)^{s-2}|x|^2,$$

where c is between 0 and x. By an easy estimate one sees, for instance, that $(1 + x)^{1/2}$ is approximately equal to $1 + \frac{1}{2}x$, and $(1 + x)^{1/3}$ is approximately equal to $1 + \frac{1}{3}x$, for small x.

Example 1. Find $\sqrt{1.2}$ to 2 decimals. We estimate R_2 with $s = \frac{1}{2}$, $x = 0.2$. Then $c \geqq 0$ and $s - 2 = -3/2$. Hence

$$(1 + c)^{s-2} \leqq 1.$$

Consequently

$$|R_2| \leqq \tfrac{1}{8}(0.04) = 0.5 \times 10^{-2}.$$

Thus

$$\sqrt{1.2} = (1 + 0.2)^{1/2} = 1.10 \pm 0.5 \times 10^{-2},$$

which is within the desired accuracy.

EXERCISES

1. Compute the cube root of 126 to 4 decimals.

2. Compute $\sqrt{97}$ to 4 decimals.

3. Estimate R_2 in the remainder of $(1 + x)^{1/3}$ for x lying in the interval

$$-0.1 \leqq x \leqq 0.1.$$

4. Estimate the remainder R_2 in the Taylor series of $(1 + x)^{1/2}$ (a) when $x = -0.2$, (b) when $x = 0.1$.

5. Estimate the remainder R_2 in the Taylor series for $(1 + x)^{1/4}$ (a) when $x = 0.01$, (b) when $x = 0.2$, (c) when $x = 0.1$.

6. Estimate the remainder R_3 in the Taylor series for $(1 + x)^{1/2}$ (a) when $x = 0.2$, (b) when $x = -0.2$, (c) when $x = 0.1$.

Supplementary Exercises

Give the first four terms of the Taylor formula for the following functions:

1. $\dfrac{1}{1 + \sin x}$
2. $\dfrac{1}{1 + \sin^2 x}$
3. $\dfrac{1}{\cos^2 x}$

4. $\sin x \cos x$
5. $\tan x$
6. $\tan^2 x$

7. $\sin x - \cos x$
8. $\sin x + \cos x$
9. $(\sin x)e^x$

10. $(\cos x)e^x$
11. $e^x + e^{-x}$
12. $e^x - e^{-x}$

13. $\dfrac{1}{e^x + e^{-x}}$
14. $1 + \pi x + 3x^2 + 2x^3$

15. Using Exercise 4(c) of §2, give the terms of degree ≤ 4 for the Taylor formula of the following functions:

(a) $(\sin x) \cos x$ (b) $(\sin x)e^x$ (c) $(\cos x)e^x$
(d) $(\arctan x) \sin x$ (e) $(\arctan x) \cos x$ (f) $(1 - x) \cos x$
(g) $(1 + x + x^2) \sin x$

16. (a) Verify the following formulas:

$$\log 2 = -7 \log \tfrac{9}{10} + 2 \log \tfrac{24}{25} + 3 \log \tfrac{81}{80}$$
$$\log 3 = -11 \log \tfrac{9}{10} + 3 \log \tfrac{24}{25} + 5 \log \tfrac{81}{80}$$

(b) Compute $\log 2$ and $\log 3$ to five decimals.

17. Compute $1/e^2$ to 4 decimals.

18. What are the first four terms of the Taylor series for

$$\log \frac{1 + x}{1 - x} ?$$

Estimate the remainder R_5.

Using the first few terms of the Taylor formula, and the estimate for the remainder, determine the following limits as x approaches 0.

19. $\dfrac{e^x - e^{-x}}{x}$
20. $\dfrac{\sin x}{e^x - e^{-x}}$
21. $\dfrac{\sin^2 x}{\sin x^2}$

22. $\dfrac{\tan x^2}{\sin^2 x}$
23. $\dfrac{\log (1 - x)}{\sin x}$
24. $\dfrac{e^x + e^{-x} - 2}{x^2}$

25. $\dfrac{e^x + e^{-x} - 2}{x \sin x}$
26. $\dfrac{\sin x - x}{x^2}$
27. $\dfrac{\sin x - x}{x^3}$

28. $\dfrac{e^x - 1 - x}{x}$ 29. $\dfrac{e^x - 1 - x}{x^2}$ 30. $\dfrac{\log (1 + x^2)}{x^2}$

31. $\dfrac{(1 + x)^{1/2} - 1 - \frac{1}{2}x}{x^2}$ 32. $\dfrac{(1 - x)^{1/3} - 1 - \frac{1}{3}x}{x^2}$

33. Let $f(x)$ be a function which has $n + 1$ continuous derivatives in an open interval containing the origin, and assume that the $(n + 1)$-th derivative is bounded by a constant M on this interval. Let $P_n(x)$ be the polynomial consisting of the terms whose degree is $\leq n$ in the Taylor formula for $f(x)$. What are the following limits?

(a) $\lim\limits_{x \to 0} \dfrac{f(x) - P_n(x)}{x^2}$ (assuming $n \geq 3$)

(b) $\lim\limits_{x \to 0} \dfrac{f(x) - P_n(x)}{x^n}$ (c) $\lim\limits_{x \to 0} \dfrac{f(x) - P_n(x)}{x^{n-1}}$ (assuming $n \geq 2$)

Determine the following limits as x approaches 0.

34. $\dfrac{\sin x + \cos x - 1}{x}$ 35. $\dfrac{\sin x + \cos x - 1 - x}{x^2}$

36. $\dfrac{\sin x - x + x^3/3!}{x^4}$ 37. $\dfrac{\sin x - x + x^3/3!}{x^5}$

38. $\dfrac{\cos x - 1 - x^2/2!}{x}$ 39. $\dfrac{\cos x - 1 - x^2/2!}{x^2}$

40. $\dfrac{\cos x - 1 + x^2/2!}{x^3}$ 41. $\dfrac{\cos x - 1 + x^2/2!}{x^4}$

42. $\dfrac{\sin x + e^x - 1}{x}$ 43. $\dfrac{\sin x - e^x + 1}{x}$

44. $\dfrac{\sin x - e^x + 1}{x^2}$ 45. $\dfrac{\cos x - e^x}{x}$

46. Estimate the following integrals to three decimals.

(a) $\displaystyle\int_0^1 \dfrac{\sin x}{x}\, dx$ (b) $\displaystyle\int_0^{0.1} \dfrac{\cos x - 1}{x}\, dx$

(c) $\displaystyle\int_0^{0.1} \dfrac{e^x - 1}{x}\, dx$ (d) $\displaystyle\int_0^1 \dfrac{\sin x^2}{x}\, dx$

(e) $\displaystyle\int_0^1 \dfrac{\cos x^2}{x^2}\, dx$ (f) $\displaystyle\int_0^1 \dfrac{\sin x^2}{x^2}\, dx$

(g) $\displaystyle\int_0^1 e^{-x^2}\, dx$ (h) $\displaystyle\int_0^1 e^{x^2}\, dx$

(i) $\displaystyle\int_0^{0.1} e^{x^2}\, dx$ (j) $\displaystyle\int_0^{0.1} e^{-x^2}\, dx$

We work out integral 46(a) as an example, to two decimals. We have:

$$\sin x = x - \frac{x^3}{3!} + R_5(x) \quad \text{and} \quad |R_5(x)| \le \frac{|x|^5}{5!}.$$

Hence

$$\frac{\sin x}{x} = 1 - \frac{x^2}{3!} + \frac{R_5(x)}{x} \quad \text{and} \quad \left|\frac{R_5(x)}{x}\right| \le \frac{|x|^4}{5!}.$$

Hence

$$\int_0^1 \frac{\sin x}{x} dx = x - \frac{x^3}{3 \cdot 3!}\Big|_0^1 + \int_0^1 \frac{R_5(x)}{x} dx$$

and

$$\int_0^1 \left|\frac{R_5(x)}{x}\right| dx \le \int_0^1 \frac{x^4}{5!} dx = \frac{x^5}{5 \cdot 5!}\Big|_0^1 = \frac{1}{600}.$$

Hence up to two decimals, our integral has the value

$$x - \frac{x^3}{3 \cdot 3!}\Big|_0^1 = 1 - \frac{1}{18} = \frac{17}{18}.$$

Chapter XV

Series

Series are a natural continuation of our study of functions. In the preceding chapter we found how to approximate our elementary functions by polynomials, with a certain error term. Conversely, one can define arbitrary functions by giving a series for them. We shall see how in the sections below.

In practice, very few tests are used to determine convergence of series. Essentially, the comparison test is the most frequent. Furthermore, the most important series are those which converge absolutely. Thus we shall put greater emphasis on these.

§1. CONVERGENT SERIES

Suppose that we are given a sequence of numbers

$$a_1, a_2, a_3, \ldots,$$

i.e. we are given a number a_n for each integer $n \geq 1$. (We picked the starting place to be 1, but we could have picked any integer.) We form the sums

$$s_n = a_1 + a_2 + \cdots + a_n.$$

It would be meaningless to form an infinite sum

$$a_1 + a_2 + a_3 + \cdots$$

because we do not know how to add infinitely many numbers. However, if our sums s_n approach a limit, as n becomes large, then we say that the sum of our sequence *converges*, and we now define its *sum* to be that limit.

The symbols

$$\sum_{n=1}^{\infty} a_n$$

will be called a *series*. We shall say that the *series converges* if the sums s_n approach a limit as n becomes large. Otherwise, we say that it does not converge, or *diverges*. If the series converges, we say that the value of the

264

series is

$$\sum_{n=1}^{\infty} a_n = \lim_{n\to\infty} s_n = \lim_{n\to\infty} (a_1 + \cdots + a_n).$$

The symbols $\lim\limits_{n\to\infty}$ are to be read: "The limit as n becomes large."

Example. Consider the sequence

$$1, \frac{1}{2}, \frac{1}{4}, \frac{1}{8}, \frac{1}{16}, \ldots,$$

and let us form the sums

$$1 + \frac{1}{2} + \frac{1}{4} + \cdots + \frac{1}{2^n}.$$

You probably know already that these sums approach a limit and that this limit is 2. To prove it, let $r = \frac{1}{2}$. Then

$$(1 + r + r^2 + \cdots + r^n) = \frac{1 - r^{n+1}}{1 - r} = \frac{1}{1 - r} - \frac{r^{n+1}}{1 - r}.$$

As n becomes large, r^{n+1} approaches 0, whence our sums approach

$$\frac{1}{1 - \frac{1}{2}} = 2.$$

Actually, the same argument works if we take for r any number such that

$$-1 < r < 1.$$

In that case, r^{n+1} approaches 0 as n becomes large, and consequently we can write

$$\sum_{n=0}^{\infty} r^n = \frac{1}{1 - r}.$$

In view of the fact that the limit of a sum is the sum of the limits, and other standard properties of limits, we get:

Theorem 1. *Let $\{a_n\}$ and $\{b_n\}$ $(n = 1, 2, \ldots)$ be two sequences and assume that the series*

$$\sum_{n=1}^{\infty} a_n \quad and \quad \sum_{n=1}^{\infty} b_n$$

converge. Then $\sum_{n=1}^{\infty} (a_n + b_n)$ also converges, and is equal to the sum of the two series. If c is a number, then

$$\sum_{n=1}^{\infty} ca = c \sum_{n=1}^{\infty} a_n.$$

Finally, if $s_n = a_1 + \cdots + a_n$ and $t_n = b_1 + \cdots + b_n$ then

$$\sum_{n=1}^{\infty} a_n \sum_{n=1}^{\infty} b_n = \lim_{n \to \infty} s_n t_n.$$

In particular, series can be added term by term. Of course, they cannot be multiplied term by term!

We also observe that a similar theorem holds for the difference of two series.

If a series $\sum a_n$ converges, then the numbers a_n must approach 0 as n becomes large. However, there are examples of sequences $\{a_n\}$ for which the series does not converge, and yet

$$\lim_{n \to \infty} a_n = 0.$$

Consider for instance

$$1 + \frac{1}{2} + \frac{1}{3} + \cdots + \frac{1}{n} + \cdots.$$

We contend that the partial sums s_n become very large when n becomes large. To see this, we look at partial sums as follows:

$$1 + \frac{1}{2} + \underbrace{\frac{1}{3} + \frac{1}{4}} + \underbrace{\frac{1}{5} + \cdots + \frac{1}{8}} + \underbrace{\frac{1}{9} + \cdots + \frac{1}{16}} + \cdots.$$

In each bunch of terms as indicated, we replace each term by that farthest to the right. This makes our sums smaller. Thus our expression is

$$\geq 1 + \frac{1}{2} + \underbrace{\frac{1}{4} + \frac{1}{4}} + \underbrace{\frac{1}{8} + \cdots + \frac{1}{8}} + \underbrace{\frac{1}{16} + \cdots + \frac{1}{16}} + \cdots$$

$$\geq 1 + \frac{1}{2} + \quad \frac{1}{2} \quad + \quad \frac{1}{2} \quad + \quad \frac{1}{2} \quad + \cdots$$

and therefore becomes arbitrarily large when n becomes large.

§2. SERIES WITH POSITIVE TERMS

Throughout this section, we shall assume that our numbers a_n are ≥ 0. Then the partial sums

$$s_n = a_1 + \cdots + a_n$$

are increasing, i.e.

$$s_1 \leq s_2 \leq s_3 \leq \cdots \leq s_n \leq s_{n+1} \leq \cdots.$$

If they are to approach a limit at all, they cannot become arbitrarily large.

Thus in that case there is a number B such that

$$s_n \leqq B$$

for all n. The collection of numbers $\{s_n\}$ has therefore a least upper bound, i.e. there is a smallest number S such that

$$s_n \leqq S$$

for all n. In that case, the partial sums s_n approach S as a limit. In other words, given any positive number $\epsilon > 0$, we have

$$S - \epsilon \leqq s_n \leqq S$$

for all n sufficiently large.

This simply expresses the fact that S is the least of all upper bounds for our collection of numbers s_n. We express this as a theorem.

Theorem 2. *Let $\{a_n\}$ $(n = 1, 2, \ldots)$ be a sequence of numbers $\geqq 0$ and let*

$$s_n = a_1 + \cdots + a_n.$$

If the sequence of numbers $\{s_n\}$ is bounded, then it approaches a limit S, which is its least upper bound.

Theorem 1 gives us a very useful criterion to determine when a series with positive terms converges:

Theorem 3. *Let*

$$\sum_{n=1}^{\infty} a_n \qquad and \qquad \sum_{n=1}^{\infty} b_n$$

be two series, with $a_n \geqq 0$ for all n and $b_n \geqq 0$ for all n. Assume that there is a number $C > 0$ such that

$$a_n \leqq Cb_n$$

for all n, and that $\displaystyle\sum_{n=1}^{\infty} b_n$ converges. Then $\displaystyle\sum_{n=1}^{\infty} a_n$ converges, and

$$\sum_{n=1}^{\infty} a_n \leqq C \sum_{n=1}^{\infty} b_n.$$

Proof. We have

$$a_1 + \cdots + a_n \leqq Cb_1 + \cdots + Cb_n = C(b_1 + \cdots + b_n) \leqq C \sum_{n=1}^{\infty} b_n.$$

This means that $C \sum_{n=1}^{\infty} b_n$ is a bound for the partial sums

$$a_1 + \cdots + a_n.$$

The least upper bound of these sums is therefore $\leq C \sum_{n=1}^{\infty} b_n$, thereby proving our theorem.

Example 1. Prove that the series $\sum_{n=1}^{\infty} \frac{1}{n^2}$ converges.
Let us look at the series:

$$\frac{1}{1^2} + \frac{1}{2^2} + \frac{1}{3^2} + \frac{1}{4^2} + \cdots + \frac{1}{8^2} + \cdots + \frac{1}{16^2} + \cdots + \cdots.$$

We look at the groups of terms as indicated. In each group of terms, if we decrease the denominator in each term, then we increase the fraction. We replace 3 by 2, then 4, 5, 6, 7 by 4, then we replace the numbers from 8 to 15 by 8, and so forth. Our partial sums are therefore less than or equal to

$$1 + \frac{1}{2^2} + \frac{1}{2^2} + \frac{1}{4^2} + \cdots + \frac{1}{4^2} + \frac{1}{8^2} + \cdots + \frac{1}{8^2} + \cdots,$$

and we note that 2 occurs twice, 4 occurs four times, 8 occurs eight times, and so forth. Hence the partial sums are less than or equal to

$$1 + \frac{2}{2^2} + \frac{4}{4^2} + \frac{8}{8^2} + \cdots = 1 + \frac{1}{2} + \frac{1}{4} + \frac{1}{8} + \cdots.$$

Thus our partial sums are less than or equal to those of the geometric series and are bounded. Hence our series converges.

Theorem 3 has an analogue to show that a series does not converge.

Theorem 3'. *Let*

$$\sum_{n=1}^{\infty} a_n \qquad and \qquad \sum_{n=1}^{\infty} b_n$$

be two series, with a_n and $b_n \geq 0$ for all n. Assume that there is a number $C > 0$ such that

$$a_n \geq C b_n$$

for all n sufficiently large, and that $\sum_{n=1}^{\infty} b_n$ does not converge. Then $\sum_{n=1}^{\infty} a_n$ diverges.

Proof. Assume $a_n \geq C b_n$ for $n \geq n_0$.
Since $\sum b_n$ diverges, we can make the partial sums

$$\sum_{n=n_0}^{N} b_n = b_{n_0} + \cdots + b_N$$

arbitrarily large as N becomes arbitrarily large. But

$$\sum_{n=n_0}^{N} a_n \geq \sum_{n=n_0}^{N} Cb_n = C \sum_{n=n_0}^{N} b_n.$$

Hence the partial sums

$$\sum_{n=1}^{N} a_n = a_1 + \cdots + a_N$$

are arbitrarily large as N becomes arbitrarily large, and hence $\sum_{n=1}^{\infty} a_n$ diverges, as was to be shown.

Example 2. Determine whether the series

$$\sum_{n=1}^{\infty} \frac{n^2}{n^3 + 1}$$

converges.
We write

$$\frac{n^2}{n^3 + 1} = \frac{1}{n + 1/n^2} = \frac{1}{n}\left(\frac{1}{1 + 1/n^3}\right).$$

Then for n sufficiently large, we see that

$$\frac{n^2}{n^3 + 1} \geq \frac{1}{2n}.$$

Since $\sum 1/n$ does not converge, it follows that the series of Example 2 does not converge either.

EXERCISES

1. Show that the series $\sum_{n=1}^{\infty} \frac{1}{n^3}$ converges.

2. (a) Show that the series $\sum \frac{\log n}{n^3}$ converges. [*Hint*: Estimate $(\log n)/n.$]

   (b) Show that the series $\sum \frac{(\log n)^2}{n^3}$ converges.

Test the following series for convergence:

3. $\displaystyle\sum_{n=1}^{\infty} \frac{1}{n^{1/2}}$ 4. $\displaystyle\sum_{n=1}^{\infty} \frac{n^2}{n^4 + n}$ 5. $\displaystyle\sum_{n=1}^{\infty} \frac{n}{n + 1}$

6. $\displaystyle\sum_{n=1}^{\infty} \frac{n}{n + 5}$ 7. $\displaystyle\sum_{n=1}^{\infty} \frac{n^2}{n^3 + n + 2}$ 8. $\displaystyle\sum_{n=1}^{\infty} \frac{|\sin n|}{n^2 + 1}$

9. $\displaystyle\sum_{n=1}^{\infty} \frac{|\cos n|}{n^2 + n}$

§3. THE RATIO TEST

We continue to consider only series with terms ≥ 0. To compare such a series with a geometric series, the simplest test is given by the ratio test.

Ratio Test. *Let* $\sum\limits_{n=1}^{\infty} a_n$ *be a series with* $a_n > 0$ *for all n. Assume that there is a number c with* $0 < c < 1$ *such that*

$$\frac{a_{n+1}}{a_n} \leq c$$

for all n sufficiently large. Then the series converges.

Proof. Suppose that there exists some integer N such that $a_{n+1}/a_n \leq c$ if $n \geq N$. Then

$$a_{N+1} \leq ca_N$$
$$a_{N+2} \leq ca_{N+1} \leq c^2 a_N$$

and in general, by induction,

$$a_{N+k} \leq c^k a_N.$$

Thus

$$\sum_{n=N}^{N+k} a_n \leq a_N + ca_N + c^2 a_N + \cdots + c^k a_N$$

$$\leq a_N(1 + c + \cdots + c^k) \leq a_N \frac{1}{1-c}.$$

Thus in effect, we have compared our series with a geometric series, and we know that the partial sums are bounded. This implies that our series converges.

Example. Show that the series

$$\sum_{n=1}^{\infty} \frac{n}{3^n}$$

converges.

We let $a_n = n/3^n$. Then

$$\frac{a_{n+1}}{a_n} = \frac{n+1}{3^{n+1}} \frac{3^n}{n} = \frac{n+1}{n} \frac{1}{3}.$$

When n is large, then $(n+1)/n$ is close to 1, and $(n+1)/3n$ is close to $1/3$. In particular, if we take $1/3 < c < 1$, we see that $a_{n+1}/a_n < c$ for all n sufficiently large. Hence we can apply the theorem to see that our series converges.

EXERCISES

Determine whether the following series converge:

1. $\sum n2^{-n}$ 2. $\sum n^2 2^{-n}$ 3. $\sum \dfrac{1}{\log n}$

4. $\sum \dfrac{\log n}{n^2}$ 5. $\sum \dfrac{\log n}{n}$ 6. $\sum \dfrac{n^{10}}{3^n}$

7. $\sum \dfrac{1}{\sqrt{n(n+1)}}$ 8. $\sum \dfrac{1}{\sqrt{n^3+1}}$ 9. $\sum \dfrac{n+1}{\sqrt{n^4+n+1}}$

10. $\sum \dfrac{n+1}{2^n}$ 11. $\sum \dfrac{n}{(4n-1)(n+15)}$ 12. $\sum \dfrac{1+\cos(\pi n/2)}{e^n}$

13. $\sum \dfrac{1}{(\log n)^{10}}$ 14. $\sum n^2 e^{-n^2}$ 15. $\sum n^2 e^{-n^3}$

16. $\sum n^5 e^{-n^2}$ 17. $\sum \dfrac{n!}{(n+2)!}$ 18. $\sum \dfrac{n^n}{(n+1)!}$

19. Let $\{a_n\}$ be a sequence of positive numbers, and assume that

$$\frac{a_{n+1}}{a_n} \geq 1 - \frac{1}{n}$$

for all n. Show that the series $\sum a_n$ diverges.

20. A ratio test can be applied in the opposite direction to determine when a series diverges. Prove the following statement: Let a_n be a sequence of positive numbers, and let $c \geq 1$. If $a_{n+1}/a_n \geq c$ for all n sufficiently large, then the series $\sum a_n$ diverges.

§4. THE INTEGRAL TEST

You must already have felt that there is an analogy between the convergence of an improper integral and the convergence of a series. We shall now make this precise.

Theorem 4. *Let f be a function which is defined and positive for all $x \geq 1$, and decreasing. The series*

$$\sum_{n=1}^{\infty} f(n)$$

converges if and only if the improper integral

$$\int_1^{\infty} f(x)\, dx$$

converges.

We visualize the situation in the following diagram.

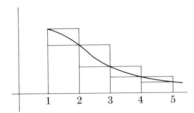

Consider the partial sums

$$f(2) + \cdots + f(n)$$

and assume that our improper integral converges. The area under the curve between 1 and 2 is greater than or equal to the area of the rectangle whose height is $f(2)$ and whose base is the interval between 1 and 2. This base has length 1. Thus

$$f(2) \leqq \int_1^2 f(x)\, dx.$$

Again, since the function is decreasing, we have a similar estimate between 2 and 3:

$$f(3) \leqq \int_2^3 f(x)\, dx.$$

We can continue up to n, and get

$$f(2) + f(3) + \cdots + f(n) \leqq \int_1^n f(x)\, dx.$$

As n becomes large, we have assumed that the integral approaches a limit. This means that

$$f(2) + f(3) + \cdots + f(n) \leqq \int_1^\infty f(x)\, dx.$$

Hence the partial sums are bounded, and hence by Theorem 2, they approach a limit. Therefore our series converges.

Conversely, assume that the partial sums

$$f(1) + \cdots + f(n)$$

approach a limit as n becomes large.

The area under the graph of f between 1 and n is less than or equal to the sum of the areas of the big rectangles. Thus

$$\int_1^2 f(x)\, dx \leqq f(1)(2 - 1) = f(1)$$

and

$$\int_2^3 f(x)\, dx \leqq f(2)(3 - 2) = f(2).$$

Proceeding stepwise, and taking the sum, we see that

$$\int_1^n f(x)\,dx \leqq f(1) + \cdots + f(n-1).$$

The partial sums on the right are less than or equal to their limit. Call this limit L. Then for all positive integers n, we have

$$\int_1^n f(x)\,dx \leqq L.$$

Given any number B, we can find an integer n such that $B \leqq n$. Then

$$\int_1^B f(x)\,dx \leqq \int_1^n f(x)\,dx \leqq L.$$

Hence the integral from 1 to B approaches a limit as B becomes large, and this limit is less than or equal to L. This proves our theorem.

Example. Prove that the series

$$\sum \frac{1}{n^2+1}$$

converges.

Let

$$f(x) = \frac{1}{n^2+1}.$$

Then f is decreasing, and

$$\int_1^B f(x)\,dx = \arctan B - \arctan 1 = \arctan B - \frac{\pi}{4}.$$

As B becomes large, $\arctan B$ approaches $\pi/2$ and therefore has a limit. Hence the integral converges. So does the series, by the theorem.

EXERCISES

1. Show that the following series diverges: $\displaystyle\sum_{n=2}^{\infty} \frac{1}{n \log n}$

2. Show that the following series converges: $\displaystyle\sum_{n=1}^{\infty} \frac{n+1}{(n+2)n!}$

Test for convergence:

3. $\displaystyle\sum_{n=1}^{\infty} ne^{-n^2}$

4. $\displaystyle\sum_{n=2}^{\infty} \frac{1}{n(\log n)^3}$

5. $\displaystyle\sum_{n=2}^{\infty} \frac{1}{n(\log n)^2}$

6. $\displaystyle\sum_{n=1}^{\infty} \frac{n!}{n^n}$

7. $\displaystyle\sum_{n=1}^{\infty} \frac{n}{e^n}$

8. $\displaystyle\sum_{n=1}^{\infty} \frac{n+1}{n^3+2}$

9. $\displaystyle\sum_{n=1}^{\infty} \frac{1}{n^2+n-1}$

10. $\displaystyle\sum_{n=1}^{\infty} \frac{n}{n^3-n+5}$

11. Let ϵ be a number > 0. Show that the series $\sum_{n=1}^{\infty} \dfrac{1}{n^{1+\epsilon}}$ converges.

12. Show that the following series converge.

(a) $\sum_{n=1}^{\infty} \dfrac{\log n}{n^2}$

(b) $\sum_{n=1}^{\infty} \dfrac{\log n}{n^{3/2}}$

(c) $\sum_{n=1}^{\infty} \dfrac{\log n}{n^{1+\epsilon}}$ if $\epsilon > 0$.

(d) $\sum_{n=1}^{\infty} \dfrac{(\log n)^2}{n^{3/2}}$

(e) $\sum_{n=1}^{\infty} \dfrac{(\log n)^3}{n^2}$

13. If $\epsilon > 0$ show that the series $\sum_{n=2}^{\infty} \dfrac{1}{n(\log n)^{1+\epsilon}}$ converges.

§5. ABSOLUTE AND ALTERNATING CONVERGENCE

We consider a series $\sum_{n=1}^{\infty} a_n$ in which we do not assume that the terms a_n are ≥ 0. We shall say that the series *converges absolutely* if the series

$$\sum_{n=1}^{\infty} |a_n|$$

formed with the absolute values of the terms a_n converges. This is now a series with terms ≥ 0, to which we can apply the tests for convergence given in the two preceding sections. This is important, because we have:

Theorem 5. *Let $\{a_n\}$ $(n = 1, 2, \ldots)$ be a sequence, and assume that the series*

$$\sum_{n=1}^{\infty} |a_n|$$

converges. Then so does the series $\sum_{n=1}^{\infty} a_n$.

Proof. Let a_n^+ be equal to 0 if $a_n < 0$ and equal to a_n itself if $a_n \geq 0$. Let a_n^- be equal to 0 if $a_n > 0$ and equal to $-a_n$ if $a_n \leq 0$. Then both a_n^+ and a_n^- are ≥ 0. By assumption and comparison with $\sum |a_n|$, we see that each one of the series

$$\sum_{n=1}^{\infty} a_n^+ \quad \text{and} \quad \sum_{n=1}^{\infty} a_n^-$$

converges. Hence so does their difference

$$\sum_{n=1}^{\infty} a_n^+ - \sum_{n=1}^{\infty} a_n^-,$$

which is equal to

$$\sum_{n=1}^{\infty} (a_n^+ - a_n^-),$$

which is none other than $\sum_{n=1}^{\infty} a_n$. This proves our theorem.

We shall use one more test for convergence of a series which may have positive and negative terms.

Theorem 6. *Let* $\sum_{n=1}^{\infty} a_n$ *be a series such that*

$$\lim_{n \to \infty} a_n = 0,$$

such that the terms a_n are alternately positive and negative, and such that $|a_{n+1}| \leq |a_n|$ for $n \geq 1$. Then the series is convergent.

Proof. Let us write the series in the form

$$b_1 - c_1 + b_2 - c_2 + b_3 - c_3 + \cdots,$$

with $b_n, c_n \geq 0$. Let

$$s_n = b_1 - c_1 + b_2 - c_2 + \cdots + b_n$$
$$t_n = b_1 - c_1 + b_2 - c_2 + \cdots + b_n - c_n.$$

Since the absolute values of the terms decrease, it follows that

$$s_1 \geq s_2 \geq s_3 \geq \cdots$$

and

$$t_1 \leq t_2 \leq t_3 \leq \cdots,$$

i.e. that the s_n are decreasing and the t_n are increasing. Indeed,

$$s_{n+1} = s_n - c_n + b_{n+1} \qquad \text{and} \qquad 0 \leq b_{n+1} \leq c_n.$$

Thus we subtract more from s_n by c_n than we add afterwards by b_{n+1}. Hence $s_n \geq s_{n+1}$. Furthermore, $s_n \geq t_n$. Hence we may visualize our sequences as follows:

$$s_n \geq s_{n+1} \geq \cdots \geq t_{n+1} \geq t_n.$$

Note that $s_n - t_n = c_n$, and that c_n approaches 0 as n becomes large. If we let L be the greatest lower bound for the sequence $\{s_n\}$, and M be the least upper bound for the sequence $\{t_n\}$, then

$$s_n \geq L \geq M \geq t_n$$

for all n. Since the difference $s_n - t_n$ becomes arbitrarily small, it follows that $L - M$ is arbitrarily small, and hence equal to 0. Thus $L = M$, and this proves that s_n and t_n approach L as a limit, whence our series $\sum a_n$ converges to L.

Example. The series

$$\sum_{n=1}^{\infty} (-1)^n \frac{1}{n}$$

is convergent, but not absolutely convergent.

EXERCISES

Determine whether the following series converge absolutely:

1. $\sum \frac{\sin n}{n^3}$

2. $\sum \frac{1 + \cos \pi n}{n!}$

3. $\sum \frac{\sin \pi n + \cos 2\pi n}{n^{3/2}}$

4. $\sum \frac{(-1)^n}{n^2 + 1}$

5. $\sum \frac{(-1)^n \sin n + \cos 3n}{n^2 + n}$

Which of the following series converge and which do not?

6. $\sum \frac{(-1)^n}{n}$

7. $\sum \frac{(-1)^n}{n^2}$

8. $\sum (-1)^n \frac{n}{n + 1}$

9. $\sum \frac{(-1)^{n+1}}{\log (n + 2)}$

10. For each number x, show that the series

$$\sum \frac{\sin n^2 x}{n^2}$$

converges absolutely. Let f be the function whose value at x is the above series. Show that f is continuous. Determine whether f is differentiable or not. (Remarkably enough, this does not seem to be known! Cf. J. P. Kahane, Bulletin of the American Mathematical Society, March 1964, p. 199.)

Determine whether the following series converge, and whether they converge absolutely.

11. $\sum \frac{(-1)^{n+1}}{\sqrt{n}}$

12. $\sum \frac{(-1)^{n+2}}{\log n}$

13. $\sum \frac{(-1)^n}{\sqrt[n]{n}}$

14. $\sum (-1)^n \frac{n^2}{n^2 + 1}$

15. $\sum (-1)^n \frac{n^2}{n^3 + 2}$

16. $\sum (-1)^{n+1} \frac{n^2 + 2}{n^3 + n - 1}$

17. $\displaystyle\sum (-1)^{n+1} \frac{\sqrt{n}}{n+2}$

18. $\displaystyle\sum \frac{(-1)^n}{n^{5/2}+n}$

19. $\displaystyle\sum (-1)^n \frac{n}{n^2+1}$

20. $\displaystyle\sum \frac{(-1)^n}{\sqrt{\log n}}$

§6. POWER SERIES

Perhaps the most important type of series are power series. Let x be any number and let $\{a_n\}$ $(n = 0, 1, \ldots)$ be a sequence of numbers. Then we can form the series

$$\sum_{n=0}^{\infty} a_n x^n.$$

The partial sums are

$$a_0 + a_1 x + a_2 x^2 + \cdots + a_n x^n.$$

We have already met such sums when we discussed Taylor's formula.

Example. The power series

$$\sum_{n=0}^{\infty} \frac{x^n}{n!}$$

converges for all x, absolutely. Indeed, given a number $R > 0$, it will suffice to prove that the above series converges for $0 < x \leq R$. We use the ratio test. Let

$$b_n = \frac{x^n}{n!}.$$

Then

$$\frac{b_{n+1}}{b_n} = \frac{x^{n+1}}{(n+1)!} \frac{n!}{x^n} = \frac{x}{n+1} \leq \frac{R}{n+1}.$$

When n is sufficiently large, it follows that $R/(n+1) < 1/2$, and we can apply the ratio test to prove our assertion.

Similarly, we could prove that the series

$$\sum_{n=0}^{\infty} (-1)^n \frac{x^{2n+1}}{(2n+1)!} \quad \text{and} \quad \sum_{n=0}^{\infty} (-1)^n \frac{x^{2n}}{(2n)!}$$

converge absolutely for all x, letting for instance

$$b_n = \frac{x^{2n+1}}{(2n+1)!}$$

for the first one. Then $b_{n+1}/b_n = x^2/(2n+3)$, and we can argue as before.

Theorem 7. *Assume that there is a number $r > 0$ such that the series*

$$\sum_{n=0}^{\infty} |a_n| r^n$$

converges. Then for all x such that $|x| \leq r$, the series

$$\sum_{n=0}^{\infty} a_n x^n$$

converges absolutely.

Proof. The absolute value of each term is

$$|a_n| \, |x|^n \leq |a_n| r^n.$$

Our assertion follows from the comparison Theorem 2.

The least upper bound of all numbers r for which we have the convergence stated in the theorem is called the *radius of convergence* of the series. If there is no upper bound for the numbers r such that the power series above converges, then we say that the radius of convergence is *infinity*. In this case, the series converges absolutely for all x.

Suppose that there is an upper bound for the numbers r above, and thus let s be the radius of convergence of the series. Then if $x > s$, the series

$$\sum_{n=0}^{\infty} |a_n| x^n$$

does *not* converge. Thus the radius of convergence s is the number such that the series converges absolutely if $0 < x < s$ but does not converge absolutely if $x > s$.

Theorem 7 allows us to define a function f; namely, for all numbers x such that $|x| < r$, we define

$$f(x) = \lim_{n \to \infty} (a_0 + a_1 x + \cdots + a_n x^n).$$

Our proofs that the remainder term in Taylor's formula approaches 0 for various functions now allow us to say that these functions are given by their Taylor series. Thus

$$\sin x = x - \frac{x^3}{3!} + \frac{x^5}{5!} - \cdots$$

$$e^x = 1 + x + \frac{x^2}{2!} + \cdots$$

for all x. Furthermore,

$$\log (1 + x) = x - \frac{x^2}{2} + \cdots$$

is valid for $-1 < x < 1$.

(Here we saw that the series converges for $x = 1$, but it does not converge absolutely, cf. §1.)

However, we can now define functions at random by means of a power series, provided we know the power series converges absolutely, for $|x| < r$.

The ratio test usually gives an easy way to determine when a power series converges, or when it diverges.

Example. Prove that the series

$$\sum_{n=2}^{\infty} \frac{\log n}{n^2} x^n$$

converges absolutely for $|x| < 1$, and diverges for $|x| > 1$.

Let $0 < c < 1$ and consider x such that $0 < x \leq c$. Let

$$b_n = \frac{\log n}{n^2} x^n.$$

Then

$$\frac{b_{n+1}}{b_n} = \frac{\log (n + 1)}{(n + 1)^2} x^{n+1} \frac{n^2}{\log n} \frac{1}{x^n} = \frac{\log (n + 1)}{\log n} \left(\frac{n}{n + 1} \right)^2 x.$$

Since $\log (n + 1)/\log n$ and $(n/(n + 1))^2$ approach 1 when n becomes very large, it follows that if $c < c_1 < 1$, then for all n sufficiently large

$$\frac{b_{n+1}}{b_n} \leq c_1$$

and hence our series converges. This is true for every c such that $0 < c < 1$, and hence the series converges absolutely for $|x| < 1$.

Let $c > 1$. If $x \geq c$ then for all n sufficiently large, it follows that $b_{n+1}/b_n \geq 1$, whence the series does not converge. This is so for all $c > 1$, and hence the series does not converge if $x > 1$. Hence 1 is the radius of convergence.

If a power series converges absolutely only for $x = 0$, then we agree to say that its radius of convergence is 0. For example, the radius of convergence of the series

$$\sum_{n=1}^{\infty} n! x^n$$

is equal to 0, as one sees by using the ratio test in the divergent case.

EXERCISES

Find the radius of convergence of the following series:

1. $\sum n^n x^n$

2. $\sum \dfrac{x^n}{n^n}$

3. $\sum \dfrac{(-1)^n}{n^2 + 1} x^n$

4. $\sum \dfrac{n}{n+5} x^n$ 5. $\sum (\log n) x^n$ 6. $\sum \dfrac{1}{\log n} x^n$

7. $\sum (\log n)^2 x^n$ 8. $\sum 2^n x^n$ 9. $\sum 2^{-n} x^n$

10. $\sum (1+n)^n x^n$ 11. $\sum \dfrac{x^n}{n}$ 12. $\sum \dfrac{x^n}{\sqrt{n}}$

13. $\sum (1+(-2)^n) x^n$ 14. $\sum (1+(-1)^n) x^n$ 15. $\displaystyle\sum_{n=1}^{\infty} \dfrac{(2n)!}{(n!)^2} x^n$

16. $\displaystyle\sum_{n=1}^{\infty} \dfrac{n^n}{n!} x^n$ 17. $\displaystyle\sum_{n=1}^{\infty} \dfrac{(n!)^3}{(3n)!} x^n$ 18. $\displaystyle\sum_{n=1}^{\infty} \dfrac{n^{5n}}{(2n)! n^{3n}} x^n$

19. $\displaystyle\sum_{n=1}^{\infty} \dfrac{(3n)!}{(n!)^2} x^n$ 20. $\displaystyle\sum_{n=1}^{\infty} \dfrac{\sin n\pi/2}{2^n} x^n$ 21. $\displaystyle\sum_{n=2}^{\infty} \dfrac{\log n}{2^n} x^n$

22. $\displaystyle\sum_{n=1}^{\infty} \dfrac{1+\cos 2\pi n}{3^n} x^n$ 23. $\displaystyle\sum_{n=2}^{\infty} n x^n$ 24. $\displaystyle\sum_{n=1}^{\infty} \dfrac{\sin 2\pi n}{n!} x^n$

25. $\displaystyle\sum_{n=2}^{\infty} n^2 x^n$ 26. $\displaystyle\sum_{n=1}^{\infty} \dfrac{\cos n^2}{n^n} x^n$ 27. $\displaystyle\sum_{n=2}^{\infty} \dfrac{n}{\log n} x^n$

28. $\displaystyle\sum_{n=2}^{\infty} \dfrac{(-1)^n}{n!-1} x^n$ 29. $\displaystyle\sum_{n=1}^{\infty} \dfrac{n!}{n^n} x^n$ 30. $\displaystyle\sum_{n=1}^{\infty} \dfrac{(-1)^n+1}{n!} x^n$

Note: For some of the above radii of convergence, recall that

$$\lim_{n\to\infty} \left(1+\frac{1}{n}\right)^n = \lim_{n\to\infty} \left(\frac{1+n}{n}\right)^n = e.$$

§7. DIFFERENTIATION AND INTEGRATION OF POWER SERIES

If we have a polynomial

$$a_0 + a_1 x + \cdots + a_n x^n$$

with numbers $a_0, a_1, \ldots, a_n$ as coefficients, then we know how to find its derivative. It is $a_1 + 2a_2 x + \cdots + n a_n x^{n-1}$. We would like to say that the derivative of a series can be taken in the same way, and that the derivative converges whenever the series does.

Theorem 8. *Let r be a number > 0 and let $\sum a_n x^n$ be a series which converges absolutely for $|x| < r$. Then the series $\sum n a_n x^{n-1}$ also converges absolutely for $|x| < r$.*

Proof. Since we are interested in the absolute convergence, we may assume that $a_n \geq 0$ for all n. Let $0 < x < r$, and let c be a number such that $x < c < r$. Recall that

$$\lim_{n\to\infty} n^{1/n} = 1.$$

We may write

$$na_nx^n = a_n(n^{1/n}x)^n.$$

Then for all n sufficiently large, we conclude that

$$n^{1/n}x < c$$

because $n^{1/n}x$ comes arbitrarily close to x. Hence for all n sufficiently large, we have

$$na_nx^n < a_nc^n.$$

We can then compare the series $\sum na_nx^n$ with $\sum a_nc^n$ to conclude that $\sum na_nx^n$ converges. Since

$$\sum na_nx^{n-1} = \frac{1}{x}\sum a_nx^n$$

we have proved Theorem 8.

A similar result holds for integration, but trivially. Indeed, if we have a series $\sum_{n=1}^{\infty} a_nx^n$ which converges absolutely for $|x| < r$, then the series

$$\sum_{n=1}^{\infty} \frac{a_n}{n+1}x^{n+1} = x\sum_{n=1}^{\infty} \frac{a_n}{n+1}x^n$$

has terms whose absolute value is smaller than in the original series.

The preceding results can be expressed by saying that an absolutely convergent power series can be integrated and differentiated term by term and still yield an absolutely convergent power series.

It is natural to expect that if

$$f(x) = \sum_{n=1}^{\infty} a_nx^n,$$

then f is differentiable and its derivative is given by differentiating the series term by term. The next theorem proves this.

Theorem 9. *Let*

$$f(x) = \sum_{n=1}^{\infty} a_nx^n$$

be a power series, which converges absolutely for $|x| < r$. Then f is differentiable for $|x| < r$, and

$$f'(x) = \sum_{n=1}^{\infty} na_nx^{n-1}.$$

Proof. Let $0 < b < r$. Let $\delta > 0$ be such that $b + \delta < r$. We consider values of x such that $|x| < b$ and values of h such that $|h| < \delta$.

We have the numerator of the Newton quotient:

$$f(x+h) - f(x) = \sum_{n=1}^{\infty} a_n(x+h)^n - \sum_{n=1}^{\infty} a_n x^n = \sum_{n=1}^{\infty} a_n[(x+h)^n - x^n].$$

By the mean value theorem, there exists a number x_n between x and $x + h$ such that

$$(x+h)^n - x^n = nx_n^{n-1}h$$

and consequently

$$f(x+h) - f(x) = \sum_{n=1}^{\infty} na_n x_n^{n-1}h.$$

Therefore

$$\frac{f(x+h) - f(x)}{h} = \sum_{n=1}^{\infty} na_n x_n^{n-1}.$$

We have to show that the Newton quotient above approaches the value of the series obtained by taking the derivative term by term. We have

$$\frac{f(x+h) - f(x)}{h} - \sum_{n=1}^{\infty} na_n x^{n-1} = \sum_{n=1}^{\infty} na_n x_n^{n-1} - \sum_{n=1}^{\infty} na_n x^{n-1}$$

$$= \sum_{n=1}^{\infty} na_n[x_n^{n-1} - x^{n-1}].$$

Using the mean value theorem again, there exists y_n between x_n and x such that the preceding expression is

$$\frac{f(x+h) - f(x)}{h} - \sum_{n=1}^{\infty} na_n x^{n-1} = \sum_{n=2}^{\infty} (n-1)na_n y_n^{n-2}(x_n - x).$$

We have $|y_n| \leq b + \delta < r$, and $|x_n - x| \leq |h|$. Consequently,

$$\left| \frac{f(x+h) - f(x)}{h} - \sum_{n=1}^{\infty} na_n x^{n-1} \right| \leq \sum_{n=2}^{\infty} (n-1)n|a_n| \, |y_n|^{n-2}|h|$$

$$\leq |h| \sum_{n=2}^{\infty} (n-1)n|a_n|(b+\delta)^{n-2}.$$

By Theorem 8 applied twice, we know that the series appearing on the right converges. It is equal to a fixed constant. As h approaches 0, it follows that the expression on the left also approaches 0. This proves that f is differentiable at x, and that its derivative is equal to $\sum_{n=1}^{\infty} na_n x^{n-1}$, for all x such that $|x| < b$. This is true for all b, $0 < b < r$, and therefore concludes the proof of our theorem.

Theorem 10. *Let* $f(x) = \sum\limits_{n=1}^{\infty} a_n x^n$ *be a power series, which converges absolutely for* $|x| < r$. *Then the relation*

$$\int f(x)\,dx = \sum_{n=1}^{\infty} \frac{a_n}{n+1} x^{n+1}$$

is valid in the interval $|x| < r$.

Proof. We know that the series for f integrated term by term converges absolutely in the interval. By the preceding theorem, its derivative term by term is the series for the derivative of the function, thereby proving our assertion.

Example. If we had never heard of the exponential function, we could define a function

$$f(x) = 1 + x + \frac{x^2}{2!} + \frac{x^3}{3!} + \cdots.$$

Taking the derivative term by term, we see that

$$f'(x) = f(x).$$

Hence by what we know from Chapter VIII, §2, Exercise 7, we conclude that

$$f(x) = Ke^x$$

for some constant K. Letting $x = 0$ shows that

$$1 = f(0) = K.$$

Thus $K = 1$ and $f(x) = e^x$.

Similarly, if we had never heard of sine and cosine, we could *define* functions

$$S(x) = x - \frac{x^3}{3!} + \frac{x^5}{5!} - \cdots, \qquad C(x) = 1 - \frac{x^2}{2!} + \frac{x^4}{4!} - \cdots.$$

Differentiating term by term shows that

$$S'(x) = C(x), \qquad C'(x) = -S(x).$$

Furthermore, $S(0) = 0$ and $C(0) = 1$. It can then be shown easily that any pair of functions $S(x)$ and $C(x)$ satisfying these properties must be the sine and cosine. This is actually carried out in an appendix.

Chapter XVI

Complex Numbers

One of the advantages of dealing with the real numbers instead of the rational numbers is that certain equations which do not have any solutions in the rational numbers have a solution in real numbers. For instance, $x^2 = 2$ is such an equation. However, we also know some equations having no solution in real numbers, for instance $x^2 = -1$, or $x^2 = -2$. In this chapter, we define a new kind of number where such equations have solutions. What we have simply called numbers in the preceding chapters will now be called *real* numbers. The new kind of numbers will be called *complex* numbers.

§1. DEFINITION

The complex numbers are a set of objects which can be added and multiplied, the sum and product of two complex numbers being also a complex number, and satisfy the following conditions.

1. Every real number is a complex number, and if α, β are real numbers, then their sum and product as complex numbers are the same as their sum and product as real numbers.
2. There is a complex number denoted by i such that $i^2 = -1$.
3. Every complex number can be written uniquely in the form $a + bi$ where a, b are real numbers.
4. The ordinary laws of arithmetic concerning addition and multiplication are satisfied. We list these laws:

If α, β, γ are complex numbers, then $(\alpha\beta)\gamma = \alpha(\beta\gamma)$, and

$$(\alpha + \beta) + \gamma = \alpha + (\beta + \gamma).$$

We have $\alpha(\beta + \gamma) = \alpha\beta + \alpha\gamma$, and $(\beta + \gamma)\alpha = \beta\alpha + \gamma\alpha$.
We have $\alpha\beta = \beta\alpha$, and $\alpha + \beta = \beta + \alpha$.
If 1 is the real number one, then $1\alpha = \alpha$.
If 0 is the real number zero, then $0\alpha = 0$.
We have $\alpha + (-1)\alpha = 0$.

We shall now draw consequences of these properties. With each complex number $a + bi$, we associate the point (a, b) in the plane.

Let $\alpha = a_1 + a_2 i$ and $\beta = b_1 + b_2 i$ be two complex numbers. Then

$$\alpha + \beta = a_1 + b_1 + (a_2 + b_2)i.$$

Hence addition of complex numbers is carried out "componentwise". For example, $(2 + 3i) + (-1 + 5i) = 1 + 8i$.

In multiplying complex numbers, we use the rule $i^2 = -1$ to simplify a product and to put it in the form $a + bi$. For instance, let $\alpha = 2 + 3i$ and $\beta = 1 - i$. Then

$$\begin{aligned}
\alpha\beta = (2 + 3i)(1 - i) &= 2(1 - i) + 3i(1 - i) \\
&= 2 - 2i + 3i - 3i^2 \\
&= 2 + i - 3(-1) \\
&= 2 + 3 + i \\
&= 5 + i.
\end{aligned}$$

Let $\alpha = a + bi$ be a complex number. We define $\bar{\alpha}$ to be $a - bi$. Thus if $\alpha = 2 + 3i$, then $\bar{\alpha} = 2 - 3i$. The complex number $\bar{\alpha}$ is called the *conjugate* of α. We see at once that

$$\alpha\bar{\alpha} = a^2 + b^2.$$

With the vector interpretation of complex numbers, we see that $\alpha\bar{\alpha}$ is the square of the distance of the point (a, b) from the origin.

We now have one more important property of complex numbers, which will allow us to divide by complex numbers other than 0.

If $\alpha = a + bi$ is a complex number $\neq 0$, and if we let

$$\lambda = \frac{\bar{\alpha}}{a^2 + b^2}$$

then $\alpha\lambda = \lambda\alpha = 1$.

The proof of this property is an immediate consequence of the law of multiplication of complex numbers, because

$$\alpha\frac{\bar{\alpha}}{a^2 + b^2} = \frac{\alpha\bar{\alpha}}{a^2 + b^2} = 1.$$

The number λ above is called the *inverse* of α, and is denoted by α^{-1} or $1/\alpha$. If α, β are complex numbers, we often write β/α instead of $\alpha^{-1}\beta$ (or $\beta\alpha^{-1}$), just as we did with real numbers. We see that we can divide by complex numbers $\neq 0$.

Example. To find the inverse of $(1 + i)$ we note that the conjugate of $1 + i$ is $1 - i$ and that $(1 + i)(1 - i) = 2$. Hence

$$(1 + i)^{-1} = \frac{1 - i}{2}.$$

Theorem 1. *Let α, β be complex numbers. Then*

$$\overline{\alpha\beta} = \bar{\alpha}\bar{\beta}, \qquad \overline{\alpha + \beta} = \bar{\alpha} + \bar{\beta}, \qquad \bar{\bar{\alpha}} = \alpha.$$

Proof. The proofs follow immediately from the definitions of addition, multiplication, and the complex conjugate. We leave them as exercises (Exercises 3 and 4).

Let $\alpha = a + bi$ be a complex number, where a, b are real. We shall call a the *real part* of α, and denote it by $\operatorname{Re}(\alpha)$. Thus

$$\alpha + \bar{\alpha} = 2a = 2\operatorname{Re}(\alpha).$$

We define the *absolute value* of a complex number $\alpha = a_1 + ia_2$ (where a_1, a_2 are real) to be

$$|\alpha| = \sqrt{a_1^2 + a_2^2}.$$

If we think of α as a point in the plane (a_1, a_2), then $|\alpha|$ is the length of the line segment from the origin to α.

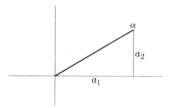

In terms of the absolute value, we can write

$$\alpha^{-1} = \frac{\bar{\alpha}}{|\alpha|^2}$$

provided $\alpha \neq 0$. Indeed, we observe that $|\alpha|^2 = \alpha\bar{\alpha}$.

If $\alpha = a_1 + ia_2$, we note that

$$|\alpha| = |\bar{\alpha}|$$

because $(-a_2)^2 = a_2^2$, so $\sqrt{a_1^2 + a_2^2} = \sqrt{a_1^2 + (-a_2)^2}$.

Theorem 2. *The absolute value of a complex number satisfies the following properties. If α, β are complex numbers, then*

$$|\alpha\beta| = |\alpha|\,|\beta|$$
$$|\alpha + \beta| \leq |\alpha| + |\beta|.$$

Proof. We have:

$$|\alpha\beta|^2 = \alpha\beta\overline{\alpha\beta} = \alpha\bar{\alpha}\beta\bar{\beta} = |\alpha|^2|\beta|^2.$$

Taking the square root, we conclude that $|\alpha| \, |\beta| = |\alpha\beta|$, thus proving the first assertion. As for the second, we have

$$|\alpha + \beta|^2 = (\alpha + \beta)(\overline{\alpha + \beta}) = (\alpha + \beta)(\bar{\alpha} + \bar{\beta})$$
$$= \alpha\bar{\alpha} + \beta\bar{\alpha} + \alpha\bar{\beta} + \beta\bar{\beta}$$
$$= |\alpha|^2 + 2\,\mathrm{Re}(\beta\bar{\alpha}) + |\beta|^2$$

because $\alpha\bar{\beta} = \overline{\beta\bar{\alpha}}$. However, we have

$$2\,\mathrm{Re}(\beta\bar{\alpha}) \leqq 2|\beta\bar{\alpha}|$$

because the real part of a complex number is $\leqq$ its absolute value. Hence

$$|\alpha + \beta|^2 \leqq |\alpha|^2 + 2|\beta\bar{\alpha}| + |\beta|^2$$
$$\leqq |\alpha|^2 + 2|\beta|\,|\alpha| + |\beta|^2$$
$$= (|\alpha| + |\beta|)^2.$$

Taking the square root yields the second assertion of the theorem.

EXERCISES

1. Express the following complex numbers in the form $x + iy$, where x, y are real numbers.

   (a) $(-1 + 3i)^{-1}$ (b) $(1 + i)(1 - i)$
   (c) $(1 + i)i(2 - i)$ (d) $(i - 1)(2 - i)$
   (e) $(7 + \pi i)(\pi + i)$ (f) $(2i + 1)\pi i$
   (g) $(\sqrt{2}\,i)(\pi + 3i)$ (h) $(i + 1)(i - 2)(i + 3)$

2. Express the following complex numbers in the form $x + iy$, where x, y are real numbers.

   (a) $(1 + i)^{-1}$ (b) $\dfrac{1}{3 + i}$ (c) $\dfrac{2 + i}{2 - i}$ (d) $\dfrac{1}{2 - i}$

   (e) $\dfrac{1 + i}{i}$ (f) $\dfrac{i}{1 + i}$ (g) $\dfrac{2i}{3 - i}$ (h) $\dfrac{1}{-1 + i}$

3. Let α be a complex number $\neq 0$. What is the absolute value of $\alpha/\bar{\alpha}$? What is $\bar{\bar{\alpha}}$?

4. Let α, β be two complex numbers. Show that $\overline{\alpha\beta} = \bar{\alpha}\bar{\beta}$ and that

$$\overline{\alpha + \beta} = \bar{\alpha} + \bar{\beta}.$$

5. Justify the assertion made in the proof of Theorem 2, that the real part of a complex number is $\leqq$ its absolute value.

6. If $\alpha = a + ib$ with a, b real, then b is called the *imaginary* part of α and we write $b = \mathrm{Im}(\alpha)$. Show that $\alpha - \bar{\alpha} = 2\,\mathrm{Im}(\alpha)$. Show that

$$\mathrm{Im}(\alpha) \leqq |\mathrm{Im}(\alpha)| \leqq |\alpha|.$$

§2. POLAR FORM

Let $(x, y) = x + iy$ be a complex number. We know that any point in the plane can be represented by polar coordinates (r, θ). We shall now see how to write our complex number in terms of such polar coordinates. Let θ be a real number. We define the expression $e^{i\theta}$ to be

$$e^{i\theta} = \cos \theta + i \sin \theta.$$

Thus $e^{i\theta}$ is a complex number.

For example, if $\theta = \pi$, then $e^{i\pi} = -1$. Also, $e^{2\pi i} = 1$, and $e^{i\pi/2} = i$. Furthermore, $e^{i(\theta + 2\pi)} = e^{i\theta}$ for any real θ.

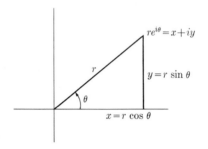

Let x, y be real numbers and $x + iy$ a complex number. Let

$$r = \sqrt{x^2 + y^2}.$$

If (r, θ) are the polar coordinates of the point (x, y) in the plane, then

$$x = r \cos \theta \quad \text{and} \quad y = r \sin \theta.$$

Hence

$$x + iy = r \cos \theta + ir \sin \theta = re^{i\theta}.$$

The expression $re^{i\theta}$ is called the *polar form* of the complex number $x + iy$.

The most important property of this polar form is given in Theorem 3. It will allow us to have a very good geometric interpretation for the product of two complex numbers.

Theorem 3. *Let θ, φ be two real numbers. Then*

$$e^{i\theta + i\varphi} = e^{i\theta} e^{i\varphi}.$$

Proof. By definition, we have

$$e^{i\theta + i\varphi} = e^{i(\theta + \varphi)} = \cos (\theta + \varphi) + i \sin (\theta + \varphi).$$

Using the addition formula for sine and cosine, we see that the preceding expression is equal to

$$\cos \theta \cos \varphi - \sin \theta \sin \varphi + i(\sin \theta \cos \varphi + \sin \varphi \cos \theta).$$

This is exactly the same expression as the one we obtain by multiplying out

$$(\cos \theta + i \sin \theta)(\cos \varphi + i \sin \varphi).$$

Our theorem is proved.

Theorem 3 justifies our notation, by showing that the exponential of complex numbers satisfies the same formal rule as the exponential of real numbers.

Let $\alpha = a_1 + ia_2$ be a complex number. We define e^α to be

$$e^{a_1}e^{ia_2}.$$

For instance, let $\alpha = 2 + 3i$. Then $e^\alpha = e^2 e^{3i}$.

Theorem 4. *Let α, β be complex numbers. Then*

$$e^{\alpha+\beta} = e^\alpha e^\beta.$$

Proof. Let $\alpha = a_1 + ia_2$ and $\beta = b_1 + ib_2$. Then

$$e^{\alpha+\beta} = e^{(a_1+b_1)+i(a_2+b_2)} = e^{a_1+b_1}e^{i(a_2+b_2)}$$
$$= e^{a_1}e^{b_1}e^{ia_2+ib_2}.$$

Using Theorem 3, we see that this last expression is equal to

$$e^{a_1}e^{b_1}e^{ia_2}e^{ib_2} = e^{a_1}e^{ia_2}e^{b_1}e^{ib_2}.$$

By definition, this is equal to $e^\alpha e^\beta$, thereby proving our theorem.

Theorem 4 is very useful in dealing with complex numbers. We shall now consider several examples to illustrate it.

Example 1. Find a complex number whose square is $4e^{i\pi/2}$.
Let $z = 2e^{i\pi/4}$. Using the rule for exponentials, we see that $z^2 = 4e^{i\pi/2}$.

Example 2. Let n be a positive integer. Find a complex number w such that $w^n = e^{i\pi/2}$.
It is clear that the complex number $w = e^{i\pi/2n}$ satisfies our requirement.
In other words, we may express Theorem 4 as follows. Let $z_1 = r_1 e^{i\theta_1}$ and $z_2 = r_2 e^{i\theta_2}$ be two complex numbers. To find the product $z_1 z_2$, we multiply the absolute values and add the angles. Thus

$$z_1 z_2 = r_1 r_2 e^{i(\theta_1+\theta_2)}.$$

In many cases, this way of visualizing the product of complex numbers is more useful than that coming out of the definition.

EXERCISES

1. Put the following complex numbers in polar form.

   (a) $1 + i$ (b) $1 + i\sqrt{2}$ (c) -3 (d) $4i$

   (e) $1 - i\sqrt{2}$ (f) $-5i$ (g) -7 (h) $-1 - i$

2. Put the following complex numbers in the ordinary form $x + iy$.

   (a) $e^{3i\pi}$ (b) $e^{2i\pi/3}$ (c) $3e^{i\pi/4}$ (d) $\pi e^{-i\pi/3}$

   (e) $e^{2\pi i/6}$ (f) $e^{-i\pi/2}$ (g) $e^{-i\pi}$ (h) $e^{-5i\pi/4}$

3. Let α be a complex number $\neq 0$. Show that there are two distinct complex numbers whose square is α.

4. Let α be a complex number $\neq 0$. Let n be a positive integer. Show that there are n distinct complex numbers z such that $z^n = \alpha$. Write these complex numbers in polar form.

5. Let $\alpha = 1$ in Exercise 4. Plot all the complex numbers z such that $z^n = 1$ on a sheet of graph paper, for $n = 2, 3, 4,$ and 5.

6. Let $a + bi$ be a complex number. Find real numbers x, y such that $(x + iy)^2 = a + bi$, expressing x, y in terms of a and b.

7. Let w be a complex number and suppose that z is a complex number such that $e^z = w$. Describe all complex numbers u such that $e^u = w$.

8. What are the complex numbers z such that $e^z = 1$?

9. If θ is real, show that

$$\cos \theta = \frac{e^{i\theta} + e^{-i\theta}}{2} \quad \text{and} \quad \sin \theta = \frac{e^{i\theta} - e^{-i\theta}}{2}.$$

§3. COMPLEX VALUED FUNCTIONS

Let S be a collection of real numbers. An association which to each element of S associates a complex number is called a *complex valued function*. For instance, the association

$$\theta \mapsto e^{i\theta}$$

is a complex valued function, defined for all real numbers θ.

Let F be a complex valued function defined on some open interval. We can write F in the form

$$F(t) = f(t) + ig(t),$$

where f and g are real valued functions. If $F(\theta) = e^{i\theta}$, then $f(\theta) = \cos \theta$ and $g(\theta) = \sin \theta$. We call f the *real part* of F, and g its *imaginary part*.

For example, the real part of the complex valued function

$$t \mapsto t^2 + 1 + i(\cos t + e^t)$$

is the function $t \mapsto t^2 + 1$.

If both the real part and imaginary part of F are differentiable, then we say that F is differentiable, and we define

$$F'(t) = f'(t) + ig'(t),$$

thus differentiating componentwise. For example, if

$$F(t) = t^2 + 1 + i(\cos t + e^t)$$

then

$$F'(t) = 2t + i(-\sin t + e^t).$$

We shall also write

$$\frac{dF(t)}{dt}$$

for the derivative, instead of $F'(t)$.

The following rules for the derivative of complex valued functions are easily verified:

(a) Let F, G be complex valued functions defined on the same interval, and differentiable. Then $F + G$ is differentiable, and $(F + G)' = F' + G'$, or in other words,

$$\frac{d(F + G)}{dt} = \frac{dF}{dt} + \frac{dG}{dt}.$$

If α is a complex number, then $(\alpha F)' = \alpha F'$, i.e.

$$\frac{d(\alpha F)}{dt} = \alpha \frac{dF}{dt}.$$

(b) Let F, G be as above. Then FG is differentiable and

$$(FG)' = FG' + F'G,$$

or in other words,

$$\frac{d(FG)}{dt} = F\frac{dG}{dt} + \frac{dF}{dt}G.$$

We shall leave the first assertion as an exercise. To prove the second, let $F(t) = f_1(t) + if_2(t)$, $G(t) = g_1(t) + ig_2(t)$. Then

$$FG = f_1g_1 - f_2g_2 + i(f_1g_2 + f_2g_1),$$

whence

$$(FG)' = f_1g_1' + f_1'g_1 - f_2g_2' - f_2'g_2$$
$$+ i(f_1g_2' + f_1'g_2 + f_2g_1' + f_2'g_1).$$

If one expands out $F'G + FG'$ according to the rule of multiplication of complex numbers, one finds precisely the same expression that we just found for $(FG)'$, as was to be shown.

We define the integral also componentwise. We say that a complex valued function

$$F(t) = f(t) + ig(t)$$

is continuous if both f and g are continuous. In this case, we define the indefinite integral

$$\int F(t)\,dt = \int f(t)\,dt + i\int g(t)\,dt,$$

and similarly, if f, g are continuous over the closed interval $[a, b]$ we define

$$\int_a^b F(t)\,dt = \int_a^b f(t)\,dt + i\int_a^b g(t)\,dt.$$

As with real valued functions, if F, G are complex valued functions on an interval such that $F' = G'$, then there is a complex number C such that $F = G + C$. Thus an indefinite integral is again determined up to a constant (complex, of course). This is seen immediately by applying the known result to the real and imaginary parts of F and G.

EXERCISES

1. Let F be a differentiable complex valued function. Show that

$$\frac{d(e^{F(t)})}{dt} = F'(t)e^{F(t)}.$$

2. Let α be a complex number $\neq 0$. Show that

$$\int e^{\alpha t}\,dt = \frac{e^{\alpha t}}{\alpha}.$$

3. Let n be an integer $\neq 0$. Find

$$\int_0^1 e^{2\pi int}\,dt.$$

4. Let F be a differentiable complex valued function defined on an interval. If $F' = 0$ show that F is constant. Also prove in detail the last assertion of the section.

Appendix 1

ϵ *and* δ

This appendix is intended to show how the notions of limits and the properties of limits can be explained and proved in terms of the notions and properties of numbers. We therefore assume the latter and carry out the proofs from there.

There remains the problem of showing how the real numbers can be defined in terms of the rational numbers, and the rational numbers in terms of integers. This takes too long to be included in this book.

Aside from the ordinary rules for addition, multiplication, subtraction, division (by non-zero numbers), ordering, positivity, and inequalities, there is one more basic property satisfied by the real numbers. This property is stated in §1. Our proofs then use only these properties.

§1. LEAST UPPER BOUND

We meet again the problem of where to jump into the theory. It would be long and tedious to jump in too early. Hence we assume known the contents of Chapter I, §1 and §2. These involve the ordinary operations of addition and multiplication, and the notion of ordering, positivity, negative numbers, and inequalities. Those who are interested in seeing the logical development of these notions are referred to books on analysis.

A collection of numbers will simply be called a *set* of numbers. This is shorter and is the usual terminology. If a set has at least one number in it, we say that it is *non-empty*. A set S' is called a *subset* of S if every element of S' is an element of S. In other words, if S' is part of S.

Let S be a non-empty set of numbers. We shall say that S is *bounded from above* if there exists a number B such that

$$x \leq B$$

for all x in our set S. We then call B an *upper bound* for S.

A *least upper bound* for S is an upper bound L such that any upper bound B for S satisfies the inequality $B \geq L$. If M is another least upper bound, then we have $M \geq L$ and $L \geq M$, whence $L = M$. Consequently, a least upper bound is unique.

Similarly, we define the notions of bounded from below, and of greatest lower bound. (Do it yourself.)

The real numbers satisfy a property which is not satisfied by the set of rational numbers, namely:

Fundamental Property. *Every non-empty set S of numbers which is bounded from above has a least upper bound. Every non-empty set of numbers S which is bounded from below has a greatest lower bound.*

Proposition 1. *Let a be a number such that*

$$0 \leqq a < \frac{1}{n}$$

for every positive integer n. Then $a = 0$. There is no number b such that $b \geqq n$ for every positive integer n.

Proof. Suppose there is a number $a \neq 0$ such that $a < 1/n$ for every positive integer n. Then $n < 1/a$ for every positive integer n. Thus to prove both our assertions, it will suffice to prove the second.

Suppose there is a number b such that $b \geqq n$ for every positive integer n. Let S be the set of positive integers. Then S is bounded, and hence has a least upper bound. Let C be this least upper bound. No number strictly less than C can be an upper bound. Since $0 < 1$, we have $C < C + 1$, whence $C - 1 < C$. Hence there is a positive integer n such that

$$C - 1 < n.$$

This implies that $C < n + 1$ and $n + 1$ is a positive integer. We have contradicted our assumption that C is an upper bound for the set of positive integers, so no such upper bound can exist.

§2. LIMITS

Let S be a set of numbers and let f be a function defined for all numbers in S. Let x_0 be a number. We shall assume that S is *arbitrarily close to* x_0, i.e. given $\epsilon > 0$ there exists an element x of S such that $|x - x_0| < \epsilon$. Let L be a number. We shall say that *$f(x)$ approaches the limit L as x approaches x_0* if the following condition is satisfied:

Given a number $\epsilon > 0$, there exists a number $\delta > 0$ such that for all x in S satisfying

$$|x - x_0| < \delta$$

we have

$$|f(x) - L| < \epsilon.$$

If that is the case, then we write

$$\lim_{x \to x_0} f(x) = L.$$

We could also rephrase this as follows. We write

$$\lim_{h \to 0} f(x_0 + h) = L$$

and say that *the limit of $f(x_0 + h)$ is L as h approaches* 0 if the following condition is satisfied:

Given $\epsilon > 0$, there exists $\delta > 0$ such that whenever h is a number with $|h| < \delta$ and $x_0 + h$ in S, then

$$|f(x_0 + h) - L| < \epsilon.$$

We note that our definition of limit depends on the set S on which f is defined. Thus we should say "limit with respect to S". The next proposition shows that this is really unnecessary.

Proposition 2. *Let S be a set of numbers arbitrarily close to x_0 and let S' be a subset of S, also arbitrarily close to x_0. Let f be a function defined on S. If*

$$\lim_{x \to x_0} f(x) = L \qquad (\textit{with respect to } S)$$

$$\lim_{x \to x_0} f(x) = M \qquad (\textit{with respect to } S')$$

then $L = M$. In particular, the limit is unique.

Proof. Given $\epsilon > 0$, there exists $\delta_1 > 0$ such that whenever x is in S' and $|x - x_0| < \delta_1$ we have

$$|f(x) - L| < \frac{\epsilon}{2},$$

and there exists $\delta_2 > 0$ such that whenever $|x - x_0| < \delta_2$ then

$$|f(x) - M| < \frac{\epsilon}{2}.$$

Let $\delta = \min(\delta_1, \delta_2)$. If $|x - x_0| < \delta$ then

$$|L - M| \le |L - f(x) + f(x) - M| < \frac{\epsilon}{2} + \frac{\epsilon}{2} = \epsilon.$$

Hence $|L - M|$ is less than any $\epsilon > 0$, and by Proposition 1 of §1, we must have $|L - M| = 0$, whence

$$L - M = 0$$

and

$$L = M.$$

In practice from now on, we omit to state that x is an element of S. The context makes it clear each time.

Furthermore, in many subsequent proofs, we shall need several simultaneous inequalities to be satisfied, just as in the preceding proof we had inequalities with δ_1 and δ_2. In each case, we use a similar trick, letting δ be the minimum of $\delta_1, \delta_2, \delta_3, \ldots$ needed to make each desired inequality valid. Thus in writing down the proofs, we omit the intermediate $\delta_1, \delta_2, \delta_3 \ldots$.

Remark. Suppose that $\lim_{x \to x_0} f(x) = L$. Then there exists $\delta > 0$ such that whenever $|x - x_0| < \delta$ we have

$$|f(x)| < |L| + 1.$$

Indeed, given $1 > 0$ there exists δ such that whenever $|x - x_0| < \delta$ we have
$$|f(x) - L| < 1,$$

so that our assertion follows from standard properties of inequalities.

Also, note that we have trivially

$$\lim_{x \to x_0} C = C$$

for any number C, viewed as a constant function on S. Indeed, given $\epsilon > 0$,

$$|C - C| < \epsilon.$$

Remark. We mention a word about limits *"when x becomes large"*. Let a be a number and f a function defined for all numbers $x \geqq a$. Let L be a number. We shall say that $f(x)$ *approaches L as x becomes large*, and we write

$$\lim_{x \to \infty} f(x) = L$$

if the following condition is satisfied. Given $\epsilon > 0$ there exists a number A such that whenever $x > A$ we have

$$|f(x) - L| < \epsilon.$$

In practice, instead of saying "when x becomes large", we sometimes say "when x approaches ∞". We leave it to you to define the analogous notion "when x becomes large negative", or "x approaches $-\infty$".

In the definition of $\lim_{x \to \infty}$ we took a function f defined for $x \geqq a$. If $a_1 > a$, and we restrict the function to all numbers $\geqq a_1$, then the limit as x becomes very large will be the same.

Let us suppose that $a \geqq 1$. Define a function g for values of x such that

$$0 < x \leqq 1/a$$

by the rule

$$g(x) = f(1/x).$$

Then a second's thought will allow you to prove that

$$\lim_{x \to 0} g(x)$$

exists if and only if

$$\lim_{x \to \infty} f(x)$$

exists, and that they are equal.

Consequently all properties which we prove concerning limits as x approaches 0 (or a number) immediately give rise to similar properties concerning limits as x becomes very large. We leave their formulations to you.

The next theorems, concerning the basic properties of limits, describe limits of sums, products, quotients, inequalities, and composite functions.

Theorem 1. *Let S be a set of numbers, and f, g two functions defined for all numbers in S. Let x_0 be a number. If*

$$\lim_{x \to x_0} f(x) = L$$

and

$$\lim_{x \to x_0} g(x) = M,$$

then $\lim_{x \to x_0} (f + g)(x)$ exists and is equal to $L + M$.

Proof. Given $\epsilon > 0$, there exists $\delta > 0$ such that, whenever $|x - x_0| < \delta$ (and x is in S), we have

$$|f(x) - L| < \frac{\epsilon}{2}$$

$$|g(x) - M| < \frac{\epsilon}{2}.$$

We observe that

$$|f(x) + g(x) - L - M| \leq |f(x) - L| + |g(x) - M| < \epsilon.$$

This proves that $L + M$ is the limit of $(f + g)(x)$ as x approaches x_0.

Theorem 2. *Let S be a set of numbers, and f, g two functions defined for all numbers in S. Let x_0 be a number. If*

$$\lim_{x \to x_0} f(x) = L$$

and

$$\lim_{x \to x_0} g(x) = M,$$

then $\lim_{x \to x_0} f(x)g(x)$ exists and is equal to LM.

Proof. Given $\epsilon > 0$ there exists $\delta > 0$ such that, whenever $|x - x_0| < \delta$, we have

$$|f(x) - L| < \frac{1}{2} \frac{\epsilon}{|M| + 1}$$

$$|g(x) - M| < \frac{1}{2} \frac{\epsilon}{|L| + 1}$$

$$|f(x)| < |L| + 1.$$

We have

$$
\begin{aligned}
|f(x)g(x) - LM| &= |f(x)g(x) - f(x)M + f(x)M - LM| \\
&\leq |f(x)g(x) - f(x)M| + |f(x)M - LM| \\
&\leq |f(x)| \, |g(x) - M| + |f(x) - L| \, |M| \\
&< (|L| + 1)\frac{1}{2} \frac{\epsilon}{|L| + 1} + \frac{1}{2} \frac{\epsilon}{|M| + 1} |M| \\
&\leq \frac{\epsilon}{2} + \frac{\epsilon}{2} \\
&\leq \epsilon.
\end{aligned}
$$

Corollary 1. *Let C be a number and let the assumptions be as in the theorem. Then*

$$\lim_{x \to x_0} Cf(x) = CL.$$

Proof. Clear.

Corollary 2. *Let the notation be as in Theorem 2. Then*

$$\lim_{x \to x_0} [f(x) - g(x)] = L - M.$$

Proof. Clear.

Theorem 3. *Let S be a set of numbers, and f a function defined for all numbers in S. Let x_0 be a number. If*

$$\lim_{x \to x_0} f(x) = L$$

and $L \neq 0$, then the limit

$$\lim_{x \to x_0} \frac{1}{f(x)}$$

exists and is equal to $1/L$.

Proof. Given $\epsilon > 0$, there exists $\delta > 0$ such that whenever $|x - x_0| < \delta$ we have

$$|f(x) - L| < \frac{|L|}{2}$$

and also

$$|f(x) - L| < \frac{\epsilon |L|^2}{2}.$$

From the first inequality, we get

$$|f(x)| \geq |L| - \frac{|L|}{2} = \frac{|L|}{2}.$$

In particular, $f(x) \neq 0$ when $|x - x_0| < \delta$. For such x we get

$$\left| \frac{1}{f(x)} - \frac{1}{L} \right| = \frac{|L - f(x)|}{|f(x)L|}$$

$$\leq \frac{2}{|L|} \frac{|L - f(x)|}{|L|}$$

$$< \frac{2}{|L|^2} \frac{\epsilon |L|^2}{2} = \epsilon.$$

Corollary. *Let the hypotheses be as in Theorem 2, and assume that $L \neq 0$. Then*

$$\lim_{x \to x_0} \frac{g(x)}{f(x)}$$

exists and is equal to M/L.

Proof. Use Theorem 2 and Theorem 3.

Theorem 4. *Let S be a set of numbers, and f a function on S. Let x_0 be a number. Let g be a function on S such that $g(x) \leq f(x)$ for all x in S. Assume that*

$$\lim_{x \to x_0} f(x) = L \qquad and \qquad \lim_{x \to x_0} g(x) = M.$$

Then $M \leq L$.

Proof. Let $\varphi(x) = f(x) - g(x)$. Then $\varphi(x) \geq 0$ for all x in S. Also,

$$\lim_{x \to x_0} \varphi(x) = L - M$$

by Corollary 2 of Theorem 2. Let K be this limit. We must show $K \geq 0$. Suppose $K < 0$. Then $-K > 0$ and $|K| = -K$. Given $\epsilon > 0$ there exists $\delta > 0$ such that whenever $|x - x_0| < \delta$ we have

$$|\varphi(x) - K| < \epsilon,$$

whence

$$|\varphi(x)| - K < \epsilon.$$

Since $\varphi(x) \geq 0$, we get $-K < \epsilon$ for all $\epsilon > 0$. In particular, for all positive integers n we get $-K < 1/n$. But $-K > 0$. This contradicts Proposition 1 of §1.

Theorem 5. *Let the notation be as in Theorem 4 and assume that M = L. Let ψ be a function on S such that*

$$g(x) \leqq \psi(x) \leqq f(x)$$

for all x in S. Then

$$\lim_{x \to x_0} \psi(x)$$

exists and is equal to L (or M).

Proof. Given $\epsilon > 0$ there exists $\delta > 0$ such that whenever $|x - x_0| < \delta$ we have

$$|g(x) - L| < \frac{\epsilon}{4}$$

$$|f(x) - L| < \frac{\epsilon}{4}.$$

We also have

$$
\begin{aligned}
|f(x) - \psi(x)| &\leqq |f(x) - g(x)| \\
&\leqq |f(x) - L + L - g(x)| \\
&\leqq |f(x) - L| + |L - g(x)| \\
&< \frac{\epsilon}{2}.
\end{aligned}
$$

But

$$
\begin{aligned}
|L - \psi(x)| &\leqq |L - f(x)| + |f(x) - \psi(x)| \\
&< \frac{\epsilon}{2} + \frac{\epsilon}{2} = \epsilon.
\end{aligned}
$$

Theorem 6. *Let S, T be sets of numbers, and let f, g be functions defined on S and T respectively. Let x_0 be arbitrarily close to S. Assume that for all x in S we have f(x) in T, so that g ∘ f is defined. Assume that*

$$\lim_{x \to x_0} f(x)$$

exists and is equal to a number y_0 arbitrarily close to T. Assume that

$$\lim_{y \to y_0} g(y)$$

exists and equals L. Then

$$\lim_{x \to x_0} g(f(x)) = L.$$

Proof. Given ϵ there exists δ such that whenever y is in T and

$$|y - y_0| < \delta$$

we have

$$|g(y) - L| < \epsilon.$$

With the above δ being given, there exists δ_1 such that whenever x is in S

and $|x - x_0| < \delta_1$ we have $|f(x) - y_0| < \delta$. From this it follows that

$$|g(f(x)) - L| < \epsilon$$

hence proving our assertion.

[*Note:* Theorem 6 justifies the limit procedure used to prove the chain rule.]

This completely proves all the statements about limits we made in Chapter III.

§3. POINTS OF ACCUMULATION

A *sequence* is a function defined on a set of integers ≥ 0. Usually, this set consists of all positive integers. In that case, a sequence amounts to giving numbers

$$a_1, a_2, a_3, \ldots$$

for each positive integer, and we denote the sequence by $\{a_n\}$ $(n = 1, 2, \ldots)$.

If the set consists of all integers ≥ 0, then we denote the sequence by $\{a_n\}$ $(n = 0, 1, 2, \ldots)$.

Let $\{a_n\}$ $(n = 1, 2, \ldots)$ be a sequence. Let C be a number. We say that C is a *point of accumulation* of the sequence if given $\epsilon > 0$ there exist infinitely many integers n such that

$$|a_n - C| < \epsilon.$$

Let $\{a_n\}$ $(n = 1, 2, \ldots)$ be a sequence, and L a number. We shall say that L is a *limit of the sequence* if given $\epsilon > 0$ there exists an integer N such that for all $n > N$ we have

$$|a_n - L| < \epsilon.$$

The limit is then unique (same type of proof as we had for limits of functions).

We shall say that the sequence $\{a_n\}$ $(n = 1, 2, \ldots)$ is *increasing* if $a_n \leq a_{n+1}$ for all positive integers n.

Theorem 7. *Let $\{a_n\}$ $(n = 1, 2, \ldots)$ be an increasing sequence, and assume that it is bounded from above. Then the least upper bound L is a limit of the sequence.*

Proof. Given $\epsilon > 0$ the number $L - (\epsilon/2)$ is not an upper bound for the sequence. Hence there exists some number a_N such that

$$L - (\epsilon/2) \leq a_N.$$

This inequality is also satisfied for all $n > N$, since the sequence is increasing. But

$$a_n \leqq L$$

because L is an upper bound. Thus

$$|L - a_n| = L - a_n \leqq \frac{\epsilon}{2} < \epsilon$$

for all $n > N$, thereby proving our assertion.

Corollary. *Let* $\{a_n\}$ *($n = 1, 2, \ldots$) be a sequence, and let A, B be two numbers such that $A \leqq a_n \leqq B$ for all positive integers n. Then there exists a point of accumulation C of the sequence between A and B.*

Proof. For each integer n we let b_n be the greatest lower bound of the set of numbers $\{a_n, a_{n+1}, a_{n+2}, \ldots\}$. Then $b_n \leqq b_{n+1} \leqq \cdots$, i.e. $\{b_n\}$ ($n = 1, 2, \ldots$) is an increasing sequence. Let L be its limit, as in Theorem 7. We leave it to you as an exercise to prove that this limit is a point of accumulation.

One can reduce the notion of limit of a sequence to that of limits defined previously.

Let S be the set of numbers

$$1, \quad \frac{1}{2}, \quad \frac{1}{3}, \quad \cdots, \quad \frac{1}{n}, \quad \cdots,$$

i.e. the set of numbers which can be written as $1/n$, where n is a positive integer.

If $\{a_n\}$ ($n = 1, 2, \ldots$) is a sequence, we let f be a function defined on S by the rule

$$f(1/n) = a_n.$$

Then you will verify immediately that

$$\lim_{n \to \infty} a_n$$

exists if and only if

$$\lim_{h \to 0} f(h)$$

exists, and in that case the two limits are equal. We say that a sequence $\{a_n\}$ *approaches a number L when n becomes large if*

$$L = \lim_{n \to \infty} a_n.$$

Thus properties concerning limits in the sense of §2 immediately give rise to properties concerning limits of sequences (for instance limits of sums, products, quotients). We leave their translations to you.

§4. CONTINUOUS FUNCTIONS

Let f be a function defined on a set of numbers S. Let x_0 be a number in S. Then S is arbitrarily close to x_0. We say that f is *continuous* at x_0 if

$$\lim_{x \to x_0} f(x) = f(x_0).$$

Note that there may be two numbers a, b with $a < x_0 < b$ such that x_0 is the only point which is in the interval and lies also in S. (In this case, one could say that x_0 is an *isolated* point of S.)

It follows at once from our definition that if $\{a_n\}$ $(n = 1, 2, \ldots)$ is a sequence of numbers in S such that

$$\lim_{n \to \infty} a_n = x_0$$

and f is continuous at x_0, then

$$\lim_{n \to \infty} f(a_n) = f(x_0).$$

It is immediate that the sum, product, quotient of continuous functions are again continuous. (In the quotient, we have to assume that $f(x_0) \neq 0$, of course.) Every constant function is continuous. The function $f(x) = x$ is continuous for all x. This is trivially verified. From the quotient theorem, we see that the function $f(x) = 1/x$ (defined for $x \neq 0$) is continuous.

Theorem 8. *Let f and g be continuous functions such that the values of f are contained in the domain of definition of g. Then $g \circ f$ is continuous.*

Proof. Let x_0 be a number at which f is defined, and let

$$y_0 = f(x_0).$$

Given $\epsilon > 0$, since g is continuous at y_0, there exists $\delta_1 > 0$ such that if $|y - y_0| < \delta_1$, then

$$|g(y) - g(y_0)| < \epsilon.$$

Now with the above δ_1 being given, there exists $\delta > 0$ such that if $|x - x_0| < \delta$ then

$$|f(x) - f(x_0)| < \delta_1.$$

Hence

$$|g(f(x)) - g(f(x_0))| < \epsilon,$$

thus proving our theorem.

Theorem 9. *Let f be a continuous function on a closed interval $a \leq x \leq b$. Then there exists a point c in the interval such that $f(c)$ is a maximum, and there exists a point d in the interval such that $f(d)$ is a minimum.*

Proof. We shall first prove that f is bounded, i.e. that there exists a number M such that $|f(x)| \leq M$ for all x in the interval.

If f is not bounded, then for every positive integer n we can find a number x_n in the interval such that $|f(x_n)| > n$. The sequence of such x_n has a point of accumulation C in the interval. We have

$$|f(x_n) - f(C)| \geq |f(x_n)| - |f(C)|$$
$$\geq n - f(C).$$

Given $\epsilon > 0$, there exists a $\delta > 0$ such that, whenever

$$|x_n - C| < \delta$$

we have $|f(x_n) - f(C)| < \epsilon$. This has to happen for infinitely many n, since C is an accumulation point. Our statements are contradictory, and we therefore conclude that the function is bounded.

Let β be the least upper bound of the set of values $f(x)$ for all x in the interval. Then given a positive integer n, we can find a number z_n in the interval such that

$$|f(z_n) - \beta| < \frac{1}{n}.$$

Let c be a point of accumulation of the sequence of numbers $\{z_n\}$ $(n = 1, 2, \ldots)$. Then $f(c) \leq \beta$. We contend that

$$f(c) = \beta$$

(this will prove our theorem).

Given $\epsilon > 0$, there exists $\delta > 0$ such that whenever $|z_n - c| < \delta$ we have

$$|f(z_n) - f(c)| < \epsilon.$$

This happens for infinitely many n, since c is a point of accumulation of the sequence $\{z_n\}$. But

$$|f(c) - \beta| \leq |f(c) - f(z_n)| + |f(z_n) - \beta|$$
$$< \epsilon + \frac{1}{n}.$$

This is true for every ϵ and infinitely many positive integers n. Hence $|f(c) - \beta| = 0$ and $f(c) = \beta$.

The proof for the minimum is similar and will be left as an exercise.

Theorem 10. *Let f be a continuous function on a closed interval $a \leq x \leq b$. Let $\alpha = f(a)$ and $\beta = f(b)$. Let γ be a number such that $\alpha < \gamma < \beta$. Then there exists a number c between a and b such that $f(c) = \gamma$.*

Proof. Let S be the set of numbers x in the interval such that $f(x) \leq \gamma$. Then S is not empty because a is in it, and b is an upper bound for S. Let c be its least upper bound. Then c is in our interval. We contend that $f(c) = \gamma$. If $f(c) < \gamma$, then $c \neq b$, and $f(x) < \gamma$ for all $x > c$ sufficiently close to c, because f is continuous at c. This contradicts the fact that c is an upper bound for S. If $f(c) > \gamma$, then $c \neq a$, and $f(x) > \gamma$ for all $x < c$ sufficiently close to c, again because f is continuous at c. This contradicts the fact that c is a least upper bound for S. We conclude that $f(c) = \gamma$, as was to be shown.

Appendix 2

Induction

In the course of several proofs, we have given a "stepwise" argument. One can formalize this type of argument, which is called *induction*. It is a property of integers which is assumed, and is stated as follows.

Suppose that we wish to prove a certain assertion concerning positive integers n. Let $A(n)$ denote the assertion concerning the integer n. To prove it for all n, it suffices to prove the following.

1. The assertion $A(1)$ is true (i.e. the assertion concerning the integer 1 is true).

2. Assuming the assertion proved for all positive integers $\leq n$, prove it for $n + 1$, i.e. prove $A(n + 1)$.

Step 2 is the procedure which allows us to proceed from one integer to the next, and step 1 gives us a starting point. We shall now give examples.

Example 1. For all integers $n \geq 1$, we have

$$1 + 2 + \cdots + n = \frac{n(n + 1)}{2}.$$

Proof. By induction. The assertion $A(n)$ is the assertion of the theorem. When $n = 1$, it simply states that

$$1 = \frac{1(1 + 1)}{2},$$

and is clearly true. Assume now that the assertion is true for n. Then:

$$1 + 2 + \cdots + n + (n + 1) = \frac{n(n + 1)}{2} + (n + 1).$$

Putting the expression on the right of the equality sign over a common denominator 2, we see that it is equal to

$$\frac{n^2 + n + 2n + 2}{2} = \frac{(n + 1)(n + 2)}{2}.$$

Hence assuming $A(n)$, we have shown that

$$1 + 2 + \cdots + (n + 1) = \frac{(n + 1)(n + 2)}{2},$$

which is none other than assertion $A(n + 1)$. This proves our theorem.

Example 2. Assume that there is a function f such that

$$f(x + y) = f(x)f(y).$$

We let $f(1) = e$, and we want to prove that $f(n) = e^n$ for all positive integers n. This is true for $n = 1$. By induction, assume the result for an integer $n \geq 1$. Then

$$f(n + 1) = f(n)f(1) = e^n e = e^{n+1},$$

thereby proving our assertion.

Example 3. We shall use induction to prove that

$$\frac{d(x^n)}{dx} = nx^{n-1}$$

for all integers $n \geq 1$. We assume known the rule for differentiating a product, namely $(fg)' = f'g + fg'$, and we also assume that we have proved the special case

$$\frac{dx}{dx} = 1.$$

Thus we have assumed the result when $n = 1$. By induction, assume the result proved for some integer $n \geq 1$. Let $f(x) = x^n$ and $g(x) = x$. Then $(fg)(x) = x^{n+1}$. Hence

$$(fg)'(x) = f'(x)g(x) + f(x)g'(x)$$
$$= nx^{n-1}x + x^n$$
$$= nx^n + x^n$$
$$= (n + 1)x^n,$$

thus proving what we wanted.

EXERCISES

1. Prove that for all integers $n \geq 1$,

$$1 + 3 + 5 + \cdots + (2n - 1) = n^2.$$

2. Prove that for all integers $n \geq 1$,

(a) $1^2 + 2^2 + 3^2 + \cdots + n^2 = \frac{1}{6}n(n + 1)(2n + 1);$

(b) $1^3 + 2^3 + 3^3 + \cdots + n^3 = \left[\dfrac{n(n+1)}{2}\right]^2$.

3. Prove that

$$1^2 + 3^2 + 5^2 + \cdots + (2n-1)^2 = \tfrac{1}{3}(4n^3 - n).$$

4. Prove that $n(n^2 + 5)$ is divisible by 6 for all integers $n \geq 1$.

5. Prove that

$$(1+x)(1+x^2)(1+x^4)\cdots(1+x^{2n}) = \dfrac{1 - x^{2n+1}}{1 - x}.$$

6. If $f_1, \ldots, f_n$ are differentiable functions, prove by induction that

$$(f_1 \cdots f_n)' = f_1' f_2 \cdots f_n + f_1 f_2' \cdots f_n + \cdots + f_1 \cdots f_{n-1}f_n'.$$

7. (a) Let f be a function such that $f(xy) = f(x) + f(y)$. Show that

$$f(a^n) = nf(a)$$

for all positive integers n.

(b) Let f be a function such that $f(x + y) = f(x) + f(y)$. Show that $f(na) = nf(a)$ for all positive integers n.

(c) Let f be a function such that $f(xy) = f(x)f(y)$. Show that $f(a^n) = f(a)^n$ for all positive integers n.

8. Let $\dbinom{n}{k}$ denote the binomial coefficient, $\dbinom{n}{k} = \dfrac{n!}{k!(n-k)!}$, where n, k are integers ≥ 0, $0 \leq k \leq n$, and $0!$ is defined to be equal to 1. Prove the following assertions.

(a) $\dbinom{n}{k} = \dbinom{n}{n-k}$ (b) $\dbinom{n}{k-1} + \dbinom{n}{k} = \dbinom{n+1}{k}$ (for $k > 0$)

9. Prove by induction that

$$(x+y)^n = \sum_{k=0}^{n} \binom{n}{k} x^k y^{n-k}.$$

Appendix 3

Sine and Cosine

In our course in calculus, we gave geometric definitions for the sine and cosine, and geometric proofs for the theorems concerning their derivatives, and the limit

$$\lim_{h \to 0} \frac{\sin h}{h} = 1$$

on which these proofs were based, drawing pictures. For the other functions, we showed how to give definitions in terms involving only properties of (real) numbers. Such definitions are called *analytic*. There is of course nothing wrong about using pictures, and it would be insane to have inhibitions about them, but it is reasonable to ask whether it is possible to develop the theory of the sine and cosine without appeal to geometric intuition, i.e. give for these notions purely analytic definitions, and prove their properties purely analytically.

In fact, in Chapter XV, we have already proved that by using suitable series, we can find functions f and g such that

$$f' = g \quad \text{and} \quad g' = -f,$$

and $f(0) = 0$, $g(0) = 1$. Using only the properties just stated, we shall develop the entire theory of sine and cosine, based only on the use of the mean value theorem and its applications (to increasing and decreasing functions), and on the intermediate value theorem proved in Appendix 1. Thus what follows gives an interesting theoretical application of the mean value theorem.

To begin with, we have a standard relation,

$$f(x)^2 + g(x)^2 = 1$$

for all x. This is proved by differentiating the left-hand side. We obtain

$$2ff' + 2gg' = 2fg - 2gf = 0.$$

Hence the left-hand side is constant, and substituting $x = 0$ we see that this constant is equal to 1, as desired.

Proposition 1. *There exists only one pair of functions f, g which are differentiable, satisfying*

$$f' = g \quad and \quad g' = -f,$$

and such that $f(0) = 0$, $g(0) = 1$.

Proof. Let f_1, g_1 be functions such that

$$f_1' = g_1 \quad and \quad g_1' = -f_1.$$

Differentiating the functions $fg_1 - f_1g$ and $ff_1 + gg_1$ we find 0, in each case. Hence there exist numbers a, b such that

$$fg_1 - f_1g = a$$
$$ff_1 + gg_1 = b.$$

We multiply the first equation by f, the second by g and add. We multiply the second equation by f, the first equation by g and subtract. Using $f^2 + g^2 = 1$, we find

(*)
$$g_1 = af + bg$$
$$f_1 = bf - ag.$$

If we assume that $f_1(0) = 0$ and $g_1(0) = 1$, then we find the values $a = 0$ and $b = 1$. This proves that $f_1 = f$ and $g_1 = g$, as was to be shown.

In view of Proposition 1, we define the functions f and g in that proposition to be the *sine* and *cosine* functions respectively, and denote them by sin and cos.

Proposition 2. *For all numbers x, y we have:*

(1) $\sin^2 x + \cos^2 x = 1$,
(2) $\sin(-x) = -\sin x$,
(3) $\cos(-x) = \cos x$,
(4) $\sin(x + y) = \sin x \cos y + \cos x \sin y$,
(5) $\cos(x + y) = \cos x \cos y - \sin x \sin y$.

Proof. The first formula has already been proved. To prove each pair of succeeding formulas, we make a suitable choice of functions f_1, g_1 and apply equations (*) of the proof of uniqueness. For instance, to prove (2) and (3), we let

$$f_1(x) = \cos(-x) \quad and \quad g_1(x) = \sin(-x).$$

Then we find numbers a, b as in the uniqueness proof such that equations (*) are satisfied. Taking the values of these functions at 0, we now find that $b = 0$ and $a = -1$. This proves what we want. To prove (4) and (5), we let y be a fixed number, and let

$$f_1(x) = \sin(x+y) \quad \text{and} \quad g_1(x) = \cos(x+y).$$

We determine the constants a, b as before, in equations (*), and find $a = -\sin y$, $b = \cos y$. Formulas (4) and (5) then drop out.

Since the functions sin and cos are differentiable, and since their derivatives are expressed in terms of each other, it follows that they are infinitely differentiable. In particular, they are continuous.

Since $\sin^2 x + \cos^2 x = 1$ for all x, it follows that the values of sin and cos lie between -1 and 1. Of course, we do not yet know that sin and cos take on all such values. This will be proved later.

Since the derivative of $\sin x$ at 0 is equal to 1, and since this derivative is continuous, it follows that the derivative of $\sin x$ (which is $\cos x$) is > 0 for all numbers x in some open interval containing 0. Hence sin is strictly increasing in such an interval, and is strictly positive for all $x > 0$ in such an interval.

We shall now prove that there is a number $x > 0$ such that $\sin x = 1$. In view of the relation between sin and cos, this amounts to proving that there exists a number $x > 0$ such that $\cos x = 0$.

Suppose that no such number exists. Since cos is continuous, we conclude that $\cos x$ cannot be negative for any value of $x > 0$ (by the intermediate value theorem). Hence sin is strictly increasing for all $x > 0$, and cos is strictly decreasing for all $x > 0$. Let $a > 0$. Then

$$0 < \cos 2a = \cos^2 a - \sin^2 a < \cos^2 a.$$

By induction, one sees that $\cos(2^n a) < (\cos a)^{2^n}$ for all integers $n > 0$. Hence $\cos(2^n a)$ approaches 0 as n becomes large, because $0 < \cos a < 1$. Since cos is strictly decreasing for $x > 0$, it follows that $\cos x$ approaches 0 as x becomes large, and hence $\sin x$ approaches 1. In particular, there exists a number $b > 0$ such that

$$\cos b < \tfrac{1}{4} \quad \text{and} \quad \sin b > \tfrac{1}{2}.$$

Then $\cos 2b = \cos^2 b - \sin^2 b < (\tfrac{1}{4})^2 - (\tfrac{1}{2})^2 < 0$, contradiction, proving that there is a number $x > 0$ such that $\sin x = 1$, $\cos x = 0$.

The set of numbers $x > 0$ such that $\cos x = 0$ (or equivalently, $\sin x = 1$) is non-empty, bounded from below. Let c be its greatest lower bound. By continuity, we must have $\cos c = 0$. We *define* π to be the number $2c$. Thus $c = \pi/2$. (We follow the Greeks. Unfortunately, it would be more practical to define π as being equal to $4c$. This would get rid of an extraneous factor of 2 appearing in almost all formulas in mathematics involving π. However, it is too late in history to change the notation.) It is clear that $c > 0$, and by definition of the greatest lower bound, there is no number x such that

$$0 \leq x < \pi/2$$

and such that $\cos x = 0$, or $\sin x = 1$.

By the intermediate value theorem, it follows that for $0 \leq x < \pi/2$ we have $0 \leq \sin x < 1$ and $0 \leq \cos x < 1$. However, by definition,

$$\cos \frac{\pi}{2} = 0 \quad \text{and} \quad \sin \frac{\pi}{2} = 1.$$

Using the addition formula, we can now find

$$\sin \pi = 0, \quad \cos \pi = -1, \quad \sin 2\pi = 0, \quad \cos 2\pi = 1.$$

For instance,

$$\sin \pi = \sin \left(\frac{\pi}{2} + \frac{\pi}{2} \right) = 2 \sin \frac{\pi}{2} \cos \frac{\pi}{2} = 0.$$

The others are proved similarly.

Proposition 3. *For all x we have:*

$$\sin \left(x + \frac{\pi}{2} \right) = \cos x \qquad \cos \left(x + \frac{\pi}{2} \right) = -\sin x$$

$$\sin (x + \pi) = -\sin x \qquad \cos (x + \pi) = -\cos x$$

$$\sin (x + 2\pi) = \sin x \qquad \cos (x + 2\pi) = \cos x.$$

Proof. Use (4) and (5) in Proposition 2, together with the values we have found above.

We shall now use systematically these relations in investigating the behavior of sin and cos between 0 and 2π.

Proposition 4. *The functions* sin *and* cos *behave as described in the following table. We use "s.i." and "s.d." to abbreviate "strictly increasing" and "strictly decreasing" respectively.*

	$\theta \leq x \leq \dfrac{\pi}{2}$	$\dfrac{\pi}{2} \leq x \leq \pi$	$\pi \leq x \leq \dfrac{3\pi}{2}$	$\dfrac{3\pi}{2} \leq x \leq 2\pi$
sin	s.i. *from* 0 *to* 1	s.d. *from* 1 *to* 0	s.d. *from* 0 *to* -1	s.i. *from* -1 *to* 0
cos	s.d. *from* 1 *to* 0	s.d. *from* 0 *to* -1	s.i. *from* -1 *to* 0	s.i. *from* 0 *to* 1.

Proof. The behavior in the first column has already been proved in the course of our discussion concerning the definition of $\pi/2$. Consider the second column. The behavior of sin in the indicated interval comes from Proposition 3 (it is the same as the behavior of cos in the preceding column). In that interval, the derivative of cos is therefore negative, and cos is strictly decreasing. Furthermore, cos decreases from 0 to -1, since we must always have $\sin^2 x + \cos^2 x = 1$.

To determine the behavior in the third and fourth columns, we can use the relations of Proposition 3, namely

$$\sin (x + \pi) = -\sin x \qquad \text{and} \qquad \cos (x + \pi) = -\cos x.$$

We see that the graph of the functions sin and cos in the third and fourth columns are similar to those of the first and second, except that they are flipped over the x-axis.

A function f is called *periodic* and a number s is called a *period*, if $f(x + s) = f(x)$ for all numbers x. From Proposition 3, we see that 2π is a period for sin and cos.

Proposition 5. *The functions* sin *and* cos *are periodic. The numbers* $2n\pi$ *(n equal to an integer) are periods, and every period is equal to* $2n\pi$ *for some integer n.*

Proof. Let s_1, s_2 be periods for the function f. Then

$$f(x + s_1 + s_2) = f(x + s_1) = f(x)$$

so that $s_1 + s_2$ is a period. If s is a period, then

$$f(x) = f(x - s + s) = f(x - s),$$

so that $-s$ is also a period. Since 2π is a period, it follows by induction that $2n\pi$ is also a period for all integers $n \geq 1$, and then also for all integers n.

Let s be a period for sin. Consider the set of integers m such that $2m\pi \leq s$. Taking m sufficiently large negative shows that this set is not empty, and is bounded from above by $s/2\pi$. Let n be its least upper bound. Then n is an integer, and $2n\pi \leq s$ but $2(n + 1)\pi > s$. Let $t = s - 2n\pi$. Then t is a period, and $0 \leq t < 2\pi$. We must have

$$\sin (0 + t) = \sin 0 = 0,$$

$$\cos (0 + t) = \cos 0 = 1.$$

From the table in Proposition 4, we see that this is possible only if $t = 0$, as was to be shown.

The preceding propositions give us all the usual properties of sin and cos.

We recall that a point (a, b) in 2-space is said to lie on the unit circle if $a^2 + b^2 = 1$. We see that for any number x, the point $(\cos x, \sin x)$ lies on the unit circle.

Proposition 6. *Given a point (a, b) on the unit circle in 2-space, there exists a unique number t such that $0 \leq t < 2\pi$ and such that $a = \cos t$, $b = \sin t$.*

Proof. We consider four different cases, according as a, b are ≥ 0 or ≤ 0. In any case, both a and b are between -1 and 1.

Consider for instance the case where $-1 \leq a \leq 0$ and $0 \leq b \leq 1$. From the table in Proposition 4, we see that there is only one possible column in which we could find a value of t satisfying our requirements, and that is the second column.

By the intermediate value theorem, we know that there is one number t such that

$$\frac{\pi}{2} \leq t \leq \pi$$

and $\sin t = b$. Since $\cos^2 x = 1 - \sin^2 x = 1 - b^2 = a^2$, and since both $\cos x$ and a are ≤ 0 in this interval, it follows that we must also have $\cos t = a$. This proves what we want.

The other cases are treated in an entirely similar way, and can be left to the reader.

This essentially concludes our theory of sine and cosine. Note that we have parametrized the circle in the usual way, i.e. we have an association

$$t \mapsto (\cos t, \sin t)$$

which to each number t associates a point on the circle of radius 1 centered at the origin in the plane. In terms of complex numbers, this is nothing else but the association

$$t \mapsto e^{it}$$

discussed in the text.

As to the limit of $(\sin h)/h$, observe that it is nothing but the limit of the Newton quotient,

$$\lim_{h \to 0} \frac{\sin h - \sin 0}{h} = \lim_{h \to 0} \frac{\sin h}{h},$$

and since the sine is differentiable, we know that this limit is equal to

$$\sin'(0) = \cos 0 = 1.$$

Thus we recover this limit in a particularly easy way.

Appendix 4

Physics and Mathematics

Mathematics consists in discovering and describing certain objects and structures. It is essentially impossible to give an all-encompassing description of these. Hence, instead of such a definition, we simply state that the objects of study of mathematics as we know it are those which you will find described in the mathematical journals of the past two centuries, and leave it at that. There are many reasons for studying these objects, among which are aesthetic reasons (some people like them), and practical reasons (some mathematics can be applied).

Physics, on the other hand, consists in describing the empirical world by means of mathematical structures. The empirical world is the world with which we come into contact through our senses, through experiments, measurements, etc. What makes a good physicist is the ability to choose, among many mathematical structures and objects, the ones which can be used to describe the empirical world. I should of course immediately qualify the above assertion in two ways: First, the description of physical situations by mathematical structures can only be done within the degree of accuracy provided by the experimental apparatus. Second, the description should satisfy certain aesthetic criteria (simplicity, elegance). After all, a complete listing of all results of all experiments performed is a description of the physical world, but is quite a distinct thing from giving at one single stroke a general principle which will account simultaneously for the results of all these experiments.

For psychological reasons, it is impossible (for most people) to learn certain mathematical theories without seeing first a geometric or physical interpretation. Hence in this book, before introducing a mathematical notion, we frequently introduce one of its geometric or physical interpretations. These two, however, should not be confused. Thus we might make two columns, as shown on the following page.

As far as the logical development of our course is concerned, we could omit the second column entirely. The second column is used, however, for many purposes: To motivate the first column (because our brain is made up in such a way that to understand something in the first column, it needs the second). To provide applications for the first column, other than pure aesthetic satisfaction (granting that you like the subject).

Mathematics	Physics and geometry
numbers	points on a line
derivative	slope of a line rate of change
$\dfrac{df}{dx} = Kf(x)$	exponential decay
integral	area work moments

Nevertheless, it is important to keep in mind that the derivative, as the limit of

$$\frac{f(x + h) - f(x)}{h},$$

and the integral, as a unique number between upper and lower sums, are not to be confused with a slope or an area respectively. It is simply our mind which interprets the mathematical notion in physical or geometric terms. Besides, we frequently assign several such interpretations to the same mathematical notion (viz. the integral being interpreted as an area, or as the work done by a force).

And by the way, the above remarks which are about physics and mathematics belong neither to physics nor to mathematics. They belong to philosophy.

Second Course

Chapter I

Vectors

The concept of a vector is basic for the whole course. It provides geometric motivation for everything that follows. Hence the properties of vectors, both algebraic and geometric, will be discussed in full.

The cross product is included for the sake of completeness. It is almost never used in the rest of the book. It is the only aspect of the theory of vectors which is valid only in three-dimensional space (not 2, nor 4, nor n-dimensional space). One significant feature of almost all the statements and proofs of this book (except for those concerning the cross product), is that they are neither easier nor harder to prove in 3- or n-space than they are in 2-space.

§1. DEFINITION OF POINTS IN n-SPACE

We have seen that a number can be used to represent a point on a line, once a unit length is selected.

A pair of numbers (i.e. a couple of numbers) (x, y) can be used to represent a point in the plane.

We now observe that a triple of numbers (x, y, z) can be used to represent a point in space, that is 3-dimensional space, or 3-space. We simply introduce one more axis. The following picture illustrates this:

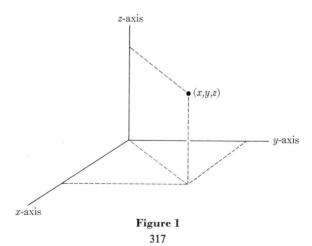

Figure 1

317

Instead of using x, y, z we could also use (x_1, x_2, x_3). The line could be called 1-space, and the plane could be called 2-space.

Thus we can say that a single number represents a point in 1-space. A couple represents a point in 2-space. A triple represents a point in 3-space.

Although we cannot draw a picture to go further, there is nothing to prevent us from considering a quadruple of numbers

$$(x_1, x_2, x_3, x_4)$$

and decreeing that this is a point in 4-space. A quintuple would be a point in 5-space, then would come a sextuple, septuple, octuple, ...

We let ourselves be carried away and *define a point in n-space* to be an n-tuple of numbers

$$(x_1, x_2, \ldots, x_n),$$

if n is a positive integer. We shall denote such an n-tuple by a capital letter X, and try to keep small letters for numbers and capital letters for points. We call the numbers $x_1, \ldots, x_n$ the *coordinates* of the point X.

Most of our examples will take place when $n = 2$ or $n = 3$. Thus the reader may visualize either of these two cases throughout the book. However, two comments must be made: First, practically no formula or theorem is simpler by making such assumptions on n. When we meet cases where a simplification occurs, we shall always treat these cases separately (e.g. in Taylor's formula for several variables). Second, the case $n = 4$ does occur in physics, and the case $n = n$ occurs often enough in practice or theory to warrant its treatment here. Furthermore, part of our purpose is in fact to show that the general case is always similar to the case when $n = 2$ or $n = 3$.

We shall now define how to add points. If A, B are two points, say

$$A = (a_1, \ldots, a_n), \qquad B = (b_1, \ldots, b_n),$$

then we define $A + B$ to be the point whose coordinates are

$$(a_1 + b_1, \ldots, a_n + b_n).$$

For example, in the plane, if $A = (1, 2)$ and $B = (-3, 5)$ then

$$A + B = (-2, 7).$$

In 3-space, if $A = (-1, \pi, 3)$ and $B = (\sqrt{2}, 7, -2)$ then

$$A + B = (\sqrt{2} - 1, \pi + 7, 1).$$

Furthermore, if c is any number, we *define* cA to be the point whose coordinates are

$$(ca_1, \ldots, ca_n).$$

If $A = (2, -1, 5)$ and $c = 7$ then $cA = (14, -7, 35)$.

We observe that the following rules are satisfied:
(1) $(A + B) + C = A + (B + C)$.
(2) $A + B = B + A$.
(3) $c(A + B) = cA + cB$.
(4) If c_1, c_2 are numbers, then

$$(c_1 + c_2)A = c_1 A + c_2 A \qquad \text{and} \qquad (c_1 c_2)A = c_1(c_2 A).$$

(5) If we let $O = (0, \ldots, 0)$ be the point all of whose coordinates are 0, then $O + A = A + O = A$ for all A.
(6) $1 \cdot A = A$, and if we denote by $-A$ the n-tuple $(-1)A$, then

$$A + (-A) = O.$$

[Instead of writing $A + (-B)$, we shall frequently write $A - B$.]

All these properties are very simple to prove, and we suggest that you verify them on some examples. We shall give in detail the proof of property (3). Let $A = (a_1, \ldots, a_n)$ and $B = (b_1, \ldots, b_n)$. Then

$$A + B = (a_1 + b_1, \ldots, a_n + b_n)$$

and

$$\begin{aligned}
c(A + B) &= \big(c(a_1 + b_1), \ldots, c(a_n + b_n)\big) \\
&= (ca_1 + cb_1, \ldots, ca_n + cb_n) \\
&= cA + cB,
\end{aligned}$$

this last step being true by definition of addition of n-tuples.

The other proofs are left as exercises.

Note. Do not confuse the number 0 and the n-tuple $(0, \ldots, 0)$. We usually denote this n-tuple by O, and also call it zero, because no difficulty can occur in practice.

We shall now interpret addition and multiplication by numbers geometrically in the plane (you can visualize simultaneously what happens in 3-space).

Take an example. Let $A = (2, 3)$ and $B = (-1, 1)$. Then

$$A + B = (1, 4).$$

The figure looks like a parallelogram (Fig. 2).

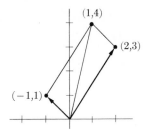

Figure 2

Take another example. Let $A = (3, 1)$ and $B = (1, 2)$. Then

$$A + B = (4, 3).$$

We see again that the geometric representation of our addition looks like a parallelogram (Fig. 3).

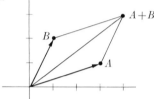

Figure 3

What is the representation of multiplication by a number?   Let $A = (1, 2)$ and $c = 3$. Then $cA = (3, 6)$ (Fig. 4a).

Multiplication by 3 amounts to stretching A by 3.   Similarly, $\frac{1}{2}A$ amounts to stretching A by $\frac{1}{2}$, i.e. shrinking A to half its size. In general, if t is a number, $t > 0$, we interpret tA as a point in the same direction as A from the origin, but t times the distance.

Multiplication by a negative number reverses the direction. Thus $-3A$ would be represented as in Fig. 4(b).

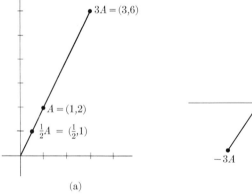

(a)   (b)   Figure 4

EXERCISES

Find $A + B$, $A - B$, $3A$, $-2B$ in each of the following cases.

1. $A = (2, -1)$, $B = (-1, 1)$ 2. $A = (-1, 3)$, $B = (0, 4)$

3. $A = (2, -1, 5)$, $B = (-1, 1, 1)$ 4. $A = (-1, -2, 3)$, $B = (-1, 3, -4)$

5. $A = (\pi, 3, -1)$, $B = (2\pi, -3, 7)$ 6. $A = (15, -2, 4)$, $B = (\pi, 3, -1)$

7. Draw the points of Exercises 1 through 4 on a sheet of graph paper.

8. Let A, B be as in Exercise 1. Draw the points $A + 2B$, $A + 3B$, $A - 2B$, $A - 3B$, $A + \frac{1}{2}B$ on a sheet of graph paper.

§2. VECTORS

We define a *located vector* to be an ordered pair of points which we write $\overrightarrow{AB}$. (This is *not* a product.) We visualize this as an arrow between A and B. We call A the *beginning point* and B the *end point* of the located vector (Fig. 5).

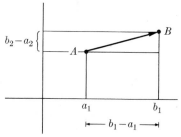

Figure 5

How are the coordinates of B obtained from those of A? We observe that in the plane,

$$b_1 = a_1 + (b_1 - a_1).$$

Similarly,

$$b_2 = a_2 + (b_2 - a_2).$$

This means that

$$B = A + (B - A).$$

Let $\overrightarrow{AB}$ and $\overrightarrow{CD}$ be two located vectors. We shall say that they are *equivalent* if $B - A = D - C$. Every located vector $\overrightarrow{AB}$ is equivalent to one whose beginning point is the origin, because $\overrightarrow{AB}$ is equivalent to $\overrightarrow{O(B - A)}$. Clearly this is the only located vector whose beginning point is the origin and which is equivalent to $\overrightarrow{AB}$. If you visualize the parallelogram law in the plane, then it is clear that equivalence of two located vectors can be interpreted geometrically by saying that the lengths of the line segments determined by the pair of points are equal, and that the "directions" in which they point are the same.

In the next figures, we have drawn the located vectors $\overrightarrow{O(B - A)}$, $\overrightarrow{AB}$, and $\overrightarrow{O(A - B)}$, $\overrightarrow{BA}$.

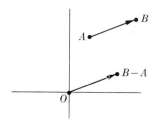

Figure 6

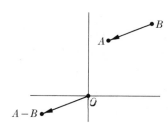

Figure 7

Given a located vector $\overrightarrow{OC}$ whose beginning point is the origin, we shall say that it is *located at the origin*. Given any located vector $\overrightarrow{AB}$, we shall say that it is *located at A*.

A located vector at the origin is entirely determined by its end point. In view of this, we shall call an n-tuple either a point or a vector, depending on the interpretation which we have in mind.

Two located vectors $\overrightarrow{AB}$ and $\overrightarrow{PQ}$ are said to be *parallel* if there is a number $c \neq 0$ such that $B - A = c(Q - P)$. They are said to have the *same direction* if there is a number $c > 0$ such that $B - A = c(Q - P)$, and to have *opposite direction* if there is a number $c < 0$ such that $B - A = c(Q - P)$. In a similar manner, any definition made concerning n-tuples can be carried over to located vectors. For instance, in the next section, we shall define what it means for n-tuples to be perpendicular. Then we can say that two located vectors $\overrightarrow{AB}$ and $\overrightarrow{PQ}$ are perpendicular if $B - A$ is perpendicular to $Q - P$. In the next figure, we have drawn a picture of such vectors in the plane.

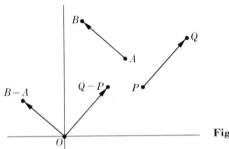

Figure 8

§3. SCALAR PRODUCT

It is understood that throughout a discussion we select vectors always in the same n-dimensional space.

Let $A = (a_1, \ldots, a_n)$ and $B = (b_1, \ldots, b_n)$ be two vectors. We define their *scalar* or *dot product* $A \cdot B$ to be

$$a_1 b_1 + \cdots + a_n b_n.$$

This product is a *number*. For instance, if

$$A = (1, 3, -2) \quad \text{and} \quad B = (-1, 4, -3)$$

then

$$A \cdot B = -1 + 12 + 6 = 17.$$

For the moment, we do not give a geometric interpretation to this scalar product. We shall do this later. We derive first some important properties. The basic ones are:

SP 1. *We have $A \cdot B = B \cdot A$.*

SP 2. *If A, B, C are three vectors then*

$$A \cdot (B + C) = A \cdot B + A \cdot C = (B + C) \cdot A.$$

SP 3. *If x is a number, then*

$$(xA) \cdot B = x(A \cdot B) \qquad \text{and} \qquad A \cdot (xB) = x(A \cdot B).$$

SP 4. *If $A = O$ is the zero vector, then $A \cdot A = 0$, and otherwise $A \cdot A > 0$.*

We shall now prove these properties.
Concerning the first, we have

$$a_1 b_1 + \cdots + a_n b_n = b_1 a_1 + \cdots + b_n a_n,$$

because for any two numbers a, b, we have $ab = ba$. This proves the first property.

For SP 2, let $C = (c_1, \ldots, c_n)$. Then

$$B + C = (b_1 + c_1, \ldots, b_n + c_n)$$

and

$$
\begin{aligned}
A \cdot (B + C) &= a_1(b_1 + c_1) + \cdots + a_n(b_n + c_n) \\
&= a_1 b_1 + a_1 c_1 + \cdots + a_n b_n + a_n c_n.
\end{aligned}
$$

Reordering the terms yields

$$a_1 b_1 + \cdots + a_n b_n + a_1 c_1 + \cdots + a_n c_n,$$

which is none other than $A \cdot B + A \cdot C$. This proves what we wanted.
We leave property SP 3 as an exercise.

Finally, for SP 4, we observe that if one coordinate a_i of A is not equal to 0, then there is a term $a_i^2 \neq 0$ and $a_i^2 > 0$ in the scalar product

$$A \cdot A = a_1^2 + \cdots + a_n^2.$$

Since every term is ≥ 0, it follows that the sum is > 0, as was to be shown.

In much of the work which we shall do concerning vectors, we shall use only the ordinary properties of addition, multiplication by numbers, and the four properties of the scalar product. We shall give a formal discussion of these later. For the moment, observe that there are other objects with which you are familiar and which can be added, subtracted, and multiplied by numbers, for instance the continuous functions on an interval $[a, b]$ (cf. Exercise 5).

Instead of writing $A \cdot A$ for the scalar product of a vector with itself, it will be convenient to write also A^2. (This is the only instance when we allow ourselves such a notation. Thus A^3 has no meaning.) As an exercise, verify the following identities:

$$(A + B)^2 = A^2 + 2A \cdot B + B^2,$$
$$(A - B)^2 = A^2 - 2A \cdot B + B^2.$$

A dot product $A \cdot B$ may very well be equal to 0 without either A or B being the zero vector. For instance, let $A = (1, 2, 3)$ and $B = (2, 1, -\frac{4}{3})$. Then $A \cdot B = 0$.

We define two vectors A, B to be *perpendicular* (or as we shall also say, *orthogonal*) if $A \cdot B = 0$. For the moment, it is not clear that in the plane, this definition coincides with our intuitive geometric notion of perpendicularity. We shall convince you that it does in the next section.

EXERCISES

1. Find $A \cdot A$ for each one of the *n*-tuples of Exercises 1 through 6 of §1.

2. Find $A \cdot B$ for each one of the *n*-tuples as above.

3. Using only the four properties of the scalar product, verify in detail the identities given in the text for $(A + B)^2$ and $(A - B)^2$.

4. Which of the following pairs of vectors are perpendicular?
   (a) $(1, -1, 1)$ and $(2, 1, 5)$ (b) $(1, -1, 1)$ and $(2, 3, 1)$
   (c) $(-5, 2, 7)$ and $(3, -1, 2)$ (d) $(\pi, 2, 1)$ and $(2, -\pi, 0)$

5. Consider continuous functions on the interval $[-1, 1]$. Define the scalar product of two such functions f, g to be

$$\int_{-1}^{+1} f(x)g(x)\, dx.$$

We denote this integral also by $\langle f, g \rangle$. Verify that the four rules for a scalar product are satisfied, in other words, show that:

SP 1. $\langle f, g \rangle = \langle g, f \rangle$.
SP 2. $\langle f, g + h \rangle = \langle f, g \rangle + \langle f, h \rangle$.
SP 3. $\langle cf, g \rangle = c \langle f, g \rangle$.
SP 4. If $f = 0$ *then* $\langle f, f \rangle = 0$ *and if* $f \neq 0$ *then* $\langle f, f \rangle > 0$.

6. If $f(x) = x$ and $g(x) = x^2$, what are $\langle f, f \rangle$, $\langle g, g \rangle$, and $\langle f, g \rangle$?

7. Consider continuous functions on the interval $[-\pi, \pi]$. Define a scalar product similar to the above for this interval. Show that the functions $\sin nx$ and $\cos mx$ are orthogonal for this scalar product (m, n being integers).

8. Let A be a vector perpendicular to every vector X. Show that $A = O$.

§4. THE NORM OF A VECTOR

The following inequality is called the *Schwarz inequality* and is fundamental in the theory of vectors.

Theorem 1. *Let A, B be two vectors. Then* $(A \cdot B)^2 \leq (A \cdot A)(B \cdot B)$.

Proof. Let $x = B \cdot B$ and $y = -A \cdot B$. Then by SP 4 we have

$$\forall x, y \in \mathbb{R}, \quad 0 \leq (xA + yB) \cdot (xA + yB).$$

We multiply out the right-hand side of this inequality and get

$$0 \leq x^2(A \cdot A) + 2xy(A \cdot B) + y^2(B \cdot B).$$

Substituting the values for x and y yields

$$0 \leq (B \cdot B)^2(A \cdot A) - 2(B \cdot B)(A \cdot B)^2 + (A \cdot B)^2(B \cdot B).$$

If $B = O$ then the inequality of the theorem is obvious, both sides being equal to 0. If $B \neq O$, then $B \cdot B \neq 0$ and we can divide this last expression by $B \cdot B$. We then obtain

$$0 \leq (A \cdot A)(B \cdot B) - (A \cdot B)^2.$$

Transposing the term $-(A \cdot B)^2$ to the other side of the inequality concludes the proof.

We define the *norm*, or *length*, of a vector A, and denote by $\|A\|$, the number

$$\|A\| = \sqrt{A \cdot A}.$$

Since $A \cdot A \geq 0$, we can take the square root. Furthermore, we note immediately that $\|A\| \neq 0$ if $A \neq O$.

In terms of coordinates, we see that

$$\|A\| = \sqrt{a_1^2 + \cdots + a_n^2},$$

and therefore that when $n = 2$ or $n = 3$, this coincides with our intuitive notion (derived from the Pythagoras theorem) of length. Indeed, when $n = 2$ and say $A = (a, b)$ then the norm of A is

$$\|A\| = \sqrt{a^2 + b^2},$$

as in the following picture.

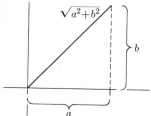

Figure 9

If $n = 3$, then the picture looks as follows, with $A = (x, y, z)$:

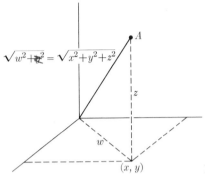

Figure 10

If we first look at the two components (x, y), then the length of the segment between $(0, 0)$ and (x, y) is equal to $w = \sqrt{x^2 + y^2}$, as indicated.
Then again the length of A by the Pythagoras theorem would be

$$\sqrt{w^2 + z^2} = \sqrt{x^2 + y^2 + z^2}.$$

Thus when $n = 3$, our definition of length is compatible with the geometry
of the Pythagoras theorem.

To take a numerical example, if $A = (1, 2, -3)$ then

$$\|A\| = \sqrt{1 + 4 + 9} = \sqrt{14}.$$

In view of our definition, we can rewrite the inequality of Theorem 1
in the form

$$|(A \cdot B)| \leq \|A\| \, \|B\|$$

by taking the square root of both sides. We shall use it in this form in
the proof of the next theorem.

Theorem 2. *Let A, B be vectors. Then*

$$\|A + B\| \leq \|A\| + \|B\|.$$

Proof. Both sides of this inequality are positive or 0. Hence it will
suffice to prove that their squares satisfy the desired inequality, in other
words,

$$(A + B) \cdot (A + B) \leq (\|A\| + \|B\|)^2.$$

To do this, we consider

$$(A + B) \cdot (A + B) = A \cdot A + 2A \cdot B + B \cdot B.$$

In view of our previous result, this satisfies the inequality

$$\leq \|A\|^2 + 2\|A\| \, \|B\| + \|B\|^2,$$

and the right-hand side is none other than

$$\left(A + B\right)^2 \leqq (\|A\| + \|B\|)^2.$$

Our theorem is proved.

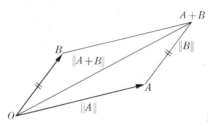

Figure 11

Theorem 2 is known as the *triangle inequality*. The reason for this is that if we draw a triangle as in Fig. 11, then Theorem 2 expresses the fact that the length of one side is $\leqq$ the sum of the lengths of the other two sides. (Cf. Exercise 11.)

Theorem 3. *Let x be a number. Then*

$$\|xA\| = |x| \, \|A\|$$

(absolute value of x times the length of A).

Proof. By definition, we have

$$\|xA\|^2 = (xA) \cdot (xA),$$

which is equal to

$$x^2(A \cdot A)$$

by the properties of the scalar product. Taking the square root now yields what we want.

We shall say that a vector U is a *unit* vector if $\|U\| = 1$. Given any vector A, let $a = \|A\|$. If $a \neq 0$ then

$$\frac{1}{a} A$$

is a unit vector, because

$$\left\|\frac{1}{a} A\right\| = \frac{1}{a} a = 1.$$

We shall say that two vectors A, B (neither of which is O) have the *same direction* if there is a number $c > 0$ such that $cA = B$. In view of this definition, we see that the vector

$$\frac{1}{\|A\|} A$$

is a unit vector in the direction of A (provided $A \neq O$).

Example 1. Let $A = (1, 2, -3)$. Then $\|A\| = \sqrt{14}$. Hence the unit vector in the direction of A is the vector

$$U = \left(\frac{1}{\sqrt{14}}, \frac{2}{\sqrt{14}}, \frac{-3}{\sqrt{14}}\right).$$

We mention in passing that two vectors A, B (neither of which is O) have *opposite directions* if there is a number $c < 0$ such that $cA = B$.

Let A, B be two n-tuples. We define the *distance* between A and B to be $\|A - B\| = \sqrt{(A - B) \cdot (A - B)}$. This definition coincides with our geometric intuition when A, B are points in the plane (Fig. 12).

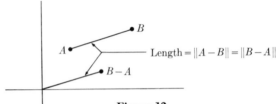

Length $= \|A - B\| = \|B - A\|$

Figure 12

It is the same thing as the length of the located vector $\overrightarrow{AB}$ or the located vector $\overrightarrow{BA}$.

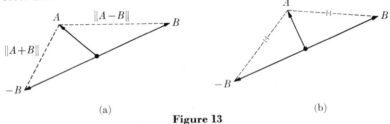

(a)   (b)

Figure 13

We are also in the position to justify our definition of perpendicularity. Given A, B in the plane, the condition that

$$\|A + B\| = \|A - B\|$$

(illustrated in Fig. 13b) coincides with the geometric property that A should be perpendicular to B.

Taking the square of each side, we see that this condition is equivalent with

$$(A + B) \cdot (A + B) = (A - B) \cdot (A - B)$$

and expanding out, this equality is equivalent with

$$A \cdot A + 2A \cdot B + B \cdot B = A \cdot A - 2A \cdot B + B \cdot B.$$

Making cancellations, we obtain the equivalent condition

$$4A \cdot B = 0$$

or

$$A \cdot B = 0.$$

This achieves what we wanted to show, namely that

$$\|A - B\| = \|A + B\| \qquad \text{if and only if} \qquad A \cdot B = 0.$$

We shall now use the notion of perpendicularity to derive the notion of projection, as on the following picture.

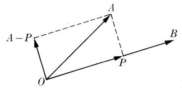

Figure 14

Let A, B be two vectors and $B \neq O$. We wish to define the projection of A along B, which will be a vector P as shown in the picture. We seek a vector P such that $A - P$ is perpendicular to B, and such that P can be written in the form $P = cB$ for some number c. Suppose that we can find such a number c, namely one satisfying

$$(A - cB) \cdot B = 0.$$

We then obtain

$$A \cdot B = cB \cdot B,$$

and therefore

$$c = \frac{A \cdot B}{B \cdot B}.$$

We see that such a number c is uniquely determined by our condition of perpendicularity. Conversely, if we let c have the above value, then we clearly have $(A - cB) \cdot B = 0$, as we see by multiplying out this dot product.

We now define the vector cB to be the *projection* of A along B, if c is the number

$$c = \frac{A \cdot B}{B \cdot B},$$

and we define c to be the *component* of A along B. *If B is a unit vector, then we have simply*

$$c = A \cdot B.$$

Example 2. Let $A = (1, 2, -3)$ and $B = (1, 1, 2)$. Then the component of A along B is the *number*

$$c = \frac{A \cdot B}{B \cdot B} = \frac{-3}{6} = -\frac{1}{2}.$$

Hence the projection of A along B is the *vector*

$$cB = (-\tfrac{1}{2}, -\tfrac{1}{2}, -1).$$

Our construction has an immediate interpretation in the plane, which gives us a geometric interpretation for the scalar product. Namely, assume $A \neq O$ and look at the angle θ between A and B (Fig. 15). Then from plane geometry we see that

$$\cos \theta = \frac{c\|B\|}{\|A\|},$$

or substituting the value for c obtained above,

$B \cdot B = \|B\|^2$

$$A \cdot B = \|A\| \, \|B\| \cos \theta.$$

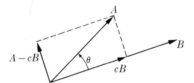

$A - cB$ $\quad \theta \quad$ cB

Figure 15

In view of Theorem 1, we know that in n-space, the number

$$\frac{A \cdot B}{\|A\| \, \|B\|}$$

has absolute value ≤ 1. Consequently,

$$-1 \leq \frac{A \cdot B}{\|A\| \, \|B\|} \leq 1,$$

and there exists a unique angle θ such that $0 \leq \theta \leq \pi$, and such that

$$\cos \theta = \frac{A \cdot B}{\|A\| \, \|B\|}.$$

We define this angle to be the *angle between A and B*.

In some treatments of vectors, one takes the relation

$$A \cdot B = \|A\| \, \|B\| \cos \theta$$

as definition of the scalar product. This is subject to the following disadvantages, not to say objections:

(a) The four properties of the scalar product SP 1 through SP 4 are then by no means obvious.

(b) Even in 3-space, one has to rely on geometric intuition to obtain the cosine of the angle between A and B, and this intuition is less clear than in the plane. In higher dimensional space, it fails even more.

(c) It is extremely hard to work with such a definition to obtain further properties of the scalar product.

Thus we prefer to lay obvious algebraic foundations, and then recover very simply all the properties. Aside from that, in analysis, one uses scalar products in the context of functions, where $\cos \theta$ becomes completely meaningless, for instance in Exercise 5 of §3, which is the starting point of the theory of Fourier series.

EXERCISES

1. Find the length of the vector A in Exercises 1 through 6 of §1.

2. Find the length of the vector B in Exercises 1 through 6 of §1.

3. Find the projection of A along B in Exercises 1 through 6 of §1.

4. Find the projection of B along A in these exercises.

5. In Exercise 6 of §3, find the projection of f along g and the projection of g along f, using the same definition of projection that has been given in the text (and did not refer to coordinates).

6. Find the norm of the functions $\sin 3x$ and $\cos x$, with respect to the scalar product on the interval $[-\pi, \pi]$ given by the integral.

7. Find the norm of the constant function 1 on the interval $[-\pi, \pi]$.

8. Find the norm of the constant function 1 on the interval $[-1, 1]$.

9. Let $A_1, \ldots, A_r$ be non-zero vectors which are mutually perpendicular, in other words $A_i \cdot A_j = 0$ if $i \neq j$. Let $c_1, \ldots, c_r$ be numbers such that

$$c_1 A_1 + \cdots + c_r A_r = 0.$$

Show that all $c_i = 0$.

10. Let A, B be two non-zero vectors in n-space. Let θ be the angle between them. If $\cos \theta = 1$, show that A and B have the same direction. If $\cos \theta = -1$, show that A and B have opposite direction.

11. If A, B are two vectors in n-space, denote by $d(A, B)$ the distance between A and B, i.e. $d(A, B) = \|B - A\|$. Show that $d(A, B) = d(B, A)$, and that for any three vectors A, B, C we have

$$d(A, B) \leq d(A, C) + d(B, C).$$

12. For any vectors A, B in n-space, prove the following relations:

    (a) $\|A + B\|^2 + \|A - B\|^2 = 2\|A\|^2 + 2\|B\|^2$.

    (b) $\|A + B\|^2 = \|A\|^2 + \|B\|^2 + 2A \cdot B$.

    (c) $\|A + B\|^2 - \|A - B\|^2 = 4A \cdot B$.

    Interpret (a) as a "parallelogram law".

13. Determine the cosine of the angles of the triangle whose vertices are $(2, -1, 1)$, $(1, -3, -5)$, $(3, -4, -4)$.

14. Show that if θ is the angle between A and B, then

$$\|A - B\|^2 = \|A\|^2 + \|B\|^2 - 2\|A\| \, \|B\| \cos \theta.$$

15. Let A, B, C be three vectors, and $A \neq 0$. If $A \cdot B = A \cdot C$, show by an example that we do not necessarily have $B = C$.

16. Let A, B be non-zero vectors, mutually perpendicular. Show that for any number c we have $\|A + cB\| \geq \|A\|$.

17. Let A, B be non-zero vectors. Assume that $\|A + cB\| \geq \|A\|$ for all numbers c. Show that A, B are perpendicular. [*Hint:* Take c to be very large positive or negative.]

18. Let $B_1, \ldots, B_m$ be vectors of length 1 in n-space, and mutually perpendicular, that is $B_i \cdot B_j = 0$ if $i \neq j$. Let A be a vector in n-space, and let c_i be the component of A along B_i. Let $x_1, \ldots, x_m$ be numbers. Show that

$$\|A - (c_1B_1 + \cdots + c_mB_m)\| \leq \|A - (x_1B_1 + \cdots + x_mB_m)\|.$$

§5. LINES AND PLANES

We define the parametric equation of a straight line passing through a point P in the direction of a vector $A \neq O$ to be

$$\boxed{X = P + tA,}$$

where t runs through all numbers (Fig. 16).

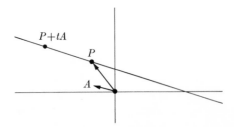

                                           Figure 16

Suppose that we work in the plane, and write the coordinates of a point X as (x, y). Let $P = (p, q)$ and $A = (a, b)$. Then in terms of the coordinates, we can write

$$x = p + ta, \qquad y = q + tb.$$

We can then eliminate t and obtain the usual equation relating x and y.

For example, let $P = (2, 1)$ and $A = (-1, 5)$. Then the parametric equation of the line through P in the direction of A gives us

(*) $$x = 2 - t, \qquad y = 1 + 5t.$$

Multiplying the first equation by 5 and adding yields

(**) $$5x + y = 11,$$

which is familiar.

This elimination of t shows that every pair (x, y) which satisfies the parametric equation (*) for some value of t also satisfies equation (**). Conversely, suppose we have a pair of numbers (x, y) satisfying (**). Let $t = 2 - x$. Then

$$y = 11 - 5x = 11 - 5(2 - t) = 1 + 5t.$$

Hence there exists some value of t which satisfies equation (*). Thus we have proved that the pairs (x, y) which are solutions of (**) are exactly the same pairs of numbers as those obtained by giving arbitrary values for t in (*). Thus the straight line can be described parametrically as in (*) or in terms of its usual equation (**). The same procedure works in general.

In higher dimensional space, we *cannot* eliminate t in this manner, and thus the parametric equation is the only one available to describe a straight line.

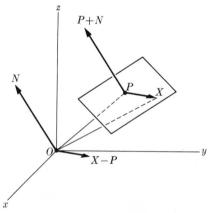

Figure 17

However, we can describe planes by an equation analogous to the single equation of the line. We proceed as follows.

Let P be a point, and consider a located vector $\overrightarrow{ON}$. We define the *hyperplane* passing through P perpendicular to $\overrightarrow{ON}$ to be the collection of all points X such that the located vector $\overrightarrow{PX}$ is perpendicular to $\overrightarrow{ON}$. According to our definitions, this amounts to the condition

$$(X - P) \cdot N = 0,$$

which can also be written as

$$X \cdot N = P \cdot N.$$

We shall also say that this hyperplane is the one perpendicular to N, and consists of all vectors X such that $X - P$ is perpendicular to N. We have drawn a typical situation in 3-space in Fig. 17.

Instead of saying that N is perpendicular to the plane, one also says that N is *normal* to the plane.

Let t be a number $\neq 0$. Then the set of points X such that

$$(X - P) \cdot N = 0$$

coincides with the set of points X such that

$$(X - P) \cdot tN = 0.$$

Thus we may say that our plane is the plane passing through P and perpendicular to the *line* in the direction of N. To find the equation of the plane, we could use any vector tN (with $t \neq 0$) instead of N.

In 3-space, we get an ordinary plane. For example, let $P = (2, 1, -1)$ and $N = (-1, 1, 3)$. Then the equation of the plane passing through P and perpendicular to N is

$$-x + y + 3z = -2 + 1 - 3$$

or

$$-x + y + 3z = -4.$$

Observe that in 2-space, with $X = (x, y)$, we are led to the equation of the line in the ordinary sense. For example, the equation of the line passing through $(4, -3)$ and perpendicular to $(-5, 2)$ is

$$-5x + 2y = -20 - 6 = -26.$$

We are now in position to interpret the coefficients $(-5, 2)$ of x and y in this equation. They give rise to a vector perpendicular to the line. In any equation

$$ax + by = c$$

the vector (a, b) is perpendicular to the line determined by the equation. Similarly, in 3-space, the vector (a, b, c) is perpendicular to the plane determined by the equation

$$ax + by + cz = d.$$

Two vectors A, B are said to be parallel if there exists a number $c \neq 0$ such that $cA = B$. Two lines are said to be *parallel* if, given two distinct points P_1, Q_1 on the first line and P_2, Q_2 on the second, the vectors

$$P_1 - Q_1$$

and

$$P_2 - Q_2$$

are parallel.

Two planes are said to be *parallel* (in 3-space) if their normal vectors are parallel. They are said to be *perpendicular* if their normal vectors are perpendicular. The *angle* between two planes is defined to be the angle between their normal vectors.

Example 1. Find the cosine of the angle between the planes

$$2x - y + z = 0,$$
$$x + 2y - z = 1.$$

This cosine is the cosine of the angle between the vectors

$$A = (2, -1, 1) \quad \text{and} \quad B = (1, 2, -1).$$

It is therefore equal to

$$\frac{A \cdot B}{\|A\| \, \|B\|} = -\frac{1}{6}.$$

Example 2. Let $Q = (1, 1, 1)$ and $P = (1, -1, 2)$. Let $N = (1, 2, 3)$. Find the point of intersection of the line through P in the direction of N, and the plane through Q perpendicular to N.

The parametric equation of the line through P in the direction of N is

(1) $$X = P + tN.$$

The equation of the plane through Q perpendicular to N is

(2) $$(X - Q) \cdot N = 0.$$

We must find the value of t such that the vector X in (1) also satisfies (2), that is

$$(P + tN - Q) \cdot N = 0,$$

or after using the rules of the dot product,

$$(P - Q) \cdot N + tN \cdot N = 0.$$

Solving for t yields

$$t = \frac{(Q - P) \cdot N}{N \cdot N} = \frac{1}{14}.$$

Thus the desired point of intersection is

$$P + tN = (1, -1, 2) + \tfrac{1}{14}(1, 2, 3) = (\tfrac{15}{14}, -\tfrac{12}{14}, \tfrac{31}{14}).$$

Example 3. Find the equation of the plane passing through the three points

$$P_1 = (1, 2, -1), \qquad P_2 = (-1, 1, 4), \qquad P_3 = (1, 3, -2).$$

We visualize schematically the three points as follows:

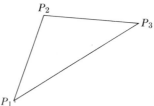

Figure 18

Then we find a vector N perpendicular to $\overrightarrow{P_1P_2}$ and $\overrightarrow{P_1P_3}$, or in other words, perpendicular to $P_2 - P_1$ and $P_3 - P_1$. We have

$$P_2 - P_1 = (-2, -1, +5),$$
$$P_3 - P_1 = (0, 1, -1).$$

Let $N = (a, b, c)$. We must solve:

$$-2a - b + 5c = 0, \quad -2a + 4c = 0$$
$$b - c = 0.$$

We take $b = c = 1$ and solve for a, getting $a = 2$. Then

$$N = (2, 1, 1)$$

satisfies our requirements. The plane perpendicular to N, passing through P_1 is the desired plane. Its equation is therefore

$$2x + y + z = 2 + 2 - 1 = 3.$$

EXERCISES

Find a parametric equation for the line passing through the following points.

1. $(1, 1, -1)$ and $(-2, 1, 3)$ 2. $(-1, 5, 2)$ and $(3, -4, 1)$

Find the equation of the line in 2-space, perpendicular to A and passing through P, for the following values of A and P.

3. $A = (1, -1),\ P = (-5, 3)$ 4. $A = (-5, 4),\ P = (3, 2)$

5. Show that the lines

$$3x - 5y = 1, \qquad 2x + 3y = 5$$

are not perpendicular.

6. Which of the following pairs of lines are perpendicular?

   (a) $3x - 5y = 1$ and $2x + y = 2$
   (b) $2x + 7y = 1$ and $x - y = 5$
   (c) $3x - 5y = 1$ and $5x + 3y = 7$
   (d) $-x + y = 2$ and $x + y = 9$

7. Find the equation of the plane perpendicular to the given vector N and passing through the given point P.

   (a) $N = (1, -1, 3)$, $P = (4, 2, -1)$
   (b) $N = (-3, -2, 4)$, $P = (2, \pi, -5)$
   (c) $N = (-1, 0, 5)$, $P = (2, 3, 7)$

8. Find the equation of the plane passing through the following three points.

   (a) $(2, 1, 1)$, $(3, -1, 1)$, $(4, 1, -1)$
   (b) $(-2, 3, -1)$, $(2, 2, 3)$, $(-4, -1, 1)$
   (c) $(-5, -1, 2)$, $(1, 2, -1)$, $(3, -1, 2)$

9. Find a vector perpendicular to $(1, 2, -3)$ and $(2, -1, 3)$, and another vector perpendicular to $(-1, 3, 2)$ and $(2, 1, 1)$.

10. Let P be the point $(1, 2, 3, 4)$ and Q the point $(4, 3, 2, 1)$. Let A be the vector $(1, 1, 1, 1)$. Let L be the line passing through P and parallel to A.

    (a) Given a point X on the line L, compute the distance between Q and X (as a function of the parameter t).
    (b) Show that there is precisely one point X_0 on the line such that this distance achieves a minimum, and that this minimum is $2\sqrt{5}$.
    (c) Show that $X_0 - Q$ is perpendicular to the line.

11. Let P be the point $(1, -1, 3, 1)$ and Q the point $(1, 1, -1, 2)$. Let A be the vector $(1, -3, 2, 1)$. Solve the same questions as in the preceding problem, except that in this case the minimum distance is $\sqrt{146/15}$.

12. Find a vector parallel to the line of intersection of the two planes

$$2x - y + z = 1, \qquad 3x + y + z = 2.$$

13. Same question for the planes,

$$2x + y + 5z = 2, \qquad 3x - 2y + z = 3.$$

14. Find a parametric equation for the line of intersection of the planes of Exercises 12 and 13.

15. Find the cosine of the angle between the following planes:

   (a) $x + y + z = 1$ (b) $2x + 3y - z = 2$
       $x - y - z = 5$ $x - y + z = 1$
   (c) $x + 2y - z = 1$ (d) $2x + y + z = 3$
       $-x + 3y + z = 2$ $-x - y + z = \pi$

16. Let $X \cdot N = P \cdot N$ be the equation of a plane in 3-space. Let Q be a point not lying in the plane. Show that there is a unique number t such that $Q + tN$ lies in the plane (i.e. satisfies the equation of the plane). What is this value in terms of P, Q, and N?

17. Let $Q = (1, -1, 2)$, $P = (1, 3, -2)$, and $N = (1, 2, 2)$. Find the point of the intersection of the line through P in the direction of N, and the plane through Q perpendicular to N.

18. Let P, Q be two points and N a vector in 3-space. Let P' be the point of intersection of the line through P, in the direction of N, and the plane through Q, perpendicular to N. We define the *distance* from P to that plane to be the distance between P and P'. Find this distance when

$$P = (1, 3, 5), \qquad Q = (-1, 1, 7), \qquad N = (-1, 1, -1).$$

19. Let $P = (1, 3, 5)$ and $A = (-2, 1, 1)$. Find the intersection of the line through P in the direction of A, and the plane

$$2x + 3y - z = 1.$$

20. Find the distance between the point $(1, 1, 2)$ and the plane

$$3x + y - 5z = 2.$$

21. Let $P = (1, 3, -1)$ and $Q = (-4, 5, 2)$. Determine the coordinates of the following points: (a) The midpoint of the line segment between P and Q. (b) The two points on this line segment lying one-third and two-thirds of the way from P to Q.

22. If P, Q are two arbitrary points in n-space, give the general formula for the midpoint of the line segment between P and Q.

§6. THE CROSS PRODUCT

This section applies only in 3-space!
Let $A = (a_1, a_2, a_3)$ and $B = (b_1, b_2, b_3)$ be two vectors in 3-space. We define their *cross product*

$$A \times B = (a_2 b_3 - a_3 b_2, a_3 b_1 - a_1 b_3, a_1 b_2 - a_2 b_1).$$

We leave the following assertions as exercises:

CP 1. $A \times B = -(B \times A)$.

CP 2. $A \times (B + C) = (A \times B) + (A \times C)$, and

$$(B + C) \times A = B \times A + C \times A.$$

CP 3. *For any number a, we have*

$$(aA) \times B = a(A \times B) = A \times (aB).$$

CP 4. $(A \times B) \times C = (A \cdot C)B - (B \cdot C)A$.

CP 5. $A \times B$ *is perpendicular to both A and B.*

As an example, we carry out this computation. We have

$$A \cdot (A \times B) = a_1(a_2b_3 - a_3b_2) + a_2(a_3b_1 - a_1b_3) + a_3(a_1b_2 - a_2b_1)$$
$$= 0$$

because all terms cancel. Similarly for $B \cdot (A \times B)$. This perpendicularity may be drawn as follows.

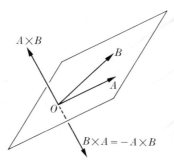

Figure 19

The vector $A \times B$ is perpendicular to the plane spanned by A and B. So is $B \times A$, but $B \times A$ points in the opposite direction.

Finally, as a last property, we have

CP 6. $(A \times B)^2 = (A \cdot A)(B \cdot B) - (A \cdot B)^2$.

Again, this can be verified by a computation on the coordinates. Namely, we have

$$(A \times B) \cdot (A \times B)$$
$$= (a_2b_3 - a_3b_2)^2 + (a_3b_1 - a_1b_3)^2 + (a_1b_2 - a_2b_1)^2,$$
$$(A \cdot A)(B \cdot B) - (A \cdot B)^2$$
$$= (a_1^2 + a_2^2 + a_3^2)(b_1^2 + b_2^2 + b_3^2) - (a_1b_1 + a_2b_2 + a_3b_3)^2.$$

Expanding everything out, we find that CP 6 drops out.

From our interpretation of the dot product, and the definition of the norm, we can rewrite CP 6 in the form

$$\|A \times B\|^2 = \|A\|^2\|B\|^2 - \|A\|^2\|B\|^2 \cos^2 \theta,$$

where θ is the angle between A and B. Hence we obtain

$$\|A \times B\|^2 = \|A\|^2\|B\|^2 \sin^2 \theta$$

or

$$\boxed{\|A \times B\| = \|A\| \, \|B\| \, |\sin \theta|.}$$

This is analogous to the formula which gave us the absolute value of $A \cdot B$.

EXERCISES

Find $A \times B$ for the following vectors.

1. $A = (1, -1, 1)$ and $B = (-2, 3, 1)$
2. $A = (-1, 1, 2)$ and $B = (1, 0, -1)$
3. $A = (1, 1, -3)$ and $B = (-1, -2, -3)$
4. Find $A \times A$ and $B \times B$, in Exercises 1 through 3.
5. Let $E_1 = (1, 0, 0)$, $E_2 = (0, 1, 0)$, and $E_3 = (0, 0, 1)$.   Find $E_1 \times E_2$, $E_2 \times E_3$, $E_3 \times E_1$.
6. Show that for any vector A in 3-space we have $A \times A = O$.
7. Compute $E_1 \times (E_1 \times E_2)$ and $(E_1 \times E_1) \times E_2$. Are these vectors equal to each other?

Chapter II

Differentiation of Vectors

We begin to acquire the flavour of the mixture of algebra, geometry, and differentiation. Each gains in appeal from being mixed with the other two.

The chain rule especially leads into the classical theory of curves. As you will see, the chain rule in its various aspects occurs very frequently in this book, and forms almost as basic a tool as the algebra of vectors, with which it will in fact be intimately mixed.

§1. DERIVATIVE

Let I be an interval. A parametrized *curve* (defined on this interval) is an association which to each point of I associates a vector. If X denotes a curve defined on I, and t is a point of I, then $X(t)$ denotes the vector associated to t by X. We often write the association $t \mapsto X(t)$ as an arrow

$$X: I \to \mathbf{R}^n.$$

Each vector $X(t)$ can be written in terms of coordinates,

$$X(t) = \big(x_1(t), \ldots, x_n(t)\big),$$

each $x_i(t)$ being a function of t. We say that this curve is *differentiable* if each function $x_i(t)$ is a differentiable function of t.

For instance, the curve defined by

$$X(t) = (\cos t, \sin t, t)$$

is a spiral (Fig. 1). Here we have

$$x(t) = \cos t,$$

$$y(t) = \sin t,$$

$$z(t) = t.$$

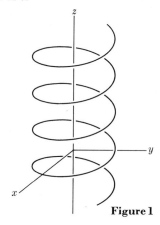

Figure 1

341

Remark. We take the intervals of definition for our curves to be open, closed, or also half open or half closed. When we define the derivative of a curve, it is understood that the interval of definition contains more than one point. In that case, at an end point the usual limit of

$$\frac{f(a + h) - f(a)}{h}$$

is taken for those h such that the quotient makes sense, i.e. $a + h$ lies in the interval. If a is a left end point, the quotient is considered only for $h > 0$. If a is a right end point, the quotient is considered only for $h < 0$. Then the usual rules for differentiation of functions are true in this greater generality, and thus Rules 1 through 4 below, and the chain rule of §2 remain true also. [An example of a statement which is not always true for curves defined over closed intervals is given in Exercise 11(b).]

Let us try to differentiate vectors using a Newton quotient. We consider

$$\frac{X(t + h) - X(t)}{h} = \left(\frac{x_1(t + h) - x_1(t)}{h}, \ldots, \frac{x_n(t + h) - x_n(t)}{h} \right)$$

and see that each component is a Newton quotient for the corresponding coordinate. If each $x_i(t)$ is differentiable, then each quotient

$$\frac{x_i(t + h) - x_i(t)}{h}$$

approaches the derivative dx_i/dt. For this reason, we define the *derivative* dX/dt to be

$$\frac{dX}{dt} = \left(\frac{dx_1}{dt}, \ldots, \frac{dx_n}{dt} \right).$$

In fact, we could also say that the vector

$$\left(\frac{dx_1}{dt}, \ldots, \frac{dx_n}{dt} \right)$$

is the limit of the Newton quotient

$$\frac{X(t + h) - X(t)}{h}$$

as h approaches 0. Indeed, as h approaches 0, each component

$$\frac{x_i(t + h) - x_i(t)}{h}$$

approaches dx_i/dt. Hence the Newton quotient approaches the vector

$$\left(\frac{dx_1}{dt}, \ldots, \frac{dx_n}{dt} \right).$$

For example, if $X(t) = (\cos t, \sin t, t)$ then

$$\frac{dX}{dt} = (-\sin t, \cos t, 1).$$

It will also be convenient to denote dX/dt by $\dot{X}$; thus in the previous example, we would also write

$$\dot{X}(t) = (-\sin t, \cos t, 1) = X'(t).$$

(The notation $\dot{X}$ is used by the physicists.)

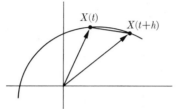

Figure 2

We define the *velocity vector* of the curve at time t to be the vector $X'(t)$. In our previous example, when

$$X(t) = (\cos t, \sin t, t),$$

the velocity vector at $t = \pi$ is

$$X'(\pi) = (0, -1, 1),$$

and for $t = \pi/4$ we get

$$X'(\pi/4) = (-1/\sqrt{2}, 1/\sqrt{2}, 1).$$

The velocity vector is located at the origin, but when we translate it to the point $X(t)$, then we visualize it as tangent to the curve, as in the next picture.

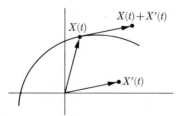

Figure 3

We define the *tangent line* to a curve X at time t to be the line passing through $X(t)$ in the direction of $X'(t)$, provided that $X'(t) \neq O$. Otherwise, we don't define a tangent line.

Example 1. Find a parametric equation of the tangent line to the curve $X(t) = (\sin t, \cos t)$ at $t = \pi/3$.

We have

$$X'(\pi/3) = (\tfrac{1}{2}, -\sqrt{3}/2) \quad \text{and} \quad X(\pi/3) = (\sqrt{3}/2, \tfrac{1}{2}).$$

Let $P = X(\pi/3)$ and $A = X'(\pi/3)$. Then a parametric equation of the tangent line at the required point is

$$L(t) = P + tA = \left(\frac{\sqrt{3}}{2}, \frac{1}{2}\right) + \left(\frac{1}{2}, -\frac{\sqrt{3}}{2}\right) t.$$

(We use another letter L because X is already occupied.) In terms of the coordinates $L(t) = (x(t), y(t))$, we can write the tangent line as

$$x(t) = \frac{\sqrt{3}}{2} + \frac{1}{2} t,$$

$$y(t) = \frac{1}{2} - \frac{\sqrt{3}}{2} t.$$

We define the *acceleration vector* to be the derivative dX'/dt, provided of course that X' is differentiable. We shall also denote the acceleration vector by X''. We define the *acceleration scalar* to be the length of the acceleration vector.

In the example given by $X(t) = (\cos t, \sin t, t)$ we find that

$$X''(t) = (-\cos t, -\sin t, 0).$$

Therefore $\|X''(t)\| = 1$ and we see that the spiral has a constant acceleration scalar, but not a constant acceleration vector.

We shall list the rules for differentiation. These will concern sums, products, and the chain rule is postponed to the next section. We make a remark concerning products. If X is a curve and f a function, defined on the same interval I, then for each t in this interval we can take the product

$$f(t)X(t)$$

of the *number* $f(t)$ by the *vector* $X(t)$. Thus if

$$X(t) = (x_1(t), \ldots, x_n(t))$$

then

$$f(t)X(t) = (f(t)x_1(t), \ldots, f(t)x_n(t)).$$

For instance, if $X(t) = (\cos t, \sin t, t)$ and $f(t) = e^t$, then

$$f(t)X(t) = (e^t \cos t, e^t \sin t, e^t t),$$

and

$$f(\pi)X(\pi) = (e^\pi(-1), e^\pi(0), e^\pi \pi) = (-e^\pi, 0, e^\pi \pi).$$

The derivative of a curve is defined componentwise. Thus the rules for the derivative will be very similar to the rules for differentiating functions.

Rule 1. *Let $X(t)$ and $Y(t)$ be two differentiable curves (defined for the same values of t). Then the sum $X(t) + Y(t)$ is differentiable, and*

$$\frac{d(X(t) + Y(t))}{dt} = \frac{dX}{dt} + \frac{dY}{dt}.$$

Rule 2. *Let c be a number, and let $X(t)$ be differentiable. Then $cX(t)$ is differentiable, and*

$$\frac{d(cX(t))}{dt} = c\frac{dX}{dt}.$$

Rule 3. *Let $f(t)$ be a differentiable function, and $X(t)$ a differentiable curve (defined for the same values of t). Then $f(t)X(t)$ is differentiable, and*

$$\frac{d(fX)}{dt} = f(t)\frac{dX}{dt} + \frac{df}{dt}X(t).$$

Rule 4. *Let $X(t)$ and $Y(t)$ be two differentiable curves (defined for the same values of t). Then $X(t) \cdot Y(t)$ is a differentiable function whose derivative is*

$$\frac{d}{dt}[X(t) \cdot Y(t)] = X'(t) \cdot Y(t) + X(t) \cdot Y'(t).$$

(This is formally analogous to the derivative of a product of functions, namely the first times the derivative of the second plus the second times the derivative of the first, except that the product is now a scalar product.)

As an example of the proofs we shall give the third one in detail, and leave the others to you as exercises.

Let $X(t) = (x_1(t), \ldots, x_n(t))$, and let $f = f(t)$ be a function. Then by definition

$$f(t)X(t) = (f(t)x_1(t), \ldots, f(t)x_n(t)).$$

We take the derivative of each component and apply the rule for the derivative of a product of functions. We obtain:

$$\frac{d(fX)}{dt} = \left(f(t)\frac{dx_1}{dt} + \frac{df}{dt}x_1(t), \ldots, f(t)\frac{dx_n}{dt} + \frac{df}{dt}x_n(t)\right).$$

Using the rule for the sum of two vectors, we see that the expression on the right is equal to

$$\left(f(t)\frac{dx_1}{dt}, \ldots, f(t)\frac{dx_n}{dt}\right) + \left(\frac{df}{dt}x_1(t), \ldots, \frac{df}{dt}x_n(t)\right).$$

We can take f out of the vector on the left and df/dt out of the vector on the right to obtain

$$f(t)\frac{dX}{dt} + \frac{df}{dt}X(t),$$

as desired.

Example 2. Let A be a fixed vector, and let f be an ordinary differentiable function of one variable. Let $F(t) = f(t)A$. Then $F'(t) = f'(t)A$. For instance, if $F(t) = (\cos t)A$ and $A = (a, b)$ where a, b are fixed numbers, then $F(t) = (a \cos t, b \cos t)$ and thus

$$F'(t) = (-a \sin t, -b \sin t) = (-\sin t)A.$$

Similarly, if A, B are fixed vectors, and

$$G(t) = (\cos t)A + (\sin t)B,$$

then

$$G'(t) = (-\sin t)A + (\cos t)B.$$

One can also give a proof for the derivative of a product which does not use coordinates and is similar to the proof for the derivative of a product of functions. We carry this proof out. We must consider the Newton quotient

$$\frac{X(t + h) \cdot Y(t + h) - X(t) \cdot Y(t)}{h}$$

$$= \frac{X(t + h) \cdot Y(t + h) - X(t) \cdot Y(t + h) + X(t) \cdot Y(t + h) - X(t) \cdot Y(t)}{h}$$

$$= \frac{X(t + h) - X(t)}{h} \cdot Y(t + h) + X(t) \cdot \frac{Y(t + h) - Y(t)}{h}.$$

Taking the limit as $h \to 0$, we find

$$X'(t) \cdot Y(t) + X(t) \cdot Y'(t)$$

as desired.

Note that this type of proof applies without change if we replace the dot product by, say, the cross product. A coordinate proof for the derivative of the cross product can also be given (cf. Exercise 25).

We define the *speed* of the curve $X(t)$ to be the length of the velocity vector. If we denote the speed by $v(t)$, then by definition we have

$$v(t) = \|X'(t)\|,$$

and thus

$$v(t)^2 = X'(t)^2 = X'(t) \cdot X'(t).$$

We can also omit the t from the notation, and write

$$v = X' \cdot X' = X'^2.$$

The length of the acceleration vector is called the *acceleration scalar*, and will be denoted by $a(t)$. *Warning:* $a(t)$ is not necessarily the derivative of $v(t)$. Almost any example shows this. For instance, let

$$X(t) = (\sin t, \cos t).$$

Then $v(t) = \|X(t)\| = 1$ so that $dv/dt = 0$. However, a simple computation shows that $X''(t) = (\cos t, -\sin t)$ and hence $a(t) = 1$.

We define the *length* of a curve X between two values a, b of t ($a \leq b$) in the interval of definition of the curve to be the integral of the speed:

$$\int_a^b v(t)\, dt = \int_a^b \|X'(t)\|\, dt.$$

By definition, we can rewrite this integral in the form

$$\int_a^b \sqrt{\left(\frac{dx_1}{dt}\right)^2 + \cdots + \left(\frac{dx_n}{dt}\right)^2}\, dt.$$

When $n = 2$, this is the same formula for the length which we gave in Volume I of this course. Thus the formula in dimension n is a very natural generalization of the formula in dimension 2. Namely, when

$$X(t) = (x(t), y(t))$$

is given by two coordinates, then the length of the curve between a and b is equal to

$$\int_a^b \sqrt{\left(\frac{dx}{dt}\right)^2 + \left(\frac{dy}{dt}\right)^2}\, dt.$$

Example 3. Let the curve be defined by

$$X(t) = (\sin t, \cos t).$$

Then $X'(t) = (\cos t, -\sin t)$ and $v(t) = \sqrt{\cos^2 t + \sin^2 t} = 1$. Hence the length of the curve between $t = 0$ and $t = 1$ is

$$\int_0^1 v(t)\, dt = t \Big|_0^1 = 1.$$

In this case, of course, the integral is easy to evaluate. There is no reason why this should always be the case.

Example 4. Set up the integral for the length of the curve

$$X(t) = (e^t, \sin t, t)$$

between $t = 1$ and $t = \pi$.

We have $X'(t) = (e^t, \cos t, 1)$. Hence the desired integral is

$$\int_1^\pi \sqrt{e^{2t} + \cos^2 t + 1}\, dt.$$

In this case, there is no easy formula for the integral. In the exercises, however, the functions are adjusted in such a way that the integral can be evaluated by elementary techniques of integration. Don't expect this to be the case in real life, though.

EXERCISES

Find the velocity vector of the following curves.

1. $(e^t, \cos t, \sin t)$ 2. $(\sin 2t, \log (1 + t), t)$

3. $(\cos t, \sin t)$ 4. $(\cos 3t, \sin 3t)$

5. In Exercises 3 and 4, show that the velocity vector is perpendicular to the position vector.

6. In Exercises 3 and 4, show that the acceleration vector is in the opposite direction from the position vector.

7. Let A, B be two constant vectors. What is the velocity vector of the curve $X = A + tB$?

8. Let $X(t)$ be a differentiable curve. A plane or line which is perpendicular to the velocity vector $X'(t)$ at the point $X(t)$ is said to be *normal* to the curve at the point t or also at the point $X(t)$. Find the equation of a line normal to the curves of Exercises 3 and 4 at the point $\pi/3$.

9. Find the equation of a plane normal to the curve

$$(e^t, t, t^2)$$

at the point $t = 1$.

10. Same question at the point $t = 0$.

11. Let $X(t)$ be a differentiable curve defined on an open interval. Let Q be a point which is not on the curve.
    (a) Write down the formula for the distance between Q and an arbitrary point on the curve.
    (b) If t_0 is a value of t such that the distance between Q and $X(t_0)$ is at a minimum, show that the vector $Q - X(t_0)$ is normal to the curve, at the point $X(t_0)$. [*Hint:* Investigate the minimum of the square of the distance.]
    (c) If $X(t)$ is the parametric equation of a straight line, show that there exists a unique value t_0 to such that the distance between Q and $X(t_0)$ is a minimum.

12. Find the length of the spiral $(\cos t, \sin t, t)$ between $t = 0$ and $t = 1$.

13. Find the length of the spiral $(\cos 2t, \sin 2t, 3t)$ between $t = 1$ and $t = 3$.

14. Assume that the differentiable curve $X(t)$ lies on the sphere of radius 1. Show that the velocity vector is perpendicular to the position vector. [*Hint:* Start from the condition $X(t)^2 = 1$.]

15. Let A be a non-zero vector, c a number, and Q a point. Let P_0 be the point of intersection of the line passing through Q, in the direction of A, and the plane $X \cdot A = c$. Show that for all points P of the plane, we have

$$\|Q - P_0\| \leq \|Q - P\|.$$

[*Hint:* If $P \neq P_0$, consider the straight line passing through P_0 and P, and use Exercise 11(c).]

16. Write a parametric equation for the tangent line to the given curve at the given point in each of the following cases.

   (a) $(\cos 4t, \sin 4t, t)$ at the point $t = \pi/8$
   (b) $(t, 2t, t^2)$ at the point $(1, 2, 1)$
   (c) $(e^{3t}, e^{-3t}, 3\sqrt{2}t)$ at $t = 1$
   (d) (t, t^3, t^4) at the point $(1, 1, 1)$

17. Find the length of the curves of Exercise 16 for the following intervals.

   (a) $t = 0$ to $t = \pi/8$.   (b) $t = 1$ to $t = 3$.   (c) $t = 0$ to $t = \frac{1}{3}$.

18. Show that the two curves $(e^t, e^{2t}, 1 - e^{-t})$ and $(1 - \theta, \cos \theta, \sin \theta)$ intersect at the point $(1, 1, 0)$. What is the angle between their tangents at that point?

19. At what points does the curve $(2t^2, 1 - t, 3 + t^2)$ intersect the plane $3x - 14y + z - 10 = 0$?

20. Let $X(t)$ be a differentiable curve and suppose that $X'(t) = O$ for all t throughout its interval of definition I. What can you say about the curve? Suppose $X'(t) \neq O$ but $X''(t) = O$ for all t in the interval. What can you say about the curve?

21. Find the length of the curve defined by

$$X(t) = (t - \sin t, 1 - \cos t)$$

between $t = 0$ and $t = 2\pi$.

22. Find the length of the curve $X(t) = (t, \log t)$ between $t = \frac{1}{2}$ and $t = 2$.

23. Find the length of the curve defined by $X(t) = (t, \log \cos t)$ between $t = 0$ and $t = \pi/4$.

24. Prove that if the acceleration of a curve is always perpendicular to its velocity, then its speed is constant.

25. Using the definition of the cross product by coordinates given in Chapter I, prove that if $X(t)$ and $Y(t)$ are two differentiable curves (defined for the same values of t), then

$$\frac{d[X(t) \times Y(t)]}{dt} = X(t) \times \frac{dY(t)}{dt} + \frac{dX(t)}{dt} \times Y(t).$$

26. Show that

$$\frac{d}{dt}[X(t) \times X'(t)] = X(t) \times X''(t).$$

27. Let $X(t) = (a \cos t, a \sin t, bt)$, where a, b are constant. Let $\theta(t)$ be the angle which the tangent line at a given point of the curve makes with the z-axis. Show that $\cos \theta(t)$ is the constant $b/\sqrt{a^2 + b^2}$.

28. Show that the velocity and acceleration vectors of the curve in Exercise 27 have constant lengths.

29. Let B be a fixed unit vector, and let $X(t)$ be a curve such that $X(t) \cdot B = e^{2t}$ for all t. Assume also that the velocity vector of the curve has a constant angle θ with the vector B, with $0 < \theta < \pi/2$.

  (a) Show that the speed is $2e^{2t}/\cos\theta$.

  (b) Determine the dot product $X'(t) \cdot X''(t)$ in terms of t and θ.

30. Let

$$X(t) = \left(\frac{2t}{1+t^2}, \frac{1-t^2}{1+t^2}, 1\right).$$

Show that the cosine of the angle between $X(t)$ and $X'(t)$ is constant.

31. Let A, B be fixed non-zero vectors. Let

$$X(t) = e^{2t}A + e^{-2t}B.$$

Show that $X''(t)$ has the same direction as $X(t)$.

32. Let $Y(t) = X(t) \times X'(t)$. Show that $Y'(t) = X(t) \times X''(t)$.

33. Let $Y(t) = X(t) \cdot (X'(t) \times X''(t))$. Show that $Y' = X \cdot (X' \times X''')$.

34. Let B be a non-zero vector, and let $X(t)$ be such that $X(t) \cdot B = t$ for all t. Assume also that the angle between $X'(t)$ and B is constant. Show that $X''(t)$ is perpendicular to $X'(t)$.

§2. THE CHAIN RULE AND APPLICATIONS

Let X be a vector and c a number. As a matter of notation it will be convenient to define Xc to be cX, in other words, we allow ourselves to multiply vectors by numbers on the right. If we have a curve $X(t)$ defined for some interval, and a function $g(t)$ defined on the same interval, then we let

$$X(t)g(t) = g(t)X(t).$$

Let $X = X(t)$ be a differentiable curve.

Let f be a function defined on some interval, such that the values of f lie in the domain of definition of the curve $X(t)$. Then we may form the composite curve $X \circ f$. If s is a number at which f is defined, we let the value of $X \circ f$ at s be

$$(X \circ f)(s) = X(f(s)).$$

For example, let $X(t) = (t^2, e^t)$ and let $f(s) = \sin s$. Then

$$X(f(s)) = (\sin^2 s, e^{\sin s}).$$

Each component of $X(f(s))$ becomes a function of s, just as when we studied the chain rule for functions.

The chain rule asserts: *If X is a differentiable curve and f is a differentiable function defined on some interval, whose values are contained in the interval* *of definition of the curve, then the composite curve $X \circ f$ is differentiable, and*

$$(X \circ f)'(s) = X'(f(s))f'(s).$$

The expression on the right can also be written $f'(s)X'(f(s))$. It is the product of the function f' times the vector X'.

In another notation, if we let $t = f(s)$, then we can write the above formula in the form

$$\frac{d(X \circ f)}{ds} = \frac{dX}{dt}\frac{dt}{ds}.$$

The proof of the chain rule is trivial, using the chain rule for functions. Indeed, let $Y(s) = X(f(s))$. Then

$$Y(s) = (x_1(f(s)), \ldots, x_n(f(s))).$$

Taking the derivative term by term, we find:

$$Y'(s) = (x_1'(f(s))f'(s), \ldots, x_n'(f(s))f'(s)).$$

We can take $f'(s)$ outside the vector, and get

$$Y'(s) = X'(f(s))f'(s),$$

which is precisely what we want.

The change of variables from t to s is also called a change of parametrization of the curve. Under certain changes of parametrization, certain formulas involving the velocity and acceleration of the curve become simpler and reflect geometric properties more clearly. We shall see examples of this in a moment.

Let us now assume that all the functions with which we dealt above have second derivatives. Using the chain rule, and the rule for the derivative of a product, we obtain the following two formulas:

(1) $Y'(s) = f'(s)X'(f(s)),$

(2) $Y''(s) = f''(s)X'(f(s)) + (f'(s))^2X''(f(s)).$

Since $t = f(s)$, we can also write these in the notation of the physicists:

(1) $Y'(s) = f'(s)\dot{X}(t),$

(2) $Y''(s) = f''(s)\dot{X}(t) + (f'(s))^2\ddot{X}(t).$

We shall consider an important special case of these formulas.
We have defined

$$v(t) = \|\dot{X}(t)\|$$

to be the speed. Let us now assume that each coordinate function of $\dot{X}(t)$ is continuous. In that case, we say that $\dot{X}(t)$ is *continuous*. Then $v(t)$ is a continuous function of t. *We shall assume throughout that $v(t) \neq 0$*

for any value of t in the interval of definition of our curve. Then $v(t) > 0$ for all such values of t. We let

$$s(t) = \int v(t) \, dt$$

be a fixed indefinite integral of $v(t)$ over our interval. (For instance, if a is a point of the interval, we could let

$$s(t) = \int_a^t v(u) \, du.$$

We know that any two indefinite integrals of v over the interval differ by a constant.) Then

$$\frac{ds}{dt} = v(t) > 0$$

for all values of t, and hence s is a strictly increasing function. Consequently, the inverse function exists. Call it

$$t = f(s).$$

We can then write

$$X(t) = X(f(s)) = Y(s).$$

Thus we are in the situation described above.

The velocity vectors of the curve depending on the two different parametrizations are related as in formula (1). From the theory of derivatives of inverse functions, we know that

$$f'(s) = \frac{df}{ds} = \left(\frac{ds}{dt}\right)^{-1}.$$

Hence $f'(s)$ is always positive. This means that in the present case, $Y'(s)$ and $\dot{X}(t)$ have the same direction when $t = f(s)$.

A curve $Y: J \to \mathbf{R}^n$ is said to be *parametrized by arc length* if $\| Y'(s) \| = 1$ for all s in the interval of definition J. The reason for this is contained in the next theorem.

Theorem 1. *Let $X: I \to \mathbf{R}^n$ be a curve whose speed $v(t)$ is > 0 for all t in the interval of definition. Let*

$$s(t) = \int_a^t v(u) \, du$$

and $t = f(s)$ be the inverse function. Then the curve given by

$$s \mapsto Y(s) = X(f(s))$$

is parametrized by arc length, and $Y'(s)$ is perpendicular to $Y''(s)$ for each value of s.

Proof. From formula (1), we get

$$\| Y'(s) \| = |f'(s)| \, \| \dot{X}(t) \| = \frac{df}{ds} \frac{ds}{dt}.$$

By what we just saw above, this last expression is equal to 1. Thus $Y'(s)$ is a vector of length 1, a unit vector, in the same direction as $\dot{X}(t)$. Thus the velocity vector of the curve Y has constant length.

In particular, we have $Y'(s)^2 = 1$. Differentiating with respect to s, we get

$$2Y' \cdot Y'' = 0.$$

Hence $Y'(s)$ is perpendicular to $Y''(s)$ for each value of s. This proves the theorem.

From (2), we see that the acceleration $Y''(s)$ has two components. First a tangential component

$$f''(s)\dot{X}(t)$$

in the direction of $\dot{X}(t)$, which involves the naive notion of scalar acceleration, namely the second derivative $f''(s)$. Second, another component in the direction of $\ddot{X}(t)$, with a coefficient

$$(f'(s))^2$$

which is positive. [We assume of course that $\ddot{X}(t) \neq O$.]

For a given value of t, let us assume that $\dot{X}(t) \neq O$ and $\ddot{X}(t) \neq O$, and also that $\dot{X}(t)$ and $\ddot{X}(t)$ do not lie on the same straight line. Then the plane passing through $X(t)$, parallel to $\dot{X}(t)$ and $\ddot{X}(t)$ is called the *osculating plane* of the curve at time t, or also at the point $X(t)$. [Actually, it is more accurate to say at time t, because there may be two numbers t_1, t_2 in the interval of definition of the curve such that $X(t_1) = X(t_2)$.]

Example 1. Let $X(t) = (\sin t, \cos t, t)$. Find the osculating plane to this curve at $t = \pi/2$.

We have

$$\dot{X}(\pi/2) = (0, -1, 1)$$

and

$$\ddot{X}(\pi/2) = (-1, 0, 0).$$

We find first a vector perpendicular to $\dot{X}(\pi/2)$ and $\ddot{X}(\pi/2)$. For instance, $N = (0, 1, 1)$ is such a vector. Furthermore, let $P = X(\pi/2) = (1, 0, \pi/2)$. Then the osculating plane at $t = \pi/2$ is the plane passing through P, perpendicular to N, and its equation is therefore

$$y + z = \pi/2.$$

In case of parametrization by arc length, or in fact in any other parametrization such that $f'(s) \neq 0$, we see from formulas (1) and (2) that the plane parallel to $\dot{X}(t)$ and $\ddot{X}(t)$ is the same as the plane parallel to $Y'(s)$ and $Y''(s)$ because from these formulas, we can solve back for $\dot{X}(t)$ and $\ddot{X}(t)$ in terms of this other pair of vectors. Thus the osculating plane does not depend on a change of parametrization $t = f(s)$ such that $f'(s) \neq 0$.

Let us assume that a curve is parametrized by arc length. Thus we write the curve as $Y(s)$, and by Theorem 1, we have $\|Y'(s)\| = 1$ *and*

$$Y'(s) \cdot Y''(s) = 0.$$

Then $Y'(s)$ and $Y''(s)$ look like this:

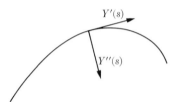

Figure 4

Example 2. Let R be a number > 0. A parametrization for the circle of radius R by arc length is given by

$$Y(s) = \left(R \cos \frac{s}{R}, R \sin \frac{s}{R} \right),$$

as one sees immediately, because $\|Y'(s)\| = 1$.

Differentiating twice shows that

$$Y''(s) = -\frac{1}{R} Y'(s),$$

and hence that

$$\|Y''(s)\| = \frac{1}{R} \quad \text{or} \quad R = \frac{1}{\|Y''(s)\|}.$$

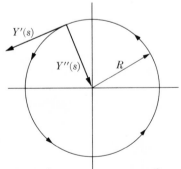

Figure 5

For an arbitrary curve Y parametrized by arc length, it is customary to make a definition which is motivated by the geometry of the special example just discussed, namely we define the *radius of curvature* $R(s)$ to be

$$R(s) = \frac{1}{\| Y''(s) \|}$$

at all points such that $\| Y''(s) \| \neq 0$. (Note that if $Y''(s) = O$ on some interval, then $Y(s) = As + B$ for suitable vectors A, B, and thus Y parametrizes a straight line. Thus intuitively, it is reasonable to view its radius of curvature as infinity.)

The same motivation as above leads us to define the *curvature* itself to be $\| Y''(s) \|$. The curvature is usually denoted by k.

Most curves are not usually given parametrized by arc length, and thus it is useful to have a formula which gives the curvature in terms of the given parameter t. This comes immediately from the chain rule. Indeed, keeping our notation $X(t)$ and $Y(s)$ with $ds/dt = v(t)$, we have the formula

$$Y''(s) = \frac{1}{v(t)} \frac{d}{dt}\left(\frac{1}{v(t)} X'(t) \right)$$

where $v(t) = \| X'(t) \|$ is the length of the velocity vector $X'(t)$.

Proof. From formula (1), we know that

$$Y'(s) = \frac{dt}{ds} X'(t) = \frac{1}{v(t)} X'(t).$$

By the chain rule,

$$Y''(s) = \frac{d(Y'(s(t)))}{dt} \frac{dt}{ds},$$

which yields precisely the formula in the box.

The curvature is then equal to the length of the vector in the box.

Example 3. Find the curvature of the curve given by

$$X(t) = (\cos t, \sin t, t).$$

We have $X'(t) = (-\sin t, \cos t, 1)$ and $v(t) = \sqrt{2}$ is constant. Then $X''(t) = (-\cos t, -\sin t, 0)$, and from the formula for the curvature we find

$$k(t) = \frac{1}{\sqrt{2}} \left\| \frac{1}{\sqrt{2}} X''(t) \right\| = \frac{1}{2}.$$

We see in particular that the curve has constant curvature.

EXERCISES

1. Find the equations of the osculating planes for each of the curves of Exercise 16, §1 at the given point.

2. Prove formula (2) from formula (1) in detail.

3. Let r be a fixed number > 0, let $c > 0$, and let

$$X(t) = (r \cos t, r \sin t, ct).$$

Find the curvature as a function of t.

4. Find the curvature of the curve

$$X(t) = (t, t^2, t^3)$$

at (a) $t = 1$, (b) $t = 0$, (c) $t = -1$.

5. Let the plane curve be defined by $X(t) = (x(t), y(t))$. Show that the curvature is given by

$$k(t) = \frac{|x'(t)y''(t) - x''(t)y'(t)|}{\left(x'^2(t) + y'^2(t)\right)^{3/2}}.$$

6. If a curve is parametrized by $x = t$, $y = f(t)$ (the natural parametrization arising from a function $y = f(x)$), find a simplification for the curvature given in the preceding exercise.

7. Find the radius of curvature of the curve $X(t) = (t, \log t)$. For which t is the radius of curvature a minimum?

8. Find the curvatures of the curves
   (a) $X(t) = (t, \sin t)$,
   (b) $X(t) = (\sin 3t, \cos 3t)$,
   (c) $X(t) = (\sin 3t, \cos 3t, t)$.

9. Find the radius of curvature of the parabola $y = x^2$.

10. Find the radius of curvature of the ellipse given by

$$X(t) = (a \cos t, b \sin t),$$

where a, b are constants.

11. Find the curvature of the curve defined by

$$x(t) = \int_0^t \cos \frac{\pi u^2}{2} \, du,$$

$$y(t) = \int_0^t \sin \frac{\pi u^2}{2} \, du.$$

12. Find the curvature of the curve defined by

$$x(t) = \int_0^t \frac{\cos u}{\sqrt{u}}\, du,$$

$$y(t) = \int_0^t \frac{\sin u}{\sqrt{u}}\, du$$

in terms of the arc length s.

13. Show that the curvature of the curve defined by

$$X(t) = (e^t, e^{-t}, \sqrt{2}\, t)$$

is equal to $\sqrt{2}/(e^t - e^{-t})^2$.

14. If a curve has constant velocity and acceleration, show that the curvature is constant. Express the curvature in terms of the lengths of the velocity and acceleration vectors.

Chapter III

Functions of Several Variables

We view functions of several variables as functions of points in space. This appeals to our geometric intuition, and also relates such functions more easily with the theory of vectors. The gradient will appear as a natural generalization of the derivative. In this chapter we are mainly concerned with basic definitions and notions. We postpone the important theorems to the next chapter.

§1. GRAPHS AND LEVEL CURVES

In order to conform with usual terminology, and for the sake of brevity, a collection of objects will simply be called a *set*. In this chapter, we are mostly concerned with sets of points in space.

Let S be a set of points in n-space. A *function* (defined on S) is an association which to each element of S associates a number.

In practice, we sometimes omit mentioning explicitly the set S, since the context usually makes it clear for which points the function is defined.

Example 1. In 2-space (the plane) we can define a function f by the rule

$$f(x, y) = x^2 + y^2.$$

It is defined for all points (x, y) and can be interpreted geometrically as the square of the distance between the origin and the point.

Example 2. Again in 2-space, let

$$f(x, y) = \frac{x^2 - y^2}{x^2 + y^2}$$

be defined for all

$$(x, y) \neq (0, 0).$$

We do not define f at $(0, 0)$ (also written O).

358

Example 3. In 3-space, we can define a function f by the rule

$$f(x, y, z) = x^2 - \sin(xyz) + yz^3.$$

Since a point and a vector are represented by the same thing (namely an n-tuple), we can think of a function such as the above also as a function of vectors. When we do not want to write the coordinates, we write $f(X)$ instead of $f(x_1, \ldots, x_n)$. As with numbers, we call $f(X)$ the *value* of f at the point (or vector) X.

Just as with functions of one variable, one can define the *graph* of a function f of n variables $x_1, \ldots, x_n$ to be the set of points in $(n + 1)$-space of the form

$$\big(x_1, \ldots, x_n, f(x_1, \ldots, x_n)\big),$$

the $(x_1, \ldots, x_n)$ being in the domain of definition of f. Thus when $n = 1$, the graph of a function f is a set of points $(x, f(x))$. When $n = 2$, the graph of a function f is the set of points $(x, y, f(x, y))$. When $n = 2$, it is already difficult to draw the graph since it involves a figure in 3-space. The graph of a function of two variables may look like this:

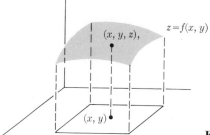

Figure 1

When we get to the graph of a function of three variables, it is of course impossible to draw it, since it exists in 4-space. However, we shall describe another means of visualizing the function.

For each number c, the equation $f(x, y) = c$ is the equation of a curve in the plane. We have considerable experience in drawing the graphs of such curves, and we may therefore assume that we know how to draw this graph in principle. This curve is called the *level curve* of f at c. It gives us the set of points (x, y) where f takes on the value c. By drawing a number of such level curves, we can get a good description of the function.

Example 1 (continued). The level curves are described by equations

$$x^2 + y^2 = c.$$

These have a solution only when $c \geqq 0$. In that case, they are circles (unless $c = 0$ in which case the circle of radius 0 is simply the origin). In Fig. 2, we have drawn the level curves for $c = 1$ and 4.

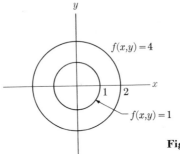

$f(x,y) = 4$

$f(x,y) = 1$

Figure 2

The graph of the function $z = f(x, y) = x^2 + y^2$ is then a figure in 3-space, which we may represent as follows.

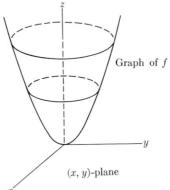

Graph of f

(x, y)-plane

Figure 3

Example 2 (continued). To find the level curves in Example 2, we have to determine the values (x, y) such that

$$x^2 - y^2 = c(x^2 + y^2)$$

for a given number c. This amounts to solving $x^2(1 - c) = y^2(1 + c)$. If $x = 0$, then $f(0, y) = -1$. Thus on the vertical line passing through the origin, our function has the constant value -1. If $x \neq 0$, then we can divide by x in the above equality, and we obtain (for $c \neq -1$)

$$\frac{y^2}{x^2} = \frac{1 - c}{1 + c}.$$

Taking the square root, we obtain two level lines, namely

$$y = ax \quad \text{and} \quad y = -ax, \quad \text{where} \quad a = \sqrt{\frac{1 - c}{1 + c}}.$$

Thus the level curves are straight lines (excluding the origin). We have drawn some of them in Fig. 4. (The numbers indicate the value of the function on the corresponding line.)

It would of course be technically much more disagreeable to draw the level lines in Example 3, and we shall not do so.

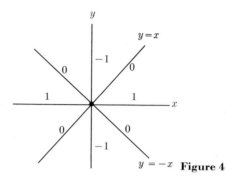

Figure 4

We see that the level lines are based on the same principle as the contour lines of a map. Each line describes, so to speak, the altitude of the function. If the graph is interpreted as a mountainous region, then each level curve gives the set of points of constant altitude. In Example 1, a person wanting to stay at a given altitude need but walk around in circles. In Example 2, such a person should walk on a straight line towards or away from the origin.

If we deal with a function of three variables, say $f(x, y, z)$, then $(x, y, z) = X$ is a point in 3-space. In that case, the set of points satisfying the equation

$$f(x, y, z) = c$$

for some constant c is a surface. The notion analogous to that of level curve is that of level surface.

In physics, a function f might be a potential function, giving the value of the potential energy at each point of space. The level surfaces are then sometimes called surfaces of *equipotential*. The function f might also give a temperature distribution (i.e. its value at a point X is the temperature at X). In that case, the level surfaces are called *isothermal* surfaces.

EXERCISES

Sketch the level curves for the functions $z = f(x, y)$, where $f(x, y)$ is given by the following expressions.

1. $x^2 + 2y^2$ 2. $y - x^2$ 3. $y - 3x^2$

4. $x - y^2$ 5. $3x^2 + 3y^2$ 6. xy

7. $(x - 1)(y - 2)$ 8. $(x + 1)(y + 3)$ 9. $\dfrac{x^2}{4} + \dfrac{y^2}{16}$

10. $2x - 3y$ 11. $\dfrac{xy}{x^2 + y^2}$ 12. $\dfrac{xy^2}{x^2 + y^4}$

13. $\dfrac{4xy(x^2 - y^2)}{x^2 + y^2}$ (try polar coordinates)

14. $\dfrac{x + y}{x - y}$ 15. $\dfrac{x^2 + y^2}{x^2 - y^2}$

(In Exercises 11, 12, and 13, the function is not defined at $(0, 0)$. In Exercise 14, it is not defined for $y = x$, and in Exercise 15 it is not defined for $y = x$ or $y = -x$.)

16. $(x - 1)^2 + (y + 3)^2$ 17. $x^2 - y^2$

§2. PARTIAL DERIVATIVES

In this section and the next, we discuss the notion of differentiability for functions of several variables. When we discussed the derivative of functions of one variable, we assumed that such a function was defined on an interval. We shall have to make a similar assumption in the case of several variables, and for this we need to introduce a new notion.

Let P be a point in n-space, and let a be a number > 0. The set of points X such that

$$\|X - P\| < a$$

will be called the *open ball* of radius a and center P. The set of points X such that

$$\|X - P\| \leqq a$$

will be called the *closed ball* of radius a and center P. The set of points X such that

$$\|X - P\| = a$$

will be called the *sphere* of radius a and center P.

Thus when $n = 1$, we are in 1-space, and the open ball of radius a is the open interval centered at P. The sphere of radius a and center P consists only of two points.

When $n = 2$, the open ball of radius a and center P is also called the open *disc*. The sphere is the *circle*.

When $n = 3$, then our terminology coincides with the obvious interpretation we might want to place on the words.

The following are the pictures of the spheres of radius 1 in 2-space and 3-space respectively centered at the origin.

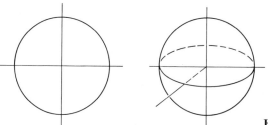

Figure 5

Let S_1 be the sphere of radius 1, centered at the origin. Let a be a number > 0. If X is a point of the sphere S_1, then aX is a point of the sphere of radius a, because

$$\|aX\| = a\|X\| = a.$$

In this manner, we get all points of the sphere of radius a. (Proof?) Thus the sphere of radius a is obtained by stretching the sphere of radius 1, through multiplication by a.

A similar remark applies to the open and closed balls of radius a, they being obtained from the open and closed balls of radius 1 through multiplication by a. (Prove this as an exercise.)

Let U be a set of points in n-space. We shall say that U is an *open set* in n-space if the following condition is satisfied: Given any point P in U, there exists an open ball B of radius $a > 0$ which is centered at P and such that B is contained in U.

Example 1. In the plane, the set consisting of the first quadrant, excluding the x- and y-axes, is an open set.

The x-axis is not open in the plane (i.e. in 2-space). Given a point on the x-axis, we cannot find an open disc centered at the point and contained in the x-axis.

On the other hand, if we view the x-axis as the set of points in 1-space, then it is open in 1-space. Similarly, the interval

$$-1 < x < 1$$

is open in 1-space, but not open in 2-space, or n-space for $n > 1$.

Example 2. Let U be the open ball of radius $a > 0$ centered at the origin. Then U is an open set. To prove this, let P be a point of this ball, so $\|P\| < a$. Say $\|P\| = b$. Let $c = a - b$. If X is a point such that $\|X - P\| < c$, then

$$\|X\| \leq \|X - P\| + \|P\| < a - b + b = a.$$

Hence the open ball of radius c centered at P is contained in U. Hence U is open.

In the next picture we have drawn an open set in the plane, consisting of the region inside the curve, but not containing any point of the boundary. We have also drawn a point P in U, and a sphere (disc) around P contained in U.

Figure 6

When we defined the derivative as a limit of

$$\frac{f(x + h) - f(x)}{h},$$

we needed the function f to be defined in some open interval around the point x.

Now let f be a function of n variables, defined on an open set U. Then for any point X in U, the function f is also defined at all points which are close to X, namely all points which are contained in an open ball centered at X and contained in U.

For small values of h, the point

$$(x_1 + h, x_2, \ldots, x_n)$$

is contained in such an open ball. Hence the function is defined at that point, and we may form the quotient

$$\frac{f(x_1 + h, x_2, \ldots, x_n) - f(x_1, \ldots, x_n)}{h}.$$

If the limit exists as h tends to 0, then we call it the *first partial derivative* of f and denote it by $D_1 f(x_1, \ldots, x_n)$, or $D_1 f(X)$, or also by

$$\frac{\partial f}{\partial x_1}.$$

Similarly, we let

$$D_i f(X) = \frac{\partial f}{\partial x_i}$$

$$= \lim_{h \to 0} \frac{f(x_1, \ldots, x_i + h, \ldots, x_n) - f(x_1, \ldots, x_n)}{h}$$

if it exists, and call it the i-th partial derivative.

When $n = 2$ and we work with variables (x, y), then the first and second partials are also noted

$$\frac{\partial f}{\partial x} \quad \text{and} \quad \frac{\partial f}{\partial y}.$$

By definition, we therefore have

$$\frac{\partial f}{\partial x} = \lim_{h \to 0} \frac{f(x + h, y) - f(x, y)}{h}$$

and

$$\frac{\partial f}{\partial y} = \lim_{k \to 0} \frac{f(x, y + k) - f(x, y)}{k}.$$

A partial derivative is therefore obtained by keeping all but one variable fixed, and taking the ordinary derivative with respect to this one variable.

Example 2. Let $f(x, y) = x^2 y^3$. Then

$$\frac{\partial f}{\partial x} = 2xy^3 \quad \text{and} \quad \frac{\partial f}{\partial y} = 3x^2 y^2.$$

We observe that when the partial derivatives are defined at all points where the function is defined, then they are themselves functions. This is the reason why the notation $D_i f$ is sometimes more useful than the notation $\partial f / \partial x_i$. It allows us to write $D_i f(P)$ for any point P in the set where the partial is defined. There cannot be any ambiguity or confusion with a (meaningless) symbol $D_i(f(P))$, since $f(P)$ is a number. Thus $D_i f(P)$ means $(D_i f)(P)$. It is the value of the function $D_i f$ at P.

Let f be defined in an open set U and assume that the partial derivatives of f exist at each point X of U. The *vector*

$$\left(\frac{\partial f}{\partial x_1}, \ldots, \frac{\partial f}{\partial x_n} \right) = (D_1 f(X), \ldots, D_n f(X)),$$

whose components are the partial derivatives, will be called the *gradient* of f at X and will be denoted by $\operatorname{grad} f(X)$. One must read this

$$(\operatorname{grad} f)(X),$$

but we shall usually omit the parentheses around $\operatorname{grad} f$.

If f is a function of two variables (x, y), then we have

$$\operatorname{grad} f(x, y) = \left(\frac{\partial f}{\partial x}, \frac{\partial f}{\partial y} \right).$$

For example, in Example 2, where $f(x, y) = x^2 y^3$, we have

$$\operatorname{grad} f(x, y) = (2xy^3, 3x^2 y^2),$$

so that in this case,

$$\operatorname{grad} f(1, 2) = (16, 12).$$

Thus the gradient of a function f associates a *vector* to a point X. This is a different kind of thing from a function, which associates a *number* to a point.

If f is a function of three variables (x, y, z), then

$$\text{grad } f(x, y, z) = \left(\frac{\partial f}{\partial x}, \frac{\partial f}{\partial y}, \frac{\partial f}{\partial z}\right).$$

Using the formula for the derivative of a sum of two functions, and the derivative of a constant times a function, we conclude at once that the gradient satisfies the following properties:

Theorem 1. *Let f, g be two functions defined on an open set U, and assume that their partial derivatives exist at every point of U. Let c be a number. Then*

$$\text{grad }(f + g) = \text{grad } f + \text{grad } g$$
$$\text{grad }(cf) = c \text{ grad } f.$$

You should carry out the details of the proof as an exercise.

We shall give later several geometric and physical interpretations for the gradient.

EXERCISES

Find the partial derivatives

$$\frac{\partial f}{\partial x}, \quad \frac{\partial f}{\partial y}, \quad \text{and} \quad \frac{\partial f}{\partial z},$$

for the following functions $f(x, y)$ or $f(x, y, z)$.

1. $xy + z$
2. $x^2 y^5 + 1$
3. $\sin(xy) + \cos z$
4. $\cos(xy)$
5. $\sin(xyz)$
6. e^{xyz}
7. $x^2 \sin(yz)$
8. xyz
9. $xz + yz + xy$
10. $x \cos(y - 3z) + \arcsin(xy)$
11. Find grad $f(P)$ if P is the point $(1, 2, 3)$ in Exercises 1, 2, 6, 8, and 9.
12. Find grad $f(P)$ if P is the point $(1, \pi, \pi)$ in Exercises 4, 5, 7.
13. Find grad $f(P)$ if

$$f(x, y, z) = \log(z + \sin(y^2 - x))$$

and

$$P = (1, -1, 1).$$

14. Find the partial derivatives of x^y.

Find the gradient of the following functions at the given point.

15. $f(x, y, z) = e^{-2x} \cos(yz)$ at $(1, \pi, \pi)$
16. $f(x, y, z) = e^{3x+y} \sin(5z)$ at $(0, 0, \pi/6)$
17. Prove that an open ball of radius $a > 0$ centered at some point Q is in fact an open set.

§3. DIFFERENTIABILITY AND GRADIENT

Let f be a function defined on an open set U. Let X be a point of U. For all vectors H such that $\|H\|$ is small (and $H \neq O$), the point $X + H$ also lies in the open set. However we *cannot* form a quotient

$$\frac{f(X + H) - f(X)}{H}$$

because it is meaningless to divide by a vector. In order to define what we mean for a function f to be differentiable, we must therefore find a way which does not involve dividing by H.

We reconsider the case of functions of one variable. Let us fix a number x. We had defined the derivative to be

$$f'(x) = \lim_{h \to 0} \frac{f(x + h) - f(x)}{h}.$$

Let

$$g(h) = \frac{f(x + h) - f(x)}{h} - f'(x).$$

Then $g(h)$ is not defined when $h = 0$, but

$$\lim_{h \to 0} g(h) = 0.$$

We can write

$$f(x + h) - f(x) = f'(x)h + hg(h).$$

This relation has meaning so far only when $h \neq 0$. However, we observe that if we define $g(0)$ to be 0, then the preceding relation is obviously true when $h = 0$ (because we just get $0 = 0$).

Furthermore, we can replace h by $-h$ if we replace g by $-g$. Thus we have shown that if f is differentiable, there exists a function g such that

(1) $$f(x + h) - f(x) = f'(x)h + |h|g(h),$$

$$\lim_{h \to 0} g(h) = 0.$$

Conversely, suppose that there exists a number a and a function $g(h)$ such that

(1a) $$f(x + h) - f(x) = ah + |h|g(h),$$

$$\lim_{h \to 0} g(h) = 0.$$

We find for $h \neq 0$,

$$\frac{f(x + h) - f(x)}{h} = a + \frac{|h|}{h} g(h).$$

Taking the limit as h approaches 0, we observe that

$$\lim_{h \to 0} \frac{|h|}{h} g(h) = 0.$$

Hence the limit of the Newton quotient exists and is equal to a. Hence f is differentiable, and its derivative $f'(x)$ is equal to a.

Therefore, the existence of a number a and a function g satisfying (1a) above could have been used as the definition of differentiability in the case of functions of one variable. The great advantage of (1) is that no h appears in the denominator. It is this relation which will suggest to us how to define differentiability for functions of several variables, and how to prove the chain rule for them.

We now consider a function of n variables.

Let f be a function defined on an open set U. Let X be a point of U. If $H = (h_1, \ldots, h_n)$ is a vector such that $\|H\|$ is small enough, then $X + H$ will also be a point of U and so $f(X + H)$ is defined. Note that

$$X + H = (x_1 + h_1, \ldots, x_n + h_n).$$

This is the generalization of the $x + h$ with which we dealt previously.

When f is a function of two variables, which we write (x, y), then we use the notation $H = (h, k)$ so that

$$X + H = (x + h, y + k).$$

The point $X + H$ is close to X and we are interested in the difference $f(X + H) - f(X)$, which is the difference of the value of the function at $X + H$ and the value of the function at X.

We say that f is *differentiable* at X if the partial derivatives $D_1 f(X), \ldots, D_n f(X)$ exist, and if there exists a function g (defined for small H) such that

$$\lim_{H \to 0} g(H) = 0 \quad \left(\text{also written } \lim_{\|H\| \to 0} g(H) = 0\right)$$

and

$$f(X + H) - f(X) = D_1 f(X)h_1 + \cdots + D_n f(X)h_n + \|H\|g(H).$$

With the other notation for partial derivatives, this last relation reads:

$$f(X + H) - f(X) = \frac{\partial f}{\partial x_1} h_1 + \cdots + \frac{\partial f}{\partial x_n} h_n + \|H\|g(H).$$

We say that f is *differentiable* in the open set U if it is differentiable at every point of U, so that the above relation holds for every point X in U.

In view of the definition of the gradient in §2, we can rewrite our fundamental relation in the form

$$(2) \qquad f(X + H) - f(X) = \left(\operatorname{grad} f(X)\right) \cdot H + \|H\|g(H).$$

The term $\|H\|g(H)$ has an order of magnitude smaller than the previous term involving the dot product. This is one advantage of the present notation. We know how to handle the formalism of dot products and are accustomed to it, and its geometric interpretation. This will help us later in interpreting the gradient geometrically.

For the moment, we observe that the gradient is the only vector which will make formula (2) valid (cf. Exercise 7).

In two variables, the definition of differentiability reads

$$f(x + h, y + k) - f(x, y) = \frac{\partial f}{\partial x} h + \frac{\partial f}{\partial y} k + \|H\|g(H).$$

We view the term

$$\frac{\partial f}{\partial x} h + \frac{\partial f}{\partial y} k$$

as an approximation to $f(X + H) - f(X)$, depending in a particularly simple way on h and k.

As an abbreviation, one sometimes writes

$$\text{grad } f = \nabla f.$$

Then formula (2) can be written

$$f(X + H) - f(X) = \nabla f(X) \cdot H + \|H\|g(H).$$

As with grad f, one must read $(\nabla f)(X)$ and not the meaningless $\nabla(f(X))$ since $f(X)$ is a number for each value of X, and thus it makes no sense to apply ∇ to a number. The symbol ∇ is applied to the function f, and $(\nabla f)(X)$ is the value of ∇f at X.

Error terms which can be written in the form $\|H\|g(H)$ for some function g such that

$$\lim_{H \to 0} g(H) = 0$$

will appear quite frequently in the sequel. Thus we make a definition. A function φ defined for small H is said to be $o(H)$ (read, "little oh of H") for $H \to O$ if

$$\lim_{H \to 0} \frac{\varphi(H)}{\|H\|} = 0.$$

If we let $g(H) = \varphi(H)/\|H\|$, then we see that $\varphi(H) = \|H\|g(H)$ is precisely of the type just considered, namely $o(H)$ for $H \to O$.

The following properties of functions which are $o(H)$ will be used constantly, and follow at once from the definition of limits:

(i) *If φ_1, φ_2 are $o(H)$ for $H \to O$, then $\varphi_1 + \varphi_2$ is also $o(H)$ for $H \to O$.*

(ii) *If φ is $o(H)$ for $H \to O$, and ψ is a bounded function defined for all sufficiently small H, then the product function $\varphi\psi$ is also $o(H)$.* [*Note: The product function is the function such that $(\varphi\psi)(H) = \varphi(H)\psi(H)$.*]

(iii) *If φ_1 is $o(H)$ for $H \to O$ and $\|\varphi_2(H)\| \leq \|\varphi_1(H)\|$ for all H sufficiently small, then φ_2 is also $o(H)$.*

As an example we indicate the proof of the first property. We have by the property of limit of a sum:

$$\lim_{H \to O} \frac{\varphi_1(H) + \varphi_2(H)}{\|H\|} = \lim_{H \to O} \frac{\varphi_1(H)}{\|H\|} + \lim_{H \to O} \frac{\varphi_2(H)}{\|H\|}$$
$$= 0.$$

We leave the others to the reader who has read the Appendix on limits.

Example. Consider the situation with $n = 2$, where we write $H = (h, k)$. Then

$$|h| \leq \sqrt{h^2 + k^2} \quad \text{and} \quad |k| \leq \sqrt{h^2 + k^2}.$$

If g is a function such that $\lim_{H \to O} g(H) = 0$, then the function φ defined by

$$\varphi(H) = hg(H)$$

is $o(H)$. Indeed,

$$|\varphi(H)| \leq \|H\| \, |g(H)|$$

and we can apply (iii). Estimates such as these will be used in Theorem 2 below.

In the new terminology of functions which are $o(H)$, we can rewrite formula (2) in the form

$$f(X + H) - f(X) = \big(\operatorname{grad} f(X)\big) \cdot H + o(H).$$

The existence of such an expression is then a restatement of the definition of differentiability of f at X.

Formula (2) is the one which is used throughout the applications of differentiability. It is therefore important to know when a function is differentiable. The next theorem will give us a criterion which can be used in practice. In all this course, the functions which will be encountered will be differentiable, and any reader allergic to theory can simply omit the proof of Theorem 2 without impairing his understanding of the rest of the book.

Let g be a function. We shall say that g is *continuous* if for every point X such that $g(X)$ is defined, we have

$$\lim_{Q \to X} g(Q) = g(X).$$

In other words, as Q approaches X, $g(Q)$ must approach $g(X)$.

Theorem 2. *Let f be a function defined on some open set U. Assume that its partial derivatives exist for every point in this open set, and that they are continuous. Then f is differentiable.*

Proof. For simplicity of notation, we shall use two variables. Thus we deal with a function $f(x, y)$. We let $H = (h, k)$. Let (x, y) be a point in U, and take H small, $H \neq (0, 0)$. We have to consider the difference $f(X + H) - f(X)$, which is simply

$$f(x + h, y + k) - f(x, y).$$

This is equal to

$$f(x + h, y + k) - f(x, y + k) + f(x, y + k) - f(x, y).$$

Applying the mean value theorem for functions of *one* variable, and applying the definition of partial derivatives, we see that there is a number s between x and $x + h$ such that

(3) $$f(x + h, y + k) - f(x, y + k) = D_1 f(s, y + k)h.$$

Similarly, there is a number t between y and $y + k$ such that

(4) $$f(x, y + k) - f(x, y) = D_2 f(x, t)k.$$

We shall now analyze the expressions on the right-hand side of equations (3) and (4).
    Let

$$g_1(H) = D_1 f(s, y + k) - D_1 f(x, y).$$

As H approaches O, $(s, y + k)$ approaches (x, y) because s is between x and $x + h$. Since $D_1 f$ is continuous, it follows that

$$\lim_{H \to 0} g_1(H) = 0.$$

But

$$D_1 f(s, y + k) = D_1 f(x, y) + g_1(H).$$

Hence equation (3) can be rewritten as

(5) $$f(x + h, y + k) - f(x, y + k) = D_1 f(x, y)h + hg_1(H).$$

By a similar argument, we can rewrite equation (4) in the form

(6) $$f(x, y + k) - f(x, y) = D_2 f(x, y)k + kg_2(H)$$

with some function $g_2(H)$ such that

$$\lim_{H \to 0} g_2(H) = 0.$$

If we add (5) and (6) we obtain

(7) $f(X + H) - f(X) = D_1 f(X)h + D_2 f(X)k + hg_1(H) + kg_2(H).$

The two expressions on the right are $o(H)$, by the Example preceding the theorem, and their sum is also $o(H)$, for $H \to O$. This proves the theorem.

Remark. If we dealt with n variables, then we would consider the expression for $f(X + H) - f(X)$ given by

$$f(x_1 + h_1, \ldots, x_n + h_n) - f(x_1, x_2 + h_2, \ldots, x_n + h_n)$$

$$+ f(x_1, x_2 + h_2, \ldots, x_n + h_n) - f(x_1, x_2, \ldots, x_n + h_n)$$

$$\vdots$$

$$+ f(x_1, \ldots, x_{n-1}, x_n + h_n) - f(x_1, \ldots, x_n).$$

We would then apply the mean value theorem at each step, take the sum, and argue in essentially the same way as with two variables.

EXERCISES

1. Show that $|h + k^2| \leq 2\|H\|^2$ if $H = (h, k)$.

2. Show that $|h^2 + 3hk| \leq 4\|H\|^2$.

3. Show that $|h^3 + h^2k + k^3| \leq 3\|H\|^3$.

4. If $\|H\| \leq 1$, show that $|h^2 + k^3 + k^2| \leq 3\|H\|^2$.

5. Show that $|(h + k)^4| \leq 16\|H\|^4$.

6. Let

$$g(h, k) = \frac{h^2 - k^2}{h^2 + k^2}$$

be defined for $(h, k) \neq (0, 0)$. Find

$$\lim_{h \to 0} g(h, k), \qquad \lim_{k \to 0} \left[\lim_{h \to 0} g(h, k) \right]$$

$$\lim_{k \to 0} g(h, k), \qquad \lim_{h \to 0} \left[\lim_{k \to 0} g(h, k) \right].$$

7. Let f be defined on an open set U. Let P be a point of U. Assume that there are two vectors A, B and two functions $g_1(H)$, $g_2(H)$ such that

$$\lim_{H \to O} g_1(H) = 0 \qquad \text{and} \qquad \lim_{H \to O} g_2(H) = 0,$$

and such that

$$f(P + H) - f(P) = A \cdot H + \|H\| g_1(H)$$
$$= B \cdot H + \|H\| g_2(H).$$

Show that $A = B$. [*Hint:* Subtract, and let $H = tK$ for any K, $t \to 0$.]

8. Let the assumptions be as in Exercise 7. Show that all partial derivatives of f exist at P, and that $A = \operatorname{grad} f(P)$. [*Hint:* Take H to be hE_i, with a unit vector E_i.]

9. Let $g(H) = g(h_1, \ldots, h_n)$ be a polynomial, i.e. an expression of the form

$$g(H) = \sum c_{i_1 \ldots i_n} h_1^{i_1} \cdots h_n^{i_n},$$

where $c_{i_1 \ldots i_n}$ are numbers, and the sum is taken over a finite number of n-tuples $(i_1, \ldots, i_n)$ of integers ≥ 0. We call $c_{i_1 \ldots i_n}$ the *coefficients* of g, and abbreviate them by $c_{(i)}$. Assume that $g(O) = 0$, and that s is an integer > 0 such that $i_1 + \cdots + i_n \geq s$ for all (i). Show that for any H with $\|H\| \leq 1$ we have

$$|g(H)| \leq NM\|H\|^s,$$

if N is the number of terms in the sum expressing g, and M is a number such that $|c_{(i)}| \leq M$ for all (i).

Chapter IV

The Chain Rule and the Gradient

In this chapter, we prove the chain rule for functions of several variables and give a number of applications. Among them will be several interpretations for the gradient. These form one of the central points of our theory. They show how powerful the tools we have accumulated turn out to be.

§1. THE CHAIN RULE

Let f be a function defined on some open set U. Let $t \mapsto X(t)$ be a curve such that the values $X(t)$ are contained in U. Then we can form the composite function $f \circ X$, which is a function of t, given by

$$(f \circ X)(t) = f(X(t)).$$

As an example, take $f(x, y) = e^x \sin(xy)$. Let $X(t) = (t^2, t^3)$. Then

$$f(X(t)) = e^{t^2} \sin(t^5).$$

This is a function of t in the old sense of functions of one variable.

The chain rule tells us how to find the derivative of this function, provided we know the gradient of f and the derivative X'. Its statement is as follows.

Let f be a function which is defined and differentiable on an open set U. Let $X: I \to \mathbf{R}^n$ be a differentiable curve (defined for some interval of numbers t) such that the values $X(t)$ lie in the open set U. Then the function

$$t \mapsto f(X(t))$$

is differentiable (as a function of t), and

$$\frac{df(X(t))}{dt} = (\text{grad } f(X(t))) \cdot X'(t).$$

In the notation dX/dt, this also reads

$$\frac{df(X(t))}{dt} = (\text{grad } f)(X(t)) \cdot \frac{dX}{dt}.$$

Before proving the chain rule, we restate it in terms of components. If $X = (x_1, \ldots, x_n)$ then

$$\boxed{\frac{d(f(X(t)))}{dt} = \frac{\partial f}{\partial x_1}\frac{dx_1}{dt} + \cdots + \frac{\partial f}{\partial x_n}\frac{dx_n}{dt}.}$$

If f is a function of two variables (x, y) then

$$\frac{df(X(t))}{dt} = \frac{\partial f}{\partial x}\frac{dx}{dt} + \frac{\partial f}{\partial y}\frac{dy}{dt}.$$

This can be applied to the seemingly more general situation when x, y are functions of more than one variable t. Suppose for instance that

$$x = \varphi(t, u) \qquad \text{and} \qquad y = \psi(t, u)$$

are differentiable functions of two variables. Let

$$g(t, u) = f(\varphi(t, u), \psi(t, u)).$$

If we keep u fixed and take the partial derivative of g with respect to t, then we can apply our chain rule, and obtain

$$\frac{\partial g}{\partial t} = \frac{\partial f}{\partial x}\frac{\partial x}{\partial t} + \frac{\partial f}{\partial y}\frac{\partial y}{\partial t}.$$

The components are of course useful in computations, to determine partial derivatives explicitly, but they will not be used in the proof.

Proof of the chain rule. By definition, we must investigate the quotient

$$\frac{f(X(t + h)) - f(X(t))}{h}.$$

Let

$$K = K(t, h) = X(t + h) - X(t).$$

Then our quotient can be rewritten in the form

$$\frac{f(X(t) + K) - f(X(t))}{h}.$$

Using the definition of differentiability for f, we have

$$f(X + K) - f(X) = (\operatorname{grad} f)(X) \cdot K + \|K\|g(K)$$

and

$$\lim_{\|K\| \to 0} g(K) = 0.$$

Replacing K by what it stands for, namely $X(t + h) - X(t)$, and dividing by h, we obtain:

$$\frac{f(X(t + h)) - f(X(t))}{h} = (\text{grad } f)(X(t)) \cdot \frac{X(t + h) - X(t)}{h}$$

$$\pm \left\| \frac{X(t + h) - X(t)}{h} \right\| g(K).$$

As h approaches 0, the first term of the sum approaches what we want, namely

$$(\text{grad } f)(X(t)) \cdot X'(t).$$

The second term approaches

$$\pm \|X'(t)\| \lim_{h \to 0} g(K),$$

and when h approaches 0, so does $K = X(t + h) - X(t)$. Hence the second term of the sum approaches 0. This proves our chain rule

Example 1. Let $f(x, y) = x^2 + 2xy$. Let $x = r \cos \theta$ and $y = r \sin \theta$. Let $g(r, \theta) = f(r \cos \theta, r \sin \theta)$ be the composite function. Find $\partial g / \partial \theta$.

We have

$$\frac{\partial x}{\partial \theta} = -r \sin \theta \quad \text{and} \quad \frac{\partial y}{\partial \theta} = r \cos \theta.$$

Hence

$$\frac{\partial g}{\partial \theta} = (2x + 2y)(-r \sin \theta) + 2x(r \cos \theta).$$

If you want the answer completely in terms of r, θ, you can substitute $r \cos \theta$ and $r \sin \theta$ for x and y respectively in this expression.

Example 2. Let $w = f(x, y, z) = e^{xy} \cos z$ and let

$$x = tu, \quad y = \sin(tu), \quad z = u^2.$$

Then

$$\frac{\partial w}{\partial u} = \frac{\partial f}{\partial x} \frac{\partial x}{\partial u} + \frac{\partial f}{\partial y} \frac{\partial y}{\partial u} + \frac{\partial f}{\partial z} \frac{\partial z}{\partial u}$$

$$= ye^{xy}(\cos z)t + xe^{xy}(\cos z)(\cos tu)t - e^{xy}(\sin z)2u$$

$$= \sin(tu)e^{tu \sin(tu)}(\cos u^2)t + tue^{tu \sin(tu)}(\cos u^2)(\cos tu)t$$

$$- e^{tu \sin(tu)}(\sin u^2)2u.$$

In this last expression, we have substituted the values for x, y, z in terms of t and u, thus giving the partial derivative completely in terms of these variables.

EXERCISES

(All functions are assumed to be differentiable as needed.)

1. If $x = u(r, s, t)$ and $y = v(r, s, t)$ and $z = f(x, y)$, write out the formula for

$$\frac{\partial z}{\partial r} \quad \text{and} \quad \frac{\partial z}{\partial t}.$$

2. Find the partial derivatives with respect to x, y, s, and t for the following functions.

   (a) $f(x, y, z) = x^3 + 3xyz - y^2z$, $x = 2t + s$, $y = -t - s$, $z = t^2 + s^2$
   (b) $f(x, y) = (x + y)/(1 - xy)$, $x = \sin 2t$, $y = \cos(3t - s)$

3. Let $f(x, y, z) = (x^2 + y^2 + z^2)^{1/2}$. Find $\partial f/\partial x$ and $\partial f/\partial y$.

4. Let $r = (x_1^2 + \cdots + x_n^2)^{1/2}$. What is $\partial r/\partial x_i$?

5. If $u = f(x - y, y - x)$, show that

$$\frac{\partial u}{\partial x} + \frac{\partial u}{\partial y} = 0.$$

6. If $u = x^3 f(y/x, z/x)$, show that

$$x\frac{\partial u}{\partial x} + y\frac{\partial u}{\partial y} + z\frac{\partial u}{\partial z} = 3u.$$

7. (a) Let $x = r \cos \theta$ and $y = r \sin \theta$. Let $z = f(x, y)$. Show that

$$\frac{\partial z}{\partial r} = \frac{\partial f}{\partial x} \cos \theta + \frac{\partial f}{\partial y} \sin \theta, \qquad \frac{1}{r}\frac{\partial z}{\partial \theta} = -\frac{\partial f}{\partial x} \sin \theta + \frac{\partial f}{\partial y} \cos \theta.$$

   (b) If we let $z = g(r, \theta) = f(r \cos \theta, r \sin \theta)$, show that

$$\left(\frac{\partial g}{\partial r}\right)^2 + \frac{1}{r^2}\left(\frac{\partial g}{\partial \theta}\right)^2 = \left(\frac{\partial f}{\partial x}\right)^2 + \left(\frac{\partial f}{\partial y}\right)^2.$$

8. (a) Let g be a function of r, let $r = \|X\|$, and $X = (x, y, z)$. Let $f(X) = g(r)$. Show that

$$\left(\frac{dg}{dr}\right)^2 = \left(\frac{\partial f}{\partial x}\right)^2 + \left(\frac{\partial f}{\partial y}\right)^2 + \left(\frac{\partial f}{\partial z}\right)^2.$$

   (b) Let $g(x, y) = f(x + y, x - y)$, where f is a differentiable function of two variables, say $f = f(u, v)$. Show that

$$\frac{\partial g}{\partial x}\frac{\partial g}{\partial y} = \left(\frac{\partial f}{\partial u}\right)^2 - \left(\frac{\partial f}{\partial v}\right)^2.$$

   (c) Let $g(x, y) = f(2x + 7y)$, where f is a differentiable function of one variable. Show that

$$2\frac{\partial g}{\partial y} = 7\frac{\partial g}{\partial x}.$$

9. Let g be a function of r, and $r = \|X\|$. Let $f(X) = g(r)$. Find $\operatorname{grad} f(X)$ for the following functions.

(a) $g(r) = 1/r$

(b) $g(r) = r^2$

(c) $g(r) = 1/r^3$

(d) $g(r) = e^{-r^2}$

(e) $g(r) = \log \dfrac{1}{r}$

(f) $g(r) = 4/r^m$ (m integer $\neq 1$)

10. Let $x = u \cos \theta - v \sin \theta$, and $y = u \sin \theta + v \cos \theta$, with θ equal to a constant. Let $f(x, y) = g(u, v)$. Show that

$$\left(\frac{\partial g}{\partial u}\right)^2 + \left(\frac{\partial g}{\partial v}\right)^2 = \left(\frac{\partial f}{\partial x}\right)^2 + \left(\frac{\partial f}{\partial y}\right)^2 .$$

11. Let f be a differentiable function (in two variables) such that $\operatorname{grad} f(X) = cX$ for some constant c and all X in 2-space. Show that f is constant on any circle of radius $a > 0$, centered at the origin. [*Hint:* Put $x = a \cos t$ and $y = a \sin t$ and find df/dt.]

12. (a) Generalize the preceding exercise to the case of n variables. You may assume that any two points on the sphere of radius a centered at the origin are connected by a differentiable curve.

(b) Let f be a differentiable function in n variables, and assume that there exists a function g such that $\operatorname{grad} f(X) = g(X)X$. Show that f is constant on the sphere of radius $a > 0$ centered at the origin. (In other words, in Exercise 11, the hypothesis about the constant c can be weakened to an arbitrary function.)

13. Let $r = \|X\|$. Let g be a differentiable function of one variable whose derivative is never equal to 0. Let $f(X) = g(r)$. Show that $\operatorname{grad} f(X)$ is parallel to X for $X \neq O$.

14. Let f be a differentiable function of two variables and assume that there is an integer $m \geq 1$ such that

$$f(tx, ty) = t^m f(x, y)$$

for all numbers t and all x, y. Prove *Euler's relation*

$$x \frac{\partial f}{\partial x} + y \frac{\partial f}{\partial y} = mf(x, y).$$

15. Generalize Exercise 14 to n variables, namely let f be a differentiable function of n variables and assume that there exists an integer $m \geq 1$ such that $f(tX) = t^m f(X)$ for all numbers t and all points X in $\mathbf{R}^n$. Show that

$$x_1 \frac{\partial f}{\partial x_1} + \cdots + x_n \frac{\partial f}{\partial x_n} = mf(X),$$

which can also be written $X \cdot \operatorname{grad} f(X) = mf(X)$. How does this exercise apply to Exercise 6?

16. Let f be a differentiable function defined on all of $\mathbf{R}^n$. Assume that $f(tP) = tf(P)$ for all numbers t and all points P in $\mathbf{R}^n$. Show that for all P we have

$$f(P) = \operatorname{grad} f(O) \cdot P.$$

17. Let A, B be two unit vectors such that $A \cdot B = 0$. Let

$$F(t) = (\cos t)A + (\sin t)B.$$

Show that $F(t)$ lies on the sphere of radius 1 centered at the origin, for each value of t.

18. Let P, Q be two points on the sphere of radius 1, centered at the origin. Let $L(t) = P + t(Q - P)$, with $0 \le t \le 1$. If there exists a value of t in $[0, 1]$ such that $L(t) = O$, show that $t = \frac{1}{2}$, and that $P = -Q$.

19. Let P, Q be two points on the sphere of radius 1. Assume that $P \ne -Q$. Show that there exists a differentiable curve joining P and Q on the sphere of radius 1, centered at the origin. [*Hint:* Divide $L(t)$ in Exercise 17 by its length.]

20. If P, Q are two unit vectors such that $P = -Q$, show that there exists a differentiable curve joining P and Q on the sphere of radius 1, centered at the origin. You may assume that there exists a unit vector A which is perpendicular to P. Then use Exercise 17.

21. Parametrize the ellipse

$$\frac{x^2}{a^2} + \frac{y^2}{b^2} = 1$$

by a differentiable curve.

§2. TANGENT PLANE

Let f be a differentiable function and c a number. The set of points X such that $f(X) = c$ and $\operatorname{grad} f(X) \ne O$ is called a *surface*.

Let $X(t)$ be a differentiable curve. We shall say that the curve *lies on* the surface if, for all t, we have

$$f(X(t)) = c.$$

This simply means that all the points of the curve satisfy the equation of the surface. If we differentiate this relation, we get from the chain rule:

$$\operatorname{grad} f(X(t)) \cdot X'(t) = 0.$$

Let P be a point of the surface, and let $X(t)$ be a curve on the surface passing through P. This means that there is a number t_0 such that $X(t_0) = P$. For this value t_0, we obtain

$$\operatorname{grad} f(P) \cdot X'(t_0) = 0.$$

Thus the gradient of f at P is perpendicular to the tangent vector of the curve at P. [We assume that $X'(t_0) \neq O$.] This is true for *any* differentiable curve passing through P. It is therefore very reasonable to *define* the *plane* (or hyperplane) *tangent* to the surface at P to be the plane passing through P and perpendicular to the vector $\operatorname{grad} f(P)$. (We know from Chapter I how to find such planes.) This definition applies only when $\operatorname{grad} f(P) \neq O$. If $\operatorname{grad} f(P) = O$, then we do not define the notion of tangent plane.

The fact that $\operatorname{grad} f(P)$ is perpendicular to every curve passing through P on the surface also gives us an interpretation of the gradient as being perpendicular to the surface

$$f(X) = c,$$

which is one of the level surfaces for the function f (Fig. 1).

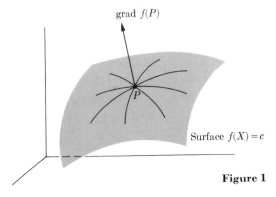

grad $f(P)$

P

Surface $f(X) = c$

Figure 1

Example 1. Find the tangent plane to the surface

$$x^2 + y^2 + z^2 = 3$$

at the point $(1, 1, 1)$.
  Let $f(X) = x^2 + y^2 + z^2$. Then at the point $P = (1, 1, 1)$,

$$\operatorname{grad} f(P) = (2, 2, 2).$$

The equation of a plane passing through P and perpendicular to a vector N is

$$X \cdot N = P \cdot N.$$

In the present case, this yields

$$2x + 2y + 2z = 2 + 2 + 2 = 6.$$

Observe that our arguments also give us a means of finding a vector perpendicular to a curve in 2-space at a given point, simply by applying the preceding discussion to the plane instead of 3-space.

Example 2. Find the tangent line to the curve

$$x^2 y + y^3 = 10$$

at the point $(1, 2)$, and find a vector perpendicular to the curve at that point.

Let $f(x, y) = x^2 y + y^3$. The gradient at the given point P is easily computed, and we find

$$\operatorname{grad} f(P) = (4, 13).$$

This is a vector N perpendicular to the curve at the given point. The tangent line is also given by $X \cdot N = P \cdot N$, and thus is

$$4x + 13y = 4 + 26 = 30.$$

Example 3. A surface may also be given in the form $z = g(x, y)$ where g is some function of two variables. In this case, the tangent plane is determined by viewing the surface as expressed by the equation

$$g(x, y) - z = 0.$$

For instance, suppose the surface is given by $z = x^2 + y^2$. We wish to determine the tangent plane at $(1, 2, 5)$. Let $f(x, y, z) = x^2 + y^2 - z$. Then $\operatorname{grad} f(x, y, z) = (2x, 2y, -1)$ and

$$\operatorname{grad} f(1, 2, 5) = (1, 4, -1).$$

The equation of the tangent plane at $P = (1, 2, 5)$ perpendicular to $N = (1, 4, -1)$ is

$$x + 4y - z = P \cdot N = 4.$$

This is the desired equation.

EXERCISES

1. Find the equation of the tangent plane and normal line to each of the following surfaces at the specific point.

   (a) $x^2 + y^2 + z^2 = 49$ at $(6, 2, 3)$
   (b) $xy + yz + zx - 1 = 0$ at $(1, 1, 0)$
   (c) $x^2 + xy^2 + y^3 + z + 1 = 0$ at $(2, -3, 4)$
   (d) $2y - z^3 - 3xz = 0$ at $(1, 7, 2)$
   (e) $x^2 y^2 + xz - 2y^3 = 10$ at $(2, 1, 4)$
   (f) $\sin xy + \sin yz + \sin xz = 1$ at $(1, \pi/2, 0)$

2. Let $f(x, y, z) = z - e^x \sin y$, and $P = (\log 3, 3\pi/2, -3)$. Find:

   (a) $\operatorname{grad} f(P)$,
   (b) the normal line at P to the level surface for f which passes through P,
   (c) the tangent plane to this surface at P.

3. Find the parametric equation of the tangent line to the curve of intersection of the following surfaces at the indicated point.

   (a) $x^2 + y^2 + z^2 = 49$ and $x^2 + y^2 = 13$ at $(3, 2, -6)$
   (b) $xy + z = 0$ and $x^2 + y^2 + z^2 = 9$ at $(2, 1, -2)$
   (c) $x^2 - y^2 - z^2 = 1$ and $x^2 - y^2 + z^2 = 9$ at $(3, 2, 2)$

   [*Note.* The tangent line above may be defined to be the line of intersection of the tangent planes of the given point.]

4. Let $f(X) = 0$ be a differentiable surface. Let Q be a point which does not lie on the surface. Given a differentiable curve $X(t)$ on the surface, defined on an open interval, give the formula for the distance between Q and a point $X(t)$. Assume that this distance reaches a minimum for $t = t_0$. Let $P = X(t_0)$. Show that the line joining Q to P is perpendicular to the curve at P.

5. Find the equation of the tangent plane to the surface $z = f(x, y)$ at the given point P when f is the following function:

   (a) $f(x, y) = x^2 + y^2$, $P = (3, 4, 25)$
   (b) $f(x, y) = x/(x^2 + y^2)^{1/2}$, $P = (3, -4, \frac{3}{5})$
   (c) $f(x, y) = \sin(xy)$ at $P = (1, \pi, 0)$

6. Find the equation of the tangent plane to the surface $x = e^{2y-z}$ at $(1, 1, 2)$.

§3. DIRECTIONAL DERIVATIVE

Let f be defined on an open set and assume that f is differentiable. Let P be a point of the open set, and let A be a unit vector (i.e. $\|A\| = 1$). Then $P + tA$ is the parametric equation of a straight line in the direction of A and passing through P. We observe that

$$\frac{d(P + tA)}{dt} = A.$$

For instance, if $n = 2$ and $P = (p, q)$, $A = (a, b)$, then

$$P + tA = (p + ta, q + tb),$$

or in terms of coordinates,

$$x = p + ta, \qquad y = q + tb.$$

Hence

$$\frac{dx}{dt} = a \quad \text{and} \quad \frac{dy}{dt} = b$$

so that

$$\frac{d(P + tA)}{dt} = (a, b) = A.$$

The same argument works in higher dimensions.

Hence by the chain rule, if we take the derivative of the function $t \mapsto f(P + tA)$, which is defined for small values of t, we obtain

$$\frac{df(P + tA)}{dt} = \operatorname{grad} f(P + tA) \cdot A.$$

When t is equal to 0, this derivative is equal to

$$\operatorname{grad} f(P) \cdot A.$$

For obvious geometrical reasons, we call it the *directional derivative* of f in the direction of A. We interpret it as the rate of change of f along the straight line in the direction of A, at the point P. Thus if we agree on the notation $D_A f(P)$ for the directional derivative of f at P in the direction of the unit vector A, then we have

$$D_A f(P) = \left. \frac{df(P + tA)}{dt} \right|_{t=0} = \operatorname{grad} f(P) \cdot A.$$

In using this formula, the reader should remember that A is taken to be a *unit vector*. When a direction is given in terms of a vector whose length is not 1, then one must first divide this vector by its length before applying the formula.

Example. Let $f(x, y) = x^2 + y^3$ and let $B = (1, 2)$. Find the directional derivative of f in the direction of B, at the point $(-1, 3)$.

We note that B is not a unit vector. Its length is $\sqrt{5}$. Let

$$A = \frac{1}{\sqrt{5}} B.$$

Then A is a unit vector having the same direction as B. Let $P = (-1, 3)$. Then $\operatorname{grad} f(P) = (-2, 27)$. Hence by our formula, the directional derivative is equal to:

$$\operatorname{grad} f(P) \cdot A = \frac{1}{\sqrt{5}} (-2 + 54) = \frac{52}{\sqrt{5}}.$$

Consider again a differentiable function f on an open set U.

Let P be a point of U. *Let us assume that* $\operatorname{grad} f(P) \neq O$, and let A be a unit vector. We know that

$$\operatorname{grad} f(P) \cdot A = \|\operatorname{grad} f(P)\| \, \|A\| \cos \theta,$$

where θ is the angle between $\operatorname{grad} f(P)$ and A. Since $\|A\| = 1$, we see that the directional derivative is equal to $\|\operatorname{grad} f(P)\| \cos \theta$. The value of $\cos \theta$ varies between -1 and $+1$ when we select all possible unit vectors A.

The maximal value of cos θ is obtained when we select A such that $\theta = 0$, i.e. when we select A to have the same direction as grad $f(P)$. In that case, the directional derivative is equal to the length of the gradient [cf. Exercise 10 of Chapter I, §4].

Thus we have obtained another interpretation for the gradient: *Its direction is that of maximal increase of the function, and its length is the rate of increase of the function in that direction.*

The directional derivative in the direction of A is at a minimum when cos $\theta = -1$. This is the case when we select A to have opposite direction to grad $f(P)$. That direction is therefore the direction of maximal decrease of the function.

For example, f might represent a temperature distribution in space. At any point P, a particle which feels cold and wants to become warmer fastest should move in the direction of grad $f(P)$. Another particle which is warm and wants to cool down fastest should move in the direction of $-\text{grad } f(P)$.

EXERCISES

1. In Exercise 2 of the preceding section, find:
   (a) the directional derivative of f at P in the direction of $(1, 2, 2)$,
   (b) the maximum and minimum values for the directional derivatives of f at P.

2. Find the directional derivatives of the following functions at the specified points in the specified directions.
   (a) $\log(x^2 + y^2)^{1/2}$ at $(1, 1)$, direction $(2, 1)$
   (b) $xy + yz + zx$ at $(-1, 1, 7)$, direction $(3, 4, -12)$
   (c) $4x^2 + 9y^2$ at $(2, 1)$ in the direction of maximum directional derivative

3. A temperature distribution in space is given by the function

$$f(x, y) = 10 + 6 \cos x \cos y + 3 \cos 2x + 4 \cos 3y.$$

   At the point $(\pi/3, \pi/3)$, find the direction of greatest increase of temperature, and the direction of greatest decrease of temperature.

4. In what direction are the following functions of X increasing most rapidly at the given point?
   (a) $x/\|X\|^{3/2}$ at $(1, -1, 2)$ $(X = (x, y, z))$
   (b) $\|X\|^5$ at $(1, 2, -1, 1)$ $(X = (x, y, z, w))$

5. Find the tangent plane to the surface $x^2 + y^2 - z^2 = 18$ at the point $(3, 5, -4)$.

6. Let $f(x, y, z) = (x + y)^2 + (y + z)^2 + (z + x)^2$. What is the direction of greatest increase of the function at the point $(2, -1, 2)$. What is the directional derivative of f in this direction at that point?

7. Let $f(x, y) = x^2 + xy + y^2$. What is the direction in which f is increasing most rapidly at the point $(-1, 1)$? Find the directional derivative of f in this direction.

§4. CONSERVATION LAW

As a final application of the chain rule, we derive the conservation law of physics.

Let U be an open set. By a *vector field* on U we mean an association which to every point of U associates a vector of the same dimension.

If f is a differentiable function on U, then we observe that grad f is a vector field, which associates the vector grad $f(P)$ to the point P of U.

A vector field in physics is often interpreted as a field of forces.

If F is a vector field on U, and X a point of U, then we denote by $F(X)$ the vector associated to X by F and call it the value of F at X, as usual.

If F is a vector field, and if there exists a differentiable function f such that $F = \text{grad} f$, then the vector field is called *conservative*. Since $-\text{grad} f = \text{grad}(-f)$, it does not matter whether we use f or $-f$ in the definition of conservative.

Let us assume that F is a conservative field on U, and let Φ be a differentiable function such that for all points X in U we have

$$F(X) = -\text{grad } \Phi.$$

In physics, one interprets Φ as a potential function. Suppose that a particle of mass m moves along a differentiable curve $X(t)$ in U, and let us assume that this particle obeys Newton's law:

$$F(X) = m\ddot{X}, \quad \text{i.e.} \quad F(X(t)) = m\ddot{X}(t)$$

for all t where $X(t)$ is defined. Then according to our hypotheses,

$$m\ddot{X} + \text{grad } \Phi(X) = O.$$

Take the dot product of both sides with $\dot{X}$. We obtain

$$m\ddot{X} \cdot \dot{X} + \text{grad } \Phi(X) \cdot \dot{X} = 0.$$

But the derivative (with respect to t) of $\dot{X}^2$ is $2\dot{X} \cdot \ddot{X}$. The derivative with respect to t of $\Phi(X(t))$ is equal to

$$\text{grad } \Phi(X) \cdot \dot{X}$$

by the chain rule. Hence the expression on the left of our last equation is the derivative of the *function*

$$\tfrac{1}{2}m\dot{X}^2 + \Phi(X),$$

and that derivative is 0. Hence this function is equal to a constant. This is what one means by the conservation law.

The function $\frac{1}{2}m\dot{X}^2$ is called the *kinetic energy*, and the conservation law states that the sum of the kinetic and potential energies is constant.

It is not true that all vector fields are conservative. We shall discuss the problem of determining which ones are conservative in the next chapter.

The fields of classical physics are for the most part conservative. For instance, consider a force which is inversely proportional to the square of the distance from the point to the origin, and in the direction of the position vector. Then there is a constant C such that for $X \neq O$ we have

$$F(X) = C\frac{1}{\|X\|^2}\frac{X}{\|X\|},$$

because $\dfrac{X}{\|X\|}$ is a unit vector in the direction of X. Thus

$$F(X) = C\frac{1}{r^3} X,$$

where $r = \|X\|$. A potential function for F is given by

$$-\frac{C}{r}.$$

This is immediately verified by taking the partial derivatives of this function.

EXERCISES

1. Find a potential function for a force field which is inversely proportional to the distance from the point to the origin, and is in the direction of the position vector.

2. Same question, replacing "distance" with "cube of the distance".

3. Let k be an integer ≥ 1. Find a potentital function for the vector field F given by

$$F(X) = \frac{1}{r^k} X, \qquad \text{where } r = \|X\|.$$

[*Hint:* Cf. Exercise 9(f) of §1.]

Chapter V

Potential Functions and Curve Integrals

We are going to deal systematically with the possibility of finding a potential function for a vector field. The discussion of the existence of such a function will be limited to the case of two variables. Actually, there is no essential difficulty in extending the results to arbitrary n-space, but we leave this to the reader.

The problem is one of integration, and the line integrals are a natural continuation of the integrals at the end of §1 (taken on vertical and horizontal lines).

§1. POTENTIAL FUNCTIONS

Let F be a vector field on an open set U. If φ is a differentiable function on U such that $F = \text{grad } \varphi$, then we say that φ is a *potential function* for F.

One can raise two questions about potential functions. Are they unique, and do they exist?

We consider the first question, and we shall be able to give a satisfactory answer to it. The problem is analogous to determining an integral for a function of one variable, up to a constant, and we shall formulate and prove the analogous statement in the present situation.

We recall that even in the case of functions of one variable, it is *not* true that whenever two functions f, g are such that

$$\frac{df}{dx} = \frac{dg}{dx},$$

then f and g differ by a constant, unless we assume that f, g are defined on some interval. As we emphasized in the *First Course*, we could for instance take

$$f(x) = \begin{cases} \dfrac{1}{x} + 5 & \text{if } x < 0, \\[2mm] \dfrac{1}{x} - \pi & \text{if } x > 0, \end{cases}$$

$$g(x) = \frac{1}{x} \quad \text{if } x \neq 0.$$

387

Def – vector field F is conservative $\Rightarrow$ ∃ function φ, $\nabla \varphi = F$

Then f, g have the same derivative, but there is no constant C such that for all $x \neq 0$ we have $f(x) = g(x) + C$.

In the case of functions of several variables, we shall have to make a similar restriction on the domain of definition of the functions.

Let U be an open set and let P, Q be two points of U. We shall say that P, Q can be joined by a *differentiable curve* if there exists a differentiable curve $X(t)$ (with t ranging over some interval of numbers) which is contained in U, and two values of t, say t_1 and t_2 in that interval, such that

$$X(t_1) = P \quad \text{and} \quad X(t_2) = Q.$$

For example, if U is the entire plane, then any two points can be joined by a straight line. In fact, if P, Q are two points, then we take

$$X(t) = P + t(Q - P).$$

When $t = 0$, then $X(0) = P$. When $t = 1$, then $X(1) = Q$.

It is not always the case that two points of an open set can be joined by a straight line. We have drawn a picture of two points P, Q in an open set U which cannot be so joined.

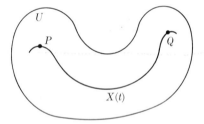

Figure 1

We are now in position to state the theorem we had in mind.

Theorem 1. *Let U be an open set, and assume that any two points in U can be joined by a differentiable curve. Let f, g be two differentiable functions on U. If* $\operatorname{grad} f(X) = \operatorname{grad} g(X)$ *for every point X of U, then there exists a constant C such that*

$$f(X) = g(X) + C$$

for all points X of U.

Proof. We note that $\operatorname{grad}(f - g) = \operatorname{grad} f - \operatorname{grad} g = O$, and we must prove that $f - g$ is constant. Letting $\varphi = f - g$, we see that it suffices to prove: If $\operatorname{grad} \varphi(X) = O$ for every point X of U, then φ is constant.

Let P be a fixed point of U and let Q be any other point. Let $X(t)$ be a differentiable curve joining P to Q, which is contained in U, and defined over an interval. The derivative of the function $\varphi(X(t))$ is, by the chain rule,

$$\operatorname{grad} \varphi\left(X(t)\right) \cdot X'(t).$$

But $X(t)$ is a point of U for all values of t in the interval. Hence by our assumption, the derivative of $\varphi(X(t))$ is 0 for all t in the interval. Hence there is a constant C such that

$$\varphi(X(t)) = C$$

for all t in the interval. In other words, the function φ is constant on the curve. Hence $\varphi(P) = \varphi(Q)$.

This result is true for any point Q of U. Hence φ is constant on U, as was to be shown.

Our theorem proves the uniqueness of potential functions (within the restrictions placed by our extra hypothesis on the open set U).

We still have the problem of determining when a vector field F admits a potential function.

We first make some remarks in the case of functions of two variables. Let F be a vector field (in 2-space), so that we can write

$$F(x, y) = \left(f(x, y), g(x, y)\right)$$

with functions f and g, defined over a suitable open set. We want to know when there exists a function $\varphi(x, y)$ such that

$$\frac{\partial \varphi}{\partial x} = f \quad \text{and} \quad \frac{\partial \varphi}{\partial y} = g.$$

Such a function would be a potential function for F, by definition. (We assume throughout that all hypotheses of differentiability are satisfied as needed.)

Suppose that such a function φ exists. Then

$$\frac{\partial f}{\partial y} = \frac{\partial}{\partial y}\left(\frac{\partial \varphi}{\partial x}\right) \quad \text{and} \quad \frac{\partial g}{\partial x} = \frac{\partial}{\partial x}\left(\frac{\partial \varphi}{\partial y}\right).$$

We shall show in the next chapter that under suitable hypotheses, the two partial derivatives on the right are equal. This means that if there exists a potential function for F, then

$$\frac{\partial f}{\partial y} = \frac{\partial g}{\partial x}.$$

This gives us a simple test in practice to tell whether a potential function may exist.

Theorem 2. *Let f, g be differentiable functions having continuous partial derivatives on an open set U in 2-space. If*

$$\frac{\partial f}{\partial y} \neq \frac{\partial g}{\partial x}$$

then the vector field given by $F(x, y) = \big(f(x, y), g(x, y)\big)$ does not have a potential function.

Example. Consider the vector field given by

$$F(x, y) = (x^2 y, \sin xy).$$

Then we let $f(x, y) = x^2 y$ and $g(x, y) = \sin xy$. We have:

$$\frac{\partial f}{\partial y} = x^2 \quad \text{and} \quad \frac{\partial g}{\partial x} = y \cos xy.$$

Since $\partial f/\partial y \neq \partial g/\partial x$, it follows that the vector field does not have a potential function.

We shall prove in §3 that the converse of Theorem 2 is true in some very important cases. Before stating and proving the pertinent theorem, we first discuss an auxiliary situation.

EXERCISES

Determine which of the following vector fields have potential functions. The vector fields are described by the functions $(f(x, y), g(x, y))$.

1. $(1/x, xe^{xy})$

2. $(\sin(xy), \cos(xy))$

3. (e^{xy}, e^{x+y})

4. $(3x^4 y^2, x^3 y)$

5. $(5x^4 y, x \cos(xy))$

6. $\left(\dfrac{x}{\sqrt{x^2 + y^2}}, 3xy^2\right)$

§2. DIFFERENTIATING UNDER THE INTEGRAL

Let f be a continuous function on a rectangle $a \leq x \leq b$ and $c \leq y \leq d$. We can then form a function of y by taking

$$\psi(y) = \int_a^b f(x, y) \, dx.$$

Example 1. We can determine explicitly the function ψ if we let $f(x, y) = \sin(xy)$, namely:

$$\psi(y) = \int_0^\pi \sin(xy) \, dx = -\left.\frac{\cos(xy)}{y}\right|_{x=0}^{x=\pi} = -\frac{\cos(\pi y) - 1}{y}.$$

We are interested in finding the derivative of ψ. The next theorem allows us to do this in certain cases, by differentiating with respect to y under the integral sign.

Theorem 3. *Assume that f is continuous on the preceding rectangle, and that $D_2 f$ exists and is continuous. Let*

$$\psi(y) = \int_a^b f(x, y)\, dx.$$

Then ψ is differentiable, and

$$\frac{d\psi}{dy} = D\psi(y) = \int_a^b D_2 f(x, y)\, dx = \int_a^b \frac{\partial f(x, y)}{\partial y}\, dx.$$

Proof. By definition, we have to investigate the Newton quotient for ψ. We have

$$\frac{\psi(y + h) - \psi(y)}{h} = \int_a^b \left[\frac{f(x, y + h) - f(x, y)}{h} \right] dx.$$

We then have to find

$$\lim_{h \to 0} \int_a^b \frac{f(x, y + h) - f(x, y)}{h}\, dx.$$

If we knew that we can put the limit sign inside the integral, we would then conclude that the preceding limit is equal to

$$\int_a^b \lim_{h \to 0} \frac{f(x, y + h) - f(x, y)}{h}\, dx = \int_a^b D_2 f(x, y)\, dx,$$

thus proving our theorem. We shall not give the argument which justifies moving the limit sign inside the integral, because it depends on (ϵ, δ) considerations which are mostly omitted in this book.

Example 2. Letting $f(x, y) = \sin(xy)$ as before, we find that

$$D_2 f(x, y) = x \cos(xy).$$

If we let

$$\psi(y) = \int_0^\pi f(x, y)\, dx,$$

then

$$D\psi(y) = \int_0^\pi D_2 f(x, y)\, dx = \int_0^\pi x \cos(xy)\, dx.$$

By evaluating this last integral, or by differentiating the expression found for ψ at the beginning of the section, the reader will find the same value, namely

$$D\psi(y) = -\left[\frac{\pi y \sin(\pi y) - \cos(\pi y)}{y^2} + \frac{1}{y^2} \right].$$

We can apply the previous theorem using any x as upper limit of the integration. Thus we may let

$$\psi(x, y) = \int_a^x f(t, y) \, dt,$$

in which case the theorem reads

$$\frac{\partial \psi}{\partial y} = D_2 \psi(x, y) = \int_a^x D_2 f(t, y) \, dt = \int_a^x \frac{\partial f(t, y)}{\partial y} \, dt.$$

We use t as a variable of integration to distinguish it from the x which is now used as an end point of the interval $[a, x]$ instead of $[a, b]$.

The preceding way of determining the derivative of ψ with respect to y is called *differentiating under the integral sign*. Note that it is completely *different from the differentiation in the fundamental theorem of calculus*. In this case, we have an integral

$$g(x) = \int_a^x f(t) \, dt,$$

and

$$\frac{dg}{dx} = Dg(x) = f(x).$$

Thus when f is a function of two variables, and ψ is defined as above, the fundamental theorem of calculus states that

$$\frac{\partial \psi}{\partial x} = D_1 \psi(x, y) = f(x, y).$$

For example, if we let

$$\psi(x, y) = \int_0^x \sin(ty) \, dt,$$

then

$$D_1 \psi(x, y) = \sin(xy),$$

but by Theorem 3,

$$D_2 \psi(x, y) = \int_0^x \cos(ty) t \, dt.$$

EXERCISES

In each of the following cases, find $D_1 \psi(x, y)$ and $D_2 \psi(x, y)$, by evaluating the integrals.

1. $\psi(x, y) = \int_1^x e^{ty} \, dt$

2. $\psi(x, y) = \int_0^x \cos(ty) \, dt$

3. $\psi(x, y) = \int_1^x (y + t)^2 \, dt$

4. $\psi(x, y) = \int_1^x e^{y+t} \, dt$

5. $\psi(x, y) = \displaystyle\int_1^x e^{y-t}\, dt$ 6. $\psi(x, y) = \displaystyle\int_0^x t^2 y^3\, dt$

7. $\psi(x, y) = \displaystyle\int_1^x \frac{\log(ty)}{t}\, dt$ 8. $\psi(x, y) = \displaystyle\int_1^x \sin(3ty)\, dt$

§3. LOCAL EXISTENCE OF POTENTIAL FUNCTIONS

We shall state a theorem which will give us conditions under which the converse of Theorem 2 is true.

Theorem 4. *Let f, g be differentiable functions on an open set of the plane. If this open set is the entire plane, or if it is an open disc, or the inside of a rectangle, if the partial derivatives of f, g exist and are continuous, and if*

$$\frac{\partial f}{\partial y} = \frac{\partial g}{\partial x},$$

then the vector field $F(x, y) = \big(f(x, y), g(x, y)\big)$ *has a potential function.*

We shall indicate how a proof of Theorem 4 might go for a rectangle after we have discussed some examples.

Example 1. Determine whether the vector field F given by

$$F(x, y) = (e^{xy}, e^{x+y})$$

has a potential function.

Here, $f(x, y) = e^{xy}$ and $g(x, y) = e^{x+y}$. We have:

$$\frac{\partial f}{\partial y} = xe^{xy} \quad \text{and} \quad \frac{\partial g}{\partial x} = e^{x+y}.$$

Since these are not equal, we know that there cannot be a potential function.

If the partial derivatives $\partial f/\partial y$ and $\partial g/\partial x$ turn out to be equal, then one can try to find a potential function by integrating with respect to one of the variables. Thus we try to find

$$\int f(x, y)\, dx,$$

keeping y constant, and taking the ordinary integral of functions of one variable. If we can find such an integral, it will be a function $\psi(x, y)$, whose partial with respect to x will be equal to $f(x, y)$ (by definition). Adding a function of y, we can then adjust it so that its partial with respect to y is equal to $g(x, y)$.

Example 2. Let $F(x, y) = (2xy, x^2 + 3y^2)$. Determine whether this vector field has a potential function, and if it does, find it.

Applying the test which we mentioned above, we find that a potential function may exist. To find it, we consider first the integral

$$\int 2xy\,dx,$$

viewing y as constant. We obtain x^2y for the indefinite integral. We must now find a function $u(y)$ such that

$$\frac{\partial}{\partial y}\left(x^2y + u(y)\right) = x^2 + 3y^2.$$

This means that we must find a function $u(y)$ such that

$$x^2 + \frac{du}{dy} = x^2 + 3y^2,$$

or in other words,

$$\frac{du}{dy} = 3y^2.$$

This is a simple integration problem in one variable, and we find $u(y) = y^3$. Thus finally, if we let

$$\varphi(x, y) = x^2y + y^3,$$

we see that φ is a potential function for F.

Proof of Theorem 4. We let the rectangle be defined by

$$a \leqq x \leqq b \qquad \text{and} \qquad c \leqq y \leqq d.$$

We let

$$\varphi(x, y) = \int_a^x f(t, y)\,dt + \int_c^y g(a, u)\,du.$$

Then the second integral on the right does not depend on x, and by the fundamental theorem of calculus,

$$D_1\varphi(x, y) = f(x, y)$$

as wanted. On the other hand, using Theorem 3, and differentiating with respect to y, we get:

$$\begin{aligned}
D_2\varphi(x, y) &= \int_a^x D_2f(t, y)\,dt + g(a, y)\\
&= \int_a^x D_1g(t, y)\,dt + g(a, y)\\
&= g(t, y)\Big|_{t=a}^{t=x} + g(a, y)\\
&= g(x, y) - g(a, y) + g(a, y)\\
&= g(x, y)
\end{aligned}$$

thus yielding the desired expression for the second partial of φ. This proves Theorem 4.

Note that the proof is entirely similar to that of the example preceding it. The first integral with respect to x solves the requirements or the first partial of φ, and we correct it by an integral involving only y in order to adjust the answer to give the desired partial with respect to y.

EXERCISES

Determine which of the following vector fields admit potential functions.

1. $(e^z, \sin xy)$ 2. $(2x^2y, y^3)$

3. $(2xy, y^2)$ 4. $(y^2x^2, x + y^4)$

Find potential functions for the following vector fields.

5. (a) $F(X) = \dfrac{1}{r} X$ (b) $F(X) = \dfrac{1}{r^2} X$

  (c) $F(X) = r^n X$ (if n is an integer $\neq -2$). In this Exercise,

$$r = \|X\|, \quad \text{and} \quad X \neq O.$$

6. $(4xy, 2x^2)$ 7. $(xy \cos xy + \sin xy, x^2 \cos xy)$

8. $(3x^2y^2, 2x^3y)$ 9. $(2x, 4y^3)$

10. (ye^{xy}, xe^{xy})

11. Let $r = \|X\|$. Let g be a differentiable function of one variable. Show that the vector field defined by

$$F(X) = \frac{g'(r)}{r} X$$

in the domain $X \neq O$ always admits a potential function. What is this potential function?

12. Generalize Theorem 4 to functions of three variables, indicating how a proof might go along the same lines as the proof we gave for two variables.

13. Find a potential function f for the following vector fields F given as $F(x, y, z)$.

(a) $(2x, 3y, 4z)$ (b) $(y + z, x + z, x + y)$

(c) $(e^{y+2z}, xe^{y+2z}, 2xe^{y+2z})$ (d) $(y \sin z, x \sin z, xy \cos z)$

§4. CURVE INTEGRALS

Let U be an open set (of n-space), and let F be a vector field on U. We can represent F by components:

$$F(X) = (f_1(X), \ldots, f_n(X)),$$

each f_i being a function. When $n = 2$,

$$F(X) = (f(x, y), g(x, y)).$$

If each function $f_1(X), \ldots, f_n(X)$ is continuous, then we shall say that F is a *continuous* vector field. If each function $f_1(X), \ldots, f_n(X)$ is differentiable, then we shall say that F is a *differentiable* vector field.

We shall also deal with curves. Rather than use the letter X to denote a curve, we shall use another letter, for instance C, to avoid certain confusions which might arise in the present context. Furthermore, it is now convenient to assume that our curve C is defined on a *closed* interval $I = [a, b]$, with $a < b$. For each number t in I, the value $C(t)$ is a point in n-space. We shall say that the curve C lies in U if $C(t)$ is a point of U for all t in I. We say that C is *continuously differentiable* if its derivative $C'(t) = dC/dt$ exists and is continuous. We abbreviate the expression "continuously differentiable" by saying that the curve is a C^1-curve, or of class C^1.

Let F be a continuous vector field on U, and let C be a continuously differentiable curve in U. The dot product

$$F(C(t)) \cdot \frac{dC}{dt}$$

is a *function* of t, and it can be shown easily that this function is continuous (by ϵ and δ techniques which we always omit).

Example 1. Let $F(x, y) = (e^{xy}, y^2)$, and $C(t) = (t, \sin t)$. Then

$$C'(t) = (1, \cos t)$$

and

$$F(C(t)) = (e^{t \sin t}, \sin^2 t).$$

Hence

$$F(C(t)) \cdot C'(t) = e^{t \sin t} + (\cos t)(\sin^2 t).$$

Suppose that C is defined on the interval $[a, b]$. We define the *integral of F along C* to be

$$\int_C F = \int_a^b F(C(t)) \cdot \frac{dC}{dt}\, dt.$$

This integral is a direct generalization of the familiar notion of the integral of functions of one variable. If we are given a function $f(u)$, and u is a function of t, then

$$\int_{u(a)}^{u(b)} f(u)\, du = \int_a^b f(u(t)) \frac{du}{dt}\, dt.$$

(This is the formula describing the substitution method for evaluating integrals.)

In n-space, $C(a)$ and $C(b)$ are points, and our curve passes through these two points. Thus the integral we have written down can be interpreted as an integral of the vector field, along the curve, between the two points. It will also be convenient to write the integral in the form

$$\int_{P,C}^{Q} F = \int_{\mathbf{C}(a)}^{\mathbf{C}(b)} F(C) \cdot dC$$

to denote the integral along the curve C, from P to Q.

Example 2. Let $F(x, y) = (x^2 y, y^3)$. Find the integral of F along the straight line from the origin to the point $(1, 1)$.

We can parametrize the line in the form

$$C(t) = (t, t).$$

Thus

$$F\big(C(t)\big) = (t^3, t^3).$$

Furthermore,

$$\frac{dC}{dt} = (1, 1).$$

Hence

$$F\big(C(t)\big) \cdot \frac{dC}{dt} = 2t^3.$$

The integral we must find is therefore equal to:

$$\int_C F = \int_0^1 2t^3 \, dt = \frac{2t^4}{4}\bigg|_0^1 = \frac{1}{2}.$$

Remark 1. Our integral of a vector field along a curve is defined for *parametrized curves.* In practice, a curve is sometimes given in a non-parametrized way. For instance, we may want to integrate over the curve defined by $y = x^2$. Then we select some parametrization which is usually the most natural, in this case

$$x = t, \qquad y = t^2.$$

In general, if a curve is defined by a function $y = g(x)$, we select the parametrization

$$x = t, \qquad y = g(t).$$

For a circle of radius R centered at the origin, we select the parametrization

$$x = R \cos t, \qquad y = R \sin t, \qquad\qquad 0 \leq t \leq 2\pi.$$

whenever we wish to integrate counterclockwise.

For a straight line segment between two points P and Q, we take the parametrization C given by

$$C(t) = P + t(Q - P), \qquad\qquad 0 \leq t \leq 1.$$

The context should always make it clear which parametrization is intended.

Remark 2. If we are given a finite number of C^1-curves forming a path as indicated in the following figure:

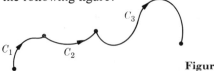

Figure 2

then the integral over the path is simply defined to be the sum of the integrals over each segment. Thus formally, we define a *path* C to be a finite sequence $\{C_1, \ldots, C_m\}$, where each C_i is a C^1-curve, defined on an interval $[a_i, b_i]$, such that the end point of C_i is the beginning point of C_{i+1}. Thus if $P_i = C_i(a_i)$ and $Q_i = C_i(b_i)$, then

$$Q_i = P_{i+1}.$$

We define the integral of F along such a path C to be the sum

$$\int_C F = \int_{C_1} F + \int_{C_2} F + \cdots + \int_{C_m} F.$$

We say that the path C is a *closed path* if the end point of C_m is the beginning point of C_1.

In the following picture, we have drawn a closed path such that the beginning point of C_1, namely P_1, is the end point of the path C_4, which joins P_4 to P_1.

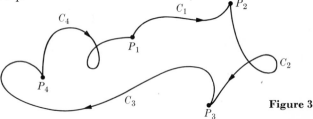

Figure 3

Example 3. Let $F(x, y) = (x^2, xy)$ and let the path consist of the segment of the parabola $y = x^2$ between $(0, 0)$ and $(1, 1)$, and the line segment from $(1, 1)$ and $(0, 0)$. (Cf. Fig. 4.)

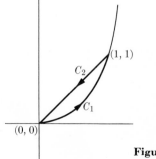

Figure 4

Then we let $C_1(t) = (t, t^2)$ and $C_2(t) = (1 - t, 1 - t)$. We let $C = \{C_1, C_2\}$. To find the integral of F along C we find the integral along C_1 and C_2, and add these integrals. We get:

$$\int_{C_1} F = \int_0^1 F(C_1(t)) \cdot (1, 2t) \, dt = \int_0^1 (t^2 + 2t^4) \, dt = \tfrac{1}{3} + \tfrac{2}{5}.$$

$$\int_{C_2} F = \int_0^1 F(C_2(t)) \cdot (-1, -1) \, dt = \int_0^1 -2(1 - 2t + t^2) \, dt = -\tfrac{2}{3}.$$

Hence

$$\int_C F = -\tfrac{1}{3} + \tfrac{2}{5}.$$

When the vector field F admits a potential function φ, then the integral of F along a curve has a simple expression in terms of φ.

Theorem 5. *Let F be a continuous vector field on the open set U and assume that $F = \operatorname{grad} \varphi$ for some differentiable function φ on U. Let C be a C^1-curve in U, joining the points P and Q. Then*

$$\int_{P,C}^Q F = \varphi(Q) - \varphi(P).$$

In particular, the integral of F is independent of the curve C joining P and Q.

Proof. Let C be defined on the interval $[a, b]$, so that $C(a) = P$ and $C(b) = Q$. By definition, we have $\nabla \Phi(c(t)) \cdot c'(t) = \varphi'(c(t))$

$$\int_{P,C}^Q F = \int_a^b F(C(t)) \cdot C'(t) \, dt = \int_a^b \operatorname{grad} \varphi \, (C(t)) \cdot C'(t) \, dt.$$

But the expression inside the integral is nothing but the derivative with respect to t of the function g given by $g(t) = \varphi(C(t))$, because of the chain rule. Thus our integral is equal to

$$\int_a^b g'(t) \, dt = g(b) - g(a) = \varphi(C(b)) - \varphi(C(a)).$$

This proves our theorem.

This theorem is easily extended to paths. We leave this to the reader.

We observe that in physics, one may interpret a vector field F as describing a force. Then the integral of this vector field along a path C describes the *work* done by the force along this path. In particular, when the vector field is conservative, as in Theorem 5, the work is expressed in terms of the potential function for F, and the end points of the path.

Example 4. Let $F(X) = kX/r^3$, where $r = \|X\|$, and k is a constant. This is the vector field inversely proportional to the square of the distance from the origin, used so often in physics. Then F has a potential function, namely the function φ such that $\varphi(X) = -k/r$. Thus the integral of F from $P = (1, 1, 1)$ to $Q = (1, 2, -1)$ is simply equal to

$$\varphi(Q) - \varphi(P) = -k\left(\frac{1}{\|Q\|} - \frac{1}{\|P\|}\right) = -k\left(\frac{1}{\sqrt{6}} - \frac{1}{\sqrt{3}}\right).$$

On the other hand, if P_1, Q_1 are two points at the same distance from the origin (i.e. lying on the same circle, centered at the origin), then the integral of F from P_1 to Q_1 along any curve is equal to 0.

EXERCISES

Compute the curve integrals of the vector field over the indicated curves.

1. $F(x, y) = (x^2 - 2xy, y^2 - 2xy)$ along the parabola $y = x^2$ from $(-2, 4)$ to $(1, 1)$.

2. $(x, y, xz - y)$ over the line segment from $(0, 0, 0)$ to $(1, 2, 4)$.

3. Let $r = (x^2 + y^2)^{1/2}$. Let $F(X) = r^{-1}X$. Find the integral of F over the circle of radius 2, taken in counterclockwise direction.

4. Let C be a circle of radius 20 with center at the origin. Let F be a vector field such that $F(X)$ has the same direction as X. What is the integral of F around C?

5. What is the work done by the force $F(x, y) = (x^2 - y^2, 2xy)$ moving a particle of mass m along the square bounded by the coordinate axes and the lines $x = 3$, $y = 3$ in counterclockwise direction?

6. Let $F(x, y) = (cxy, x^6y^2)$, where c is a positive constant. Let a, b be numbers > 0. Find a value of a in terms of c such that the line integral of F along the curve $y = ax^b$ from $(0, 0)$ to the line $x = 1$ is independent of b.

Find the values of the indicated integrals of vector fields along the given curves in Exercises 7 through 13.

7. $(y^2, -x)$ along the parabola $x = y^2/4$ from $(0, 0)$ to $(1, 2)$.

8. $(x^2 - y^2, x)$ along the arc in the first quadrant of the circle $x^2 + y^2 = 4$ from $(0, 2)$ to $(2, 0)$.

9. (x^2y^2, xy^2) along the closed path formed by parts of the line $x = 1$ and the parabola $y^2 = x$, counterclockwise.

10. $(x^2 - y^2, x)$ counterclockwise around the circle $x^2 + y^2 = 4$.

11. The vector field

$$\left(\frac{-y}{x^2 + y^2}, \frac{x}{x^2 + y^2}\right)$$

counterclockwise along the circle $x^2 + y^2 = 2$ from $(1, 1)$ to $(-\sqrt{2}, 0)$.

12. The same vector field along the line $x + y = 1$ from $(0, 1)$ to $(1, 0)$.

13. $(2xy, -3xy)$ clockwise around the square bounded by the lines $x = 3$, $x = 5$, $y = 1$, $y = 3$.

14. Let $C = (C_1, \ldots, C_m)$ be a piecewise C^1-path in an open set U. Let F be a continuous vector field on U, admitting a differentiable potential function φ. Let P be the beginning point of the path and Q its end point. Show that

$$\int_{P,C}^Q F = \varphi(Q) - \varphi(P).$$

[*Hint:* Apply Theorem 5 to the beginning point P_i and end point Q_i for each curve C_i.]

15. Find the integral of the vector field $F(x, y, z) = (2x, 3y, 4z)$ along the straight line $C(t) = (t, t, t)$ between the points $(0, 0, 0)$ and $(1, 1, 1)$.

16. Find the integral of the vector field $F(x, y, z) = (y + z, x + z, x + y)$ along the straight line $C(t) = (t, t, t)$ between $(0, 0, 0)$ and $(1, 1, 1)$.

17. Find the integral of the vector field given in Exercises 15 and 16 between the given points along the curve $C(t) = (t, t^2, t^4)$. Compare your answers with those previously found.

18. Let $F(x, y, z) = (y, x, 0)$. Find the integral of F along the straight line from $(1, 1, 1)$ to $(3, 3, 3)$.

19. Let P, Q be points of 3-space. Show that the integral of the vector field given by

$$F(x, y, z) = (z^2, 2y, 2xz)$$

from P to Q is independent of the curve selected between P and Q.

20. Let $F(x, y) = (x/r^3, y/r^3)$ where $r = (x^2 + y^2)^{1/2}$. Find the integral of F along the curve $C(t) = (e^t \cos t, e^t \sin t)$ from the point $(1, 0)$ to the point $(e^{2\pi}, 0)$.

21. Let $F(x, y, z) = (z^2, 2y, 2xz)$. Show that the integral of F between two points is independent of the curve between the points.

§5. DEPENDENCE OF THE INTEGRAL ON THE PATH

By a path from now on, we mean a piecewise C^1-path, and all vector fields are assumed continuous.

Given two points P, Q in some open set U, and a vector field F on U, it may be that the integral of F along two paths from P to Q depends on the path. The main theorem of this section gives three equivalent conditions that this integral should be independent of the path. Before discussing this theorem, we describe what we mean by integrating along a curve in opposite direction.

Let $C: [a, b] \to \mathbf{R}^n$ be a curve. We define the *opposite curve* C^- (or the negative curve) by letting

$$C^-(t) = C(a + b - t).$$

Thus when $t = b$ we find that $C^-(b) = C(a)$, and when $t = a$ we find that $C^-(a) = C(b)$. As t increases from a to b, we see that $a + b - t$

decreases from b to a and thus we visualize C^- as going from $C(b)$ to $C(a)$ in reverse direction from C (Fig. 5).

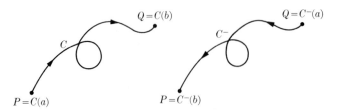

Figure 5

Lemma. *Let F be a vector field on the open set U, and let C be a curve in U, of class C^1, defined on the interval $[a, b]$. Then*

$$\int_{C^-} F = -\int_C F.$$

Proof. This is a simple application of the change of variables formula. Let $u = a + b - t$. Then $du/dt = -1$. By definition and the chain rule, we get:

$$\int_{C^-} F = \int_a^b F(C^-(t)) \cdot \frac{dC^-}{dt}\, dt$$

$$= \int_a^b F(C(a + b - t)) \cdot C'(a + b - t)(-1)\, dt.$$

We now change variables, with $du = -dt$. When $t = a$ then $u = b$, and when $t = b$ then $u = a$. Thus our integral is equal to

$$\int_b^a F(C(u)) \cdot C'(u)\, du = -\int_a^b F(C(u)) \cdot C'(u)\, du,$$

thereby proving the lemma.

The lemma expresses the expected result, that if we integrate the vector field along the opposite direction, then the value of the integral is the negative of the value obtained by integrating F along the curve itself.

Theorem 6. *Let U be an open set in $\mathbf{R}^n$ and let F be a vector field on U. Assume that any two points of U can be connected by a path in U. Then the following conditions are equivalent:*

 (i) *The vector field F has a potential function.*
 (ii) *The integral of F along any closed path in U is equal to 0.*
 (iii) *If P, Q are two points in U then the integral of F from P to Q is independent of the path.*

Proof. Assume condition (i). Let $C = (C_1, \ldots, C_m)$ be a path in U where each C_i is a C^1-curve. Let P_i be the beginning point of C_i and let Q_i be its end point, so that $Q_i = P_{i+1}$. By Theorem 5, we find that

$$\int_C F = \varphi(Q_m) - \varphi(P_m) + \varphi(Q_{m-1}) - \varphi(P_{m-1}) + \cdots + \varphi(Q_1) - \varphi(P_1).$$

All intermediate terms cancel, leaving the first and the last terms, and our integral is equal to

$$\varphi(Q_m) - \varphi(P_1).$$

If the path is a closed path, then $Q_m = P_1$ and thus the integral is equal to 0. If $P_1 = P$ and $Q_m = Q$, then we see that the value of the integral is independent of the path; it depends only on P, Q and the potential function, namely $\varphi(Q) - \varphi(P)$. *Thus both conditions* (ii) *and* (iii) *follow from* (i).

Furthermore, condition (ii) *implies* (iii). Indeed, let C and D be paths from P to Q in U. Let $D = (D_1, \ldots, D_k)$ where each D_j is a C^1-curve. Then we may form the opposite path

$$D^- = (D_k^-, \ldots, D_1^-),$$

and by the lemma,

$$\int_{D^-} F = - \int_D F.$$

If $C = (C_1, \ldots, C_m)$, then the path $(C_1, \ldots, C_m, D_k^-, \ldots, D_1^-)$ is a closed path from P to P (Fig. 6), and assuming (ii), we conclude that the integral of F along this closed path is equal to 0. Thus

$$\int_C F + \int_{D^-} F = 0.$$

From this it follows that

$$\int_C F = \int_D F,$$

whence condition (iii) holds.

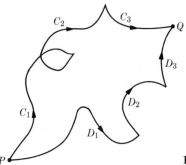

Figure 6

We shall now prove that condition (iii) implies (i). Let P_0 be a fixed point of U and define a function φ on U by the rule

$$\varphi(P) = \int_{P_0}^{P} F,$$

where the integral is taken along any path from P_0 to P. By assumption, this integral does not depend on the path, so we don't need to specify the path in the notation. We must show that the partial derivatives $D_i\varphi(P)$ exist for all P in U, and if the vector field F has coordinate functions

$$F = (f_1, \ldots, f_n),$$

then $D_i\varphi(P) = f_i(P)$.

To do this, let E_i be the unit vector with 1 in the i-th component and 0 in the other components. Then for any vector $X = (x_1, \ldots, x_n)$ we have $X \cdot E_i = x_i$. To determine $D_i\varphi(P)$ we must consider the Newton quotient

$$\frac{\varphi(P + hE_i) - \varphi(P)}{h} = \frac{1}{h}\left[\int_{P_0}^{P+hE_i} F - \int_{P_0}^{P} F\right]$$

and show that its limit as $h \to 0$ is $f_i(P)$. The integral from P_0 to $P + hE_i$ can be taken along a path going first from P_0 to P and then from P to $P + hE_i$.

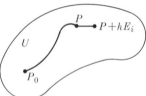

Figure 7

We can then cancel the integrals from P_0 to P and obtain

$$\frac{\varphi(P + hE_i) - \varphi(P)}{h} = \frac{\int_{P}^{P+hE_i} F(C) \cdot dC}{h},$$

taking the integral along any curve C between P and $P + hE_i$. In fact, we take C to be the parametrized straight line segment given by

$$C(t) = P + tE_i$$

with $0 \leq t \leq h$ in case h is positive. (The case of h negative is handled similarly. Cf. Exercise 1.) Then $C'(t) = E_i$ and

$$F(C(t)) \cdot C'(t) = f_i(C(t)).$$

The Newton quotient is therefore equal to

$$\frac{\int_0^h f_i(C(t))\, dt}{h}.$$

By the fundamental theorem of calculus, for any continuous function g we have (cf. Remark after the proof):

$$\lim_{h \to 0} \frac{1}{h} \int_0^h g(t)\, dt = g(0).$$

We apply this to the function given by $g(t) = f_i(C(t))$. Then

$$g(0) = f_i(C(0)) = f_i(P + 0E_i) = f_i(P).$$

Therefore we obtain the limit

$$\lim_{h \to 0} \frac{\varphi(P + hE_i) - \varphi(P)}{h} = f_i(P).$$

This proves what we wanted.

Remark. The use of the fundamental theorem of calculus in the preceding proof should be recognized as absolutely straightforward. If G is an indefinite integral for g, then

$$\int_0^h g(t)\, dt = G(h) - G(0),$$

and hence

$$\frac{1}{h} \int_0^h g(t)\, dt = \frac{G(h) - G(0)}{h}$$

is the ordinary Newton quotient for G. The fundamental theorem of calculus asserts precisely that the limit as $h \to 0$ is equal to $G'(0) = g(0)$.

EXERCISE

1. To take care of the case when h is negative in the proof of Theorem 6, use the parametrization $C(t) = P + thE_i$ with $0 \leq t \leq 1$. Making a change of variables, $u = th$, $du = h\, dt$, show that the proof follows exactly the same pattern as that given in the text.

Chapter VI

Higher Derivatives

In this chapter, we discuss two things which are of independent interest. First, we define partial differential operators (with constant coefficients). It is very useful to have facility in working with these formally.

Secondly, we apply them to the derivation of Taylor's formula for functions of several variables, which will be very similar to the formula for one variable. The formula, as before, tells us how to approximate a function by means of polynomials. In the present theory, these polynomials involve several variables, of course. We shall see that they are hardly more difficult to handle than polynomials in one variable in the matters under consideration.

The proof that the partial derivatives commute is tricky. It can be omitted without harm in a class allergic to theory, because the technique involved never reappears in the rest of this book.

§1. REPEATED PARTIAL DERIVATIVES

Let f be a function of two variables, defined on an open set U in 2-space. Assume that its first partial derivative exists. Then $D_1 f$ (which we also write $\partial f/\partial x$ if x is the first variable) is a function defined on U. We may then ask for its first or second partial derivatives, i.e. we may form $D_2 D_1 f$ or $D_1 D_1 f$ if these exist. Similarly, if $D_2 f$ exists, and if the first partial derivative of $D_2 f$ exists, we may form $D_1 D_2 f$.

Suppose that we write f in terms of the two variables (x, y). Then we can write

$$D_1 D_2 f(x, y) = \frac{\partial}{\partial x}\left(\frac{\partial f}{\partial y}\right) = (D_1(D_2 f))(x, y),$$

and

$$D_2 D_1 f(x, y) = \frac{\partial}{\partial y}\left(\frac{\partial f}{\partial x}\right) = (D_2(D_1 f))(x, y).$$

For example, let $f(x, y) = \sin(xy)$. Then

$$\frac{\partial f}{\partial x} = y \cos(xy) \qquad \text{and} \qquad \frac{\partial f}{\partial y} = x \cos(xy).$$

Hence

$$D_2 D_1 f(x, y) = -xy \sin(xy) + \cos(xy).$$

406

But differentiating $\partial f/\partial y$ with respect to x, we see that

$$D_1 D_2 f(x, y) = -xy \sin(xy) + \cos(xy).$$

These two repeated partial derivatives are equal!

The next theorem tells us that in practice, this will always happen.

Theorem 1. *Let f be a function of two variables, defined on an open set U of 2-space. Assume that the partial derivatives $D_1 f$, $D_2 f$, $D_1 D_2 f$, and $D_2 D_1 f$ exist and are continuous. Then*

$$D_1 D_2 f = D_2 D_1 f.$$

Proof. A direct use of the definition of these partial and repeated partial derivatives would lead to a blind alley. Hence we shall have to use a special trick to pull through.

Let (x, y) be a point in U, and let $H = (h, k)$ be small, $h \neq 0$, $k \neq 0$. We consider the expression

$$g(x) = f(x, y + k) - f(x, y).$$

If we apply the mean value theorem to g, then we conclude that there exists a number s_1 between x and $x + h$ such that

$$g(x + h) - g(x) = g'(s_1)h,$$

or in other words, using the definitions of partial derivative:

(1) $g(x + h) - g(x) = [D_1 f(s_1, y + k) - D_1 f(s_1, y)]h.$

But the difference on the left of this equation is

(2) $f(x + h, y + k) - f(x + h, y) - f(x, y + k) + f(x, y).$

On the other hand, we can now apply the mean value theorem to the expression in brackets in (1) *with respect to the second variable.* If we do this, we see that the long expression in (2) is equal to

(3) $D_2 D_1 f(s_1, s_2)kh$

for some number s_2 lying between y and $y + k$.

We now start all over again, and consider the expression

$$g_2(y) = f(x + h, y) - f(x, y).$$

We apply the mean value theorem to g_2, and conclude that there is a number t_2 between y and $y + k$ such that

$$g_2(y + k) - g_2(y) = g_2'(t_2)k,$$

or in other words, is equal to

(4) $[D_2 f(x + h, t_2) - D_2 f(x, t_2)]k.$

If you work out $g_2(y + k) - g_2(y)$, you will see that it is equal to the long expression of (2). Furthermore, proceeding as before, and applying the mean value theorem to the first variable in (4), we see that (4) becomes

$$(5) \qquad\qquad D_1 D_2 f(t_1, t_2) hk$$

for some number t_1 between x and $x + h$. Since (5) and (3) are both equal to the long expression in (2), they are equal to each other. Thus finally we obtain

$$D_2 D_1 f(s_1, s_2) kh = D_1 D_2 f(t_1, t_2) hk.$$

Since we assume from the beginning that $h \neq 0$ and $k \neq 0$, we can cancel hk, and get

$$D_2 D_1 f(s_1, s_2) = D_1 D_2 f(t_1, t_2).$$

Now as h, k approach 0, the left side of this equation approaches $D_2 D_1 f(x, y)$ because $D_2 D_1 f$ is assumed to be continuous. Similarly, the right-hand side approaches $D_1 D_2 f(x, y)$. We can therefore conclude that

$$D_1 D_2 f(x, y) = D_2 D_1 f(x, y),$$

as desired.

Consider now a function of three variables $f(x, y, z)$. We can then take three kinds of partial derivatives: D_1, D_2, or D_3 (in other notation, $\partial/\partial x$, $\partial/\partial y$, and $\partial/\partial z$). Let us assume throughout that all the partial derivatives which we shall consider exist and are continuous, so that we may form as many repeated partial derivatives as we please. Then using Theorem 1, we can show that it does not matter in which order we take these partials.

For instance, we see that

$$D_3 D_1 f = D_1 D_3 f.$$

This is simply an application of Theorem 1, keeping the second variable fixed. We may take a further partial derivative, for instance

$$D_1 D_3 D_1 f.$$

Here D_1 occurs twice and D_3 once. Then this expression will be equal to any other repeated partial derivative of f in which D_1 occurs twice and D_3 once. For example, we apply the theorem to the function $(D_1 f)$. Then the theorem allows us to interchange D_1 and D_3 in front of $(D_1 f)$ (always assuming that all partials we want to take exist and are continuous). We obtain

$$D_1 D_3 (D_1 f) = D_3 D_1 (D_1 f).$$

As another example, consider

$$(6) \qquad\qquad D_2 D_1 D_3 D_2 f.$$

We wish to show that it is equal to $D_1D_2D_2D_3f$. By Theorem 1, we have $D_3D_2f = D_2D_3f$. Hence:

(7) $D_2D_1(D_3D_2f) = D_2D_1(D_2D_3f).$

We then apply Theorem 1 again, and interchange D_2 and D_1 to obtain the desired expression.

In general, suppose that we are given three positive integers m_1, m_2, and m_3. We wish to take the repeated partial derivatives of f by using m_1 times the first partial D_1, using m_2 times the second partial D_2, and using m_3 times the third partial D_3. Then it does not matter in which order we take these partial derivatives, we shall always get the same answer.

To see this, note that by repeated application of Theorem 1, we can always interchange any occurrence of D_3 with D_2 or D_1 so as to push D_3 towards the right. We can perform such interchanges until all occurrences of D_3 occur furthest to the right, in the same way as we pushed D_3 towards the right going from expression (6) to expression (7). Once this is done, we start interchanging D_2 with D_1 until all occurrences of D_2 pile up just behind D_3. Once this is done, we are left with D_1 repeated a certain number of times on the left.

No matter with what arrangement of D_1, D_2, D_3 we started, we end up with the *same* arrangement, namely

$$\underbrace{D_1 \cdots D_1}_{m_1} \underbrace{D_2 \cdots D_2}_{m_2} \underbrace{D_3 \cdots D_3}_{m_3} f,$$

with D_1 occurring m_1 times, D_2 occurring m_2 times, and D_3 occurring m_3 times.

Exactly the same argument works for functions of more variables.

EXERCISES

In all problems, functions are assumed to be differentiable as needed.

Find the partial derivatives of order 2 for the following functions and verify explicitly in each case that $D_1D_2f = D_2D_1f$.

1. e^{xy} 2. $\sin(xy)$

3. $x^2y^3 + 3xy$ 4. $2xy + y^2$

5. $e^{x^2+y^2}$ 6. $\sin(x^2 + y)$

7. $\cos(x^3 + xy)$ 8. $\arctan(x^2 - 2xy)$

9. e^{x+y} 10. $\sin(x + y)$.

Find $D_1D_2D_3f$ and $D_3D_2D_1f$ in the following cases.

11. xyz 12. x^2yz

13. e^{xyz} 14. $\sin(xyz)$

15. $\cos(x + y + z)$ 16. $\sin(x + y + z)$

17. $(x^2 + y^2 + z^2)^{-1}$ 18. $x^3 y^2 z + 2(x + y + z)$.

19. Let $x = r \cos \theta$ and $y = r \sin \theta$. Let $f(x, y) = g(r, \theta)$. Show that

$$\frac{\partial f}{\partial x} = \cos \theta \frac{\partial g}{\partial r} - \frac{\sin \theta}{r} \frac{\partial g}{\partial \theta}$$

$$\frac{\partial f}{\partial y} = \sin \theta \frac{\partial g}{\partial r} + \frac{\cos \theta}{r} \frac{\partial g}{\partial \theta}.$$

[*Hint:* Using the chain rule, find first $\dfrac{\partial g}{\partial r}$ and $\dfrac{\partial g}{\partial \theta}$ in terms of $\dfrac{\partial f}{\partial x}$ and $\dfrac{\partial f}{\partial y}$. Then solve back a system of two equations in two unknowns.]

20. Let $x = r \cos \theta$ and $y = r \sin \theta$. Let $f(x, y) = g(r, \theta)$. Show that

$$\frac{\partial^2 g}{\partial r^2} + \frac{1}{r}\frac{\partial g}{\partial \theta} + \frac{1}{r^2}\frac{\partial^2 g}{\partial \theta^2} = \frac{\partial^2 f}{\partial x^2} + \frac{\partial^2 f}{\partial y^2}.$$

21. Let $f(X) = g(r)$ (with $r = \|X\|$), and assume $X = (x, y, z)$. Show that

$$\frac{d^2 g}{dr^2} + \frac{2}{r}\frac{dg}{dr} = \frac{\partial^2 f}{\partial x^2} + \frac{\partial^2 f}{\partial y^2} + \frac{\partial^2 f}{\partial z^2}.$$

22. Let $f(x, y)$ satisfy $f(tx, ty) = t^n f(x, y)$ for all t (n being some integer ≥ 1). Show that

$$x\frac{\partial f}{\partial x} + y\frac{\partial f}{\partial y} = nf(x, y).$$

23. Let f be as in Exercise 22. Show that

$$x^2 \frac{\partial^2 f}{\partial x^2} + 2xy\frac{\partial^2 f}{\partial x \, \partial y} + y^2 \frac{\partial^2 f}{\partial y^2} = n(n - 1)f(x, y).$$

(It is understood throughout that all functions are as many times differentiable as is necessary.)

24. A function of three variables $f(x, y, z)$ is said to satisfy *Laplace's equation* if

$$\frac{\partial^2 f}{\partial x^2} + \frac{\partial^2 f}{\partial y^2} + \frac{\partial^2 f}{\partial z^2} = 0.$$

Verify that the following functions satisfy Laplace's equation.

(a) $x^2 + y^2 - 2z^2$

(b) $\log \sqrt{x^2 + y^2 + z^2}$

(c) $\dfrac{1}{\sqrt{x^2 + y^2 + z^2}}$

(d) $e^{3x+4y} \cos(5z)$

25. Let $z = f(u, v)$ and $u = x + y, v = x - y$. Show that

$$\frac{\partial^2 z}{\partial x \, \partial y} = \frac{\partial^2 z}{\partial u^2} - \frac{\partial^2 z}{\partial v^2}.$$

26. Let $z = f(x + y) - g(x - y)$, where f, g are functions of one variable. Let $u = x + y$ and $v = x - y$. Show that

$$\frac{\partial^2 z}{\partial x^2} = \frac{\partial^2 z}{\partial y^2} = f''(u) + g''(v).$$

27. Let c be a constant, and let $z = \sin(x + ct) + \cos(2x + 2ct)$. Show that

$$\frac{\partial^2 z}{\partial t^2} = c^2 \frac{\partial^2 z}{\partial x^2}.$$

28. Let $z = f\left(\dfrac{x - y}{y}\right)$. Show that $x(\partial z/\partial x) + y(\partial z/\partial y) = 0$.

29. Let c be a constant, and let $z = f(x + ct) + g(x - ct)$. Let $u = x + ct$ and $v = x - ct$. Show that

$$\frac{\partial^2 z}{\partial t^2} = c^2 \frac{\partial^2 z}{\partial x^2} = c^2(f''(u) + g''(v)).$$

30. Let F be a vector field on an open set in 3-space, so that F is given by three coordinate functions, say $F = (f_1, f_2, f_3)$. Define the *curl* of F to be the vector field given by

$$(\text{curl } F)(x_1, x_2, x_3) = \left(\frac{\partial f_3}{\partial x_2} - \frac{\partial f_2}{\partial x_3}, \frac{\partial f_1}{\partial x_3} - \frac{\partial f_3}{\partial x_1}, \frac{\partial f_2}{\partial x_1} - \frac{\partial f_1}{\partial x_2}\right).$$

Define the *divergence* of F to be the function $g = \text{div } F$ given by

$$g(x, y, z) = \frac{\partial f_1}{\partial x} + \frac{\partial f_2}{\partial y} + \frac{\partial f_3}{\partial z}.$$

(a) Prove that if $F = \text{grad } \varphi$ for some function φ, then

$$\text{div grad } \varphi = 0.$$

(b) Prove that curl grad $\varphi = O$.

§2. PARTIAL DIFFERENTIAL OPERATORS

We shall continue the discussion at the end of the last section, but we shall build up a convenient system to talk about iterated partial derivatives.

For simplicity, let us begin with functions of one variable x. We can then take only one type of derivative,

$$D = \frac{d}{dx}.$$

Let f be a function of one variable, and let us assume that all the iterated derivatives of f exist. Let m be a positive integer. Then we can take the

m-th derivative of f, which we once denoted by $f^{(m)}$. We now write it

$$DD\cdots Df \quad \text{or} \quad \frac{d}{dx}\left(\frac{d}{dx}\cdots\left(\frac{df}{dx}\right)\cdots\right),$$

the derivative D (or d/dx) being iterated m times. What matters here is the number of times D occurs. We shall use the notation D^m or $(d/dx)^m$ to mean the iteration of D, m times. Thus we write

$$D^m f \quad \text{or} \quad \left(\frac{d}{dx}\right)^m f$$

instead of the above expressions. This is shorter. But even better, we have the rule

$$D^m D^n f = D^{m+n} f$$

for any positive integers m, n. So this iteration of derivatives begins to look like a multiplication. Furthermore, if we define $D^0 f$ to be simply f, then the rule above also holds if m, n are ≥ 0.

The expression D^m will be called a *simple differential operator of order m* (in one variable, so far).

Let us now look at the case of two variables, say (x, y). We can then take two partials D_1 and D_2 (or $\partial/\partial x$ and $\partial/\partial y$). Let m_1, m_2 be two integers ≥ 0. Instead of writing

$$\underbrace{D_1\cdots D_1}_{m_1}\underbrace{D_2\cdots D_2}_{m_2}f \quad \text{or} \quad \underbrace{\frac{\partial}{\partial x}\cdots\left(\frac{\partial}{\partial x}}_{m_1}\underbrace{\left(\frac{\partial}{\partial y}\cdots\left(\frac{\partial f}{\partial y}\right)\cdots\right)}_{m_2}\right),$$

we shall write

$$D_1^{m_1}D_2^{m_2}f \quad \text{or} \quad \left(\frac{\partial}{\partial x}\right)^{m_1}\left(\frac{\partial}{\partial y}\right)^{m_2}f.$$

For instance, taking $m_1 = 2$ and $m_2 = 5$ we would write

$$D_1^2 D_2^5 f.$$

This means: take the first partial twice and the second partial five times (in any order). (We assume throughout that all repeated partials exist and are continuous.)

An expression of type

$$D_1^{m_1} D_2^{m_2}$$

will be called a simple differential operator, and we shall say that its *order* is $m_1 + m_2$. In the example we just gave, the order is $5 + 2 = 7$.

It is now clear how to proceed with three or more variables, and it is no harder to express our thoughts in terms of n variables than in terms of three. Consequently, if we deal with functions of n variables, all of whose repeated partial derivatives exist and are continuous in some open set U, and if $D_1, \ldots, D_n$ denote the partial derivatives with respect to these variables, then we call an expression

$$D_1^{m_1} \cdots D_n^{m_n} \quad \text{or} \quad \left(\frac{\partial}{\partial x_1}\right)^{m_1} \cdots \left(\frac{\partial}{\partial x_n}\right)^{m_n}$$

a *simple differential operator*, $m_1, \ldots, m_n$ being integers ≥ 0. We say that its *order* is $m_1 + \cdots + m_n$.

Given a function f (satisfying the above stated conditions), and a simple differential operator D, we write Df to mean the function obtained from f by applying repeatedly the partial derivatives $D_1, \ldots, D_n$, the number of times being the number of times each D_i occurs in D.

Example 1. Consider functions of three variables (x, y, z). Then

$$D = \left(\frac{\partial}{\partial x}\right)^3 \left(\frac{\partial}{\partial y}\right)^5 \left(\frac{\partial}{\partial z}\right)^2$$

is a simple differential operator of order $3 + 5 + 2 = 10$. Let f be a function of three variables satisfying the usual hypotheses. To take Df means that we take the partial derivative with respect to z twice, the partial with respect to y five times, and the partial with respect to x three times.

We observe that a simple differential operator gives us a rule which to each function f associates another function Df.

As a matter of notation, referring to Example 1, one would also write the differential operator D in the form

$$D = \frac{\partial^{10}}{\partial x^3 \partial y^5 \partial z^2}.$$

In this notation, one would thus have

$$\left(\frac{\partial}{\partial x}\right)^2 f = \frac{\partial^2 f}{\partial x^2}$$

and

$$\frac{\partial}{\partial x}\left(\frac{\partial f}{\partial y}\right) = \frac{\partial^2 f}{\partial x \, \partial y}.$$

All the above notations are used in the scientific literature, and this is the reason for including them here.

Warning. Do not confuse the two expressions

$$\left(\frac{\partial}{\partial x}\right)^2 f = \frac{\partial^2 f}{\partial x^2} \quad \text{and} \quad \left(\frac{\partial f}{\partial x}\right)^2,$$

which are usually **not** equal. For instance, if $f(x, y) = x^2 y$, then

$$\frac{\partial^2 f}{\partial x^2} = 2y \quad \text{and} \quad \left(\frac{\partial f}{\partial x}\right)^2 = 4x^2 y^2.$$

We shall now show how one can add simple differential operators and multiply them by constants.

Let D, D' be two simple differential operators. For any function f we define $(D + D')f$ to be $Df + D'f$. If c is a number, then we define $(cD)f$ to be $c(Df)$. In this manner, taking iterated sums, and products with constants, we obtain what we shall call *differential operators*. Thus a *differential operator* D is a sum of terms of type

$$c D_1^{m_1} \cdots D_n^{m_n},$$

where c is a number and $m_1, \ldots, m_n$ are integers ≥ 0.

Example 2. Dealing with two variables, we see that

$$D = 3\frac{\partial}{\partial x} + 5\left(\frac{\partial}{\partial x}\right)^2 - \pi \frac{\partial}{\partial x} \frac{\partial}{\partial y}$$

is a differential operator. Let $f(x, y) = \sin(xy)$. We wish to find Df. By definition,

$$Df(x, y) = 3\frac{\partial f}{\partial x} + 5\left(\frac{\partial}{\partial x}\right)^2 f - \pi \frac{\partial}{\partial x} \frac{\partial f}{\partial y}$$

$$= 3y\cos(xy) + 5(-y^2 \sin(xy))$$
$$- \pi[y(-\sin(xy))x + \cos(xy)].$$

We see that a differential operator associates with each function f (satisfying the usual conditions) another function Df.

Let c be a number and f a function. Let D_i be any partial derivative. Then
$$D_i(cf) = cD_i f.$$

This is simply the old property that the derivative of a constant times a function is equal to the constant times the derivative of the function. Iterating partial derivatives, we see that this same property applies to differential operators. For any differential operator D, and any number c, we have
$$D(cf) = cDf.$$

Furthermore, if f, g are two functions (defined on the same open set, and having continuous partial derivatives of all orders), then for any partial derivative D_i, we have

$$D_i(f + g) = D_i f + D_i g.$$

Iterating the partial derivatives, we find that for any differential operator D, we have

$$D(f + g) = Df + Dg.$$

Having learned how to add differential operators, we now learn how to multiply them.

Let D, D' be two differential operators. Then we define the differential operator DD' to be the one obtained by taking first D' and then D. In other words, if f is a function, then

$$(DD')f = D(D'f).$$

Example 3. Let

$$D = 3\frac{\partial}{\partial x} + 2\frac{\partial}{\partial y} \quad \text{and} \quad D' = \frac{\partial}{\partial x} + 4\frac{\partial}{\partial y}.$$

Then

$$DD' = \left(3\frac{\partial}{\partial x} + 2\frac{\partial}{\partial y}\right)\left(\frac{\partial}{\partial x} + 4\frac{\partial}{\partial y}\right)$$

$$= 3\left(\frac{\partial}{\partial x}\right)^2 + 14\frac{\partial}{\partial x}\frac{\partial}{\partial y} + 8\left(\frac{\partial}{\partial y}\right)^2.$$

Differential operators multiply just like polynomials and numbers, and their addition and multiplication satisfy all the rules of addition and multiplication of polynomials. For instance:

If D, D' are two differential operators, then

$$DD' = D'D.$$

If D, D', D'' are three differential operators, then

$$D(D' + D'') = DD' + DD''.$$

It would be tedious to list all the properties here and to give in detail all the proofs (even though they are quite simple). We shall therefore omit these proofs. The main purpose of this section is to insure that you develop as great a facility in adding and multiplying differential operators as you have in adding and multiplying numbers or polynomials.

When a differential operator is written as a sum of terms of type

$$cD_1^{m_1} \cdots D_n^{m_n},$$

then we shall say that it is in *standard form*.

For example,

$$3\left(\frac{\partial}{\partial x}\right)^2 + 14\frac{\partial}{\partial x}\frac{\partial}{\partial y} + 8\left(\frac{\partial}{\partial y}\right)^2$$

is in standard form, but

$$\left(3\frac{\partial}{\partial x} + 2\frac{\partial}{\partial y}\right)\left(\frac{\partial}{\partial x} + 4\frac{\partial}{\partial y}\right)$$

is not.

Each term

$$cD_1^{m_1} \cdots D_n^{m_n}$$

is said to have degree $m_1 + \cdots + m_n$. If a differential operator is expressed as a sum of simple differential operators which all have the same degree, say m, then we say that it is *homogeneous* of degree m.

The differential operator of Example 2 is not homogeneous. The differential operator DD' of Example 3 is homogeneous of degree 2.

EXERCISES

Put the following differential operators in standard form.

1. $(3D_1 + 2D_2)^2$ 2. $(D_1 + D_2 + D_3)^2$
3. $(D_1 - D_2)(D_1 + D_2)$ 4. $(D_1 + D_2)^2$
5. $(D_1 + D_2)^3$ 6. $(D_1 + D_2)^4$
7. $(2D_1 - 3D_2)(D_1 + D_2)$ 8. $(D_1 - D_3)(D_2 + 5D_3)$

9. $\left(\dfrac{\partial}{\partial x} + 4\dfrac{\partial}{\partial y}\right)^3$ 10. $\left(2\dfrac{\partial}{\partial x} + \dfrac{\partial}{\partial y}\right)^2$

11. $\left(h\dfrac{\partial}{\partial x} + k\dfrac{\partial}{\partial y}\right)^2$ 12. $\left(h\dfrac{\partial}{\partial x} + k\dfrac{\partial}{\partial y}\right)^3$

Find the values of the differential operator of Exercise 10 applied to the following functions at the given point.

13. x^2y at $(0, 1)$ 14. xy at $(1, 1)$
15. $\sin(xy)$ at $(0, \pi)$ 16. e^{xy} at $(0, 0)$

17. Let f, g be two functions (of two variables) with continuous partial derivatives of order ≤ 2 in an open set U. Assume that

$$\frac{\partial f}{\partial x} = -\frac{\partial g}{\partial y} \quad \text{and} \quad \frac{\partial f}{\partial y} = \frac{\partial g}{\partial x}.$$

Show that

$$\frac{\partial^2 f}{\partial x^2} + \frac{\partial^2 f}{\partial y^2} = 0.$$

18. Let f be a function of three variables, defined for $X \neq O$ by $f(X) = 1/\|X\|$. Show that

$$\frac{\partial^2 f}{\partial x^2} + \frac{\partial^2 f}{\partial y^2} + \frac{\partial^2 f}{\partial z^2} = 0.$$

19. In Exercise 20 of the preceding section, compute

$$\left(\frac{\partial}{\partial x}\right)^2 + \left(\frac{\partial}{\partial y}\right)^2$$

in terms of $\partial/\partial r$ and $\partial/\partial\theta$. Watch out! The coefficients are not constant.

§3. TAYLOR'S FORMULA

In the theory of functions of one variable, we derived an expression for the values of a function f near a point a by means of the derivatives, namely

$$f(a + h) = f(a) + f'(a)h + \frac{f^{(2)}(a)}{2!}h^2 + \cdots + \frac{f^{(r-1)}(a)}{(r-1)!}h^{r-1} + R_r,$$

where

$$R_r = \frac{f^{(r)}(c)}{r!}h^r,$$

for some point c between a and $a + h$. We shall now derive a similar formula for functions of several variables. We begin with the case of two variables.

We let $P = (a, b)$ and $H = (h, k)$. We assume that P is in an open set U and that f is a function on U all of whose partial derivatives up to order n exist and are continuous. We are interested in finding an expression

$$f(P + H) = f(P) + ?\,?\,?$$

The idea is to reduce the problem to the one variable case. Thus we define the function

$$g(t) = f(P + tH) = f(a + th, b + tk)$$

for $0 \le t \le 1$. We assume that U contains all points $P + tH$ for $0 \le t \le 1$. Then

$$g(1) = f(P + H) \qquad \text{and} \qquad g(0) = f(P).$$

We can use Taylor's formula in one variable applied to the function g and we know that

$$g(1) = g(0) + \frac{g'(0)}{1!} + \cdots + \frac{g^{(r-1)}(0)}{(r-1)!} + \frac{g^{(r)}(\tau)}{r!}$$

for some number τ between 0 and 1, provided that g has r continuous derivatives. We shall now prove that the derivatives of g can be expressed in terms of the partial derivatives of f, and thus obtain the desired Taylor formula for f. We shall first do it for $n = 2$.

We let $x = a + th$ and $y = b + tk$. By the chain rule:

(1) $$g'(t) = \frac{\partial f}{\partial x}\frac{\partial x}{\partial t} + \frac{\partial f}{\partial y}\frac{\partial y}{\partial t} = \frac{\partial f}{\partial x}h + \frac{\partial f}{\partial y}k.$$

For the second derivative, we must find the derivative with respect to t of each one of the functions $\partial f/\partial x$ and $\partial f/\partial y$. By the chain rule applied to each such function, we have:

$$\frac{d}{dt}\left(\frac{\partial f}{\partial x}\right) = \frac{\partial^2 f}{\partial x^2}\frac{dx}{dt} + \frac{\partial^2 f}{\partial y\,\partial x}\frac{dy}{dt} = \frac{\partial^2 f}{\partial x^2}h + \frac{\partial^2 f}{\partial y\,\partial x}k,$$

(2)

$$\frac{d}{dt}\left(\frac{\partial f}{\partial y}\right) = \frac{\partial^2 f}{\partial x\,\partial y}h + \frac{\partial^2 f}{\partial y^2}k.$$

Hence using (2) to take the derivative of (1), we find:

$$g''(t) = h\left[\frac{\partial^2 f}{\partial x^2}h + \frac{\partial^2 f}{\partial y\,\partial x}k\right] + k\left[\frac{\partial^2 f}{\partial x\,\partial y}h + \frac{\partial^2 f}{\partial y^2}k\right]$$

$$= h^2\frac{\partial^2 f}{\partial x^2} + 2hk\frac{\partial^2 f}{\partial x\,\partial y} + k^2\frac{\partial^2 f}{\partial y^2}.$$

This expression can be rewritten more easily in terms of differential operators, namely we see that the expression for $g''(t)$ is equal to

$$\left(h\frac{\partial}{\partial x} + k\frac{\partial}{\partial y}\right)^2 f.$$

If we wish to free the notation from the x and y, then we can use the notation

$$g''(t) = (hD_1 + kD_2)^2 f(P + tH)$$
$$= (hD_1 + kD_2)^2 f(a + th, b + tk).$$

As usual, this means that we apply $(hD_1 + kD_2)^2$ to f, and then evaluate this function at the point $(a + th, b + tk)$.

The expression $hD_1 + kD_2$ looks like a dot product, and thus it is useful to abbreviate the notation and write

$$hD_1 + kD_2 = H \cdot \nabla.$$

With this abbreviation, our first derivative for g can then be written [from (1)]:

$$g'(t) = (H \cdot \nabla)f(P + tH),$$

and the second derivative can be written

$$g''(t) = (H \cdot \nabla)^2 f(P + tH).$$

Here again, we emphasize that $(H \cdot \nabla)$ and $(H \cdot \nabla)^2$ are first applied to f, so that strictly speaking we should write an extra set of parentheses, e.g.

$$g'(t) = ((H \cdot \nabla)f)(a + th, b + tk)$$

and similarly for $g''(t)$.

The higher derivatives of g are determined similarly by induction.

Theorem 2. *Let r be a positive integer. Let f be a function defined on an open set U, and having continuous partial derivatives of orders $\leq r$. Let P be a point of U, and H a vector. Let $g(t) = f(P + tH)$. Then*

$$g^{(r)}(t) = ((H \cdot \nabla)^r f)(P + tH)$$

for all values of t such that $P + tH$ lies in U.

Proof. The case $r = 1$ (even $r = 2$) has already been verified. Suppose our formula proved for some integer r. Let $\psi = (H \cdot \nabla)^r f$. Then

$$g^{(r)}(t) = \psi(P + tH).$$

Hence by the case for $r = 1$ we get

$$g^{(r+1)}(t) = ((H \cdot \nabla)\psi)(P + tH).$$

Substituting the value for ψ yields

$$g^{(r+1)}(t) = ((H \cdot \nabla)^{r+1} f)(P + tH),$$

thus proving our theorem by induction.

In terms of the $\partial/\partial x$ and $\partial/\partial y$ notation, we see that

$$g^{(r)}(t) = \left(h\frac{\partial}{\partial x} + k\frac{\partial}{\partial y} \right)^r f(P + tH).$$

Taylor's Formula. *Let f be a function defined on an open set U, and having continuous partial derivatives up to order r. Let P be a point of U, and H a vector. Assume that the line segment*

$$P + tH, \qquad 0 \leq t \leq 1,$$

is contained in U. Then there exists a number τ between 0 and 1 such that

$$f(P + H) = f(P) + \frac{(H \cdot \nabla)f(P)}{1!} + \cdots + \frac{(H \cdot \nabla)^{r-1}f(P)}{(r-1)!}$$

$$+ \frac{(H \cdot \nabla)^r f(P + \tau H)}{r!}.$$

Proof. This is obtained by plugging the expression for the derivatives of the function $g(t) = f(P + tH)$ into the Taylor formula for one variable. We see that

$$g^{(s)}(0) = (H \cdot \nabla)^s f(P)$$

and

$$g^{(r)}(\tau) = (H \cdot \nabla)^r (P + \tau H).$$

This proves Taylor's formula as stated.

Rewritten in terms of the $\partial/\partial x$ and $\partial/\partial y$ notation, we have

$$f(a + h, b + k) = f(a, b) + \left(h\frac{\partial}{\partial x} + k\frac{\partial}{\partial y}\right) f(a, b) + \cdots$$
$$+ \left(h\frac{\partial}{\partial x} + k\frac{\partial}{\partial y}\right)^{r-1} f(a, b)$$
$$+ \left(h\frac{\partial}{\partial x} + k\frac{\partial}{\partial y}\right)^{r} f(a + \tau h, b + \tau k).$$

The powers of the differential operators

$$\left(h\frac{\partial}{\partial x} + k\frac{\partial}{\partial y}\right)^{s}$$

are found by the usual binomial expansion. For instance:

$$\left(h\frac{\partial}{\partial x} + k\frac{\partial}{\partial y}\right)^{2} = h^2\frac{\partial^2}{\partial x^2} + 2hk\frac{\partial^2}{\partial x\,\partial y} + k^2\frac{\partial^2}{\partial y^2},$$
$$\left(h\frac{\partial}{\partial x} + k\frac{\partial}{\partial y}\right)^{3} = h^3\left(\frac{\partial}{\partial x}\right)^3 + 3h^2k\left(\frac{\partial}{\partial x}\right)^2\left(\frac{\partial}{\partial y}\right)$$
$$+ 3hk^2\left(\frac{\partial}{\partial x}\right)\left(\frac{\partial}{\partial y}\right)^2 + k^3\left(\frac{\partial}{\partial y}\right)^3.$$

Example 1. Find the terms of degree ≤ 2 in the Taylor formula for the function $f(x, y) = \log(1 + x + 2y)$ at the point $(2, 1)$.

We compute the partial derivatives. They are:

$$f(2, 1) = \log 5,$$

$$D_1 f(x, y) = \frac{1}{1 + x + 2y}, \qquad\qquad D_1 f(2, 1) = \frac{1}{5} = \frac{\partial f}{\partial x}(2, 1),$$

$$D_2 f(x, y) = \frac{2}{1 + x + 2y}, \qquad\qquad D_2 f(2, 1) = \frac{2}{5} = \frac{\partial f}{\partial y}(2, 1),$$

$$D_1^2 f(x, y) = -\frac{1}{(1 + x + 2y)^2}, \qquad D_1^2 f(2, 1) = -\frac{1}{25} = \frac{\partial^2 f}{\partial x^2}(2, 1),$$

$$D_2^2 f(x, y) = -\frac{4}{(1 + x + 2y)^2}, \qquad D_2^2 f(2, 1) = -\frac{4}{25} = \frac{\partial^2 f}{\partial y^2}(2, 1),$$

$$D_1 D_2 f(x, y) = -\frac{2}{(1 + x + 2y)^2}, \qquad D_1 D_2 f(2, 1) = -\frac{2}{25} = \frac{\partial^2 f}{\partial x\,\partial y}(2, 1).$$

Hence

$$f(2 + h, 1 + k) = \log 5 + \left(\frac{1}{5}h + \frac{2}{5}k\right)$$
$$+ \frac{1}{2!}\left[-\frac{1}{25}h^2 - \frac{4}{25}hk - \frac{4}{25}k^2\right] + \cdots.$$

In many cases, we take $P = O$ and we wish to approximate $f(x, y)$ by a polynomial in x, y. Thus we let $H = (x, y)$. In that case, the notation $\partial/\partial x$ and $\partial/\partial y$ becomes even worse than usual since it is not entirely clear in taking the square

$$\left(x \frac{\partial}{\partial x} + y \frac{\partial}{\partial y} \right)^2$$

what is to be treated as a constant and what is not. Thus it is better to write

$$(xD_1 + yD_2)^2,$$

and similarly for higher powers. We then obtain a polynomial expression for f, with a remainder term. The terms of degree ≤ 3 are as follows:

$$f(x, y)$$
$$= f(0, 0) + D_1 f(0, 0)x + D_2 f(0, 0)y$$
$$+ \frac{1}{2!} [D_1^2 f(0, 0)x^2 + 2D_1 D_2 f(0, 0)xy + D_2^2 f(0, 0)y^2]$$
$$+ \frac{1}{3!} [D_1^3 f(0, 0)x^3 + 3D_1^2 D_2 f(0, 0)x^2 y + 3D_1 D_2^2 f(0, 0)xy^2 + D_2^3 f(0, 0)y^3]$$
$$+ R_4.$$

In general, the Taylor formula gives us an expression

$$f(x, y) = f(0, 0) + G_1(x, y) + \cdots + G_{r-1}(x, y) + R_r,$$

where $G_d(x, y)$ is a homogeneous polynomial in x, y of degree d, and R_r is the remainder term. We call

$$f(0, 0) + G_1(x, y) + \cdots + G_s(x, y)$$

the *polynomial approximation of f*, of degree $\leq s$.

Example 2. Find the polynomial approximation of the function

$$f(x, y) = \log (1 + x + 2y)$$

up to degree 2.

We computed the partial derivatives in Example 1. For the present application, we have

$$f(0, 0) = 0,$$
$$D_1 f(0, 0) = 1, \qquad D_2 f(0, 0) = 2,$$
$$D_1^2 f(0, 0) = -1, \qquad D_2^2 f(0, 0) = -4,$$
$$D_1 D_2 f(0, 0) = -2.$$

Hence the polynomial approximation of f up to degree 2 is

$$G(x, y) = x + 2y - \tfrac{1}{2}(x^2 + 4xy + 4y^2).$$

Example 3. In some special cases, there is a way of getting the polynomial approximation to the function more simply by using more directly the Taylor formula for one variable. Consider for instance the function $f(x, y) = \sin(xy)$. For any number u we know that

$$\sin u = u + R_3(u)$$

where $R_3(u)$ is the remainder of the Taylor formula for the sine function of one variable. From the *First Course in Calculus*, you should know that this remainder term satisfies the estimate

$$|R_3(u)| \leq \frac{|u|^3}{3!}.$$

Thus if we let $u = xy$, then we find that

$$\sin(xy) = xy + R_3(xy),$$

and hence

$$|\sin(xy) - xy| \leq \frac{|xy|^3}{3!}.$$

Also we see that, for example, for $y \neq 0$, we have

$$\frac{\sin(xy) - xy}{y} = \frac{R_3(xy)}{y}.$$

In particular, we get the estimate

$$\left|\frac{\sin(xy) - xy}{y}\right| \leq \frac{|x|^3|y|^2}{3!}.$$

From this we see that the limit of

$$\frac{\sin(xy) - xy}{y}$$

as (x, y) approaches $(0, 0)$ is equal to 0.

Finally, we observe that the treatment of functions of several variables follows exactly the same pattern. In this case, we let

$$H = (h_1, \ldots, h_n)$$

and

$$H \cdot \nabla = h_1 D_1 + \cdots + h_n D_n = h_1 \frac{\partial}{\partial x_1} + \cdots + h_n \frac{\partial}{\partial x_n}.$$

Not a single word need be changed in Theorems 2 and 3 to get Taylor's formula for several variables.

EXERCISES

Find the terms up to order 2 in the Taylor formula of the following functions (taking $P = O$).

1. $\sin(xy)$ 2. $\cos(xy)$ 3. $\log(1 + xy)$

4. $\sin(x^2 + y^2)$ 5. e^{x+y} 6. $\cos(x^2 + y)$

7. $(\sin x)(\cos y)$ 8. $e^x \sin y$ 9. $x + xy + 2y^2$

10. Does $\dfrac{\sin(xy)}{x}$ approach a limit as (x, y) approaches $(0, 0)$? If so, what limit?

11. Same questions for

$$\frac{e^{xy} - 1}{x} \quad \text{and} \quad \frac{\log(1 + x^2 + y^2)}{x^2 + y^2}.$$

12. Same questions for

$$\frac{\cos(xy) - 1}{x}.$$

13. Same questions for

$$\frac{\sin(xy) - xy}{x^2 y}.$$

14. Find the terms up to order 3 in Taylor's formula for the function $e^x \cos y$.

15. What is the term of degree 7 in Taylor's formula for the function

$$x^3 - 2xy^4 + (x - 1)^2 y^{10}?$$

16. Show that if $f(x, y, z)$ is a polynomial in x, y, z, then it is equal to its own Taylor series, i.e. there exists an integer n such that $R_n = 0$.

17. Find the polynomial approximation of the function

$$f(x, y) = \log(1 + x + 2y)$$

up to degree 3.

18. In each one of Exercises 1 through 9, find the terms of degree ≤ 2 in the Taylor expansion of the function at the indicated point.

1. $P = (1, \pi)$ 2. $P = (\pi/2, \pi)$ 3. $P = (2, 3)$

4. $P = (\pi, \pi)$ 5. $P = (1, 2)$ 6. $P = (0, \pi)$

7. $P = (\pi/2, \pi)$ 8. $P = (2, \pi/4)$ 9. $P = (1, 1)$

19. Let f be a function of two variables with continuous partial derivatives of order ≤ 2. Assume that $f(0) = 0$ and also that $f(ta, tb) = t^2 f(a, b)$ for all numbers t and all vectors (a, b). Show that for all points $P = (a, b)$ we have

$$f(P) = \frac{(P \cdot \nabla)^2 f(0)}{2!}.$$

20. Let U be an open set having the following property. Given two points X, Y in U, the line segment joining X and Y is contained in the open set.

(a) What is the parametric equation for this line segment?

(b) Let f have continuous partial derivatives in U. Assume that

$$\|\operatorname{grad} f(P)\| \leq M$$

for some number M, and all points P in U. Show that for any two points X, Y in U we have

$$|f(X) - f(Y)| \leq M\|X - Y\|.$$

§4. INTEGRAL EXPRESSIONS

Quite often, instead of the mean value type of remainder obtained previously in Taylor's formula, it is useful to deal with an integral form of the remainder. For instance, we have

$$(1) \qquad f(x, y) = f(0, 0) + \int_0^1 \frac{d}{dt} \left(f(tx, ty) \right) dt.$$

This is a direct application of the definition of the integral, since we can put $\psi(t) = f(tx, ty)$, and since

$$\int_0^1 \frac{d\psi}{dt} dt = \psi(1) - \psi(0).$$

If we now evaluate the derivative with respect to t under the integral, using the chain rule, we obtain

$$f(x, y) = f(0, 0) + \int_0^1 [D_1 f(tx, ty)x + D_2 f(tx, ty)y] dt$$

or

$$\boxed{f(x, y) = f(0, 0) + x g_1(x, y) + y g_2(x, y),}$$

where

$$g_1(x, y) = \int_0^1 D_1 f(tx, ty) dt \qquad \text{and} \qquad g_2(x, y) = \int_0^2 D_2 f(tx, ty) dt.$$

The advantage of such an expression is that the dependence of g_1 and g_2 on (x, y) is quite smooth—just as smooth as that of $D_1 f$ and $D_2 f$. From Chapter V, §2 we know that we can differentiate under the integral sign with respect to x and y. Thus this type of expression is often better than the remainder of Taylor's formula, with an undetermined τ which usually cannot be given explicitly, and depends on the specific choice of (x, y).

EXERCISE

1. Let f be a function of two variables, with continuous partials of order ≤ 2. Assume that $f(0, 0) = 0$ and $D_i f(0, 0) = 0$ for $i = 1, 2$. Show that there exist continuous functions h_i such that

$$f(x, y) = h_1(x, y)x^2 + h_2(x, y)xy + h_3(x, y)y^2.$$

[*Hint:* Apply the arguments of the text to the functions

$$D_1 f(tx, ty) \qquad \text{and} \qquad D_2 f(tx, ty)$$

using an integral with respect to some new variable, say s.]

Chapter VII

Maximum and Minimum

When we studied functions of one variable, we found maxima and minima by first finding critical points, i.e. points where the derivative is equal to 0, and then determining by inspection which of these are maxima or minima. We can carry out a similar investigation for functions of several variables. The condition that the derivative is equal to 0 must be replaced by the vanishing of all partial derivatives.

§1. CRITICAL POINTS

Let f be a differentiable function defined on an open set U. Let P be a point of U. If all partial derivatives of f are equal to 0 at P, then we say that P is a *critical point* of the function. In other words, for P to be a critical point, we must have

$$D_1 f(P) = 0, \quad \ldots, \quad D_n f(P) = 0.$$

Example. Find the critical points of the function $f(x, y) = e^{-(x^2 + y^2)}$. Taking the partials, we see that

$$\frac{\partial f}{\partial x} = -2x e^{-(x^2+y^2)} \quad \text{and} \quad \frac{\partial f}{\partial y} = -2y e^{-(x^2+y^2)}.$$

The only value of (x, y) for which both these quantities are equal to 0 is $x = 0$ and $y = 0$. Hence the only critical point is $(0, 0)$.

A critical point of a function of one variable is a point where the derivative is equal to 0. We have seen examples where such a point need not be a local maximum or a local minimum, for instance as in the following picture:

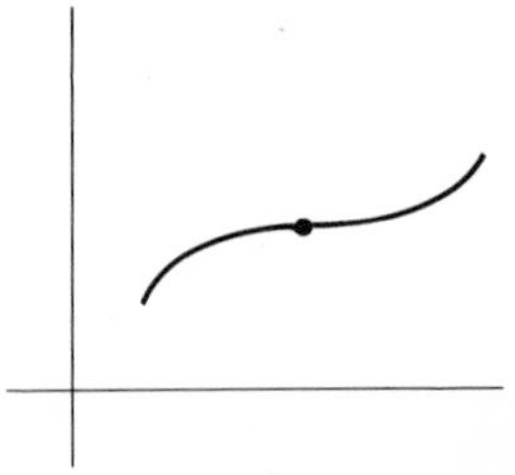

Figure 1

A fortiori, a similar thing may occur for functions of several variables. However, once we have found critical points, it is usually not too difficult to tell by inspection whether they are of this type or not.

Let f be any function (differentiable or not), defined on an open set U. We shall say that a point P of U is a *local maximum* for the function if there exists an open ball (of positive radius) B, centered at P, such that for all points X of B, we have

$$f(X) \leq f(P).$$

As an exercise, define *local minimum* in an analogous manner.

In the case of functions of one variable, we took an open interval instead of an open ball around the point P. Thus our notion of local maximum in n-space is the natural generalization of the notion in 1-space.

Theorem 1. *Let f be a function which is defined and differentiable on an open set U. Let P be a local maximum for f in U. Then P is a critical point of f.*

Proof. The proof is exactly the same as for functions of one variable. In fact, we shall prove that the directional derivative of f at P in any direction is 0. Let H be a non-zero vector. For small values of t, $P + tH$ lies in the open set U, and $f(P + tH)$ is defined. Furthermore, for small values of t, tH is small, and hence $P + tH$ lies in our open ball such that

$$f(P + tH) \leq f(P).$$

Hence the function of one variable $g(t) = f(P + tH)$ has a local maximum at $t = 0$. Hence its derivative $g'(0)$ is equal to 0. By the chain rule, we obtain as usual:

$$\operatorname{grad} f(P) \cdot H = 0.$$

This equation is true for every non-zero vector H, and hence

$$\operatorname{grad} f(P) = O.$$

This proves what we wanted.

EXERCISES

Find the critical points of the following functions.

1. $x^2 + 4xy - y^2 - 8x - 6y$
2. $x + y \sin x$
3. $x^2 + y^2 + z^2$
4. $(x + y)e^{-xy}$
5. $xy + xz$
6. $\cos(x^2 + y^2 + z^2)$
7. $x^2 y^2$
8. $x^4 + y^2$
9. $(x - y)^4$
10. $x \sin y$
11. $x^2 + 2y^2 - x$
12. $e^{-(x^2 + y^2 + z^2)}$
13. $e^{(x^2 + y^2 + z^2)}$

14. In each of the preceding exercises, find the minimum value of the given function, and give all points where the value of the function is equal to this minimum. [*Do this exercise after you have read* §3.]

§2. THE QUADRATIC FORM

Let f be a differentiable function on an open set U, and assume that all partial derivatives up to order 3 exist and are continuous. Let P be a point of U, and assume that P is a critical point of f. We assume that we work in 2-space, so that we can express f near the point $P = (a, b)$ in the form

$$f(a + h, b + k) = f(a, b)$$
$$+ \frac{1}{2}\left[h^2 \frac{\partial^2 f}{\partial x^2}(a, b) + 2hk \frac{\partial^2 f}{\partial x\, \partial y}(a, b) + k^2 \frac{\partial^2 f}{\partial y^2}(a, b) \right]$$
$$+ R_3,$$

where R_3 is a remainder term. Actually, we prefer to write in the other notation:

$$f(a + h, b + k) = f(a, b)$$
$$+ \tfrac{1}{2}[h^2 D_1^2 f(a, b) + 2hk D_1 D_2 f(a, b) + k^2 D_2^2 f(a, b)]$$
$$+ R_3$$

because we want to use x, y for other purposes.

The *function* $q(x, y)$ of x, y given by

$$q(x, y) = \tfrac{1}{2}[x^2 D_1^2 f(P) + 2xy D_1 D_2 f(P) + y^2 D_2^2 f(P)]$$

is called the *quadratic form* associated with f at P, whenever P is a critical point of f. This quadratic form approximates the values of f so that one gets some general idea of the behavior of f near P when the terms of degree 1 vanish.

Example 1. Let $f(x, y) = e^{-(x^2+y^2)}$. Then it is a simple matter to verify that

$$\operatorname{grad} f(0, 0) = 0.$$

We let $P = (0, 0)$ be the origin. Standard computations show that

$$D_1^2 f(O) = -2, \qquad D_1 D_2 f(O) = 0, \qquad D_2^2 f(O) = -2.$$

Substituting these values in the general formula gives the expression for the quadratic form, namely

$$q(x, y) = -(x^2 + y^2).$$

We see that the quadratic form is nothing but the term of degree 2 in the Taylor expansion of the function at the given point.

We shall now describe the level curves for some quadratic forms to get an idea of their behavior near the origin.

Example 2. $q(x, y) = x^2 + y^2$. Then a graph of the function q and the level curves look like those in Figs. 2 and 3.

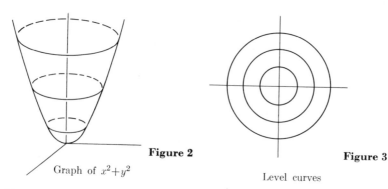

Figure 2

Graph of $x^2 + y^2$

Figure 3

Level curves

In this example, we see that the origin $(0, 0)$ is a local minimum point for the form.

Example 3. $q(x, y) = -(x^2 + y^2)$. The graph and level curves look like these:

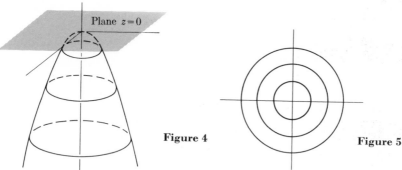

Plane $z = 0$

Figure 4

Figure 5

The origin is a local maximum for the form.

Example 4. $q(x, y) = x^2 - y^2$. The level curves are then hyperbolas, determined for each number c by the equation $x^2 - y^2 = c$:

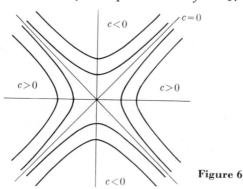

$c < 0$ $c = 0$

$c > 0$ $c > 0$

$c < 0$ **Figure 6**

Of course, when $c = 0$, we get the two straight lines as shown.

Example 5. $q(x, y) = xy$. The level curves look like the following
(similar to the preceding example, but turned around):

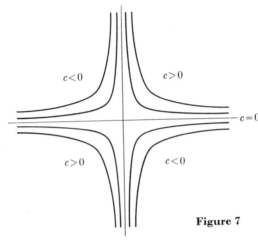

$c < 0$ $c > 0$

$c = 0$

$c > 0$ $c < 0$

Figure 7

In Examples 4 and 5, we see that the origin, which is a critical point,
is neither a local maximum nor local minimum.

EXERCISES

1. Let $f(x, y) = 3x^2 - 4xy + y^2$. Show that the origin is a critical point of f.

2. More generally, let a, b, c be numbers. Show that the function f given by
   $f(x, y) = ax^2 + bxy + cy^2$ has the origin as a critical point.

3. Find the quadratic form associated to the function f at the critical points
   P in the Exercises of §1.

4. Sketch the level curves for the following quadratic forms. Determine
   whether the origin is a local maximum, minimum, or neither.

   (a) $q(x, y) = 2x^2 - y^2$ (b) $q(x, y) = 3x^2 + 4y^2$
   (c) $q(x, y) = -(4x^2 + 5y^2)$ (d) $q(x, y) = y^2 - x^2$
   (e) $q(x, y) = 2y^2 - x^2$ (f) $q(x, y) = y^2 - 4x^2$
   (g) $q(x, y) = -(3x^2 + 2y^2)$ (h) $q(x, y) = 2xy$

§3. BOUNDARY POINTS

In considering intervals, we had to distinguish between closed and open
intervals. We must make an analogous distinction when considering sets
of points in space.

Let S be a set of points, in some n-space. Let P be a point of S. We
shall say that P is an *interior point* of S if there exists an open ball B of
positive radius, centered at P, and such that B is contained in S. The

next picture illustrates an interior point (for the set consisting of the region enclosed by the curve).

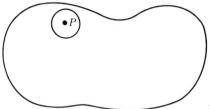

Figure 8

We have also drawn an open ball around P.

From the very definition, we conclude that the set consisting of all interior points of S is an open set.

A point P (not necessarily in S) is called a *boundary point* of S if every open ball B centered at P includes a point of S, and also a point which is not in S. We illustrate a boundary point in the following picture:

Figure 9

For example, the set of boundary points of the closed ball of radius $a > 0$ is the sphere of radius a. In 2-space, the plane, the region consisting of all points with $y > 0$ is open. Its boundary points are the points lying on the x-axis.

If a set contains all of its boundary points, then we shall say that the set is *closed*.

Finally, a set is said to be *bounded* if there exists a number $b > 0$ such that, for every point X of the set, we have

$$\|X\| \leqq b.$$

We are now in a position to state the existence of maxima and minima for continuous functions.

Theorem 2. *Let S be a closed and bounded set. Let f be a continuous function defined on S. Then f has a maximum and a minimum in S. In other words, there exists a point P in S such that*

$$f(P) \geqq f(X)$$

for all X in S, and there exists a point Q in S such that

$$f(Q) \leqq f(X)$$

for all X in S.

We shall not prove this theorem. It depends on an analysis which is beyond the level of this course.

When trying to find a maximum (say) for a function f, one should first determine the critical points of f in the interior of the region under consideration. If a maximum lies in the interior, it must be among these critical points.

Next, one should investigate the function on the boundary of the region. By parametrizing the boundary, one frequently reduces the problem of finding a maximum on the boundary to a lower-dimensional problem, to which the technique of critical points can also be applied.

Finally, one has to compare the possible maximum of f on the boundary and in the interior to determine which points are maximum points.

Example. In the Example in §1, we observe that the function

$$f(x, y) = e^{-(x^2+y^2)}$$

becomes very small as x or y becomes large. Consider some big closed disc centered at the origin. We know by Theorem 2 that the function has a maximum in this disc. Since the value of the function is small on the boundary, it follows that this maximum must be an interior point, and hence that the maximum is a critical point. But we found in the Example in §1 that the only critical point is at the origin. Hence we conclude that the origin is *the* only maximum of the function $f(x, y)$. The value of f at the origin is $f(0, 0) = 1$. Furthermore, the function has no minimum, because $f(x, y)$ is always positive and approaches 0 as x and y become large.

EXERCISES

Find the maximum and minimum points of the following functions in the indicated region.

1. $x + y$ in the square with corners at $(\pm 1, \pm 1)$

2. (a) $x + y + z$ in the region $x^2 + y^2 + z^2 < 1$
   (b) $x + y$ in the region $x^2 + y^2 < 1$

3. $xy - (1 - x^2 - y^2)^{1/2}$ in the region $x^2 + y^2 \leq 1$

4. $144x^3y^2(1 - x - y)$ in the region $x \geq 0$ and $y \geq 0$ (the first quadrant together with its boundary)

5. $(x^2 + 2y^2)e^{-(x^2+y^2)}$ in the plane

6. (a) $(x^2 + y^2)^{-1}$ in the region $(x - 2)^2 + y^2 \leq 1$
   (b) $(x^2 + y^2)^{-1}$ in the region $x^2 + (y - 2)^2 \leq 1$

7. Which of the following functions have a maximum and which have a minimum in the whole plane?

(a) $(x + 2y)e^{-x^2-y^4}$

(b) e^{x-y}

(c) $e^{x^2-y^2}$

(d) $e^{x^2+y^{10}}$

(e) $(3x^2 + 2y^2)e^{-(4x^2+y^2)}$

(f) $-x^2 e^{x^4+y^{10}}$

(g) $\begin{cases} \dfrac{x^2 + y^2}{|x| + |y|} & \text{if } (x, y) \neq (0, 0) \\ 0 & \text{if } (x, y) = (0, 0) \end{cases}$

8. Which is the point on the curve $(\cos t, \sin t, \sin(t/2))$ farthest from the origin?

§4. LAGRANGE MULTIPLIERS

In this section, we shall investigate another method for finding the maximum or minimum of a function on some set of points. This method is particularly well adapted to the case when the set of points is described by means of an equation.

We shall work in 3-space. Let g be a differentiable function of three variables x, y, z. We consider the surface

$$g(X) = 0.$$

Let U be an open set containing this surface, and let f be a differentiable function defined for all points of U. We wish to find those points P on the surface $g(X) = 0$ such that $f(P)$ is a maximum or a minimum on the surface. In other words, we wish to find all points P such that $g(P) = 0$, and either

$$f(P) \geq f(X) \quad \text{for all } X \text{ such that } g(X) = 0,$$

or

$$f(P) \leq f(X) \quad \text{for all } X \text{ such that } g(X) = 0.$$

Any such point will be called an *extremum for f subject to the constraint g*.

In what follows, we consider only points P such that $g(P) = 0$ but grad g $(P) \neq 0$.

Theorem 3. *Let g be a continuously differentiable function on an open set U. Let S be the set of points X in U such that $g(X) = 0$ but*

$$\text{grad } g \ (X) \neq O.$$

Let f be a continuously differentiable function on U and assume that P is a point of S such that P is an extremum for f. (In other words, P is an extremum for f, subject to the constraint g.) Then there exists a number λ such that

$$\text{grad} f \ (P) = \lambda \text{ grad } g \ (P).$$

Proof. Let $X: J \to S$ be a differentiable curve on the surface S passing through P, say $X(t_0) = P$. Then the function $t \mapsto f(X(t))$ has a maximum or a minimum at t_0. Its derivative

$$\frac{d}{dt} f(X(t))$$

is therefore equal to 0 at t_0. But this derivative is equal to

$$\text{grad} f(P) \cdot X'(t_0) = 0.$$

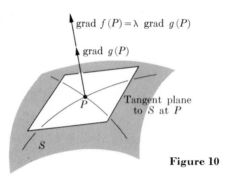

Figure 10

Hence $\text{grad} f(P)$ is perpendicular to every curve on the surface passing through P (Fig. 10). It can be shown that under these circumstances, and the hypothesis that grad $g(P) \neq O$, there exists a number λ such that

(1) $\text{grad} f(P) = \lambda \text{ grad } g(P),$

or in other words, $\text{grad} f(P)$ has the same, or opposite direction, as grad $g(P)$, provided it is not O. Intuitively, this is rather clear, since the direction of grad $g(P)$ is the direction perpendicular to the surface, and we have seen that grad $f(P)$ is also perpendicular to the surface. To give a complete proof would require technical arguments in linear algebra, which we shall omit here. One can use the result proved in Chapter XVI, Theorem 7, §2, that for a subspace W of $\mathbf{R}^3$ we have

$$\dim W + \dim W^\perp = 3.$$

Conversely, when we want to find an extremum point for f subject to the constraint g, we find all points P such that $g(P) = 0$, and such that relation (1) is satisfied. We can then find our extremum points among these by inspection.

(Note that this procedure is analogous to the procedure used to find maxima or minima for functions of one variable. We first determined all points at which the derivative is equal to 0, and then determined maxima or minima by inspection.)

Example 1. Find the maximum of the function $f(x, y) = x + y$ subject to the constraint $x^2 + y^2 = 1$.

We let $g(x, y) = x^2 + y^2 - 1$, so that S consists of all points (x, y) such that $g(x, y) = 0$. We have

$$\text{grad } f(x, y) = (1, 1),$$
$$\text{grad } g(x, y) = (2x, 2y).$$

Let (x_0, y_0) be a point for which there exists a number λ satisfying

$$\text{grad } f(x_0, y_0) = \lambda \text{ grad } g(x_0, y_0),$$

or in other words

$$1 = 2x_0\lambda \quad \text{and} \quad 1 = 2y_0\lambda.$$

Then $x_0 \neq 0$ and $y_0 \neq 0$. Hence $\lambda = 1/2x_0 = 1/2y_0$, and consequently $x_0 = y_0$. Since the point (x_0, y_0) must satisfy the equation $g(x_0, y_0) = 1$, we get the possibilities:

$$x_0 = \pm \frac{1}{\sqrt{2}} \quad \text{and} \quad y_0 = \pm \frac{1}{\sqrt{2}}.$$

It is then clear that $(1/\sqrt{2}, 1/\sqrt{2})$ is a maximum for f since the only other possibility $(-1/\sqrt{2}, -1/\sqrt{2})$ is a point at which f takes on a negative value, and $f(1/\sqrt{2}, 1/\sqrt{2}) = 2/\sqrt{2} > 0$.

Example 2. Find the extrema for the function $x^2 + y^2 + z^2$ subject to the constraint $x^2 + 2y^2 - z^2 - 1 = 0$.

Computing the partial derivatives of the functions f and g, we find that we must solve the system of equations

(a) $2x = \lambda \cdot 2x$,　　　　　　　　(b) $2y = \lambda \cdot 4y$,

(c) $2z = \lambda \cdot (-2z)$,　　　　　　(d) $g(X) = x^2 + 2y^2 - z^2 - 1 = 0$.

Let (x_0, y_0, z_0) be a solution. If $z_0 \neq 0$, then from (c) we conclude that $\lambda = -1$. The only way to solve (a) and (b) with $\lambda = -1$ is that $x = y = 0$. In that case, from (d), we would get

$$z_0^2 = -1,$$

which is impossible. Hence any solution must have $z_0 = 0$.

If $x_0 \neq 0$, then from (a) we conclude that $\lambda = 1$. From (b) and (c) we then conclude that $y_0 = z_0 = 0$. From (d), we must have $x_0 = \pm 1$. In this manner, we have obtained two solutions satisfying our conditions, namely

$$(1, 0, 0) \quad \text{and} \quad (-1, 0, 0).$$

Similarly, if $y_0 \neq 0$, we find two more solutions, namely

$$(0, \sqrt{\tfrac{1}{2}}, 0) \quad \text{and} \quad (0, -\sqrt{\tfrac{1}{2}}, 0).$$

These four points are therefore the extrema of the function f subject to the constraint g.

If we ask for the minimum of f, then a direct computation shows that the last two points

$$(0, \pm\sqrt{\tfrac{1}{2}}, 0)$$

are the only possible solutions (because $1 > \tfrac{1}{2}$).

EXERCISES

1. Find the minimum of the function $x + y^2$ subject to the constraint $2x^2 + y^2 = 1$.

2. Find the maximum value of $x^2 + xy + y^2 + yz + z^2$ on the sphere of radius 1.

3. Let $A = (1, 1, -1)$, $B = (2, 1, 3)$, $C = (2, 0, -1)$. Find the point at which the function

$$f(X) = (X - A)^2 + (X - B)^2 + (X - C)^2$$

reaches its minimum, and find the minimum value.

4. Do Exercise 3 in general, for any three distinct vectors

$$A = (a_1, a_2, a_3), \qquad B = (b_1, b_2, b_3), \qquad C = (c_1, c_2, c_3).$$

5. Find the maximum of the function $3x^2 + 2\sqrt{2}\,xy + 4y^2$ on the circle of radius 3 in the plane.

6. Find the maximum of the functions xyz subject to the constraints $x \geq 0$, $y \geq 0$, $z \geq 0$, and $xy + yz + xz = 2$.

7. Find the maximum and minimum distance from points on the curve

$$5x^2 + 6xy + 5y^2 = 0$$

and the origin in the plane.

8. Find the extreme values of the function $\cos^2 x + \cos^2 y$ subject to the constraint $x - y = \pi/4$ and $0 \leq x \leq \pi$.

9. Find the points on the surface $z^2 - xy = 1$ nearest to the origin.

10. Find the extreme values of the function xy subject to the condition $x + y = 1$.

11. Find the shortest distance between the point $(1, 0)$ and the curve $y^2 = 4x$.

12. Find the maximum and minimum points of the function

$$f(x, y, z) = x + y + z$$

in the region $x^2 + y^2 + z^2 \leq 1$.

13. Find the extremum values of the function $f(x, y, z) = x - 2y + 2z$ on the sphere $x^2 + y^2 + z^2 = 1$.

14. Find the maximum of the function $f(x, y, z) = x + y + z$ on the sphere $x^2 + y^2 + z^2 = 4$.

15. Find the extreme values of the function f given by $f(x, y, z) = xyz$ subject to the condition $x + y + z = 1$.

16. Find the extreme values of the function given by $f(x, y, z) = (x + y + z)^2$ subject to the condition $x^2 + 2y^2 + 3z^2 = 1$.

17. Find the maximum of the function $f(x, y, z) = x^2 + y^2 + z^2$ subject to the condition $3x + 2y - 7z = 5$.

18. In general, if a, b, c, d are numbers with not all of a, b, c equal to 0, find the maximum of the function $x^2 + y^2 + z^2$ subject to the condition

$$ax + by + cz = d.$$

19. Find the points on the curve $x^2 + y^4 + 3xy = 2$ which are closest to the origin. Find the points which are farthest from the origin.

Chapter VIII

Vector Spaces

As usual, a collection of objects will be called a *set*. A member of the collection is also called an *element* of the set. It is useful in practice to use short symbols to denote certain sets. For instance we denote by **R** the set of all numbers. To say that "x is a number" or that "x is an element of **R**" amounts to the same thing. The set of n-tuples of numbers will be denoted by $\mathbf{R}^n$. Thus "X is an element of $\mathbf{R}^n$" and "X is an n-tuple" mean the same thing. Instead of saying that u is an element of a set S, we shall also frequently say that u *lies in* S. If S and S' are two sets, and if every element of S' is an element of S, then we say that S' is a *subset* of S. Thus the set of rational numbers is a subset of the set of (real) numbers. To say that S is a subset of S' is to say that S is part of S'. To denote the fact that S is a subset of S', we write $S \subset S'$.

If S_1, S_2 are sets, then the *intersection* of S_1 and S_2, denoted by $S_1 \cap S_2$, is the set of elements which lie in both S_1 and S_2. The *union* of S_1 and S_2, denoted by $S_1 \cup S_2$, is the set of elements which lie in S_1 or S_2.

§1. DEFINITIONS

We have met already several types of objects which can be added and multiplied by numbers. Among these are vectors (of the same dimension) and functions. It is now convenient to define in general a notion which includes these as a special case.

A *vector space* V is a set of objects which can be added and multiplied by numbers, in such a way that the sum of two elements of V is again an element of V, the product of an element of V by a number is an element of V, and the following properties are satisfied:

VS 1. *Given elements u, v, w of V, we have*

$$(u + v) + w = u + (v + w).$$

VS 2. *There is an element of V, denoted by O, such that*

$$O + u = u + O = u$$

for all elements u of V.

VS 3. *Given an element u of V, the element* $(-1)u$ *is such that*

$$u + (-1)u = O.$$

VS 4. *For all elements u, v of V, we have*

$$u + v = v + u.$$

VS 5. *If c is a number, then* $c(u + v) = cu + cv.$

VS 6. *If a, b are two numbers, then* $(a + b)v = av + bv.$

VS 7. *If a, b are two numbers, then* $(ab)v = a(bv).$

VS 8. *For all elements u of V, we have* $1 \cdot u = u$ (1 *here is the number one*).

We have used all these rules when dealing with vectors, or with functions but we wish to be more systematic from now on, and hence have made a list of them. Further properties which can be easily deduced from these are given in the exercises and will be assumed from now on.

The sum $u + (-1)v$ is usually written $u - v$. We also write $-v$ instead of $(-1)v$.

We shall use 0 to denote the number zero, and O to denote the element of any vector space V satisfying property VS 2. We also call it zero, but there is never any possibility of confusion. We observe that this zero element O is uniquely determined by condition VS 2 (cf. Exercise 5).

It is possible to add several elements of a vector space. Suppose we wish to add four elements, say u, v, w, z. We first add any two of them, then a third, and finally a fourth. Using the rules VS 1 and VS 4, we see that it does not matter in which order we perform the additions. This is exactly the same situation as we had with vectors. For example, we have

$$((u + v) + w) + z = (u + (v + w)) + z$$
$$= ((v + w) + u) + z$$
$$= (v + w) + (u + z) \quad \text{etc.}$$

Thus it is customary to leave out the parentheses, and write simply

$$u + v + w + z.$$

The same remark applies to the sum of any number n of elements of V, and a formal proof could easily be given by induction.

Let V be a vector space, and let W be a subset of V. Assume that W satisfies the following conditions.

   (i) If v, w are elements of W, their sum $v + w$ is also an element of W.
   (ii) If v is an element of W and c a number, then cv is an element of W.
   (iii) The element O of V is also an element of W.

Then W itself is a vector space. Indeed, properties VS 1 through VS 8, being satisfied for all elements of V, are satisfied a fortiori for the elements of W. We shall call W a *subspace* of V.

Example 1. Let $V = \mathbf{R}^n$ and let W be the set of vectors in V whose last coordinate is equal to 0. Then W is a subspace of V, which we could identify with $\mathbf{R}^{n-1}$.

Example 2. Let V be an arbitrary vector space, and let $v_1, \ldots, v_n$ be elements of V. Let $x_1, \ldots, x_n$ be numbers. An expression of type

$$x_1 v_1 + \cdots + x_n v_n$$

is called a *linear combination* of $v_1, \ldots, v_n$. The set of all linear combinations of $v_1, \ldots, v_n$ is a subspace of V.

Proof. Let $y_1, \ldots, y_n$ be numbers. Then

$$(x_1 v_1 + \cdots + x_n v_n) + (y_1 v_1 + \cdots + y_n v_n)$$
$$= (x_1 + y_1)v_1 + \cdots + (x_n + y_n)v_n.$$

Thus the sum of two elements of W is again an element of W, i.e. a linear combination of $v_1, \ldots, v_n$. Furthermore, if c is a number, then

$$c(x_1 v_1 + \cdots + x_n v_n) = cx_1 v_1 + \cdots + cx_n v_n$$

is a linear combination of $v_1, \ldots, v_n$, and hence is an element of W. Finally,

$$O = 0v_1 + \cdots + 0v_n$$

is an element of W. This proves that W is a subspace of V.

In Example 2, the subspace W is called the subspace *generated* by $v_1, \ldots, v_n$. If $W = V$, i.e. if every element of V is a linear combination of $v_1, \ldots, v_n$, then we say that $v_1, \ldots, v_n$ *generate* V.

Example 3. Let V be the set of all functions defined for all numbers. If f, g are two functions, then we know how to form their sum $f + g$. It is the function whose value at a number t is $f(t) + g(t)$. We also know how to multiply f by a number c. It is the function cf whose value at a number t is $cf(t)$. In dealing with functions, we have used properties VS 1 through VS 8 many times. We now realize that the set of functions is a vector space.

If f, g are two continuous functions, then $f + g$ is continuous. If c is a number, then cf is continuous. The zero function is continuous. Hence the continuous functions form a subspace of the vector space of all functions.

If f, g are two differentiable functions, then their sum $f + g$ is differentiable. If c is a number, then cf is differentiable. The zero function is differentiable. Hence the differentiable functions form a subspace of the vector space of all functions. Furthermore, every differentiable function is continuous. Hence the differentiable functions form a subspace of the vector space of continuous functions.

Consider the two functions e^t, e^{2t}. These generate a subspace of the space of all differentiable functions. The function $3e^t + 2e^{2t}$ is an element of this subspace. So is the function $\sqrt{2}\, e^t + \pi e^{2t}$.

EXERCISES

1. Let V be a vector space. Using the properties VS 1 through VS 8, show that if v is an element of V and 0 is the number zero, then $0v = O$.

2. Let c be a number $\neq 0$, and v an element of V. Prove that if $cv = O$, then $v = O$.

3. In the vector space of functions, what is the function satisfying the condition VS 2?

4. Let V be a vector space and v, w two elements of V. If $v + w = O$, show that $w = -v$.

5. Let V be a vector space, and v, w two elements of V such that $v + w = v$. Show that $w = O$.

§2. BASES

Let V be a vector space, and let $v_1, \ldots, v_n$ be elements of V. We shall say that $v_1, \ldots, v_n$ are *linearly dependent* if there exist numbers $a_1, \ldots, a_n$ not all equal to 0 such that

$$a_1 v_1 + \cdots + a_n v_n = O.$$

If there do not exist such numbers, then we say that $v_1, \ldots, v_n$ are *linearly independent*. In other words, vectors $v_1, \ldots, v_n$ are linearly independent if and only if the following condition is satisfied:

Whenever $a_1, \ldots, a_n$ are numbers such that

$$a_1 v_1 + \cdots + a_n v_n = 0,$$

then $a_i = 0$ for all $i = 1, \ldots, n$.

Example 1. Let $V = \mathbf{R}^n$ and consider the vectors

$$E_1 = (1, 0, \ldots, 0)$$
$$\vdots$$
$$E_n = (0, 0, \ldots, 1).$$

Then $E_1, \ldots, E_n$ are linearly independent. Indeed, let $a_1, \ldots, a_n$ be numbers such that $a_1 E_1 + \cdots + a_n E_n = O$. Since

$$a_1 E_1 + \cdots + a_n E_n = (a_1, \ldots, a_n),$$

it follows that all $a_i = 0$.

Example 2. Let V be the vector space of all functions of a variable t. Let $f_1, \ldots, f_n$ be n functions. To say that they are linearly dependent is to say that there exist n numbers $a_1, \ldots, a_n$ not all equal to 0 such that

$$a_1 f_1(t) + \cdots + a_n f_n(t) = 0$$

for *all* values of t.

The two functions e^t, e^{2t} are linearly independent. To prove this, suppose that there are numbers a, b such that

$$ae^t + be^{2t} = 0$$

(for all values of t). Differentiate this relation. We obtain

$$ae^t + 2be^{2t} = 0.$$

Subtract the first from the second relation. We obtain $be^t = 0$, and hence $b = 0$. From the first relation, it follows that $ae^t = 0$, and hence $a = 0$. Hence e^t, e^{2t} are linearly independent.

Consider again an arbitrary vector space V. Let $v_1, \ldots, v_n$ be linearly independent elements of V. Let $x_1, \ldots, x_n$ and $y_1, \ldots, y_n$ be numbers. Suppose that we have

$$x_1 v_1 + \cdots + x_n v_n = y_1 v_1 + \cdots + y_n v_n.$$

In other words, two linear combinations of $v_1, \ldots, v_n$ are equal. Then we must have $x_i = y_i$ for each $i = 1, \ldots, n$. Indeed, subtracting the right-hand side from the left-hand side, we get

$$x_1 v_1 - y_1 v_1 + \cdots + x_n v_n - y_n v_n = O.$$

We can write this relation also in the form

$$(x_1 - y_1) v_1 + \cdots + (x_n - y_n) v_n = O.$$

By definition, we must have $x_i - y_i = 0$ for all $i = 1, \ldots, n$, thereby proving our assertion.

If elements $v_1, \ldots, v_n$ of V generate V and in addition are linearly independent, then the set consisting of these elements is called a *basis* of V. We shall also say that the elements $v_1, \ldots, v_n$ *constitute* or *form* a basis of V.

As a matter of notation, if $s_1, \ldots, s_n$ are objects, then the set consisting of these objects is denoted by $\{s_1, \ldots, s_n\}$. If elements $v_1, \ldots, v_n$ of V generate V and are linearly independent, then we shall say that $\{v_1, \ldots, v_n\}$ is a basis.

The vectors $E_1, \ldots, E_n$ of Example 1 form a basis of $\mathbf{R}^n$.

Let W be the vector space of functions generated by the two functions e^t, e^{2t}. Then $\{e^t, e^{2t}\}$ is a basis of W.

Let V be a vector space, and let $\{v_1, \ldots, v_n\}$ be a basis of V. The elements of V can be represented by n-tuples relative to this basis, as follows. If an element v of V is written as a linear combination

$$v = x_1 v_1 + \cdots + x_n v_n$$

of the basis elements, then we call $(x_1, \ldots, x_n)$ the *coordinates* of v with respect to our basis, and we call x_i the i-th coordinate.

For example, let V be the vector space of functions generated by the two functions e^t, e^{2t}. Then the coordinates of the function

$$3e^t + 5e^{2t}$$

with respect to the basis e^t, e^{2t} are $(3, 5)$.

Example 3. Show that the vectors $(1, 1)$ and $(-3, 2)$ are linearly independent.

Let a, b be two numbers such that

$$a(1, 1) + b(-3, 2) = O.$$

Writing this equation in terms of components, we find

$$a - 3b = 0,$$
$$a + 2b = 0.$$

This is a system of two equations which we solve for a and b. Subtracting the second from the first, we get $-5b = 0$, whence $b = 0$. Substituting in either equation, we find $a = 0$. Hence a, b are both 0, and our vectors are linearly independent.

Example 4. Find the coordinates of $(1, 0)$ with respect to the two vectors $(1, 1)$ and $(-1, 2)$.

We must find numbers a, b such that

$$a(1, 1) + b(-1, 2) = (1, 0).$$

Writing this equation in terms of coordinates, we find

$$a - b = 1,$$
$$a + 2b = 0.$$

Solving for a and b in the usual manner yields $b = -\frac{1}{3}$ and $a = \frac{2}{3}$. Hence the coordinates of $(1, 0)$ with respect to $(1, 1)$ and $(-1, 2)$ are $(\frac{2}{3}, -\frac{1}{3})$.

Let $\{v_1, \ldots, v_n\}$ be a set of elements of a vector space V. Let r be a positive integer $\leq n$. We shall say that $\{v_1, \ldots, v_r\}$ is a *maximal* subset of linearly independent elements if $v_1, \ldots, v_r$ are linearly independent, and if in addition, given any v_i with $i > r$, the elements $v_1, \ldots, v_r, v_i$ are linearly dependent.

The next theorem gives us a useful criterion to determine when a set of elements of a vector space is a basis.

Theorem 1. *Let* $\{v_1, \ldots, v_n\}$ *be a set of generators of a vector space* V. *Let* $\{v_1, \ldots, v_r\}$ *be a maximal subset of linearly independent elements. Then* $\{v_1, \ldots, v_r\}$ *is a basis of* V.

Proof. We must prove that $v_1, \ldots, v_r$ generate V. We shall first prove that each v_i (for $i > r$) is a linear combination of $v_1, \ldots, v_r$. By hypothesis, given v_i, there exist numbers $x_1, \ldots, x_r, y$ not all 0 such that

$$x_1 v_1 + \cdots + x_r v_r + y v_i = O.$$

Furthermore, $y \neq 0$, because otherwise, we would have a relation of linear dependence for $v_1, \ldots, v_r$. Hence we can solve for v_i, namely

$$v_i = \frac{x_1}{-y} v_1 + \cdots + \frac{x_r}{-y} v_r,$$

thereby showing that v_i is a linear combination of $v_1, \ldots, v_r$.

Next, let v be any element of V. There exist numbers $c_1, \ldots, c_n$ such that

$$v = c_1 v_1 + \cdots + c_n v_n.$$

In this relation, we can replace each v_i $(i > r)$ by a linear combination of $v_1, \ldots, v_r$. If we do this, and then collect terms, we find that we have expressed v as a linear combination of $v_1, \ldots, v_r$. This proves that $v_1, \ldots, v_r$ generate V, and hence form a basis of V.

EXERCISES

1. Show that the following vectors are linearly independent.

    (a) $(1, 1, 1)$ and $(0, 1, -1)$ (b) $(1, 0)$ and $(1, 1)$

    (c) $(-1, 1, 0)$ and $(0, 1, 2)$ (d) $(2, -1)$ and $(1, 0)$

    (e) $(\pi, 0)$ and $(0, 1)$ (f) $(1, 2)$ and $(1, 3)$

    (g) $(1, 1, 0), (1, 1, 1)$ and $(0, 1, -1)$ (h) $(0, 1, 1), (0, 2, 1)$ and $(1, 5, 3)$

2. Express the given vector X as a linear combination of the given vectors A, B, and find the coordinates of X with respect to A, B.

    (a) $X = (1, 0)$, $A = (1, 1)$, $B = (0, 1)$

    (b) $X = (2, 1)$, $A = (1, -1)$, $B = (1, 1)$

    (c) $X = (1, 1)$, $A = (2, 1)$, $B = (-1, 0)$

    (d) $X = (4, 3)$, $A = (2, 1)$, $B = (-1, 0)$

3. Find the coordinates of the vector X with respect to the vectors A, B, C.

    (a) $X = (1, 0, 0)$, $A = (1, 1, 1)$, $B = (-1, 1, 0)$, $C = (1, 0, -1)$

    (b) $X = (1, 1, 1)$, $A = (0, 1, -1)$, $B = (1, 1, 0)$, $C = (1, 0, 2)$

    (c) $X = (0, 0, 1)$, $A = (1, 1, 1)$, $B = (-1, 1, 0)$, $C = (1, 0, -1)$

4. Let (a, b) and (c, d) be two vectors in the plane. If $ad - bc = 0$, show that they are linearly dependent. If $ad - bc \neq 0$, show that they are linearly independent.

5. Consider the vector space of all functions of a variable t. Show that the following pairs of functions are linearly independent.

   (a) $1, t$ (b) t, t^2 (c) t, t^4 (d) e^t, t (e) te^t, e^{2t} (f) $\sin t, \cos t$ (g) $t, \sin t$ (h) $\sin t, \sin 2t$ (i) $\cos t, \cos 3t$

6. Consider the vector space of functions defined for $t > 0$. Show that the following pairs of functions are linearly independent.

   (a) $t, 1/t$ (b) $e^t, \log t$

7. What are the coordinates of the function $3 \sin t + 5 \cos t = f(t)$ with respect to the basis $\{\sin t, \cos t\}$?

8. Let D be the derivative d/dt. Let $f(t)$ be as in Exercise 7. What are the coordinates of the function $Df(t)$ with respect to the basis of Exercise 7?

9. Let $A_1, \ldots, A_r$ be vectors in $\mathbf{R}^n$ and assume that they are mutually perpendicular (i.e. any two of them are perpendicular), and that none of them is equal to O. Prove that they are linearly independent.

10. Let V be the vector space of continuous functions on the interval $[-\pi, \pi]$. If f, g are two continuous functions on this interval, define their scalar product $\langle f, g \rangle$ to be

$$\langle f, g \rangle = \int_{-\pi}^{\pi} f(t)g(t) \, dt.$$

Show that the functions $\sin nt$ $(n = 1, 2, 3, \ldots)$ are mutually perpendicular, i.e. that the scalar product of any two of them is equal to 0.

11. Show that the functions $\sin t, \sin 2t, \sin 3t, \ldots, \sin nt$ are linearly independent, for any integer $n \geq 1$.

Chapter IX

Linear Equations and Bases

You have met linear equations in elementary school. Linear equations are simply equations like

$$2x + y + z = 1,$$
$$5x - y + 7z = 0.$$

You have learned to solve such equations by the successive elimination of the variables. In this chapter, we shall review the theory of such equations, dealing with equations in n variables, and interpreting our results from the point of view of vectors. Several geometric interpretations for the solutions of the equations will be given.

§1. MATRICES

We consider a new kind of object, matrices.

Let n, m be two integers ≥ 1. An array of numbers

$$\begin{pmatrix} a_{11} & a_{12} & a_{13} & \cdots & a_{1n} \\ a_{21} & a_{22} & a_{23} & \cdots & a_{2n} \\ \vdots & \vdots & \vdots & & \vdots \\ a_{m1} & a_{m2} & a_{m3} & \cdots & a_{mn} \end{pmatrix}$$

is called a *matrix*. We can abbreviate the notation for this matrix by writing it (a_{ij}), $i = 1, \ldots, m$ and $j = 1, \ldots, n$. We say that it is an m by n matrix, or an $m \times n$ matrix. The matrix has m *rows* and n *columns*. For instance, the first column is

$$\begin{pmatrix} a_{11} \\ a_{21} \\ \vdots \\ a_{m1} \end{pmatrix}$$

and the second row is $(a_{21}, a_{22}, \ldots, a_{2n})$. We call a_{ij} the *ij-entry* or *ij-component* of the matrix.

Example 1. The following is a 2×3 matrix:

$$\begin{pmatrix} 1 & 1 & -2 \\ -1 & 4 & -5 \end{pmatrix}.$$

It has two rows and three columns.

446

The rows are $(1, 1, -2)$ and $(-1, 4, -5)$. The columns are

$$\begin{pmatrix} 1 \\ -1 \end{pmatrix}, \quad \begin{pmatrix} 1 \\ 4 \end{pmatrix}, \quad \begin{pmatrix} -2 \\ -5 \end{pmatrix}.$$

Thus the rows of a matrix may be viewed as n-tuples, and the columns may be viewed as vertical m-tuples. A vertical m-tuple is also called a *column vector*.

A vector $(x_1, \ldots, x_n)$ is a $1 \times n$ matrix. A column vector

$$\begin{pmatrix} x_1 \\ \vdots \\ x_n \end{pmatrix}$$

is an $n \times 1$ matrix.

When we write a matrix in the form (a_{ij}), then i denotes the row and j denotes the column. In Example 1, we have for instance $a_{11} = 1$, $a_{23} = -5$.

A single number (a) may be viewed as a 1×1 matrix.

Let (a_{ij}), $i = 1, \ldots, m$ and $j = 1, \ldots, n$ be a matrix. If $m = n$, then we say that it is a *square* matrix. Thus

$$\begin{pmatrix} 1 & 2 \\ -1 & 0 \end{pmatrix} \quad \text{and} \quad \begin{pmatrix} 1 & -1 & 5 \\ 2 & 1 & -1 \\ 3 & 1 & -1 \end{pmatrix}$$

are both square matrices.

We have a *zero matrix*, in which $a_{ij} = 0$ for all i, j. It looks like this:

$$\begin{pmatrix} 0 & 0 & 0 & \cdots & 0 \\ 0 & 0 & 0 & \cdots & 0 \\ \vdots & \vdots & \vdots & & \vdots \\ 0 & 0 & 0 & \cdots & 0 \end{pmatrix}.$$

We shall write it O. We note that we have met so far with the zero number, zero vector, and zero matrix.

We shall now define addition of matrices and multiplication of matrices by numbers.

We define addition of matrices only when they have the same size. Thus let m, n be fixed integers ≥ 1. Let $A = (a_{ij})$ and $B = (b_{ij})$ be two $m \times n$ matrices. We define $A + B$ to be the matrix whose entry in the i-th row and j-th column is $a_{ij} + b_{ij}$. In other words, we add matrices of the same size componentwise.

Example 2. Let

$$A = \begin{pmatrix} 1 & -1 & 0 \\ 2 & 3 & 4 \end{pmatrix} \quad \text{and} \quad B = \begin{pmatrix} 5 & 1 & -1 \\ 2 & 1 & -1 \end{pmatrix}.$$

Then

$$A + B = \begin{pmatrix} 6 & 0 & -1 \\ 4 & 4 & 3 \end{pmatrix}.$$

If A, B are both $1 \times n$ matrices, i.e. n-tuples, then we note that our addition of matrices coincides with the addition which we defined in Chapter I for n-tuples.

If O is the zero matrix, then for any matrix A (of the same size, of course), we have $O + A = A + O = A$. This is trivially verified.

We shall now define the multiplication of a matrix by a number. Let c be a number, and $A = (a_{ij})$ be a matrix. We define cA to be the matrix whose ij-component is ca_{ij}. We write $cA = (ca_{ij})$. Thus we multiply each component of A by c.

Example 3. Let A, B be as in Example 2. Let $c = 2$. Then

$$2A = \begin{pmatrix} 2 & -2 & 0 \\ 4 & 6 & 8 \end{pmatrix} \quad \text{and} \quad 2B = \begin{pmatrix} 10 & 2 & -2 \\ 4 & 2 & -2 \end{pmatrix}.$$

We also have:

$$(-1)A = -A = \begin{pmatrix} -1 & 1 & 0 \\ -2 & -3 & -4 \end{pmatrix}.$$

For all matrices A, we find that $A + (-1)A = O$.

We leave it as an exercise to verify that all properties VS 1 through VS 8 are satisfied by our rules for addition of matrices and multiplication of matrices by numbers. The main thing to observe here is that addition of matrices is defined in terms of the components, and for the addition of components, the conditions analogous to VS 1 through VS 4 are satisfied. They are standard properties of numbers. Similarly, VS 5 through VS 8 are true for multiplication of matrices by numbers, because the corresponding properties for the multiplication of numbers are true.

We see that the matrices (of a given size $m \times n$) form a vector space, which we may denote by $\mathfrak{M}_{m,n}$.

We define one more notion related to a matrix. Let $A = (a_{ij})$ be an $m \times n$ matrix. The $n \times m$ matrix $B = (b_{ji})$ such that $b_{ji} = a_{ij}$ is called the *transpose* of A, and is also denoted by ${}^tA$. Taking the transpose of a matrix amounts to changing rows into columns and vice versa. If A is the matrix which we wrote down at the beginning of this section, then ${}^tA$ is the matrix

$$\begin{pmatrix} a_{11} & a_{21} & a_{31} & \cdots & a_{m1} \\ a_{12} & a_{22} & a_{32} & \cdots & a_{m2} \\ \vdots & \vdots & \vdots & & \vdots \\ a_{1n} & a_{2n} & a_{3n} & \cdots & a_{mn} \end{pmatrix}.$$

To take a special case:

$$\text{If } A = \begin{pmatrix} 2 & 1 & 0 \\ 1 & 3 & 5 \end{pmatrix} \quad \text{then} \quad {}^t A = \begin{pmatrix} 2 & 1 \\ 1 & 3 \\ 0 & 5 \end{pmatrix}.$$

If $A = (2, 1, -4)$ is a *row vector*, then

$${}^t A = \begin{pmatrix} 2 \\ 1 \\ -4 \end{pmatrix}$$

is a *column vector*.

EXERCISES

1. Let

$$A = \begin{pmatrix} 1 & 2 & 3 \\ -1 & 0 & 2 \end{pmatrix} \quad \text{and} \quad B = \begin{pmatrix} -1 & 5 & -2 \\ 1 & 1 & -1 \end{pmatrix}.$$

   Find $A + B$, $3B$, $-2B$, $A + 2B$, $2A + B$, $A - B$, $A - 2B$, $B - A$.

2. Let

$$A = \begin{pmatrix} 1 & -1 \\ 2 & 1 \end{pmatrix} \quad \text{and} \quad B = \begin{pmatrix} -1 & 1 \\ 0 & -3 \end{pmatrix}.$$

   Find $A + B$, $3B$, $-2B$, $A + 2B$, $A - B$, $B - A$.

3. In Exercise 1, find ${}^t A$ and ${}^t B$.

4. In Exercise 2, find ${}^t A$ and ${}^t B$.

5. If A, B are arbitrary $m \times n$ matrices, show that

$${}^t(A + B) = {}^t A + {}^t B.$$

6. If c is a number, show that ${}^t(cA) = c{}^t A$.

7. If $A = (a_{ij})$ is a square matrix, then the elements a_{ii} are called the *diagonal elements*. How do the diagonal elements of A and ${}^t A$ differ?

8. Find ${}^t(A + B)$ and ${}^t A + {}^t B$ in Exercise 2.

9. Find $A + {}^t A$ and $B + {}^t B$ in Exercise 2.

10. A matrix A is said to be *symmetric* if $A = {}^t A$. Show that for any square matrix A, the matrix $A + {}^t A$ is symmetric.

11. Write down the row vectors and column vectors of the matrices A, B in Exercise 1.

12. Write down the row vectors and column vectors of the matrices A, B in Exercise 2.

§2. HOMOGENEOUS LINEAR EQUATIONS

Let $A = (a_{ij})$, $i = 1, \ldots, m$ and $j = 1, \ldots, n$ be a matrix. Let $b_1, \ldots, b_m$ be numbers. Equations like

$$
\begin{aligned}
a_{11}x_1 + \cdots + a_{1n}x_n &= b_1 \\
&\vdots \\
a_{m1}x_1 + \cdots + a_{mn}x_n &= b_m
\end{aligned}
$$

(*)

are called linear equations. We also say that (*) is a system of linear equations. The system is said to be *homogeneous* if all the numbers $b_1, \ldots, b_m$ are equal to 0. The number n is called the number of *unknowns*, and m is the number of equations.

The system of equations

$$
\begin{aligned}
a_{11}x_1 + \cdots + a_{1n}x_n &= 0 \\
&\vdots \\
a_{m1}x_1 + \cdots + a_{mn}x_n &= 0
\end{aligned}
$$

(**)

will be called the *homogeneous system associated with* (*). In this section, we study the homogeneous system (**).

The system (**) always has a solution, namely the solution obtained by letting all $x_i = 0$. This solution will be called the *trivial* solution. A solution $(x_1, \ldots, x_n)$ such that some x_i is $\neq 0$ is called *non-trivial*.

We shall be interested in the case when the number of unknowns is greater than the number of equations, and we shall see that in that case, there always exists a non-trivial solution.

Before dealing with the general case, we shall study examples.

First, suppose that we have a single equation, like

$$2x + y - 4z = 0.$$

To find a non-trivial solution, we give all the variables except the first a special value $\neq 0$, say $y = 1$, $z = 1$. We then solve for x. We find $2x - (-y) + 4z = 3$, whence $x = \frac{2}{3}$.

Next, consider a pair of equations, say

(1) $2x + 3y - z = 0,$

(2) $x + y + z = 0.$

We reduce the problem of solving these simultaneous equations to the preceding case of one equation, by eliminating one variable. Thus we multiply the second equation by 2 and subtract it from the first equation, getting

(3) $y - 3z = 0.$

Now we meet one equation in more than one variable. We give z any value $\neq 0$, say $z = 1$, and solve for y, namely $y = 3$. We then solve for x

from the second equation, and obtain $x = -4$. The values which we have obtained for x, y, z are also solutions of the first equation, because the first equation is (in an obvious sense) the sum of equation (2) multiplied by 2, and equation (3).

The procedure which we shall use in general is merely the general formulation of the elimination carried out above on numerical examples.

Consider our system of homogeneous equations (**). Let $A_1, \ldots, A_m$ be the row vectors of the matrix (a_{ij}). Then we can rewrite our equations (**) in the form

(**)
$$A_1 \cdot X = 0$$
$$\vdots$$
$$A_m \cdot X = 0.$$

Geometrically, to find a solution of (**) amounts to finding a vector X which is perpendicular to $A_1, \ldots, A_m$. Using the notation of the dot product will make it easier to formulate the proof of our main theorem, namely:

Theorem 1. *Let*

$$a_{11}x_1 + \cdots + a_{1n}x_n = 0$$
$$\vdots$$
$$a_{m1}x_1 + \cdots + a_{mn}x_n = 0$$

be a system of m linear equations in n unknowns, and assume that $n > m$. Then the system has a non-trivial solution.

Proof. The proof will be carried out by induction.

Consider first the case of one equation in n unknowns, $n > 1$:

$$a_1x_1 + \cdots + a_nx_n = 0.$$

If all coefficients $a_1, \ldots, a_n$ are equal to 0, then any value of the variables will be a solution, and a non-trivial solution certainly exists. Suppose that some coefficient a_i is $\neq 0$. After renumbering the variables and the coefficients, we may assume that it is a_1. Then we give $x_2, \ldots, x_n$ arbitrary values, for instance we let $x_2 = \cdots = x_n = 1$, and solve for x_1, letting

$$x_1 = \frac{-1}{a_1}(a_2 + \cdots + a_n).$$

In that manner, we obtain a non-trivial solution for our system of equations.

Let us now assume that our theorem is true for a system of $m - 1$ equations in more than $m - 1$ unknowns. We shall prove that it is true for m equations in n unknowns when $n > m$. We consider the system (**).

If all coefficients (a_{ij}) are equal to 0, we can give any non-zero value to our variables to get a solution. If some coefficient is not equal to 0, then after renumbering the equations and the variables, we may assume that it is a_{11}. We shall subtract a multiple of the first equation from the others to eliminate x_1. Namely, we consider the system of equations

$$\left(A_2 - \frac{a_{21}}{a_{11}} A_1\right) \cdot X = 0$$
$$\vdots$$
$$\left(A_m - \frac{a_{m1}}{a_{11}} A_1\right) \cdot X = 0,$$

which can also be written in the form

(***)
$$A_2 \cdot X - \frac{a_{21}}{a_{11}} A_1 \cdot X = 0$$
$$\vdots$$
$$A_m \cdot X - \frac{a_{m1}}{a_{11}} A_1 \cdot X = 0.$$

In this system, the coefficient of x_1 is equal to 0. Hence we may view (***) as a system of $m-1$ equations in $n-1$ unknowns, and $n-1 > m-1$.

According to our assumption, we can find a non-trivial solution $(x_2, \ldots, x_n)$ for this system. We can then solve for x_1 in the first equation, namely

$$x_1 = \frac{-1}{a_{11}} (a_{12}x_2 + \cdots + a_{1n}x_n).$$

In that way, we find a solution of $A_1 \cdot X = 0$. But according to (***), we have

$$A_i \cdot X = \frac{a_{i1}}{a_{11}} A_1 \cdot X$$

for $i = 2, \ldots, m$. Hence $A_i \cdot X = 0$ for $i = 2, \ldots, m$, and therefore we have found a non-trivial solution to our original system (**).

The argument we have just given allows us to proceed stepwise from one equation to two equations, then from two to three, and so forth. This concludes the proof.

EXERCISES

1. Let V be a subspace of $\mathbf{R}^n$. Let W be the set of elements of $\mathbf{R}^n$ which are perpendicular to every element of V. Show that W is a subspace of $\mathbf{R}^n$.

2. Let $A_1, \ldots, A_r$ be generators of a substance V of $\mathbf{R}^n$. Let W be the set of all elements of $\mathbf{R}^n$ which are perpendicular to $A_1, \ldots, A_r$. Show that the vectors of W are perpendicular to every element of V.

3. Interpret the solutions of a homogeneous system of linear equations in the light of Exercises 1 and 2.

4. Consider the inhomogeneous system (*) consisting of all X such that $X \cdot A_i = b_i$ for $i = 1, \ldots, m$. If X and X' are two solutions of this system, show that there exists a solution Y of the homogeneous system (**) such that $X' = X + Y$. Conversely, if X is any solution of (*), and Y a solution of (**), show that $X + Y$ is a solution of (*).

§3. INVARIANCE OF DIMENSION

This section consists of applications of Theorem 1.

Theorem 2. *Let V be a vector space, and let $\{v_1, \ldots, v_m\}$ be a basis of V. Let $w_1, \ldots, w_n$ be elements of V and assume that $n > m$. Then $w_1, \ldots, w_n$ are linearly dependent.*

Proof. Since $\{v_1, \ldots, v_m\}$ is a basis, there exist numbers (a_{ij}) such that we can write

$$w_1 = a_{11}v_1 + \cdots + a_{m1}v_m$$
$$\vdots \qquad \vdots \qquad \vdots$$
$$w_n = a_{1n}v_1 + \cdots + a_{mn}v_m.$$

If $x_1, \ldots, x_n$ are numbers, then

$$x_1 w_1 + \cdots + x_n w_n$$
$$= (x_1 a_{11} + \cdots + x_n a_{1n})v_1 + \cdots + (x_1 a_{m1} + \cdots + x_n a_{mn})v_m$$

(just add up the coefficients of $v_1, \ldots, v_m$ vertically downward). According to Theorem 1, the system of equations

$$x_1 a_{11} + \cdots + x_n a_{1n} = 0$$
$$\vdots$$
$$x_1 a_{m1} + \cdots + x_n a_{mn} = 0$$

has a non-trivial solution, because $n > m$. In view of the preceding remark, such a solution $(x_1, \ldots, x_n)$ is such that

$$x_1 w_1 + \cdots + x_n w_n = 0,$$

as desired.

Theorem 3. *Let V be a vector space and suppose that one basis has n elements, and another basis has m elements. Then $m = n$.*

Proof. We apply Theorem 2 to the two bases. Theorem 2 implies that both alternatives $n > m$ and $m > n$ are impossible, and hence $m = n$.

Let V be a vector space having a basis consisting of n elements. We shall say that n is the *dimension* of V. If V consists of O alone, then V does not have a basis, and we shall say that V has dimension 0.

We shall now give criteria which allow us to tell when elements of a vector space constitute a basis.

Let $v_1, \ldots, v_n$ be linearly independent elements of a vector space V. We shall say that they form a *maximal set of linearly independent elements* of V if given any element w of V, the elements $w, v_1, \ldots, v_n$ are linearly dependent.

Theorem 4. *Let V be a vector space, and $\{v_1, \ldots, v_n\}$ a maximal set of linearly independent elements of V. Then $\{v_1, \ldots, v_n\}$ is a basis of V.*

Proof. We must show that $v_1, \ldots, v_n$ generate V, i.e. that every element of V can be expressed as a linear combination of $v_1, \ldots, v_n$. Let w be an element of V. The elements $w, v_1, \ldots, v_n$ of V must be linearly dependent by hypothesis, and hence there exist numbers $x_0, x_1, \ldots, x_n$ not all 0 such that

$$x_0 w + x_1 v_1 + \cdots + x_n v_n = O.$$

We cannot have $x_0 = 0$, because if that were the case, we would obtain a relation of linear dependence among $v_1, \ldots, v_n$. Therefore we can solve for w in terms of $v_1, \ldots, v_n$, namely

$$w = -\frac{x_1}{x_0} v_1 - \cdots - \frac{x_n}{x_0} v_n.$$

This proves that w is a linear combination of $v_1, \ldots, v_n$, and hence that $\{v_1, \ldots, v_n\}$ is a basis.

Theorem 5. *Let V be a vector space of dimension n, and let $v_1, \ldots, v_n$ be linearly independent elements of V. Then $v_1, \ldots, v_n$ constitute a basis of V.*

Proof. According to Theorem 2, $\{v_1, \ldots, v_n\}$ is a maximal set of linearly independent elements of V. Hence it is a basis by Theorem 4.

Theorem 6. *Let V be a vector space having a basis consisting of n elements. Let W be a subspace which does not consist of O alone. Then W has a basis, and the dimension of W is $\leq n$.*

Proof. Let w_1 be a non-zero element of W. If $\{w_1\}$ is not a maximal set of linearly independent elements of W, we can find an element w_2 of W such that w_1, w_2 are linearly independent. Proceeding in this manner, one element at a time, there must be an integer $m \leq n$ such that we can find linearly independent elements $w_1, w_2, \ldots, w_m$, and such that $\{w_1, \ldots, w_m\}$ is a maximal set of linearly independent elements of W (by Theorem 2, we cannot go on indefinitely finding linearly independent elements, and the number of such elements is at most n). If we now use Theorem 4, we conclude that $\{w_1, \ldots, w_m\}$ is a basis for W.

EXERCISES

1. What is the dimension of the space of $m \times n$ matrices? Give a basis for this space.

2. What is the dimension of the space of $n \times n$ matrices all of whose components are 0 except possibly the diagonal components?

3. What is the dimension of the space of $n \times n$ matrices which are upper-triangular, i.e. of the following type:

$$\begin{pmatrix} a_{11} & a_{12} & \cdots & a_{1n} \\ 0 & a_{22} & \cdots & a_{2n} \\ \vdots & \vdots & & \vdots \\ 0 & 0 & \cdots & a_{nn} \end{pmatrix} ?$$

§4. MULTIPLICATION OF MATRICES

We shall now define the product of matrices. Let $A = (a_{ij})$, $i = 1, \ldots, m$ and $j = 1, \ldots, n$ be an $m \times n$ matrix. Let $B = (b_{jk})$, $j = 1, \ldots, n$ and $k = 1, \ldots, s$ be an $n \times s$ matrix.

$$A = \begin{pmatrix} a_{11} & \cdots & a_{1n} \\ \vdots & & \vdots \\ a_{m1} & \cdots & a_{mn} \end{pmatrix}, \qquad B = \begin{pmatrix} b_{11} & \cdots & b_{1s} \\ \vdots & & \vdots \\ b_{n1} & \cdots & b_{ns} \end{pmatrix}.$$

We define the product AB to be the $m \times s$ matrix whose ik-coordinate is

$$\sum_{j=1}^{n} a_{ij} b_{jk} = a_{i1} b_{1k} + a_{i2} b_{2k} + \cdots + a_{in} b_{nk}.$$

If $A_1, \ldots, A_m$ are the row vectors of the matrix A, and if $B^1, \ldots, B^s$ are the column vectors of the matrix B, then the ik-coordinate of the product AB is equal to $A_i \cdot B^k$. Thus

$$AB = \begin{pmatrix} A_1 \cdot B^1 & \cdots & A_1 \cdot B^s \\ \vdots & & \vdots \\ A_m \cdot B^1 & \cdots & A_m \cdot B^s \end{pmatrix}.$$

Multiplication of matrices is therefore a generalization of the dot product.

Example 1. Let

$$A = \begin{pmatrix} 2 & 1 & 5 \\ 1 & 3 & 2 \end{pmatrix}, \qquad B = \begin{pmatrix} 3 & 4 \\ -1 & 2 \\ 2 & 1 \end{pmatrix}.$$

Then AB is a 2×2 matrix, and computations show that

$$AB = \begin{pmatrix} 2 & 1 & 5 \\ 1 & 3 & 2 \end{pmatrix} \begin{pmatrix} 3 & 4 \\ -1 & 2 \\ 2 & 1 \end{pmatrix} = \begin{pmatrix} 15 & 15 \\ 4 & 12 \end{pmatrix}.$$

Example 2. Let

$$C = \begin{pmatrix} 1 & 3 \\ -1 & -1 \end{pmatrix}.$$

Let A, B be as in Example 1. Then:

$$BC = \begin{pmatrix} 3 & 4 \\ -1 & 2 \\ 2 & 1 \end{pmatrix} \begin{pmatrix} 1 & 3 \\ -1 & -1 \end{pmatrix} = \begin{pmatrix} -1 & 5 \\ -3 & -5 \\ 1 & 5 \end{pmatrix}$$

and

$$A(BC) = \begin{pmatrix} 2 & 1 & 5 \\ 1 & 3 & 2 \end{pmatrix} \begin{pmatrix} -1 & 5 \\ -3 & -5 \\ 1 & 5 \end{pmatrix} = \begin{pmatrix} 0 & 30 \\ -8 & 0 \end{pmatrix}.$$

Compute $(AB)C$. What do you find?

Let A be an $m \times n$ matrix and let B be an $n \times 1$ matrix, i.e. a column vector. Then AB is again a column vector. The product looks like this:

$$\begin{pmatrix} a_{11} & \cdots & a_{1n} \\ \vdots & & \vdots \\ a_{m1} & \cdots & a_{mn} \end{pmatrix} \begin{pmatrix} b_1 \\ \vdots \\ b_n \end{pmatrix} = \begin{pmatrix} c_1 \\ \vdots \\ c_m \end{pmatrix}$$

where

$$c_i = \sum_{j=1}^{n} a_{ij}b_j = a_{i1}b_1 + \cdots + a_{in}b_n.$$

If $X = (x_1, \ldots, x_m)$ is a row vector, i.e. a $1 \times m$ matrix, then we can form the product XA, which looks like this:

$$(x_1, \ldots, x_m) \begin{pmatrix} a_{11} & \cdots & a_{1n} \\ \vdots & & \vdots \\ a_{m1} & \cdots & a_{mn} \end{pmatrix} = (y_1, \ldots, y_n),$$

where

$$y_k = x_1 a_{1k} + \cdots + x_m a_{mk}.$$

In this case, XA is a $1 \times n$ matrix, i.e. a row vector.

If A is a square matrix, then we can form the product AA, which will be a square matrix of the same size as A. It is denoted by A^2. Similarly, we can form A^3, A^4, and in general, A^n for any positive integer n.

We define the unit $n \times n$ matrix to be the matrix having diagonal components all equal to 1, and all other components equal to 0. Thus the unit $n \times n$ matrix, denoted by I_n, looks like this:

$$\begin{pmatrix} 1 & 0 & 0 & \cdots & & 0 \\ 0 & 1 & 0 & \cdots & & 0 \\ 0 & 0 & 1 & \cdots & & 0 \\ \vdots & \vdots & \vdots & \ddots & & \vdots \\ 0 & 0 & 0 & & 1 & 0 \\ 0 & 0 & 0 & \cdots & & 1 \end{pmatrix}$$

We can then define $A^0 = I$ (the unit matrix of the same size as A).

Theorem 7. *Let A, B, C be matrices. Assume that A, B can be multiplied, and A, C can be multiplied, and B, C can be added. Then A, $B + C$ can be multiplied, and we have*

$$A(B + C) = AB + AC.$$

If x is a number, then

$$A(xB) = x(AB).$$

Proof. Let A_i be the i-th row of A, and let B^k, C^k be the k-th column of B and C respectively. Then $B^k + C^k$ is the k-th column of $B + C$. By definition, the ik-component of AB is $A_i \cdot B^k$, the ik-component of AC is $A_i \cdot C^k$, and the ik-component of $A(B + C)$ is $A_i \cdot (B^k + C^k)$. Since

$$A_i \cdot (B^k + C^k) = A_i \cdot B^k + A_i \cdot C^k,$$

our first assertion follows. As for the second, observe that the k-th column of xB is xB^k. Since

$$A_i \cdot xB^k = x(A_i \cdot B^k),$$

our second assertion follows.

Theorem 8. *Let A, B, C be matrices such that A, B can be multiplied and B, C can be multiplied. Then A, BC can be multiplied, so can AB, C, and we have*

$$(AB)C = A(BC).$$

Proof. Let $A = (a_{ij})$ be an $m \times n$ matrix, let $B = (b_{jk})$ be an $n \times r$ matrix, and let $C = (c_{kl})$ be an $r \times s$ matrix. The product AB is an $m \times r$ matrix, whose ik-component is equal to the sum

$$a_{i1}b_{1k} + a_{i2}b_{2k} + \cdots + a_{in}b_{nk}.$$

We shall abbreviate this sum using our $\sum$ notation by writing

$$\sum_{j=1}^{n} a_{ij}b_{jk}.$$

By definition, the il-component of $(AB)C$ is equal to

$$\sum_{k=1}^{r} \left[\sum_{j=1}^{n} a_{ij}b_{jk} \right] c_{kl} = \sum_{k=1}^{r} \left[\sum_{j=1}^{n} a_{ij}b_{jk}c_{kl} \right].$$

The sum on the right can also be described as the sum of all terms

$$a_{ij}b_{jk}c_{kl},$$

where j, k range over all integers $1 \leq j \leq n$ and $1 \leq k \leq r$ respectively.

If we had started with the jl-component of BC and then computed the il-component of $A(BC)$ we would have found exactly the same sum, thereby proving the theorem.

In terms of multiplication of matrices, we can now write a system of linear equations in the form

$$AX = B,$$

where A is an $m \times n$ matrix, X is a column vector of size n, and B is a column vector of size m.

EXERCISES

1. Let I be the unit $n \times n$ matrix. Let A be an $n \times r$ matrix. What is IA? If A is an $m \times n$ matrix, what is AI?

2. Let O be the matrix all of whose coordinates are 0. Let A be a matrix of a size such that the product AO is defined. What is AO?

3. In each one of the following cases, find $(AB)C$ and $A(BC)$.

(a) $A = \begin{pmatrix} 2 & 1 \\ 3 & 1 \end{pmatrix}$, $B = \begin{pmatrix} -1 & 1 \\ 1 & 0 \end{pmatrix}$, $C = \begin{pmatrix} 1 & 4 \\ 2 & 3 \end{pmatrix}$

(b) $A = \begin{pmatrix} 2 & 1 & -1 \\ 3 & 1 & 2 \end{pmatrix}$, $B = \begin{pmatrix} 1 & 1 \\ 2 & 0 \\ 3 & -1 \end{pmatrix}$, $C = \begin{pmatrix} 1 \\ 3 \end{pmatrix}$

(c) $A = \begin{pmatrix} 2 & 4 & 1 \\ 3 & 0 & -1 \end{pmatrix}$, $B = \begin{pmatrix} 1 & 1 & 0 \\ 2 & 1 & -1 \\ 3 & 1 & 5 \end{pmatrix}$, $C = \begin{pmatrix} 1 & 2 \\ 3 & 1 \\ -1 & 4 \end{pmatrix}$

4. Let A, B be square matrices of the same size, and assume that $AB = BA$. Show that $(A + B)^2 = A^2 + 2AB + B^2$, and

$$(A + B)(A - B) = A^2 - B^2,$$

using the properties of matrices stated in Theorem 7.

5. Let

$$A = \begin{pmatrix} 1 & 2 \\ 3 & -1 \end{pmatrix}, \qquad B = \begin{pmatrix} 2 & 0 \\ 1 & 1 \end{pmatrix}.$$

Find AB and BA.

6. Let

$$C = \begin{pmatrix} 7 & 0 \\ 0 & 7 \end{pmatrix}.$$

Let A, B be as in Exercise 5. Find CA, AC, CB, and BC. State the general rule including this exercise as a special case.

7. Let $X = (1, 0, 0)$ and let

$$A = \begin{pmatrix} 3 & 1 & 5 \\ 2 & 0 & 1 \\ 1 & 1 & 7 \end{pmatrix}.$$

What is XA?

8. Let $X = (0, 1, 0)$, and let A be an arbitrary 3×3 matrix. How would you describe XA? What if $X = (0, 0, 1)$? Generalize to similar statements concerning $n \times n$ matrices, and their products with unit vectors.

9. Let A, B be the matrices of Exercise 3(a). Verify by computation that $^t(AB) = {}^tB{}^tA$. Do the same for 3(b) and 3(c). Prove the same rule for any two matrices A, B (which can be multiplied). If A, B, C are matrices which can be multiplied, show that $^t(ABC) = {}^tC{}^tB{}^tA$.

10. Let M be an $n \times n$ matrix such that $^tM = M$. Given two row vectors in n-space, say A and B define $\langle A, B \rangle$ to be AM^tB. (Identify a 1×1 matrix with a number.) Show that the conditions of a scalar product are satisfied, except possibly the condition concerning positivity. Give an example of a matrix M and vectors A, B such that AM^tB is negative (taking $n = 2$).

11. (a) Let A be the matrix

$$\begin{pmatrix} 0 & 1 & 1 \\ 0 & 0 & 1 \\ 0 & 0 & 0 \end{pmatrix}.$$

Find A^2, A^3. Generalize to 4×4 matrices.

(b) Let A be the matrix

$$\begin{pmatrix} 1 & 1 & 1 \\ 0 & 1 & 1 \\ 0 & 0 & 1 \end{pmatrix}.$$

Compute A^2, A^3, and A^4.

12. Let X be the indicated column vector, and A the indicated matrix. Find AX as a column vector.

(a) $X = \begin{pmatrix} 3 \\ 2 \\ 1 \end{pmatrix}$, $A = \begin{pmatrix} 1 & 0 & 1 \\ 2 & 1 & 1 \\ 2 & 0 & -1 \end{pmatrix}$ (b) $X = \begin{pmatrix} 1 \\ 1 \\ 0 \end{pmatrix}$, $A = \begin{pmatrix} 2 & 1 & 5 \\ 0 & 1 & 1 \end{pmatrix}$

(c) $X = \begin{pmatrix} x_1 \\ x_2 \\ x_3 \end{pmatrix}$, $A = \begin{pmatrix} 0 & 1 & 0 \\ 0 & 0 & 0 \end{pmatrix}$ (d) $X = \begin{pmatrix} x_1 \\ x_2 \\ x_3 \end{pmatrix}$, $A = \begin{pmatrix} 0 & 0 & 0 \\ 1 & 0 & 0 \end{pmatrix}$

13. Let

$$A = \begin{pmatrix} 2 & 1 & 3 \\ 4 & 1 & 5 \end{pmatrix}.$$

Find AX for each of the following values of X.

(a) $X = \begin{pmatrix} 1 \\ 0 \\ 0 \end{pmatrix}$ (b) $X = \begin{pmatrix} 0 \\ 1 \\ 1 \end{pmatrix}$ (c) $X = \begin{pmatrix} 0 \\ 0 \\ 1 \end{pmatrix}$

14. Let

$$A = \begin{pmatrix} 3 & 7 & 5 \\ 1 & -1 & 4 \\ 2 & 1 & 8 \end{pmatrix}.$$

Find AX for each of the values of X given in Exercise 3.

15. Let

$$X = \begin{pmatrix} 0 \\ 1 \\ 0 \\ 0 \end{pmatrix} \quad \text{and} \quad A \begin{pmatrix} a_{11} & \cdots & a_{14} \\ \vdots & & \vdots \\ a_{m1} & \cdots & a_{m4} \end{pmatrix}.$$

What is AX?

16. Let X be a column vector having all its components equal to 0 except the i-th component which is equal to 1. Let A be an arbitrary matrix, whose size is such that we can form the product AX. What is AX?

17. Let $A = (a_{ij})$, $i = 1, \ldots, m$ and $j = 1, \ldots, n$, be an $m \times n$ matrix. Let $B = (b_{jk})$, $j = 1, \ldots, n$ and $k = 1, \ldots, s$, be an $n \times s$ matrix. Let $AB = C$. Show that the k-th column C^k can be written

$$C^k = b_{1k}A^1 + \cdots + b_{nk}A^n.$$

(This will be useful in finding the determinant of a product.)

18. Let a, b be numbers, and let

$$A = \begin{pmatrix} 1 & a \\ 0 & 1 \end{pmatrix} \quad \text{and} \quad B = \begin{pmatrix} 1 & b \\ 0 & 1 \end{pmatrix}.$$

What is AB? What is A^n where n is a positive integer?

19. If A is a square $n \times n$ matrix, we call a square matrix B an *inverse* for A if $AB = BA = I_n$. Show that if B, C are inverses for A, then $B = C$.

20. Show that the matrix A in Exercise 18 has an inverse. What is this inverse?

21. Show that if A, B are $n \times n$ matrices which have inverses, then AB has an inverse.

22. Determine all 2×2 matrices A such that $A^2 = O$.

23. Let $A = \begin{pmatrix} \cos \theta & -\sin \theta \\ \sin \theta & \cos \theta \end{pmatrix}$. Show that $A^2 = \begin{pmatrix} \cos 2\theta & -\sin 2\theta \\ \sin 2\theta & \cos 2\theta \end{pmatrix}$.

Determine A^n by induction for any positive integer n.

24. Find a 2×2 matrix A such that $A^2 = -I = \begin{pmatrix} -1 & 0 \\ 0 & -1 \end{pmatrix}$.

Chapter X

Linear Mappings

We shall first define the general notion of a mapping, which generalizes the notion of a function. Among mappings, the linear mappings are the most important. A good deal of mathematics is devoted to reducing questions concerning arbitrary mappings to linear mappings. For one thing, they are interesting in themselves, and many mappings are linear. On the other hand, it is often possible to approximate an arbitrary mapping by a linear one, whose study is much easier than the study of the original mapping. (Cf. Chapter XIII.)

§1. MAPPINGS

Let S, S' be two sets. A *mapping* from S to S' is an association which to every element of S associates an element of S'. Instead of saying that F is a mapping from S into S', we shall often write the symbols $F: S \to S'$. A mapping will also be called a *map*, for the sake of brevity.

A function is a special type of mapping, namely it is a mapping from a set into the set of numbers, i.e. into **R**.

We extend to mappings some of the terminology we have used for functions. For instance, if $T: S \to S'$ is a mapping, and if u is an element of S, then we denote by $T(u)$, or Tu, the element of S' associated to u by T. We call $T(u)$ the *value* of T at u, or also the *image* of u under T. The symbols $T(u)$ are read "T of u". The set of all elements $T(u)$, when u ranges over all elements of S, is called the *image* of T. If W is a subset of S, then the set of elements $T(w)$, when w ranges over all elements of W, is called the *image* of W under T, and is denoted by $T(W)$.

Let $F: S \to S'$ be a map from a set S into a set S'. If x is an element of S, we often write

$$x \mapsto F(x)$$

with a special arrow $\mapsto$ to denote the image of x under F. Thus, for instance, we would speak of the map F such that $F(x) = x^2$ as the map $x \mapsto x^2$.

Example 1. Let S and S' be both equal to $\mathbf{R}$. Let $f\colon \mathbf{R} \to \mathbf{R}$ be the function $f(x) = x^2$ (i.e. the function whose value at a number x is x^2). Then f is a mapping from $\mathbf{R}$ into $\mathbf{R}$. Its image is the set of numbers ≥ 0.

Example 2. Let S be the set of numbers ≥ 0, and let $S' = \mathbf{R}$. Let $g\colon S \to S'$ be the function such that $g(x) = x^{1/2}$. Then g is a mapping from S into $\mathbf{R}$.

Example 3. Let S be the set of functions having derivatives of all orders on the interval $0 < t < 1$, and let $S' = S$. Then the derivative $D = d/dt$ is a mapping from S into S. Indeed, our map D associates the function $df/dt = Df$ to the function f. According to our terminology, Df is the value of the mapping D at f.

Example 4. Let S be the set of continuous functions on the interval $[0, 1]$ and let S' be the set of differentiable functions on that interval. We shall define a mapping $\mathscr{g}\colon S \to S'$ by giving its value at any function f in S. Namely, we let $\mathscr{g}f$ (or $\mathscr{g}(f)$) be the function whose value at x is

$$(\mathscr{g}f)(x) = \int_0^x f(t)\, dt.$$

Then $\mathscr{g}(f)$ is a differentiable function.

Example 5. Let S be the set $\mathbf{R}^3$, i.e. the set of 3-tuples. Let $A = (2, 3, -1)$. Let $L\colon \mathbf{R}^3 \to \mathbf{R}$ be the mapping whose value at a vector $X = (x, y, z)$ is $A \cdot X$. Then $L(X) = A \cdot X$. If $X = (1, 1, -1)$, then the value of L at X is 6.

Just as we did with functions, we describe a mapping by giving its values. Thus, instead of making the statement in Example 5 describing the mapping L, we would also say: Let $L\colon \mathbf{R}^3 \to \mathbf{R}$ be the mapping $L(X) = A \cdot X$. This is somewhat incorrect, but is briefer, and does not usually give rise to confusion. More correctly, we can write $X \mapsto L(X)$ or $X \mapsto A \cdot X$ with the special arrow $\mapsto$ to denote the effect of the map L on the element X.

Example 6. Let $F\colon \mathbf{R}^2 \to \mathbf{R}^2$ be the mapping given by

$$F(x, y) = (2x, 2y).$$

Describe the image under F of the points lying on the circle $x^2 + y^2 = 1$. Let (x, y) be a point on the circle of radius 1. Let $u = 2x$ and $v = 2y$. Then u, v satisfy the relation

$$(u/2)^2 + (v/2)^2 = 1$$

or in other words,

$$\frac{u^2}{4} + \frac{v^2}{4} = 1.$$

Hence (u, v) is a point on the circle of radius 2. Therefore the image under F of the circle of radius 1 is a subset of the circle of radius 2. Conversely, given a point (u, v) such that

$$u^2 + v^2 = 4,$$

let $x = u/2$ and $y = v/2$. Then the point (x, y) satisfies the equation $x^2 + y^2 = 1$, and hence is a point on the circle of radius 1. Furthermore, $F(x, y) = (u, v)$. Hence every point on the circle of radius 2 is the image of some point on the circle of radius 1. We conclude finally that the image of the circle of radius 1 under F is precisely the circle of radius 2.

Note. In general, let S, S' be two sets. To prove that $S = S'$, one frequently proves that S is a subset of S' and that S' is a subset of S. This is what we did in the preceding argument.

Example 7. Let S be a set. A mapping from S into $\mathbf{R}$ will be called a *function*, and the set of such functions will be called the set of functions defined on S. Let f, g be two functions defined on S. We can define their sum just as we did for functions of numbers, namely $f + g$ is the function whose value at an element t of S is $f(t) + g(t)$. We can also define the product of f by a number c. It is the function whose value at t is $cf(t)$. Then the set of mappings from S into $\mathbf{R}$ is a vector space.

Example 8. Let S be a set and let V be a vector space. Let F, G be two mappings from S into V. We can define their sum in the same way as we defined the sum of functions, namely the sum $F + G$ is the mapping whose value at an element t of S is $F(t) + G(t)$. We also define the product of F by a number c to be the mapping whose value at an element t of S is $cF(t)$. It is easy to verify that conditions VS 1 through VS 8 are satisfied.

Example 9. Let $F: \mathbf{R} \to \mathbf{R}^n$ be a mapping. For each number t, the value of F at t is a vector $F(t)$. The coordinates of $F(t)$ depend on t. Hence there are functions $f_1, \ldots, f_n$ such that

$$F(t) = \big(f_1(t), \ldots, f_n(t)\big).$$

Each f_i is a function from $\mathbf{R}$ into $\mathbf{R}$. These functions are called the *coordinate functions* of F.

Let $G: \mathbf{R} \to \mathbf{R}^n$ be another mapping from $\mathbf{R}$ into $\mathbf{R}^n$, and let $g_1, \ldots, g_n$ be its coordinate functions. Then

$$G(t) = \big(g_1(t), \ldots, g_n(t)\big).$$

Then

$$(F + G)(t) = F(t) + G(t) = \big(f_1(t) + g_1(t), \ldots, f_n(t) + g_n(t)\big)$$

and for any number c,

$$(cF)(t) = cF(t) = \big(cf_1(t), \ldots, cf_n(t)\big).$$

If all the functions $f_1, \ldots, f_n$ are differentiable, then we say that the mapping F above is *differentiable*. The set of all differentiable mappings from $\mathbf{R}$ into $\mathbf{R}^n$ is a subspace of the vector space of all mappings.

If J is an interval and $F: J \to \mathbf{R}^n$ is a mapping, then we see that F is nothing else but what we previously called a parametrized curve.

Let U, V, W be sets. Let $F: U \to V$ and $G: V \to W$ be mappings. Then we can form the composite mapping from U into W, denoted by $G \circ F$. It is by definition the mapping defined by

$$(G \circ F)(t) = G\big(F(t)\big)$$

for all $t \in U$.

Example 10. If $f: \mathbf{R} \to \mathbf{R}$ is a function and $g: \mathbf{R} \to \mathbf{R}$ is also a function, then $g \circ f$ is the composite function we studied long ago. We have also considered composite mappings in Chapter IV, §1, in connection with the chain rule, which gives the formula for the derivative of composite mappings under special circumstances.

The following statement is an important property of mappings.
Let U, V, W, S be sets. Let

$$F: U \to V, \qquad G: V \to W, \qquad and \qquad H: W \to S$$

be mappings. Then

$$H \circ (G \circ F) = (H \circ G) \circ F.$$

Proof. Here again, the proof is very simple. By definition, we have, for any element u of U:

$$\big(H \circ (G \circ F)\big)(u) = H\big((G \circ F)(u)\big) = H\big(G(F(u))\big).$$

On the other hand,

$$\big((H \circ G) \circ F\big)(u) = (H \circ G)\big(F(u)\big) = H\big(G(F(u))\big).$$

By definition, this means that $(H \circ G) \circ F = H \circ (G \circ F)$.

Finally, we define inverse mappings. Let $F: S \to S'$ be a mapping from one set into another set. We say that F has an *inverse* if there exists a mapping $G: S' \to S$ such that

$$G \circ F = Id_S \qquad and \qquad F \circ G = Id_{S'}.$$

By this we mean that the composite maps $G \circ F$ and $F \circ G$ are the identity mappings of S and S' respectively.

Example 11. Let $S = S'$ be the set of all numbers ≥ 0. Let

$$f: S \to S'$$

be the map such that $f(x) = x^2$. Then f has an inverse mapping, namely the map $g: S \to S$ such that $g(x) = \sqrt{x}$.

Example 12. Let $\mathbf{R}^+$ be the set of numbers > 0 and let $f: \mathbf{R} \to \mathbf{R}^+$ be the map such that $f(x) = e^x$. Then f has an inverse mapping which is nothing but the logarithm.

Example 13. This example is particularly important in geometric applications. Let V be a vector space, and let u be a fixed element of V. We let

$$T_u: V \to V$$

be the map such that $T_u(v) = v + u$. We call T_u the *translation* by u. If S is any subset of V, then $T_u(S)$ is called the translation of S by u, and consists of all vectors $v + u$, with $v \in S$. We often denote it by $S + u$. In the next picture, we draw a set S and its translation by a vector u.

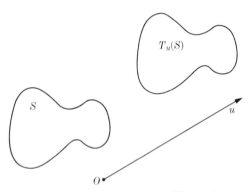

Figure 1

As exercises, we leave the proofs of the following statements to the reader:

If u_1, u_2 are elements of V, then $T_{u_1+u_2} = T_{u_1} \circ T_{u_2}$.
If u is an element of V then $T_u: V \to V$ has an inverse mapping which is nothing but the translation T_{-u}.

EXERCISES

1. In Example 3, give Df when f is the function:

    (a) $f(x) = \sin x$ (b) $f(x) = e^x$ (c) $f(x) = \log x$

2. In Example 4, give $\mathcal{G}(f)$ when f is the function:

   (a) $f(x) = e^x$ (b) $f(x) = \dfrac{1}{1 + x^2}$ (c) $f(x) = \cos x$

3. In Example 5, give $L(X)$ when X is the vector:

   (a) $(1, 2, -3)$ (b) $(-1, 5, 0)$ (c) $(2, 1, 1)$

4. Let $F: \mathbf{R} \to \mathbf{R}^2$ be the mapping such that $F(t) = (e^t, t)$. What is $F(1)$, $F(0)$, $F(-1)$?

5. Let $G: \mathbf{R} \to \mathbf{R}^2$ be the mapping such that $G(t) = (t, 2t)$. Let F be as in Exercise 4. What is $(F + G)(1)$, $(F + G)(2)$, $(F + G)(0)$?

6. Let F be as in Exercise 4. What is $(2F)(0)$, $(\pi F)(1)$?

7. Let $A = (1, 1, -1, 3)$. Let $F: \mathbf{R}^4 \to \mathbf{R}$ be the mapping such that for any vector $X = (x_1, x_2, x_3, x_4)$ we have $F(X) = X \cdot A + 2$. What is the value of $F(X)$ when (a) $X = (1, 1, 0, -1)$ and (b) $X = (2, 3, -1, 1)$?

In Exercises 8 through 12, refer to Example 6. In each case, to prove that the image is equal to a certain set S, you must prove that the image is contained in S, and also that every element of S is in the image.

8. Let $F: \mathbf{R}^2 \to \mathbf{R}^2$ be the mapping defined by $F(x, y) = (2x, 3y)$. Describe the image of the points lying on the circle $x^2 + y^2 = 1$.

9. Let $F: \mathbf{R}^2 \to \mathbf{R}^2$ be the mapping defined by $F(x, y) = (xy, y)$. Describe the image under F of the straight line $x = 2$.

10. Let F be the mapping defined by $F(x, y) = (e^x \cos y, e^x \sin y)$. Describe the image under F of the line $x = 1$. Describe more generally the image under F of a line $x = c$, where c is a constant.

11. Let F be the mapping defined by $F(t, u) = (\cos t, \sin t, u)$. Describe geometrically the image of the (t, u)-plane under F.

12. Let F be the mapping defined by $F(x, y) = (x/3, y/4)$. What is the image under F of the ellipse

$$\frac{x^2}{9} + \frac{y^2}{16} = 1?$$

13. Prove the statement about translations at the end of the section.

§2. LINEAR MAPPINGS

Let V, V' be two vector spaces. A *linear mapping*

$$T: V \to V'$$

is a mapping which satisfies the following two properties. First, for any elements u, v in V, we have

LM 1. $\qquad\qquad T(u + v) = T(u) + T(v)$.

Secondly, for any number c, we have

LM 2. $\qquad\qquad T(cu) = cT(u)$.

Example 1. Let V be the set of functions which have derivatives of all orders. Then the derivative $D: V \to V$ is a linear mapping. This is simply a brief way of summarizing properties of the derivative which we have known for a long time, namely

$$D(f + g) = Df + Dg,$$
$$D(cf) = cD(f).$$

Example 2. Let $V = \mathbf{R}^3$ be the vector space of vectors in 3-space. Let $V' = \mathbf{R}^2$ be the vector space of vectors in 2-space. We can define a mapping

$$F: \mathbf{R}^3 \to \mathbf{R}^2$$

by the projection, namely $F(x, y, z) = (x, y)$. We leave it to you to check that the conditions LM 1 and LM 2 are satisfied.

Example 3. Let $A = (1, 2, -1)$. Let $V = \mathbf{R}^3$ and $V' = \mathbf{R}$. We can define a mapping $L = L_A: \mathbf{R}^3 \to \mathbf{R}$ by the rule

$$L(X) = X \cdot A$$

for any vector X in 3-space. The fact that L is linear summarizes two known properties of the scalar product, namely, for any two vectors X, Y we have

$$(X + Y) \cdot A = X \cdot A + Y \cdot A,$$
$$(cX) \cdot A = c(X \cdot A).$$

Example 4. Let V be any vector space. The mapping which associates to any element u of V this element itself is obviously a linear mapping, which is called the *identity* mapping. We denote it by *Id* or simply *I*. Thus $Id(u) = u$.

Example 5. Let V, V' be any vector spaces. The mapping which associates the element O in V' to any element u of V is called the *zero* mapping and is obviously linear.

Example 6. Let V, V' be two vector spaces. We consider the set of all linear mappings from V into V', and denote this set by $\mathcal{L}$. We shall define the addition of linear mappings and their multiplication by numbers in such a way as to make $\mathcal{L}$ into a vector space.

Let $T: V \to V'$ and let $F: V \to V'$ be two linear mappings. We define their *sum* $T + F$ to be the map whose value at an element u of V is $T(u) + F(u)$. Thus we may write

$$(T + F)(u) = T(u) + F(u).$$

The map $T + F$ is then a linear map. Indeed, it is easy to verify that the two conditions which define a linear map are satisfied. For any elements u, v of V, we have

$$
\begin{aligned}
(T + F)(u + v) &= T(u + v) + F(u + v) \\
&= T(u) + T(v) + F(u) + F(v) \\
&= T(u) + F(u) + T(v) + F(v) \\
&= (T + F)(u) + (T + F)(v).
\end{aligned}
$$

Furthermore, if c is a number, then

$$
\begin{aligned}
(T + F)(cu) &= T(cu) + F(cu) \\
&= cT(u) + cF(u) \\
&= c[T(u) + F(u)] \\
&= c[(T + F)(u)].
\end{aligned}
$$

Hence $T + F$ is a linear map.

If a is a number, and $T: V \rightarrow V'$ is a linear map, we define a map aT from V into V' by giving its value at an element u of V, namely $(aT)(u) = aT(u)$. Then it is easily verified that aT is a linear map. We leave this as an exercise.

We have just defined operations of addition and multiplication by numbers in our set $\mathcal{L}$. Furthermore, if $T: V \rightarrow V'$ is a linear map, i.e. an element of $\mathcal{L}$, then we can define $-T$ to be $(-1)T$, i.e. the product of the number -1 by T. Finally, we have the *zero-map*, which to every element of V associates the element O of V'. Then $\mathcal{L}$ is a vector space. In other words, the set of linear maps from V into V' is itself a vector space. The verification that the rules VS 1 through VS 8 for a vector space are satisfied is easy and is left to the reader.

Example 7. Let $V = V'$ be the vector space of functions which have derivatives of all orders. Let D be the derivative, and let Id be the identity. If f is in V, then

$$(D + Id)f = Df + f.$$

Thus, when $f(x) = e^x$, then $(D + Id)f$ is the function whose value at x is $e^x + e^x = 2e^x$.

If $f(x) = \sin x$, then $((D + Id)f)(x) = \cos x + \sin x$.

We note that $3 \cdot Id$ is a linear map, whose value at f is $3f$. Thus $(D + 3 \cdot Id)f = Df + 3f$. At any number x, the value of $(D + 3 \cdot Id)f$ is $Df(x) + 3f(x)$. We can also write $(D + 3I)f = Df + 3f$.

Let $T: V \rightarrow V'$ be a linear mapping. Let u, v, w be elements of V. Then

$$T(u + v + w) = T(u) + T(v) + T(w).$$

This can be seen stepwise, using the definition of linear mappings. Thus

$$T(u + v + w) = T(u + v) + T(w) = T(u) + T(v) + T(w).$$

Similarly, given a sum of more than three elements, an analogous property is satisfied. For instance, let $u_1, \ldots, u_n$ be elements of V. Then

$$T(u_1 + \cdots + u_n) = T(u_1) + \cdots + T(u_n).$$

The sum on the right can be taken in any order. A formal proof can easily be given by induction, and we omit it.

If $a_1, \ldots, a_n$ are numbers, then

$$T(a_1 u_1 + \cdots + a_n u_n) = a_1 T(u_1) + \cdots + a_n T(u_n).$$

We show this for three elements.

$$T(a_1 u + a_2 v + a_3 w) = T(a_1 u) + T(a_2 v) + T(a_3 w)$$
$$= a_1 T(u) + a_2 T(v) + a_3 T(w).$$

The next theorem will show us how a linear map is determined when we know its value on basis elements.

Theorem 1. *Let V and W be vector spaces. Let $\{v_1, \ldots, v_n\}$ be a basis of V, and let $w_1, \ldots, w_n$ be arbitrary elements of W. Then there exists a unique linear mapping $T: V \to W$ such that*

$$T(v_1) = w_1, \ldots, T(v_n) = w_n.$$

If $x_1, \ldots, x_n$ are numbers, then

$$T(x_1 v_1 + \cdots + x_n v_n) = x_1 w_1 + \cdots + x_n w_n.$$

Proof. We shall prove that a linear map T satisfying the required conditions exists. Let v be an element of V, and let $x_1, \ldots, x_n$ be the unique numbers such that $v = x_1 v_1 + \cdots + x_n v_n$. We let

$$T(v) = x_1 w_1 + \cdots + x_n w_n.$$

We then have defined a mapping T from V into W, and we contend that T is linear. If v' is an element of V, and if $v' = y_1 v_1 + \cdots + y_n v_n$, then

$$v + v' = (x_1 + y_1)v_1 + \cdots + (x_n + y_n)v_n.$$

By definition, we obtain

$$T(v + v') = (x_1 + y_1)w_1 + \cdots + (x_n + y_n)w_n$$
$$= x_1 w_1 + y_1 w_1 + \cdots + x_n w_n + y_n w_n$$
$$= T(v) + T(v').$$

Let c be a number. Then $cv = cx_1 v_1 + \cdots + cx_n v_n$, and hence

$$T(cv) = cx_1 w_1 + \cdots + cx_n w_n = cT(v).$$

We have therefore proved that T is linear, and hence that there exists a linear map as asserted in the theorem.

Such a map is unique, because for any element $x_1 v_1 + \cdots + x_n v_n$ of V, any linear map $F: V \to W$ such that $F(v_i) = w_i$ $(i = 1, \ldots, n)$ must also satisfy

$$F(x_1 v_1 + \cdots + x_n v_n) = x_1 F(v_1) + \cdots + x_n F(v_n)$$
$$= x_1 w_1 + \cdots + x_n w_n.$$

This concludes the proof.

EXERCISES

1. Determine which of the following mappings F are linear.

   (a) $F: \mathbf{R}^3 \to \mathbf{R}^2$ defined by $F(x, y, z) = (x, z)$.

   (b) $F: \mathbf{R}^4 \to \mathbf{R}^4$ defined by $F(X) = -X$.

   (c) $F: \mathbf{R}^3 \to \mathbf{R}^3$ defined by $F(X) = X + (0, -1, 0)$.

   (d) $F: \mathbf{R}^2 \to \mathbf{R}^2$ defined by $F(x, y) = (2x + y, y)$.

   (e) $F: \mathbf{R}^2 \to \mathbf{R}^2$ defined by $F(x, y) = (2x, y - x)$.

   (f) $F: \mathbf{R}^2 \to \mathbf{R}^2$ defined by $F(x, y) = (y, x)$.

   (g) $F: \mathbf{R}^2 \to \mathbf{R}$ defined by $F(x, y) = xy$.

   (h) Let U be an open subset of $\mathbf{R}^3$, and let V be the vector space of differentiable functions on U. Let V' be the vector space of vector fields on U. Then $\operatorname{grad}: V \to V'$ is a mapping. Is it linear?

2. Let $T: V \to W$ be a linear map from one vector space into another. Show that $T(O) = O$.

3. Let T be as in Exercise 2. Let u, v be elements of V, and let $Tu = w$. If $Tv = O$, show that $T(u + v)$ is also equal to w.

4. Determine all elements z of V such that $Tz = w$.

5. Let $T: V \to W$ be a linear map. Let v be an element of V. Show that $T(-v) = -T(v)$.

6. Let V be a vector space, and $f: V \to \mathbf{R}$, $g: V \to \mathbf{R}$ two linear mappings. Let $F: V \to \mathbf{R}^2$ be the mapping defined by $F(v) = (f(v), g(v))$. Show that F is linear. Generalize.

7. Let V, W be two vector spaces and let $F: V \to W$ be a linear map. Let U be the subset of V consisting of all elements v such that $F(v) = O$. Prove that U is a subspace of V.

8. Which of the mappings in Exercises 4, 7, 8, 9 of §1 are linear?

9. Let $F: \mathbf{R}^3 \to \mathbf{R}^4$ be a linear map. Let P be a point of $\mathbf{R}^3$, and A a nonzero element of $\mathbf{R}^3$. Describe the image of the straight line $P + tA$ under F. [Distinguish the cases when $F(A) = O$ and $F(A) \neq O$.]

   Let V be a vector space, and let v_1, v_2 be two elements of V which are linearly independent. The set of elements of V which can be written in the form $t_1 v_1 + t_2 v_2$ with numbers t_1, t_2 satisfying

   $$0 \leq t_1 \leq 1 \quad \text{and} \quad 0 \leq t_2 \leq 1,$$

   is called a *parallelogram*, spanned by v_1, v_2.

10. Let V and W be vector spaces, and let $F: V \to W$ be a linear map. Let v_1, v_2 be linearly independent elements of V, and assume that $F(v_1), F(v_2)$ are linearly independent. Show that the image under F of the parallelogram spanned by v_1 and v_2 is the parallelogram spanned by $F(v_1), F(v_2)$.

11. Let F be a linear map from $\mathbf{R}^2$ into itself such that

$$F(E_1) = (1, 1) \quad \text{and} \quad F(E_2) = (-1, 2).$$

Let S be the square whose corners are at $(0, 0)$, $(1, 0)$, $(1, 1)$, and $(0, 1)$. Show that the image of this square under F is a parallelogram.

12. Let A, B be two non-zero vectors in the plane such that there is no constant $c \neq 0$ such that $B = cA$. Let T be a linear mapping of the plane into itself such that $T(E_1) = A$ and $T(E_2) = B$. Describe the image under T of the rectangle whose corners are $(0, 1)$, $(3, 0)$, $(0, 0)$, and $(3, 1)$.

13. Let A, B be two non-zero vectors in the plane such that there is no constant $c \neq 0$ such that $B = cA$. Describe geometrically the set of points $tA + uB$ for values of t and u such that $0 \leq t \leq 5$ and $0 \leq u \leq 2$.

14. Let $T_u: V \to V$ be the translation by a vector u. For which vectors u is T_u a linear map?

15. Let V, W be two vector spaces, and $F: V \to W$ a linear map. Let $w_1, \ldots, w_n$ be elements of W which are linearly independent, and let $v_1, \ldots, v_n$ be elements of V such that $F(v_i) = w_i$ for $i = 1, \ldots, n$. Show that $v_1, \ldots, v_n$ are linearly independent.

16. Let V be a vector space and $F: V \to \mathbf{R}$ a linear map. Let W be the subset of V consisting of all elements v such that $F(v) = O$. Assume that $W \neq V$, and let v_0 be an element of V which does not lie in W. Show that every element of V can be written as a sum $w + cv_0$, with some w in W and some number c.

17. In Exercise 16, show that W is a subspace of V. Let $\{v_1, \ldots, v_n\}$ be a basis of W. Show that $\{v_0, v_1 \ldots, v_n\}$ is a basis of V.

§3. THE KERNEL AND IMAGE OF A LINEAR MAP

Let V, W be vector spaces, and let $F: V \to W$ be a linear map. We contend that the following two conditions are equivalent:

1. If v is an element of V such that $F(v) = O$, then $v = O$.

2. If v, w are elements of V such that $F(v) = F(w)$, then $v = w$.

To prove our contention, assume first that F satisfies the first condition, and suppose that v, w are such that $F(v) = F(w)$. Then

$$F(v - w) = F(v) - F(w) = O.$$

By assumption, $v - w = O$, and hence $v = w$.

Conversely, assume that F satisfies the second condition. If v is such that $F(v) = F(O) = O$, we conclude that $v = O$.

Let $F: V \to W$ be as above. The set of elements v of V such that $F(v) = O$ is called the *kernel* of F. We leave it as an exercise to prove that the kernel of F is a subspace of V (Exercise 7 of §2).

Theorem 2. *Let $F: V \to W$ be a linear map whose kernel is $\{O\}$. If $v_1, \ldots, v_n$ are linearly independent elements of V, then $F(v_1), \ldots, F(v_n)$ are linearly independent elements of W.*

Proof. Let $x_1, \ldots, x_n$ be numbers such that

$$x_1 F(v_1) + \cdots + x_n F(v_n) = O.$$

By linearity, we get

$$F(x_1 v_1 + \cdots + x_n v_n) = O.$$

Hence $x_1 v_1 + \cdots + x_n v_n = O$. Since $v_1, \ldots, v_n$ are linearly independent it follows that $x_i = 0$ for $i = 1, \ldots, n$. This proves our theorem.

Let $F: V \to W$ be a linear map. The *image* of F is the set of elements w in W such that there exists an element v of V such that $F(v) = w$. *The image of F is a subspace of W.* To prove this, observe first that $F(O) = O$, and hence O is in the image. Next, suppose that w_1, w_2 are in the image. Then there exist elements v_1, v_2 of V such that $F(v_1) = w_1$ and $F(v_2) = w_2$. Hence $F(v_1 + v_2) = F(v_1) + F(v_2) = w_1 + w_2$, thereby proving that $w_1 + w_2$ is in the image. If c is a number, then

$$F(cv_1) = cF(v_1) = cw_1.$$

Hence cw_1 is in the image. This proves that the image is a subspace of W.

We often abbreviate kernel and image by writing Ker and Im respectively. The next theorem relates the dimensions of the kernel and image of a linear map, with the dimension of the space on which the map is defined.

Theorem 3. *Let V be a vector space. Let $L: V \to W$ be a linear map of V into another space W. Let n be the dimension of V, q the dimension of the kernel of L, and s the dimension of the image of L. Then $n = q + s$. In other words,*

$$\dim V = \dim \text{Ker } L + \dim \text{Im } L.$$

Proof. If the image of L consists of O only, then our assertion is trivial We may therefore assume that $s > 0$. Let $\{w_1, \ldots, w_s\}$ be a basis of the image of L. Let $v_1, \ldots, v_s$ be elements of V such that $L(v_i) = w_i$ for $i = 1, \ldots, s$. If the kernel of L is not $\{O\}$, let $\{u_1, \ldots, u_q\}$ be a basis of the kernel. If the kernel is $\{O\}$, it is understood that all reference to $\{u_1, \ldots, u_q\}$ is to be omitted in what follows. We contend that

$\{v_1, \ldots, v_s, u_1, \ldots, u_q\}$ is a basis of V. This will suffice to prove our assertion. Let v be any element of V. Then there exist numbers $x_1, \ldots, x_s$ such that

$$L(v) = x_1 w_1 + \cdots + x_s w_s,$$

because $\{w_1, \ldots, w_s\}$ is a basis of the image of L. By linearity,

$$L(v) = L(x_1 v_1 + \cdots + x_s v_s),$$

and again by linearity, subtracting the right-hand side from the left-hand side, it follows that

$$L(v - x_1 v_1 - \cdots - x_s v_s) = O.$$

Hence $v - x_1 v_1 - \cdots - x_s v_s$ lies in the kernel of L, and there exist numbers $y_1, \ldots, y_q$ such that

$$v - x_1 v_1 - \cdots - x_s v_s = y_1 u_1 + \cdots + y_q u_q.$$

Hence

$$v = x_1 v_1 + \cdots + x_s v_s + y_1 u_1 + \cdots + y_q u_q$$

is a linear combination of $v_1, \ldots, v_s, u_1, \ldots, u_q$. This proves that these $s + q$ elements of V generate V.

We now show that they are linearly independent, and hence that they constitute a basis. Suppose that there exists a linear relation.

$$x_1 v_1 + \cdots + x_s v_s + y_1 u_1 + \cdots + y_q u_q = O.$$

Applying L to this relation, and using the fact that $L(u_j) = O$ for $j = 1, \ldots, q$, we obtain

$$x_1 L(v_1) + \cdots + x_s L(v_s) = O.$$

But $L(v_1), \ldots, L(v_s)$ are none other than $w_1, \ldots, w_s$, which have been assumed linearly independent. Hence $x_i = 0$ for $i = 1, \ldots, s$. Hence

$$y_1 u_1 + \cdots + y_q u_q = 0.$$

But $u_1, \ldots, u_q$ constitute a basis of the kernel of L, and in particular, are linearly independent. Hence all $y_j = 0$ for $j = 1, \ldots, q$. This concludes the proof of our assertion.

EXERCISES

1. Let A, B be two vectors in $\mathbf{R}^2$ forming a basis of $\mathbf{R}^2$. Let $F: \mathbf{R}^2 \to \mathbf{R}^n$ be a linear map. Show that either $F(A), F(B)$ are linearly independent, or the image of F has dimension 1, or the image of F is $\{O\}$.

2. Let A be a non-zero vector in $\mathbf{R}^2$. Let $F: \mathbf{R}^2 \to W$ be a linear map such that $F(A) = O$. Show that the image of F is either a straight line or $\{O\}$.

3. Let $F: V \to W$ be a linear map, whose kernel is $\{O\}$. Assume that V and W have both the same dimension n. Show that the image of F is all of W.

4. Let $F: V \to W$ be a linear map and assume that the image of F is all of W. Assume that V and W have the same dimension n. Show that the kernel of F is $\{O\}$.

5. Let $L: V \to W$ be a linear map. Let w be an element of W. Let v_0 be an element of V such that $L(v_0) = w$. Show that any solution of the equation $L(X) = w$ is of type $v_0 + u$, where u is an element of the kernel of L.

6. Let V be the vector space of functions which have derivatives of all orders, and let $D: V \to V$ be the derivative. What is the kernel of D?

7. Let D^2 be the second derivative (i.e. the iteration of D taken twice). What is the kernel of D^2? In general, what is the kernel of D^n (n-th derivative)?

8. Let V be as in Exercise 6. We write the functions as functions of a variable t, and let $D = d/dt$. Let $a_1, \ldots, a_m$ be numbers. Let g be an element of V. Describe how the problem of finding a solution of the differential equation

$$a_m \frac{d^m f}{dt^m} + a_{m-1} \frac{d^{m-1} f}{dt^{m-1}} + \cdots + a_0 f = g$$

can be interpreted as fitting the abstract situation described in Exercise 5.

9. Let V, D be as in Exercise 6. Let $L = D - I$, where I is the identity mapping of V. What is the kernel of L?

10. Same question of $L = D - aI$, where a is a number.

§4. COMPOSITION AND INVERSE OF LINEAR MAPPINGS

In §1 we have mentioned the fact that we can compose arbitrary maps. We can say something additional in the case of linear maps.

Theorem 4. *Let U, V, W be vector spaces. Let*

$$F: U \to V \quad \text{and} \quad G: V \to W$$

be linear maps. Then the composite map $G \circ F$ is also a linear map.

Proof. This is very easy to prove. Let u, v be elements of U. Since F is linear, we have $F(u + v) = F(u) + F(v)$. Hence

$$(G \circ F)(u + v) = G\big(F(u + v)\big) = G\big(F(u) + F(v)\big).$$

Since G is linear, we obtain

$$G\big(F(u) + F(v)\big) = G\big(F(u)\big) + G\big(F(v)\big).$$

Hence

$$(G \circ F)(u + v) = (G \circ F)(u) + (G \circ F)(v).$$

Next, let c be a number. Then

$$
\begin{aligned}
(G \circ F)(cu) &= G\big(F(cu)\big) \\
&= G\big(cF(u)\big) \qquad \text{(because } F \text{ is linear)} \\
&= cG\big(F(u)\big) \qquad \text{(because } G \text{ is linear)}.
\end{aligned}
$$

This proves that $G \circ F$ is a linear mapping.

The next theorem states that some of the rules of arithmetic concerning the product and sum of numbers also apply to the composition and sum of linear mappings.

Theorem 5. *Let U, V, W be vector spaces. Let*

$$F \colon U \to V$$

be a linear mapping, and let G, H be two linear mappings of V into W. Then

$$(G + H) \circ F = G \circ F + H \circ F.$$

If c is a number, then

$$(cG) \circ F = c(G \circ F).$$

If $T \colon U \to V$ is a linear mapping from U into V, then

$$G \circ (F + T) = G \circ F + G \circ T.$$

The proofs are all simple. We shall just prove the first assertion and leave the others as exercises.

Let u be an element of U. We have:

$$
\begin{aligned}
\big((G + H) \circ F\big)(u) &= (G + H)(F(u)) = G\big(F(u)\big) + H\big(F(u)\big) \\
&= (G \circ F)(u) + (H \circ F)(u).
\end{aligned}
$$

By definition, it follows that $(G + H) \circ F = G \circ F + H \circ F$.

It may happen that $U = V = W$. Let $F \colon U \to U$ and $G \colon U \to U$ be two linear mappings. Then we may form $F \circ G$ and $G \circ F$. It is not always true that these two composite mappings are equal. As an example, let $U = \mathbf{R}^3$. Let F be the linear mapping given by

$$F(x, y, z) = (x, y, 0)$$

and let G be the linear mapping given by

$$G(x, y, z) = (x, z, 0).$$

Then $(G \circ F)(x, y, z) = (x, 0, 0)$, but $(F \circ G)(x, y, z) = (x, z, 0)$.

Theorem 6. *Let $F \colon U \to V$ be a linear map, and assume that this map has an inverse mapping $G \colon V \to U$. Then G is a linear map.*

Proof. This proof will be left as an exercise.

§5. GEOMETRIC APPLICATIONS

Let V be a vector space, and let v, w be elements of V. We define the *straight line segment* between v and w to be the set of all points (Fig. 2)

$$v + t(w - v), \qquad\qquad 0 \leq t \leq 1.$$

Observe that we can rewrite the expression for these points in the form

(1) $$\qquad\qquad (1 - t)v + tw, \qquad\qquad 0 \leq t \leq 1,$$

and letting $s = 1 - t$, $t = 1 - s$, we can also write it as

$$sv + (1 - s)w, \qquad\qquad 0 \leq s \leq 1.$$

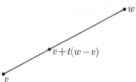

Figure 2

Finally, we can write the points of our line segment in the form

(2) $$\qquad\qquad t_1 v + t_2 w$$

with t_1, $t_2 \geq 0$ and $t_1 + t_2 = 1$. Indeed, letting $t = t_2$, we see that every point which can be written in the form (2) satisfies (1). Conversely, we let $t_1 = 1 - t$ and $t_2 = t$ and see that every point of the form (1) can be written in the form (2).

We shall now generalize this discussion to higher dimensional figures.

Let v, w be linearly independent elements of the vector space V. We define the *parallelogram* spanned by v, w to be the set of all points

$$t_1 v + t_2 w, \qquad 0 \leq t_i \leq 1 \quad \text{for} \quad i = 1, 2.$$

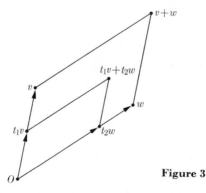

Figure 3

This definition is clearly justified since $t_1 v$ is a point of the segment between O and v (Fig. 3), and $t_2 w$ is a point of the segment between

O and w. For all values of t_1, t_2 ranging independently between 0 and 1, we see geometrically that $t_1v + t_2w$ describes all points of the parallelogram.

At the end of §1 we defined *translations*. We obtain the most general parallelogram (Fig. 4) by taking the translation of the parallelogram just described. Thus if u is an element of V, the translation by u of the parallelogram spanned by v and w consists of all points

$$u + t_1v + t_2w, \quad 0 \le t_i \le 1 \quad \text{for} \quad i = 1, 2.$$

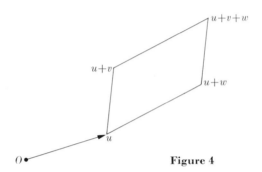

Figure 4

We shall now describe triangles. We begin with triangles located at the origin. Let v, w again be linearly independent. We define the *triangle spanned* by O, v, w to be the set of all points

(3) $t_1v + t_2w, \quad 0 \le t_i \quad \text{and} \quad t_1 + t_2 \le 1.$

We must convince ourselves that this is a reasonable definition. We do this by showing that the triangle defined above coincides with the set of points on all line segments between v and all the points of the segment between O and w. From Fig. 5, this second description of a triangle does coincide with our geometric intuition.

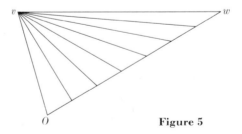

Figure 5

We denote the line segment between O and w by $\overline{Ow}$. A point on $\overline{Ow}$ can then be written tw with $0 \le t \le 1$. The set of points between v and tw is the set of points

(4) $sv + (1 - s)tw, \quad\quad\quad 0 \le s \le 1.$

Let $t_1 = s$ and $t_2 = (1 - s)t$. Then

$$t_1 + t_2 = s + (1 - s)t \leqq s + (1 - s) \leqq 1.$$

Hence all points satisfying (4) also satisfy (3). Conversely, suppose given a point $t_1 v + t_2 w$ satisfying (3), so that $t_1 + t_2 \leqq 1$. Then $t_2 \leqq 1 - t_1$ and we let

$$s = t_1, \qquad t = t_2/(1 - t_1).$$

Then

$$t_1 v + t_2 w = t_1 v + (1 - t_1) \frac{t_2}{(1 - t_1)} w = sv + (1 - s)tw,$$

which shows that every point satisfying (3) also satisfies (4). This justifies our definition of a triangle.

As with parallelograms, an arbitrary triangle is obtained by translating a triangle located at the origin. In fact, we have the following description of a triangle.

Let v_1, v_2, v_3 be elements of V such that $v_1 - v_3$ and $v_2 - v_3$ are linearly independent. Let $v = v_1 - v_3$ and $w = v_2 - v_3$. Let S be the set of points

(5) $\qquad\qquad t_1 v_1 + t_2 v_2 + t_3 v_3, \qquad\qquad 0 \leqq t_i \ \text{ for } \ i = 1, 2, 3$
$$t_1 + t_2 + t_3 = 1.$$

Then S is the translation by v_3 of the triangle spanned by O, v, w. (Cf. Fig. 6.)

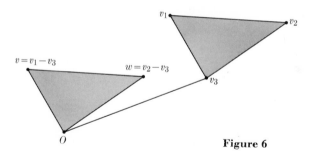

Figure 6

Proof. Let $P = t_1 v_1 + t_2 v_2 + t_3 v_3$ be a point satisfying (5). Then

$$P = t_1(v_1 - v_3) + t_2(v_2 - v_3) + t_1 v_3 + t_2 v_3 + t_3 v_3$$
$$= t_1 v + t_2 w + v_3,$$

and $t_1 + t_2 \leqq 1$. Hence our point P is a translation by v_3 of a point satisfying (3). Conversely, given a point satisfying (3), which we translate by v_3, we let $t_3 = 1 - t_2 - t_1$, and we can then reverse the steps we have just taken to see that

$$t_1 v + t_2 w + v_3 = t_1 v_1 + t_2 v_2 + t_3 v_3.$$

This proves what we wanted.

Actually, it is (5) which is the most useful description of a triangle, because the vertices v_1, v_2, v_3 occupy a symmetric position in this definition. Furthermore, the conditions of (5) are those which generalize to the fruitful concept of convex set which we now discuss.

Let S be a subset of a vector space V. We shall say that S is *convex* if given points P, Q in S the line segment between P and Q is contained in S.

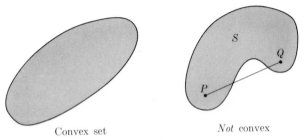

Convex set   *Not* convex

Figure 7

The set on the left is convex. The set on the right is not convex since the line segment between P and Q is not entirely contained in S.

Theorem 7. *Let $P_1, \ldots, P_n$ be points of a vector space V. Let S be the set of all linear combinations*

$$t_1 P_1 + \cdots + t_n P_n$$

with $0 \leq t_i$ and $t_1 + \cdots + t_n = 1$. Then S is convex.

Proof. Let

$$P = t_1 P_1 + \cdots + t_n P_n \quad \text{and} \quad Q = s_1 P_1 + \cdots + s_n P_n$$

with $0 \leq t_i$, $0 \leq s_i$, and $t_1 + \cdots + t_n = 1$, $s_1 + \cdots + s_n = 1$. Let $0 \leq t \leq 1$. Then:

$$(1 - t)P + tQ$$
$$= (1 - t)t_1 P_1 + \cdots + (1 - t)t_n P_n + ts_1 P_1 + \cdots + ts_n P_n$$
$$= [(1 - t)t_1 + ts_1]P_1 + \cdots + [(1 - t)t_n + ts_n]P_n.$$

We have $0 \leq (1 - t)t_i + ts_i$ for all i, and

$$(1 - t)t_1 + ts_1 + \cdots + (1 - t)t_n + ts_n$$
$$= (1 - t)(t_1 + \cdots + t_n) + t(s_1 + \cdots + s_n)$$
$$= (1 - t) + t$$
$$= 1.$$

This proves our theorem.

From Theorem 7, we see that a triangle, as we have defined it analytically, is convex. The convex set of Theorem 7 is therefore a natural
generalization of a triangle. It looks like this:

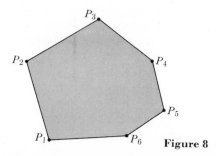

Figure 8

We shall call the convex set of Theorem 7 the convex set *spanned* by
$P_1, \ldots, P_n$. Although we shall not need the next result, it shows that
this convex set is the smallest convex set containing all the points
$P_1, \ldots, P_n$.

Theorem 8. *Let $P_1, \ldots, P_n$ be points of a vector space V. Any convex
set S' which contains $P_1, \ldots, P_n$ also contains all linear combinations*

$$t_1 P_1 + \cdots + t_n P_n$$

with $0 \leqq t_i$ for all i and $t_1 + \cdots + t_n = 1$.

Proof. We prove this by induction. If $n = 1$, then $t_1 = 1$, and our
assertion is obvious. Assume the theorem proved for some integer
$n - 1 \geqq 1$. We shall prove it for n. Let $t_1, \ldots, t_n$ be numbers satisfying
the conditions of the theorem. If $t_n = 1$, then our assertion is trivial
because $t_1 = \cdots = t_{n-1} = 0$. Suppose that $t_n \neq 1$. Then the linear
combination $t_1 P_1 + \cdots + t_n P_n$ is equal to

$$(1 - t_n) \left(\frac{t_1}{1 - t_n} P_1 + \cdots + \frac{t_{n-1}}{1 - t_n} P_{n-1} \right) + t_n P_n.$$

Let

$$s_i = \frac{t_i}{1 - t_i} \quad \text{for} \quad i = 1, \ldots, n - 1.$$

Then $s_i \geqq 0$ and $s_1 + \cdots + s_{n-1} = 1$ so that by induction, we conclude
that the point

$$Q = s_1 P_1 + \cdots + s_{n-1} P_{n-1}$$

lies in S'. But then

$$(1 - t_n)Q + t_n P_n = t_1 P_1 + \cdots + t_n P_n$$

lies in S' by definition of a convex set, as was to be shown.

One of the advantages of giving a definition of a triangle as we did it, is that it is then easy to see what happens to a triangle under a linear map, and similarly for parallelograms and convex sets. For instance, let $L: V \to W$ be a linear map, and let v, w be elements of V which are linearly independent. Assume that $L(v)$ and $L(w)$ are also linearly independent. Let S be the triangle spanned by O, v, w. Then the image of S under L, namely $L(S)$, is the triangle spanned by O, $L(v)$, $L(w)$. Indeed, it is the set of all points

$$L(t_1 v + t_2 w) = t_1 L(v) + t_2 L(w)$$

with

$$0 \leqq t_i \quad \text{and} \quad t_1 + t_2 \leqq 1.$$

Similarly, let R be the parallelogram spanned by v, w. Then the image of R under L, namely $L(R)$, is the set of all points

$$L(t_1 v + t_2 w) = t_1 L(v) + t_2 L(w)$$

with

$$0 \leqq t_i \leqq 1 \quad \text{for} \quad i = 1, 2.$$

Thus it is also a parallelogram.

Finally, we give an example showing that a certain set is convex. *Let V be a vector space, and let $L: V \to \mathbf{R}$ be a linear map. We contend that the set S of all elements v in V such that $L(v) < 0$ is convex.*

Proof. Let $L(v) < 0$ and $L(w) < 0$. Let $0 < t < 1$. Then

$$L(tv + (1 - t)w) = tL(v) + (1 - t)L(w).$$

Then $tL(v) < 0$ and $(1 - t)L(w) < 0$ so $tL(v) + (1 - t)L(w) < 0$, whence $tv + (1 - t)w$ lies in S. If $t = 0$ or $t = 1$, then $tv + (1 - t)w$ is equal to v or w and thus also lies in S. This proves our assertion.

EXERCISES

1. Show that the image under a linear map of a convex set is convex.

2. Let S_1 and S_2 be convex sets in V. Show that the intersection $S_1 \cap S_2$ is convex.

3. Let $L: \mathbf{R}^n \to \mathbf{R}$ be a linear map. Let S be the set of all points A in $\mathbf{R}^n$ such that $L(A) \geqq 0$. Show that S is convex.

4. Let $L: \mathbf{R}^n \to \mathbf{R}$ be a linear map and c a number. Show that the set S consisting of all points A in $\mathbf{R}^n$ such that $L(A) > c$ is convex.

5. Let A be a non-zero vector in $\mathbf{R}^n$ and c a number. Show that the set of points X such that $X \cdot A \geqq c$ is convex.

6. Let $L: V \to W$ be a linear map. Let S' be a convex set in W. Let S be the set of all elements P in V such that $L(P)$ is in S'. Show that S is convex.

7. Show that a parallelogram is convex.

8. Let S be a convex set in V and let u be an element of V. Let $T_u: V \to V$ be the translation by u. Show that the image $T_u(S)$ is convex.

9. Let S be a convex set in the vector space V and let c be a number. Let cS denote the set of all elements cv with v in S. Show that cS is convex.

Chapter XI

Linear Maps and Matrices

§1. THE LINEAR MAP ASSOCIATED WITH A MATRIX

Let

$$A = \begin{pmatrix} a_{11} & \cdots & a_{1n} \\ \vdots & & \vdots \\ a_{m1} & \cdots & a_{mn} \end{pmatrix}$$

be an $m \times n$ matrix. We can then associate with A a map

$$L_A \colon \mathbf{R}^n \to \mathbf{R}^m$$

by letting

$$L_A(X) = AX$$

for every column vector X in $\mathbf{R}^n$. Thus L_A is defined by the association $X \mapsto AX$, the product being the product of matrices. That L_A is linear is simply a special case of Theorem 7, Chapter IX, §4, namely the theorem concerning properties of multiplication of matrices. Indeed, we have

$$A(X + Y) = AX + AY \quad \text{and} \quad A(cX) = cAX$$

for all vectors X, Y in $\mathbf{R}^n$ and all numbers c. We call L_A the linear map *associated* with the matrix A.

Example. If

$$A = \begin{pmatrix} 2 & 1 \\ -1 & 5 \end{pmatrix} \quad \text{and} \quad X = (3, 7)$$

then

$$L_A(X) = \begin{pmatrix} 2 & 1 \\ -1 & 5 \end{pmatrix} \begin{pmatrix} 3 \\ 7 \end{pmatrix} = \begin{pmatrix} 6 - 7 \\ -3 + 35 \end{pmatrix} = \begin{pmatrix} -1 \\ 32 \end{pmatrix},$$

which we may also write as horizontal vector $(-1, 32)$.

Theorem 1. *If A, B are $m \times n$ matrices and if $L_A = L_B$, then $A = B$. In other words, if matrices A, B give rise to the same linear map, then they are equal.*

Proof. By definition, we have $A_i \cdot X = B_i \cdot X$ for all i, if A_i is the i-th row of A and B_i is the i-th row of B. Hence $(A_i - B_i) \cdot X = 0$ for all i and all X. Hence $A_i - B_i = O$, and $A_i = B_i$ for all i. Hence $A = B$.

We can give a new interpretation for a system of homogeneous linear equations in terms of the linear map associated with a matrix. Indeed, such a system can be written

$$AX = 0,$$

and hence we see that *the set of solutions is the kernel of the linear map L_A.*

EXERCISES

1. In each case, find the vector $L_A(X)$. View X as a column vector.

(a) $A = \begin{pmatrix} 2 & 1 \\ 1 & 0 \end{pmatrix}$, $X = (3, -1)$ (b) $A = \begin{pmatrix} 1 & 0 \\ 0 & 0 \end{pmatrix}$, $X = (5, 1)$

(c) $A = \begin{pmatrix} 1 & 1 \\ 0 & 1 \end{pmatrix}$, $X = (4, 1)$ (d) $A = \begin{pmatrix} 0 & 0 \\ 0 & 1 \end{pmatrix}$, $X = (7, -3)$

§2. THE MATRIX ASSOCIATED WITH A LINEAR MAP

Let $L: \mathbf{R}^n \to \mathbf{R}^m$ be a linear map. As usual, let $E_1, \ldots, E_n$ be the unit vectors in $\mathbf{R}^n$, and let $E'_1, \ldots, E'_m$ be the unit vectors in $\mathbf{R}^m$. We can write any vector X in $\mathbf{R}^n$ as a linear combination

$$X = x_1 E_1 + \cdots + x_n E_n,$$

where x_j is the j-th component of X. We view $E_1, \ldots, E_n$ as column vectors. By linearity, we find that

$$L(X) = x_1 L(E_1) + \cdots + x_n L(E_n)$$

and we can write each $L(E_j)$ in terms of $E'_1, \ldots, E'_m$. In other words, there exist numbers a_{ij} such that

$$L(E_1) = a_{11} E'_1 + \cdots + a_{m1} E'_m$$
$$\vdots \qquad \vdots \qquad \qquad \vdots$$
$$L(E_n) = a_{1n} E'_1 + \cdots + a_{mn} E'_n$$

or in terms of the column vectors,

(*) $$L(E_1) = \begin{pmatrix} a_{11} \\ \vdots \\ a_{m1} \end{pmatrix}, \quad \ldots, \quad L(E_n) = \begin{pmatrix} a_{1n} \\ \vdots \\ a_{mn} \end{pmatrix}.$$

Hence

$$L(X) = x_1(a_{11}E_1' + \cdots + a_{m1}E_m') + \cdots + x_n(a_{1n}E_1' + \cdots + a_{mn}E_n')$$
$$= (a_{11}x_1 + \cdots + a_{1n}x_n)E_1' + \cdots + (a_{m1}x_1 + \cdots + a_{mn}x_n)E_m'.$$

Consequently, if we let $A = (a_{ij})$, then we see that

$$L(X) = AX.$$

Thus $L = L_A$ is the linear map associated with the matrix A. We also call A *the matrix associated with the linear map* L. We know that this matrix is uniquely determined by Theorem 1.

Example 1. Let $F: \mathbf{R}^3 \to \mathbf{R}^2$ be the projection, in other words the mapping such that $F(x_1, x_2, x_3) = (x_1, x_2)$. Then the matrix associated with F is

$$\begin{pmatrix} 1 & 0 & 0 \\ 0 & 1 & 0 \end{pmatrix}.$$

Example 2. Let $F: \mathbf{R}^n \to \mathbf{R}^n$ be the identity. Then the matrix associated with F relative to the usual bases is the matrix

$$\begin{pmatrix} 1 & 0 & 0 & \cdots & 0 \\ 0 & 1 & 0 & \cdots & 0 \\ & \cdot & \cdot & & \cdot \\ & \cdot & \cdot & \cdot & \cdot \\ & \cdot & \cdot & & \cdot \\ 0 & 0 & 0 & \cdots & 1 \end{pmatrix},$$

having components equal to 1 on the diagonal, and 0 otherwise.

Example 3. According to Theorem 1 of Chapter X, §2, there exists a unique linear map $L: \mathbf{R}^4 \to \mathbf{R}^2$ such that

$$L(E_1) = \begin{pmatrix} 2 \\ 1 \end{pmatrix}, \quad L(E_2) = \begin{pmatrix} 3 \\ -1 \end{pmatrix}, \quad L(E_3) = \begin{pmatrix} -5 \\ 4 \end{pmatrix}, \quad L(E_4) = \begin{pmatrix} 1 \\ 7 \end{pmatrix}.$$

According to the relations (*), we see that the matrix associated with L is the matrix

$$\begin{pmatrix} 2 & 3 & -5 & 1 \\ 1 & -1 & 4 & 7 \end{pmatrix}.$$

Example 4 (Rotations). We can define a rotation in terms of matrices. Indeed, we call a linear map $L: \mathbf{R}^2 \to \mathbf{R}^2$ a *rotation* if its associated matrix can be written in the form

$$\begin{pmatrix} \cos\theta & -\sin\theta \\ \sin\theta & \cos\theta \end{pmatrix}.$$

The geometric justification for this definition comes from the following picture.

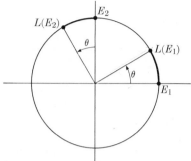

We see that

$$L(E_1) = (\cos \theta)E_1 + (\sin \theta)E_2,$$
$$L(E_2) = (-\sin \theta)E_1 + (\cos \theta)E_2.$$

Thus our definition corresponds precisely to the picture. When the matrix of the rotation is as above, we say that the rotation is by an angle θ. For example, the matrix associated with a rotation by an angle $\pi/2$ is

$$\begin{pmatrix} 0 & -1 \\ 1 & 0 \end{pmatrix}.$$

We observe finally that the operations on matrices correspond to the operations on the associated linear map. For instance, if A, B are $m \times n$ matrices, then

$$L_{A+B} = L_A + L_B$$

and if c is a number, then

$$L_{cA} = cL_A.$$

This is obvious, because

$$(A + B)X = AX + BX \qquad \text{and} \qquad (cA)X = c(AX).$$

Similarly for composition of mappings. Indeed, let

$$F: \mathbf{R}^n \to \mathbf{R}^m \qquad \text{and} \qquad G: \mathbf{R}^m \to \mathbf{R}^s$$

be linear maps, and let A, B be the matrices associated with F and G respectively. Then for any vector X in $\mathbf{R}^n$ we have

$$(G \circ F)(X) = G\bigl(F(X)\bigr) = B(AX) = (BA)X.$$

Hence the product BA is the matrix associated with the composite linear map $G \circ F$.

EXERCISES

1. Assume that $\mathbf{R}^n$, $\mathbf{R}^m$ have their usual bases. Find the matrix associated with the following linear maps. (Although the vectors are written horizontally, for typographical reasons, view them as column vectors.)

   (a) $F: \mathbf{R}^4 \to \mathbf{R}^2$ given by $F(x_1, x_2, x_3, x_4) = (x_1, x_2)$ (the projection)

   (b) The projection from $\mathbf{R}^4$ to $\mathbf{R}^3$

   (c) $F: \mathbf{R}^2 \to \mathbf{R}^2$ given by $F(x, y) = (3x, 3y)$

   (d) $F: \mathbf{R}^n \to \mathbf{R}^n$ given by $F(X) = 7X$

   (e) $F: \mathbf{R}^n \to \mathbf{R}^n$ given by $F(X) = -X$

   (f) $F: \mathbf{R}^4 \to \mathbf{R}^4$ given by $F(x_1, x_2, x_3, x_4) = (x_1, x_2, 0, 0)$

2. Find the matrix associated with the rotation for each of the following values of θ.

   (a) $\pi/2$ (b) $\pi/4$ (c) π (d) $-\pi$ (e) $-\pi/3$

   (f) $\pi/6$ (g) $5\pi/4$

3. In general, let $\theta > 0$. What is the matrix associated with the rotation by an angle $-\theta$ (i.e. clockwise rotation by θ)?

4. Let $X = (1, 2)$ be a point of the plane. Let F be the rotation through an angle of $\pi/4$. What are the coordinates of $F(X)$ relative to the usual basis $\{E_1, E_2\}$?

5. Same question when $X = (-1, 3)$, and F is the rotation through $\pi/2$.

6. Let $F: \mathbf{R}^n \to \mathbf{R}^n$ be a linear map which is invertible. Show that if A is the matrix associated with F, then A^{-1} is the matrix associated with the inverse of F.

7. Let F be a rotation through an angle θ. Show that for any vector X in $\mathbf{R}^2$ we have $\|X\| = \|F(X)\|$ (i.e. F preserves norms).

8. Let c be a number, and let $L: \mathbf{R}^n \to \mathbf{R}^n$ be the linear map such that $L(X) = cX$. What is the matrix associated with this linear map?

9. Let F_θ be one rotation by an angle θ. If θ, φ are numbers, compute the matrix of the linear map $F_\theta \circ F_\varphi$ and show that it is the matrix of $F_{\theta+\varphi}$.

Chapter XII

Determinants

We have worked with vectors for some time, and we have often felt the need of a method to determine when vectors are linearly independent. Up to now, the only method available to us was to solve a system of linear equations by the elimination method. In this chapter, we shall exhibit a very efficient computational method to solve linear equations, and determine when vectors are linearly independent.

§1. DETERMINANTS OF ORDER 2

Before stating the general properties of an arbitrary determinant, we shall consider a special case.

Let

$$A = \begin{pmatrix} a & b \\ c & d \end{pmatrix}$$

be a 2×2 matrix. We define its determinant to be $ad - cb$. Thus the determinant is a number.

The determinant can be viewed as a function of the matrix A. It can also be viewed as a function of its two columns. Let these be A^1 and A^2 as usual. Then we write the determinant as

$$D(A), \quad \text{Det}(A), \quad \text{or} \quad D(A^1, A^2).$$

The following properties are easily verified by direction computation, which you should carry out completely.

As a function of the column vectors, the determinant is linear. This means: let b', d' be two numbers. Then

$$\text{Det}\begin{pmatrix} a & b + b' \\ c & d + d' \end{pmatrix} = \text{Det}\begin{pmatrix} a & b \\ c & d \end{pmatrix} + \text{Det}\begin{pmatrix} a & b' \\ c & d' \end{pmatrix}.$$

Furthermore, *if t is a number, then*

$$\text{Det}\begin{pmatrix} a & tb \\ c & td \end{pmatrix} = t \,\text{Det}\begin{pmatrix} a & b \\ c & d \end{pmatrix}.$$

The analogous properties also hold with respect to the first column.

If the two columns are equal, then the determinant is equal to 0.

If A is the unit matrix,

$$A = \begin{pmatrix} 1 & 0 \\ 0 & 1 \end{pmatrix},$$

then $\text{Det}(A) = 1$.

The determinant also satisfies the following additional properties.

If one adds a multiple of one column to the other, then the value of the determinant does not change.

In other words, let t be a number. The determinant of the matrix

$$\begin{pmatrix} a + tb & b \\ c + td & d \end{pmatrix}$$

is the same as $D(A)$, and similarly when we add a multiple of the first column to the second.

If the two columns are interchanged, then the determinant changes by a sign.

In other words, we have

$$\text{Det} \begin{pmatrix} a & b \\ c & d \end{pmatrix} = -\text{Det} \begin{pmatrix} b & a \\ d & c \end{pmatrix}.$$

The determinant of A is equal to the determinant of its transpose, i.e. $D(A) = D(^tA)$.

Explicitly, we have

$$\text{Det} \begin{pmatrix} a & b \\ c & d \end{pmatrix} = \text{Det} \begin{pmatrix} a & c \\ b & d \end{pmatrix}.$$

The vectors $\begin{pmatrix} a \\ c \end{pmatrix}$ *and* $\begin{pmatrix} b \\ d \end{pmatrix}$ *are linearly dependent if and only if the determinant* $ad - bc$ *is equal to* 0.

In the next section, we shall consider determinants of $n \times n$ matrices, and the analogous properties will give us a method for computing the determinant in general.

§2. PROPERTIES OF DETERMINANTS

Let A be an $n \times n$ matrix. It would be possible to define its determinant by a sum, just as we defined the determinant of a 2×2 matrix. However, to write such a sum is a little complicated, and it turns out that to find the value of a determinant, it is not necessary to have this expression. What is needed is a set of properties which can be used to compute it.

Some of these properties are already contained in the following theorem.

Theorem 1. *To each $n \times n$ matrix A we can associate a number, called its determinant, and denoted by $D(A)$, or $D(A^1, \ldots, A^n)$, if $A^1, \ldots, A^n$ are the columns of A, satisfying the following properties:*

1. *As a function of each column vector, the determinant is linear,* i.e. *if the j-th column A^j is equal to a sum of two column vectors, say $A^j = C + C'$, then*

$$D(A^1, \ldots, C + C', \ldots, A^n)$$
$$= D(A^1, \ldots, C, \ldots, A^n) + D(A^1, \ldots, C', \ldots, A^n).$$

Furthermore, if t is a number, then

$$D(A^1, \ldots, tA^j, \ldots, A^n) = tD(A^1, \ldots, A^j, \ldots, A^n).$$

2. *If two adjacent columns are equal,* i.e. *if $A^j = A^{j+1}$ for some $j = 1, \ldots, n - 1$, then the determinant $D(A)$ is equal to 0.*

3. *If I is the unit matrix, then $D(I) = 1$.*

Determinants are uniquely determined by the above three properties.

We shall prove in §4 that determinants exist. Here, we shall prove more simple properties which follow from (1), (2), and (3). We shall also use the notation $\text{Det}(A)$ instead of $D(A)$. Furthermore, the determinant of the matrix (a_{ij}) is also denoted by two vertical bars surrounding the matrix:

$$D(A) = \begin{vmatrix} a_{11} & \cdots & a_{1n} \\ & \cdots & \\ a_{n1} & \cdots & a_{nn} \end{vmatrix}$$

4. *Let j be some integer, $1 \leq j < n$. If the j-th and $(j + 1)$-th columns are interchanged, then the determinant changes by a sign.*

Proof. In the matrix A, we replace the j-th and $(j + 1)$-th columns by $A^j + A^{j+1}$. We obtain a matrix with two equal adjacent columns and by (2) we have:

$$0 = D(\ldots, A^j + A^{j+1}, A^j + A^{j+1}, \ldots).$$

Expanding out using (1) repeatedly yields

$$0 = D(\ldots, A^j, A^j, \ldots) + D(\ldots, A^{j+1}, A^j, \ldots)$$
$$+ D(\ldots, A^j, A^{j+1}, \ldots) + D(\ldots, A^{j+1}, A^{j+1}, \ldots).$$

Using (2), we see that two of these four terms are equal to 0, and hence that

$$0 = D(\ldots, A^{j+1}, A^j, \ldots) + D(\ldots, A^j, A^{j+1}, \ldots).$$

In this last sum, one term must be equal to minus the other, as desired.

5. *If two columns A^j, A^i of A are equal, $j \neq i$, then the determinant of A is equal to 0.*

Proof. Assume that two columns of the matrix A are equal. We can change the matrix by a successive interchange of adjacent columns until we obtain a matrix with equal adjacent columns. (This could be proved formally by induction.) Each time that we make such an adjacent interchange, the determinant changes by a sign, which does not affect its being 0 or not. Hence we conclude by (2) that $D(A) = 0$ if two columns are equal.

6. *If one adds a scalar multiple of one column to another then the value of the determinant does not change.*

Proof. Consider two distinct columns, say the k-th and j-th columns A^k and A^j with $k \neq j$. Let t be a scalar. We add tA^j to A^k. By (1), the determinant becomes

$$D(\ldots, \underset{\underset{k}{\uparrow}}{A^k + tA^j}, \ldots) = D(\ldots, \underset{\underset{k}{\uparrow}}{A^k}, \ldots) + D(\ldots, \underset{\underset{k}{\uparrow}}{tA^j}, \ldots)$$

(the k points to the k-th column). In both terms on the right, the indicated column occurs in the k-th place. But $D(\ldots, A^k, \ldots)$ is simply $D(A)$. Furthermore,

$$D(\ldots, \underset{\underset{k}{\uparrow}}{tA^j}, \ldots) = tD(\ldots, \underset{\underset{k}{\uparrow}}{A^j}, \ldots).$$

Since $k \neq j$, the determinant on the right has two equal columns, because A^j occurs in the k-th place and also in the j-th place. Hence it is equal to 0. Hence

$$D(\ldots, A^k + tA^j, \ldots) = D(\ldots, A^k, \ldots),$$

thereby proving our property (6).

EXERCISE

1. Let c be a number and let A be an $n \times n$ matrix. Show that

$$D(cA) = c^n D(A).$$

§3. CRAMER'S RULE

The properties of the preceding section are already sufficient to prove a well-known rule used in solving linear equations.

Theorem 2. *Let $A^1, \ldots, A^n$ be column vectors such that*

$$D(A^1, \ldots, A^n) \neq 0.$$

Let B be a column vector. If $x_1, \ldots, x_n$ are numbers such that

$$x_1 A^1 + \cdots + x_n A^n = B,$$

then for each $j = 1, \ldots, n$ we have

$$x_j = \frac{D(A^1, \ldots, B, \ldots, A^n)}{D(A^1, \ldots, A_n)},$$

where B occurs in the j-th column instead of A^j. In other words,

$$x_j = \begin{vmatrix} a_{11} & \cdots & b_1 & \cdots & a_{1n} \\ a_{21} & \cdots & b_2 & \cdots & a_{2n} \\ \vdots & & \vdots & & \vdots \\ a_{n1} & \cdots & b_n & \cdots & a_{nn} \\ a_{11} & \cdots & a_{ij} & \cdots & a_{1n} \\ a_{21} & \cdots & a_{2j} & \cdots & a_{2n} \\ \vdots & & \vdots & & \vdots \\ a_{n1} & \cdots & a_{nj} & \cdots & a_{nn} \end{vmatrix}.$$

(The numerator is obtained from A by replacing the j-th column A^j by B. The denominator is the determinant of the matrix A.)

Theorem 2 gives us an explicit way of finding the coordinates of B with respect to $A^1, \ldots, A^n$. In the language of linear equations, Theorem 2 allows us to solve explicitly in terms of determinants the system of n linear equations in n unknowns:

$$x_1 a_{11} + \cdots + x_n a_{1n} = b_1,$$
$$\cdots$$
$$x_1 a_{n1} + \cdots + x_n a_{nn} = b_n.$$

We now prove Theorem 2.

Let B be written as in the statement of the theorem, and consider the determinant of the matrix obtained by replacing the j-th column of A by B. Then

$$D(A^1, \ldots, B, \ldots, A^n) = D(A^1, \ldots, x_1 A_1^1 + \cdots + x_n A_n^1, \ldots, A^n).$$

We use property (1) and obtain a sum:

$$D(A^1, \ldots, x_1 A^1, \ldots, A^n) + \cdots + D(A^1, \ldots, x_j A^j, \ldots, A^n)$$
$$+ \cdots + D(A^1, \ldots, x_n A^n, \ldots, A^n),$$

which by property (1) again, is equal to

$$x_1 D(A^1, \ldots, A^1, \ldots, A^n) + \cdots + x_j D(A^1, \ldots, A^n)$$
$$+ \cdots + x_n D(A^1, \ldots, A^n, \ldots, A^n).$$

In every term of this sum except the j-th term, two column vectors are equal. Hence every term except the j-th term is equal to 0, by property (5). The j-th term is equal to

$$x_j D(A^1, \ldots, A^n),$$

and is therefore equal to the determinant we started with, namely $D(A^1, \ldots, B, \ldots, A^n)$. We can solve for x_j, and obtain precisely the expression given in the statement of the theorem.

The rule of Theorem 2, giving us the solution to the system of linear equations by means of determinants, is known as *Cramer's rule*.

Example. Solve the system of linear equations:

$$3x + 2y + 4z = 1,$$
$$2x - y + z = 0,$$
$$x + 2y + 3z = 1.$$

We have:

$$x = \frac{\begin{vmatrix} 1 & 2 & 4 \\ 0 & -1 & 1 \\ 1 & 2 & 3 \end{vmatrix}}{\begin{vmatrix} 3 & 2 & 4 \\ 2 & -1 & 1 \\ 1 & 2 & 3 \end{vmatrix}}, \quad y = \frac{\begin{vmatrix} 3 & 1 & 4 \\ 2 & 0 & 1 \\ 1 & 1 & 3 \end{vmatrix}}{\begin{vmatrix} 3 & 2 & 4 \\ 2 & -1 & 1 \\ 1 & 2 & 3 \end{vmatrix}}, \quad z = \frac{\begin{vmatrix} 3 & 2 & 1 \\ 2 & -1 & 0 \\ 1 & 2 & 1 \end{vmatrix}}{\begin{vmatrix} 3 & 2 & 4 \\ 2 & -1 & 1 \\ 1 & 2 & 3 \end{vmatrix}}.$$

Observe how the column

$$B = \begin{pmatrix} 1 \\ 0 \\ 1 \end{pmatrix}$$

shifts from the first column when solving for x, to the second column when solving for y, to the third column when solving for z. The denominator in all three expressions is the same, namely it is the determinant of the matrix of coefficients of the equations.

In the next section we shall give a method for computing the determinant. One then finds $x = -\frac{1}{5}$, $y = 0$, $z = \frac{2}{5}$.

Determinants also allow us to determine when vectors are linearly independent.

Theorem 3. *Let $A^1, \ldots, A^n$ be column vectors (of dimension n). If they are linearly dependent, then*

$$D(A^1, \ldots, A^n) = 0.$$

If $D(A^1, \ldots, A^n) \neq 0$, then $A^1, \ldots, A^n$ are linearly independent.

Proof. The second assertion is merely an equivalent formulation of the first. It will therefore suffice to prove the first. Assume that $A^1, \ldots, A^n$ are linearly dependent. We can find numbers $x_1, \ldots, x_n$ not all 0 such that

$$x_1 A^1 + \cdots + x_n A^n = O.$$

Suppose $x_j \neq 0$. Then

$$x_j A^j = -x_1 A^1 - \cdots - x_n A^n = \sum_{k \neq j} x_k A^k,$$

it being understood that the j-th term on the right-hand side does not appear. Dividing by x_j, we obtain A^j as a linear combination of $A^1, \ldots, A^n$ (omitting A^j). In other words, there are numbers $y_1, \ldots, y_n$ such that

$$A^j = y_1 A^1 + \cdots + y_n A^n = -\sum_{k \neq j} y_k A^k,$$

the j-th term in the sum being omitted. We get:

$$D(A^1, \ldots, A^n) = D(A^1, \ldots, y_1 A^1 + \cdots + y_n A^n, \ldots, A^n),$$

which we can expand out using property (1). This yields

$$y_1 D(A^1, \ldots, A^1, \ldots, A^n) + \cdots + y_n D(A^1, \ldots, A^n, \ldots, A^n).$$

Here again, the j-term is omitted. In the other terms, we always have two equal columns, and hence each such term is equal to 0 by property (5). This proves Theorem 3.

Corollary. *If $A^1, \ldots, A^n$ are column vectors of $\mathbf{R}^n$ such that $D(A^1, \ldots, A^n) \neq 0$, and if B is a column vector of $\mathbf{R}^n$, then there exist numbers $x_1, \ldots, x_n$ such that*

$$x_1 A^1 + \cdots + x_n A^n = B.$$

Proof. According to the theorem, $A^1, \ldots, A^n$ are linearly independent, and hence form a basis of $\mathbf{R}^n$. Hence any vector of $\mathbf{R}^n$ can be written as a linear combination of $A^1, \ldots, A^n$.

EXERCISE

1. Solve the following systems of linear equations after you have read the next section.

(a) $3x + y - z = 0$
  $x + y + z = 0$
    $y - z = 1$

(b) $2x - y + z = 1$
  $x + 3y - 2z = 0$
  $4x - 3y + z = 2$

(c) $4x + y + z + w = 1$
  $x - y + 2z - 3w = 0$
  $2x + y + 3z + 5w = 0$
  $x + y - z - w = 2$

(d) $x + 2y - 3z + 5w = 0$
  $2x + y - 4z - w = 1$
  $x + y + z + w = 0$
  $-x - y - z + w = 4$

§4. EXISTENCE OF DETERMINANTS

We come to the question of existence, and the problem of computing determinants. We shall define determinants by induction, and give a formula for computing them at the same time. We first deal with the 3×3 case.

We have already defined 2×2 determinants. Let

$$A = (a_{ij}) = \begin{pmatrix} a_{11} & a_{12} & a_{13} \\ a_{21} & a_{22} & a_{23} \\ a_{31} & a_{32} & a_{33} \end{pmatrix}$$

be a 3×3 matrix. We define its determinant according to the formula known as the expansion by a row, say the first row. That is, we define

(*) $\mathrm{Det}(A) = a_{11} \begin{vmatrix} a_{22} & a_{23} \\ a_{32} & a_{33} \end{vmatrix} - a_{12} \begin{vmatrix} a_{21} & a_{23} \\ a_{31} & a_{33} \end{vmatrix} + a_{13} \begin{vmatrix} a_{21} & a_{22} \\ a_{31} & a_{32} \end{vmatrix}.$

We may describe this sum as follows. Let A_{ij} be the matrix obtained from A by deleting the i-th row and j-th column. Then the sum expressing $\mathrm{Det}(A)$ can be written

$$a_{11} \mathrm{Det}(A_{11}) - a_{12} \mathrm{Det}(A_{12}) + a_{13} \mathrm{Det}(A_{13}).$$

In other words, each term consists of the product of an element of the first row and the determinant of the 2×2 matrix obtained by deleting the first row and the j-th column, and putting the appropriate sign to this term as shown.

Example 1. Let

$$A = \begin{pmatrix} 2 & 1 & 0 \\ 1 & 1 & 4 \\ -3 & 2 & 5 \end{pmatrix}.$$

Then

$$A_{11} = \begin{pmatrix} 1 & 4 \\ 2 & 5 \end{pmatrix}, \qquad A_{12} = \begin{pmatrix} 1 & 4 \\ -3 & 5 \end{pmatrix}, \qquad A_{13} = \begin{pmatrix} 1 & 1 \\ -3 & 2 \end{pmatrix}$$

and our formula for the determinant of A yields

$$\begin{aligned} \mathrm{Det}(A) &= 2 \begin{vmatrix} 1 & 4 \\ 2 & 5 \end{vmatrix} - 1 \begin{vmatrix} 1 & 4 \\ -3 & 5 \end{vmatrix} + 0 \begin{vmatrix} 1 & 1 \\ -3 & 2 \end{vmatrix} \\ &= 2(5 - 8) - 1(5 + 12) + 0 \\ &= -23. \end{aligned}$$

A direct computation shows that the definition of the determinant by (*) satisfies the three properties of Theorem 1, and consequently the other properties proved in §1 from these three. For instance, suppose that the first column is a sum of two columns:

$$A^1 = B + C, \qquad \text{that is,} \qquad \begin{pmatrix} a_{11} \\ a_{21} \\ a_{31} \end{pmatrix} = \begin{pmatrix} b_1 \\ b_2 \\ b_3 \end{pmatrix} + \begin{pmatrix} c_1 \\ c_2 \\ c_3 \end{pmatrix}.$$

Substituting in each term of (*), we see that each term splits into a sum of two terms corresponding to B and C. For instance,

$$a_{11} \begin{vmatrix} a_{22} & a_{23} \\ a_{31} & a_{33} \end{vmatrix} = b_1 \begin{vmatrix} a_{22} & a_{23} \\ a_{31} & a_{33} \end{vmatrix} + c_1 \begin{vmatrix} a_{22} & a_{23} \\ a_{31} & a_{33} \end{vmatrix},$$

$$a_{12} \begin{vmatrix} b_2 + c_2 & a_{23} \\ b_3 + c_3 & a_{33} \end{vmatrix} = a_{12} \begin{vmatrix} b_2 & a_{23} \\ b_3 & a_{33} \end{vmatrix} + a_{12} \begin{vmatrix} c_2 & a_{23} \\ c_3 & a_{33} \end{vmatrix},$$

and similarly for the third term. The proof with respect to the other columns is analogous. Furthermore, if t is a number, then

$$\mathrm{Det}(tA^1, A^2, A^3) = ta_{11} \begin{vmatrix} a_{22} & a_{23} \\ a_{32} & a_{33} \end{vmatrix} - a_{12} \begin{vmatrix} ta_{21} & a_{23} \\ ta_{31} & a_{33} \end{vmatrix} + a_{13} \begin{vmatrix} ta_{21} & a_{22} \\ ta_{31} & a_{32} \end{vmatrix}$$

$$= t \, \mathrm{Det}(A^1, A^2, A^3)$$

because each 2×2 determinant is linear in the first column, and we can take t outside each one of the second and third terms. Again the proof is similar with respect to the other columns. A direct substitution shows that if two adjacent columns are equal, then formula (*) yields 0 for the determinant. Finally, one sees at once that if A is the unit matrix, then $\mathrm{Det}(A) = 1$. Thus the three properties are verified.

In the above proof, we see that the properties of 2×2 determinants are used to prove the properties of 3×3 determinants.

Furthermore, there is no particular reason why we selected the expansion according to the first row. We could also have used the second row, and write a similar sum, namely:

$$-a_{21} \begin{vmatrix} a_{12} & a_{13} \\ a_{32} & a_{33} \end{vmatrix} + a_{22} \begin{vmatrix} a_{11} & a_{13} \\ a_{31} & a_{33} \end{vmatrix} - a_{23} \begin{vmatrix} a_{11} & a_{12} \\ a_{31} & a_{32} \end{vmatrix}$$

$$= -a_{21} \operatorname{Det}(A_{21}) + a_{22} \operatorname{Det}(A_{22}) - a_{23} \operatorname{Det}(A_{23}).$$

Again, each term is the product of a_{2j}, the determinant of the 2×2 matrix obtained by deleting the second row and j-th column, and putting the appropriate sign in front of each term. This sign is determined according to the pattern:

$$\begin{pmatrix} + & - & + \\ - & + & - \\ + & - & + \end{pmatrix}.$$

One can see directly that the determinant can be expanded according to any row by multiplying out all the terms, and expanding the 2×2 determinants, thus obtaining:

$$(**) \quad \operatorname{Det}(A) = a_{11}a_{22}a_{33} - a_{11}a_{32}a_{23} - a_{12}a_{21}a_{33} + a_{12}a_{23}a_{31}$$

$$+ a_{13}a_{21}a_{32} - a_{13}a_{22}a_{31}.$$

Furthermore, we can also expand according to columns following the same principle. For instance, expanding out according to the first column:

$$a_{11} \begin{vmatrix} a_{22} & a_{23} \\ a_{32} & a_{33} \end{vmatrix} - a_{21} \begin{vmatrix} a_{12} & a_{13} \\ a_{32} & a_{33} \end{vmatrix} + a_{31} \begin{vmatrix} a_{12} & a_{13} \\ a_{22} & a_{23} \end{vmatrix}$$

yields precisely the same six terms as in (**). Thus in the case of 3×3 determinants, we have the following result.

Theorem 4. *Determinants satisfy the rule for expansion according to rows and columns, and* $\operatorname{Det}(A) = \operatorname{Det}({}^t A)$. *In other words, the determinant of a matrix is equal to the determinant of its transpose.*

This last assertion follows because taking the transpose of a matrix changes rows into columns and vice versa. We shall see in the next section that the proofs given here for the 3×3 case apply in the general case.

With the above means at our disposal, we can now compute 3×3 determinants very efficiently. In doing so, we apply the operations described in property (6), which we now see are valid for rows or columns, since $\operatorname{Det}(A) = \operatorname{Det}({}^t A)$. We try to make as many entries in the matrix A

equal to 0. We try especially to make all but one element of a column (or row) equal to 0, and then expand according to that column (or row). The expansion will contain only one term, and reduces our computation to a 2 × 2 determinant.

Example 2. Compute the determinant

$$\begin{vmatrix} 3 & 0 & 1 \\ 1 & 2 & 5 \\ -1 & 4 & 2 \end{vmatrix}.$$

We already have 0 in the first row. We subtract twice the second row from the third row. Our determinant is then equal to

$$\begin{vmatrix} 3 & 0 & 1 \\ 1 & 2 & 5 \\ -3 & 0 & -8 \end{vmatrix}.$$

We expand according to the second column. The expansion has only one term $\neq 0$, with a + sign, and that is:

$$2\begin{vmatrix} 3 & 1 \\ -3 & -8 \end{vmatrix}.$$

The 2 × 2 determinant can be evaluated by our definition $ad - bc$, and we find $2(-24 - (-3)) = -42$.

In the sequel, we deal mostly with 2 × 2 and 3 × 3 matrices, so that the reader may omit the discussion of the general case, or simply read the statement of the definitions and properties, and omit the proofs.

The general case of $n \times n$ determinants is done by induction. Suppose that we have been able to define determinants of $n \times n$ matrices for all integers $< n$, satisfying our properties. Let i, j be a pair of integers between 1 and n. If we cross out the i-th row and j-th column in the $n \times n$ matrix A, we obtain an $(n - 1) \times (n - 1)$ matrix, which we denote by A_{ij}. It looks like this:

$$i\begin{pmatrix} a_{11} & \cdots & \overset{\displaystyle j}{|} & \cdots & a_{1n} \\ \vdots & & | & & \vdots \\ \rule{0pt}{0pt} & & \!\!\!\!\!\!\!\!a_{ij} & & \\ \vdots & & | & & \vdots \\ a_{n1} & \cdots & | & \cdots & a_{nn} \end{pmatrix}.$$

We give an expression for the determinant of an $n \times n$ matrix in terms of determinants of $(n - 1) \times (n - 1)$ matrices. Let i be an integer, $1 \leqq i \leqq n$. We define

$$D(A) = (-1)^{i+1}a_{i1} \operatorname{Det}(A_{i1}) + \cdots + (-1)^{i+n}a_{in} \operatorname{Det}(A_{in}).$$

Each A_{ij} is an $(n - 1) \times (n - 1)$ matrix.

This sum can be described in words. For each element of the i-th row, we have a contribution of one term in the sum. This term is equal to $+$ or $-$ the product of this element, times the determinant of the matrix obtained from A by deleting the i-th row and the corresponding column. The sign $+$ or $-$ is determined according to the chess-board pattern:

$$\begin{pmatrix} + & - & + & - & \cdots \\ - & + & - & + & \cdots \\ + & - & + & - & \cdots \\ & & \cdots & & \end{pmatrix}$$

This sum is called the *expansion of the determinant according to the i-th row*. We shall prove that this function D satisfies properties (1), (2), and (3).

Note that $D(A)$ is a sum of terms

$$(-1)^{i+j}a_{ij} \operatorname{Det}(A_{ij})$$

as j ranges from 1 to n.

1. Consider D as a function of the k-th column, and consider any term

$$(-1)^{i+j}a_{ij} \operatorname{Det}(A_{ij}).$$

If $j \neq k$, then a_{ij} does not depend on the k-th column, and $\operatorname{Det}(A_{ij})$ depends linearly on the k-th column. If $j = k$, then a_{ij} depends linearly on the k-th column, and $\operatorname{Det}(A_{ij})$ does not depend on the k-th column. In any case, our term depends linearly on the k-th column. Since $D(A)$ is a sum of such terms, it depends linearly on the k-th column, and property (1) follows.

2. Suppose two adjacent columns of A are equal, namely $A^k = A^{k+1}$. Let j be an index $\neq k$ or $k + 1$. Then the matrix A_{ij} has two adjacent equal columns, and hence its determinant is equal to 0. Thus the term corresponding to an index $j \neq k$ or $k + 1$ gives a zero contribution to $D(A)$. The other two terms can be written

$$(-1)^{i+k}a_{ik} \operatorname{Det}(A_{ik}) + (-1)^{i+k+1}a_{i,k+1} \operatorname{Det}(A_{i,k+1}).$$

The two matrices A_{ik} and $A_{i,k+1}$ are equal because of our assumption that the k-th column of A is equal to the $(k + 1)$-th column. Similarly, $a_{ik} = a_{i,k+1}$. Hence these two terms cancel since they occur with opposite signs. This proves property (2).

3. Let A be the unit matrix. Then $a_{ij} = 0$ unless $i = j$, in which case $a_{ii} = 1$. Each A_{ij} is the unit $(n - 1) \times (n - 1)$ matrix. The only term in the sum which gives a non-zero contribution is

$$(-1)^{i+i} a_{ii} \operatorname{Det}(A_{ii}),$$

which is equal to 1. This proves property (3).

Example 3. We wish to compute the determinant

$$\begin{vmatrix} 1 & 2 & 1 \\ -1 & 3 & 1 \\ 0 & 1 & 5 \end{vmatrix}.$$

We use the expansion according to the third row (because it has a zero in it), and only two non-zero terms occur:

$$(-1) \begin{vmatrix} 1 & 1 \\ -1 & 1 \end{vmatrix} + (-5) \begin{vmatrix} 1 & 2 \\ -1 & 3 \end{vmatrix}.$$

We can compute explicitly the 2×2 determinants as in §1, and thus we get the value -27 for the determinant of our 3×3 matrix.

It will be shown in a subsequent section that the determinant of a matrix A is equal to the determinant of its transpose. When we have proved this result, we will obtain:

Theorem 4_n. *Determinants satisfy the rule for expansion according to rows and columns. For any column A^j of the matrix $A = (a_{ij})$, we have*

$$D(A) = (-1)^{1+j} a_{1j} D(A_{1j}) + \cdots + (-1)^{n+j} a_{nj} D(A_{nj}).$$

In practice, the computation of a determinant is always done by using an expansion according to some row or column.

Example 4. We wish to compute the determinant

$$\begin{vmatrix} 1 & 3 & 1 & 1 \\ 2 & 1 & 5 & 2 \\ 1 & -1 & 2 & 3 \\ 4 & 1 & -3 & 7 \end{vmatrix}.$$

We add the third row to the second row, and then add the third row to the fourth row. This yields

$$\begin{vmatrix} 1 & 3 & 1 & 1 \\ 3 & 0 & 7 & 5 \\ 1 & -1 & 2 & 3 \\ 4 & 1 & -3 & 7 \end{vmatrix} = \begin{vmatrix} 1 & 3 & 1 & 1 \\ 3 & 0 & 7 & 5 \\ 1 & -1 & 2 & 3 \\ 5 & 0 & -1 & 10 \end{vmatrix}.$$

We then add three times the third row to the first row and get

$$\begin{vmatrix} 4 & 0 & 7 & 10 \\ 3 & 0 & 7 & 5 \\ 1 & -1 & 2 & 3 \\ 5 & 0 & -1 & 10 \end{vmatrix}$$

which we expand according to the third row. There is only one term, namely

$$\begin{vmatrix} 4 & 7 & 10 \\ 3 & 7 & 5 \\ 5 & -1 & 10 \end{vmatrix}$$

We subtract twice the second row from the first row, and then from the third row, yielding

$$\begin{vmatrix} -2 & -7 & 0 \\ 3 & 7 & 5 \\ -1 & -15 & 0 \end{vmatrix}$$

which we expand according to the third column, and get

$$- 5(30 - 7) = -5(23) = -115.$$

EXERCISES

1. Compute the following determinants.

(a) $\begin{vmatrix} 2 & 1 & 2 \\ 0 & 3 & -1 \\ 4 & 1 & 1 \end{vmatrix}$ (b) $\begin{vmatrix} 3 & -1 & 5 \\ -1 & 2 & 1 \\ -2 & 4 & 3 \end{vmatrix}$ (c) $\begin{vmatrix} 2 & 4 & 3 \\ -1 & 3 & 0 \\ 0 & 2 & 1 \end{vmatrix}$

(d) $\begin{vmatrix} 1 & 2 & -1 \\ 0 & 1 & 1 \\ 0 & 2 & 7 \end{vmatrix}$ (e) $\begin{vmatrix} -1 & 5 & 3 \\ 4 & 0 & 0 \\ 2 & 7 & 8 \end{vmatrix}$

2. Compute the following determinants.

(a) $\begin{vmatrix} 1 & 1 & -2 & 4 \\ 0 & 1 & 1 & 3 \\ 2 & -1 & 1 & 0 \\ 3 & 1 & 2 & 5 \end{vmatrix}$

(b) $\begin{vmatrix} -1 & 1 & 2 & 0 \\ 0 & 3 & 2 & 1 \\ 0 & 4 & 1 & 2 \\ 3 & 1 & 5 & 7 \end{vmatrix}$

(c) $\begin{vmatrix} 3 & 1 & 1 \\ 2 & 5 & 5 \\ 8 & 7 & 7 \end{vmatrix}$

(d) $\begin{vmatrix} 4 & -9 & 2 \\ 4 & -9 & 2 \\ 3 & 1 & 0 \end{vmatrix}$

(e) $\begin{vmatrix} 4 & -1 & 1 \\ 2 & 0 & 0 \\ 1 & 5 & 7 \end{vmatrix}$

(f) $\begin{vmatrix} 2 & 0 & 0 \\ 1 & 1 & 0 \\ 8 & 5 & 7 \end{vmatrix}$

(g) $\begin{vmatrix} 4 & 0 & 0 \\ 0 & 1 & 0 \\ 0 & 0 & 27 \end{vmatrix}$

(h) $\begin{vmatrix} 5 & 0 & 0 \\ 0 & 3 & 0 \\ 0 & 0 & 9 \end{vmatrix}$

3. In general, what is the determinant of a diagonal matrix

$$\begin{vmatrix} a_{11} & 0 & 0 & \cdots & 0 \\ 0 & a_{22} & 0 & \cdots & 0 \\ \vdots & \vdots & & & \vdots \\ 0 & 0 & \ddots & & 0 \\ 0 & 0 & 0 & \cdots & a_{nn} \end{vmatrix} \ ?$$

4. Compute the determinant $\begin{vmatrix} \cos\theta & -\sin\theta \\ \sin\theta & \cos\theta \end{vmatrix}$.

5. (a) Let x_1, x_2, x_3 be numbers. Show that

$$\begin{vmatrix} 1 & x_1 & x_1^2 \\ 1 & x_2 & x_2^2 \\ 1 & x_3 & x_3^2 \end{vmatrix} = (x_2 - x_1)(x_3 - x_1)(x_3 - x_2).$$

(b) If $x_1, \ldots, x_n$ are numbers, then show by induction that

$$\begin{vmatrix} 1 & x_1 & \cdots & x_1^{n-1} \\ 1 & x_2 & \cdots & x_2^{n-1} \\ & & \cdots & \\ 1 & x_n & \cdots & x_n^{n-1} \end{vmatrix} = \prod_{i<j} (x_j - x_i),$$

the symbol on the right meaning that it is the product of all terms $x_j - x_i$ with $i < j$ and i, j integers from 1 to n. This determinant is called the *Vandermonde* determinant V_n. To do the induction easily, multiply each column by x_1 and subtract it from the next column on the right, starting from the right-hand side. You will find that

$$V_n = (x_n - x_1) \cdots (x_2 - x_1)V_{n-1}.$$

6. Let A be a triangular $n \times n$ matrix, say a matrix such that all components below the diagonal are equal to 0.

$$A = \begin{pmatrix} a_{11} & & & & \\ 0 & a_{22} & & * & \\ 0 & 0 & \ddots & & \\ \vdots & \vdots & & \ddots & \\ 0 & 0 & \cdots & & a_{nn} \end{pmatrix}$$

What is $D(A)$?

7. If $a(t)$, $b(t)$, $c(t)$, $d(t)$ are functions of t, one can form the determinant

$$\begin{vmatrix} a(t) & b(t) \\ c(t) & d(t) \end{vmatrix},$$

just as with numbers. Write out in full the determinant

$$\begin{vmatrix} \sin t & \cos t \\ -\cos t & \sin t \end{vmatrix}.$$

8. Write out in full the determinant

$$\begin{vmatrix} t+1 & t-1 \\ t & 2t+5 \end{vmatrix}.$$

9. Let $f(t)$, $g(t)$ be two functions having derivatives of all orders. Let $\varphi(t)$ be the function obtained by taking the determinant

$$\varphi(t) = \begin{vmatrix} f(t) & g(t) \\ f'(t) & g'(t) \end{vmatrix}.$$

Show that

$$\varphi'(t) = \begin{vmatrix} f(t) & g(t) \\ f''(t) & g''(t) \end{vmatrix},$$

i.e. the derivative is obtained by taking the derivative of the bottom row.

10. Let

$$A(t) = \begin{pmatrix} b_1(t) & c_1(t) \\ b_2(t) & c_2(t) \end{pmatrix}$$

be a 2×2 matrix of differentiable functions. Let $B(t)$ and $C(t)$ be its column vectors. Let

$$\varphi(t) = \mathrm{Det}(A(t)).$$

Show that

$$\varphi'(t) = D\big(B'(t), C(t)\big) + D\big(B(t), C'(t)\big).$$

11. Let $\alpha_1, \ldots, \alpha_n$ be distinct numbers, $\neq 0$. Show that the functions

$$e^{\alpha_1 t}, \ldots, e^{\alpha_n t}$$

are linearly independent over the complex numbers. [*Hint:* Suppose we have a linear relation

$$c_1 e^{\alpha_1 t} + \cdots + c_n e^{\alpha_n t} = 0$$

with constants c_i, valid for all t. If not all c_i are 0, without loss of generality, we may assume that none of them is 0. Differentiate the above relation $n - 1$ times. You get a system of linear equations. The determinant of its coefficients must be zero. (Why?) Get a contradiction from this.]

12. For this exercise, we assume that the reader is acquainted with polynomials. If he is not, he can do it after reading further into the book.

    (a) Let P_{ij} $(i, j = 1, \ldots, n)$ be polynomials. Assume that all polynomials in a given column in the matrix

    $$\begin{pmatrix} P_{11} & \cdots & P_{1n} \\ \vdots & & \vdots \\ P_{n1} & \cdots & P_{nn} \end{pmatrix}$$

    have the same degree, and let $d_1, \ldots, d_n$ be these degrees. Let c_{ij} $(\neq 0)$ be the leading coefficient of P_{ij}. Let Q be the determinant of the above matrix. Show that Q has an expression

    $$Q(t) = ct^d + \text{terms of degree} < d$$

    where $c = \text{Det}(c_{ij})$. Hence if $\text{Det}(c_{ij}) \neq 0$, we see that $Q \neq 0$. (If you wish, do this only for $n = 2$, and then $n = 3$ using the expansion according to a column. The general case can be done by induction. Similarly, you may assume $n = 2$ or 3 in the subsequent parts of the exercise.)

    (b) Let D denote the derivative, $D = d/dt$. Let P be a polynomial, and α a number, $\alpha \neq 0$. Show that

    $$D(P(t)e^{\alpha t}) = (D + \alpha)P(t)e^{\alpha t},$$

    and by induction,

    $$D^k(P(t)e^{\alpha t}) = (D + \alpha)^k P(t)e^{\alpha t}.$$

    (c) Let $\alpha_1, \ldots, \alpha_n$ be distinct numbers $\neq 0$. Show that the functions $e^{\alpha_1 t}, \ldots, e^{\alpha_n t}$ are linearly independent over the polynomials, i.e. that if $P_1, \ldots, P_n$ are polynomials such that

    $$P_1(t)e^{\alpha_1 t} + \cdots + P_n(t)e^{\alpha_n t} = 0$$

    for all t, then $P_1, \ldots, P_n$ are the zero polynomials. [*Hint:* Differentiate the above expression $n - 1$ times. Prove that if $\alpha \neq 0$, then

$$\deg(D + \alpha)^k P = \deg P$$

for any polynomial P, and integer $k \geq 0$. You obtain a system of linear equations

$$P_{k1}(t)e^{\alpha_1 t} + \cdots + P_{kn}(t)e^{\alpha_n t} = 0$$

with $k = 0, \ldots, n - 1$. Hence the determinant $\mathrm{Det}(P_{kj})$ must be 0. Apply part (a) to get a contradiction. You should recognize the determinant of leading coefficients as being a special kind of determinant.]

§5. PERMUTATIONS

(*Note.* The reader who is allergic to combinatorial arguments is advised to understand only the statements of the propositions, and to omit their proofs.)

We shall deal only with permutations of the set of integers $\{1, \ldots, n\}$, which we denote by J_n. By definition, a *permutation* of this set is a map

$$\sigma : \{1, \ldots, n\} \to \{1, \ldots, n\}$$

of J_n into itself such that, if $i, j \in J_n$ and $i \neq j$ then $\sigma(i) \neq \sigma(j)$. If σ is such a permutation, then the set of integers

$$\{\sigma(1), \ldots, \sigma(n)\}$$

has n distinct elements, and hence consists again of the integers $1, \ldots, n$ in a different arrangement. Thus to each integer $j \in J_n$ there exists a unique integer k such that $\sigma(k) = j$. We can define the *inverse permutation*, denoted by σ^{-1}, as the map

$$\sigma^{-1} : J_n \to J_n$$

such that $\sigma^{-1}(k) =$ unique integer $j \in J_n$ such that $\sigma(j) = k$. If σ, τ are permutations of J_n, then we can form their composite map

$$\sigma \circ \tau,$$

and this map will again be a permutation. We shall usually omit the small circle, and write $\sigma\tau$ for the composite map. Thus

$$(\sigma\tau)(i) = \sigma\big(\tau(i)\big).$$

By definition, for any permutation σ, we have

$$\sigma\sigma^{-1} = id \qquad \text{and} \qquad \sigma^{-1}\sigma = id,$$

where id is the identity permutation, that is, the permutation such that $id(i) = i$ for all $i = 1, \ldots, n$.

If $\sigma_1, \ldots, \sigma_r$ are permutations of J_n, then the inverse of the composite map

$$\sigma_1 \cdots \sigma_r$$

is the permutation

$$\sigma_r^{-1} \cdots \sigma_1^{-1}.$$

This is trivially seen by direct multiplication.

A *transposition* is a permutation which interchanges two numbers and leaves the others fixed. The inverse of a transposition is obviously a transposition.

Proposition 1. *Every permutation of J_n can be expressed as a product of transpositions.*

Proof. We shall prove our assertion by induction on n. For $n = 1$, there is nothing to prove. Let $n > 1$ and assume the assertion proved for $n - 1$. Let σ be a permutation of J_n. Let $\sigma(n) = k$. Let τ be the transposition of J_n such that $\tau(k) = n$, $\tau(n) = k$. Then $\tau\sigma$ is a permutation such that

$$\tau\sigma(n) = \tau(k) = n.$$

In other words, $\tau\sigma$ leaves n fixed. We may therefore view $\tau\sigma$ as a permutation of J_{n-1}, and by induction, there exist transpositions $\tau_1, \ldots, \tau_s$ of J_{n-1}, leaving n fixed, such that

$$\tau\sigma = \tau_1 \cdots \tau_s.$$

We can now write

$$\sigma = \tau^{-1}\tau_1 \cdots \tau_s = \tau\tau_1 \cdots \tau_s,$$

thereby proving our proposition.

Example 1. A permutation σ of the integers $\{1, \ldots, n\}$ is denoted by

$$\begin{bmatrix} 1 & \cdots & n \\ \sigma(1) & \cdots & \sigma(n) \end{bmatrix}.$$

Thus

$$\begin{bmatrix} 1 & 2 & 3 \\ 2 & 1 & 3 \end{bmatrix}$$

denotes the permutation σ such that $\sigma(1) = 2$, $\sigma(2) = 1$, and $\sigma(3) = 3$. This permutation is in fact a transposition. If σ' is the permutation

$$\begin{bmatrix} 1 & 2 & 3 \\ 3 & 1 & 2 \end{bmatrix},$$

then $\sigma\sigma' = \sigma \circ \sigma'$ is the permutation such that

$$\sigma\sigma'(1) = \sigma\big(\sigma'(1)\big) = \sigma(3) = 3,$$
$$\sigma\sigma'(2) = \sigma\big(\sigma'(2)\big) = \sigma(1) = 2,$$
$$\sigma\sigma'(3) = \sigma\big(\sigma'(3)\big) = \sigma(2) = 1,$$

so that we can write

$$\sigma\sigma' = \begin{bmatrix} 1 & 2 & 3 \\ 3 & 2 & 1 \end{bmatrix}.$$

Example 2. We wish to express the permutation

$$\sigma = \begin{bmatrix} 1 & 2 & 3 \\ 3 & 1 & 2 \end{bmatrix}$$

as a product of permutations. Let τ be the transposition which interchanges 3 and 1, and leaves 2 fixed. Then using the definition, we find that

$$\tau\sigma = \begin{bmatrix} 1 & 2 & 3 \\ 1 & 3 & 2 \end{bmatrix}$$

so that $\tau\sigma$ is a transposition, which we denote by τ'. We can then write $\tau\sigma = \tau'$, so that

$$\sigma = \tau^{-1}\tau' = \tau\tau'$$

because $\tau^{-1} = \tau$. This is the desired product.

Example 3. Express the permutation

$$\sigma = \begin{bmatrix} 1 & 2 & 3 & 4 \\ 2 & 3 & 4 & 1 \end{bmatrix}$$

as a product of transpositions.

Let τ_1 be the transposition which interchanges 1 and 2, and leaves 3, 4 fixed. Then

$$\tau_1\sigma = \begin{bmatrix} 1 & 2 & 3 & 4 \\ 1 & 3 & 4 & 2 \end{bmatrix}.$$

Now let τ_2 be the transposition which interchanges 2 and 3, and leaves 1, 4 fixed. Then

$$\tau_2\tau_1\sigma = \begin{bmatrix} 1 & 2 & 3 & 4 \\ 1 & 2 & 4 & 3 \end{bmatrix}$$

and we see that $\tau_2\tau_1\sigma$ is a transposition, which we may denote by τ_3. Then we get $\tau_2\tau_1\sigma = \tau_3$ so that

$$\sigma = \tau_1\tau_2\tau_3.$$

The proof of the next proposition is the only long one of this section, and can be omitted without harm.

Proposition 2. *To each permutation σ of J_n it is possible to assign a sign 1 or -1, denoted by $\epsilon(\sigma)$, satisfying the following conditions:*
(a) *If τ is a transposition, then $\epsilon(\tau) = -1$.*
(b) *If σ, σ' are permutations of J_n, then*

$$\epsilon(\sigma\sigma') = \epsilon(\sigma)\epsilon(\sigma').$$

Proof. Let $x_1, \ldots, x_n$ be variables, and let σ be a permutation of J_n. Let P^+ be the set of pairs (i, j) with $1 \leq i < j \leq n$ such that $\sigma(i) < \sigma(j)$. Let P^- be the set of pairs (i, j) with $1 \leq i < j \leq n$ such that $\sigma(i) > \sigma(j)$. Let m be the number of pairs in P^-. This number m is called the number of *inversions* of σ. We let P be the set of all pairs (i, j) with $1 \leq i < j \leq n$. Then P is the union of P^+ and P^-, and P^+, P^- have no elements in common.

We consider the expression

$$\Delta_\sigma = \prod_{(i,j)\in P} [x_{\sigma(j)} - x_{\sigma(i)}].$$

The product symbol means that we must take the product over all pairs in P, of the terms $x_{\sigma(j)} - x_{\sigma(i)}$. Then we may decompose our product into two products, the first taken over all pairs in P^+, and the second taken over all pairs in P^-. Thus we may write our product in the form

$$\Delta_\sigma = \prod_{(i,j)\in P^+} [x_{\sigma(j)} - x_{\sigma(i)}] \prod_{(k,l)\in P^-} [x_{\sigma(l)} - x_{\sigma(k)}].$$

Inverting each factor in the second product, we find

$$\Delta_\sigma = \prod_{(i,j)\in P^+} [x_{\sigma(j)} - x_{\sigma(i)}] (-1)^m \prod_{(k,l)\in P^-} [x_{\sigma(k)} - x_{\sigma(l)}].$$

The pairs $(\sigma(i), \sigma(j))$ with $(i, j) \in P^+$ are all distinct, and similarly, the pairs $(\sigma(l), \sigma(k))$ with $(k, l) \in P^-$ are all distinct because σ is a permutation.

Furthermore, no pair $(\sigma(l), \sigma(k))$ with $(k, l) \in P^-$ can be equal to a pair $(\sigma(i), \sigma(j))$ with $(i, j) \in P^+$, for otherwise, $l = i$ and $k = j$, contradicting the fact that $k < l$. Hence the set of pairs

$$S = \begin{cases} (\sigma(i), \sigma(j)) & \text{with} \quad (i, j) \in P^+ \\ (\sigma(k), \sigma(l)) & \text{with} \quad (k, l) \in P^- \end{cases}$$

has as many elements as there are pairs in the union $P = P^+ \cup P^-$. But $P^+ \cup P^-$ is the set of all pairs of integers (i, j) with $1 \leq i < j \leq n$. Hence $S = P$.

We define $\epsilon(\sigma)$ to be $(-1)^m$, where m is the number of inversions of σ.

Then our products for Δ_σ may be rewritten

$$\prod_{(i,j)\in P} [x_{\sigma(j)} - x_{\sigma(i)}] = \epsilon(\sigma) \prod_{(i,j)\in P} [x_j - x_i].$$

Let σ' be a permutation. Substitute $\sigma'(\lambda)$ for x_λ, for each value $\lambda = 1, \ldots, n$. Then on the one hand,

$$\prod_{i<j} [\sigma'(\sigma(j)) - \sigma'(\sigma(i))] = \epsilon(\sigma) \prod_{i<j} [\sigma'(j) - \sigma'(i)]$$
$$= \epsilon(\sigma)\epsilon(\sigma') \prod_{i<j} (j - i),$$

and on the other hand, the product on the left is equal to

$$\epsilon(\sigma'\sigma) \prod_{i<j} (j - i).$$

From this we conclude that $\epsilon(\sigma'\sigma) = \epsilon(\sigma')\epsilon(\sigma)$.

To determine the sign of a transposition, we consider the set of pairs P^- associated with a transposition σ. Suppose that $1 \leq \alpha < \beta \leq n$ and that σ is a transposition such that $\sigma(\alpha) = \beta$ and $\sigma(\beta) = \alpha$. Then P^- consists of all pairs

$$(\alpha, l) \quad \text{with} \quad \alpha + 1 \leq l \leq \beta,$$
$$(k, \beta) \quad \text{with} \quad \alpha + 1 \leq k \leq \beta - 1.$$

Hence P^- will contain an odd number of pairs, whence the sign of the transposition is -1. This proves our proposition.

Corollary 1. *If a permutation σ of J_n is expressed as a product of transpositions,*

$$\sigma = \tau_1 \cdots \tau_s,$$

where each τ_i is a transposition, then s is even or odd according as $\epsilon(\sigma) = 1$ or -1.

Proof. We have

$$\epsilon(\sigma) = (-1)^s,$$

whence our assertion is clear.

Corollary 2. *If σ is a permutation of J_n, then*

$$\epsilon(\sigma) = \epsilon(\sigma^{-1}).$$

Proof. We have

$$1 = \epsilon(id) = \epsilon(\sigma\sigma^{-1}) = \epsilon(\sigma)\epsilon(\sigma^{-1}).$$

Hence either $\epsilon(\sigma)$ and $\epsilon(\sigma^{-1})$ are both equal to 1, or both equal to -1, as desired.

As a matter of terminology, a permutation is called *even* if its sign is 1, and it is called *odd* if its sign is -1. Thus every transposition is odd.

Example 4. The sign of the permutation σ in Example 2 is equal to 1 because $\sigma = \tau\tau'$. The sign of the permutation σ in Example 3 is equal to -1 because $\sigma = \tau_1\tau_2\tau_3$.

EXERCISES

1. Determine the sign of the following permutations.

(a) $\begin{bmatrix} 1 & 2 & 3 \\ 2 & 3 & 1 \end{bmatrix}$
(b) $\begin{bmatrix} 1 & 2 & 3 \\ 3 & 1 & 2 \end{bmatrix}$
(c) $\begin{bmatrix} 1 & 2 & 3 \\ 3 & 2 & 1 \end{bmatrix}$

(d) $\begin{bmatrix} 1 & 2 & 3 & 4 \\ 2 & 3 & 1 & 4 \end{bmatrix}$
(e) $\begin{bmatrix} 1 & 2 & 3 & 4 \\ 2 & 1 & 4 & 3 \end{bmatrix}$
(f) $\begin{bmatrix} 1 & 2 & 3 & 4 \\ 3 & 2 & 4 & 1 \end{bmatrix}$

(g) $\begin{bmatrix} 1 & 2 & 3 & 4 \\ 4 & 2 & 1 & 3 \end{bmatrix}$
(h) $\begin{bmatrix} 1 & 2 & 3 & 4 \\ 3 & 1 & 4 & 2 \end{bmatrix}$
(i) $\begin{bmatrix} 1 & 2 & 3 & 4 \\ 2 & 4 & 1 & 3 \end{bmatrix}$

2. In each one of the cases of Exercise 1, write the inverse of the permutation.

3. Show that the number of odd permutations of $\{1, \ldots, n\}$ for $n \geq 2$ is equal to the number of even permutations.

§6. UNIQUENESS

Before proceeding with the main part of the argument, we make some remarks on repeated linear maps, as in property (1). Consider first the case $n = 2$. If we have to expand

$$D(3A + 5B, 2A - B),$$

where A, B are 2-vectors, then using property (1), we obtain a sum of four terms, namely

$$D(3A, 2A - B) + D(5B, 2A - B)$$
$$= D(3A, 2A) + D(3A, -B) + D(5B, 2A) + D(5B, -B)$$
$$= 6D(A, A) - 3D(A, B) + 10D(B, A) - 5D(B, B).$$

Observe that we have used the fact that when $c = -1$ in property (1),

$$D(A, -B) = -D(A, B).$$

In such an expression, we note that $D(A, A) = 0$ and $D(B, B) = 0$. Thus only two terms remain to give a contribution which is not *a priori* equal to 0.

To give another example, let us expand $D(2A + B - C, 3E + F)$ where A, B, C, E, F are vectors. Using (1) repeatedly, we obtain six terms, namely

$$6D(A, E) + 2D(A, F) + 3D(B, E) + D(B, F) - 3D(C, E) - D(C, F).$$

More generally, suppose that we have a determinant

$$D(x_1 A^1 + \cdots + x_n A^n, y_1 B^1 + \cdots + y_m B^m)$$

with numbers $x_1, \ldots, x_n, y_1, \ldots, y_m$ and vectors

$$A^1, \ldots, A^n, B^1, \ldots, B^m.$$

Using (1) repeatedly, this determinant is equal to

$$D(x_1 A^1, y_1 B^1 + \cdots + y_m B^m) + \cdots + D(x_n A^n, y_1 B^1 + \cdots + y_m B^m).$$

Each expression can then be further expanded, and our determinant is equal to a double sum,

$$D(x_1 A^1, y_1 B^1) + \cdots + D(x_1 A^1, y_m B^m)$$
$$\vdots \qquad\qquad\qquad \vdots$$
$$+ D(x_n A^n, y_1 B^1) + \cdots + D(x_n A^n, y_m B^m).$$

The principle involved in expanding such a determinant is the following. We select one term from the first sum, one term from the second sum, and take the sum over all such terms. Thus our double sum may be written

$$\sum_{i=1}^{n} \sum_{j=1}^{m} x_i y_j D(A^i, B^j).$$

The same principle applies when we deal with more general expansions.

We shall find an explicit expression of a determinant satisfying conditions (1), (2) and (3) in terms of the components of the matrix. Since properties (4), (5) and (6) are consequences of (1), (2), and (3), we may use them freely.

We shall now give the uniqueness proof in the case of 2×2 determinants. Let

$$A = \begin{pmatrix} a & b \\ c & d \end{pmatrix}$$

be a 2×2 matrix, and let

$$A^1 = \begin{pmatrix} a \\ c \end{pmatrix}, \qquad A^2 = \begin{pmatrix} b \\ d \end{pmatrix}$$

be its column vectors. We can write

$$A^1 = aE^1 + cE^2 \qquad \text{and} \qquad A^2 = bE^1 + dE^2,$$

where E^1, E^2 are the unit column vectors. Then

$$
\begin{aligned}
D(A) = D(A^1, A^2) &= D(aE^1 + cE^2, bE^1 + dE^2) \\
&= ab\,D(E^1, E^1) + cb\,D(E^2, E^1) + ad\,D(E^1, E^2) + cd\,D(E^2, E^2) \\
&= -bc\,D(E^1, E^2) + ad\,D(E^1, E^2) \\
&= ad - bc.
\end{aligned}
$$

This proves that any function D satisfying the basic properties of a determinant is given by the formula of §1, namely $ad - bc$.

The proof in general is entirely similar, taking into account the n components. It is based on an expansion similar to the one we have just used in the 2×2 case. We can formulate it in a lemma.

Lemma. Let $X^1, \ldots, X^n$ be n vectors in n-space. Let $B = (b_{ij})$ be an $n \times n$ matrix, and let

$$
\begin{aligned}
A^1 &= b_{11}X^1 + \cdots + b_{n1}X^n \\
&\;\;\vdots \qquad\qquad\;\; \vdots \\
A^n &= b_{1n}X^1 + \cdots + b_{nn}X^n.
\end{aligned}
$$

Then

$$
D(A^1, \ldots, A^n) = \sum_{\sigma} \epsilon(\sigma) b_{\sigma(1),1} \cdots b_{\sigma(n),n} D(X^1, \ldots, X_n),
$$

where the sum is taken over all permutations σ of $\{1, \ldots, n\}$.

Proof. We must compute

$$
D(b_{11}X^1 + \cdots + b_{n1}X^n, \ldots, b_{1n}X^1 + \cdots + b_{nn}X^n).
$$

Using property (1), we can express this as a sum of terms

$$
D(b_{\sigma(1),1} X^{\sigma(1)}, \ldots, b_{\sigma(n),n} X^{\sigma(n)}),
$$

where $\sigma(1), \ldots, \sigma(n)$ denote a choice of an integer between 1 and n for each value of $1, \ldots, n$. Thus σ is a mapping of the set of integers $\{1, \ldots, n\}$ into itself. By property (1), each one of the above terms can also be written

$$
b_{\sigma(1),1} \cdots b_{\sigma(n),n} D(X^{\sigma(1)}, \ldots, X^{\sigma(n)}).
$$

If some σ assigns the same integer to distinct values i, j between 1 and n, then the determinant on the right has two equal columns, and hence is equal to 0. Consequently we can take our sum only for those σ which are such that $\sigma(i) \neq \sigma(j)$ whenever $i \neq j$, namely *permutations*. Instead of saying that we take the sum for all permutations σ, we abbreviate the notation with the usual $\sum$ symbol. Thus we can write

$$
D(A^1, \ldots, A^n) = \sum_{\sigma} b_{\sigma(1),1} \cdots b_{\sigma(n),n} D(X^{\sigma(1)}, \ldots, X^{\sigma(n)}).
$$

The vectors $X^{\sigma(1)}, \ldots, X^{\sigma(n)}$ occur in a permutation of the standard arrangement $X^1, \ldots, X^n$. If we interchange any two distinct columns, this corresponds to a transposition of $\{1, \ldots, n\}$, and thus the determinant changes by a sign. By a succession of interchanges of adjacent columns, we can reestablish the standard order for the vectors. If $m(\sigma)$ is the number of transpositions of adjacent column vectors which have to be carried out to reestablish the standard ordering of the unit vectors, then

$$D(X^{\sigma(1)}, \ldots, X^{\sigma(n)}) = (-1)^{m(\sigma)} D(X^1, \ldots, X^n)$$
$$= \epsilon(\sigma) D(X^1, \ldots, X^n).$$

Substituting this for our expression of $D(A^1, \ldots, A^n)$ obtained above, we find the desired expression of the lemma.

Theorem 5. *Determinants are uniquely determined by properties* (1), (2), *and* (3). *Let* $A = (a_{ij})$. *This determinant satisfies the expression*

$$D(A^1, \ldots, A^n) = \sum_{\sigma} \epsilon(\sigma) a_{\sigma(1),1} \cdots a_{\sigma(n),n},$$

where the sum is taken over all permutations of the integers $\{1, \ldots, n\}$.

Proof. We let $X^j = E^j$ be the unit vector having 1 in the j-th component, and we let $b_{ij} = a_{ij}$ in the Lemma. Since by hypothesis we have $D(E^1, \ldots, E^n) = 1$, we see that the formula of Theorem 5 drops out at once.

EXERCISES

1. Let $A^1, \ldots, A^n$ be column vectors of dimension n and assume that they are linearly independent. Show that $D(A^1, \ldots, A^n) \neq 0$. [*Hint:* Express each one of the standard unit vectors $E^1, \ldots, E^n$ viewed as column vectors as linear combinations of $A^1, \ldots, A^n$. Using the fact that $D(E^1, \ldots, E^n) = 1$, and properties (1) and (2), prove the assertion.] Thus in view of Theorem 3, we can now say that $A^1, \ldots, A^n$ are linearly dependent if and only if $D(A^1, \ldots, A^n) = 0$.

2. Let V, V' be vector spaces. Suppose that we have a product, defined between pairs of elements of V, and denoted by $v \wedge w$ for v, w elements of V. We assume that the values of the product lie in the space V', that is $v \wedge w$ is an element of V' for all v, w in V. Assume that the product satisfies the following conditions:

   AP 1. *We have* $(u + v) \wedge w = u \wedge w + v \wedge w$ *and*

   $$u \wedge (v + w) = u \wedge v + u \wedge w$$

   for all u, v, w *in* V. *Also for any number* c,

   $$(cu) \wedge v = c(u \wedge v) = u \wedge (cv).$$

AP 2. *We have* $u \wedge u = 0$ *for all* u *in* V.

Prove the following statements:

(a) We have $u \wedge v = -v \wedge u$.

(b) Let z be an element of V', and assume that $V = \mathbf{R}^2$. Let e^1, e^2 be the two unit vectors of $\mathbf{R}^2$. Show that a product satisfying AP 1, AP 2, and the condition that $e^1 \wedge e^2 = z$ is uniquely determined by these three conditions.

(c) Let z_1, z_2, z_3 be elements of V' and let $V = \mathbf{R}^3$. Let e^1, e^2, e^3 be the three unit vectors of $\mathbf{R}^3$. Show that a product satisfying AP 1, AP 2, and the conditions

$$e^1 \wedge e^2 = z_1, \qquad e^1 \wedge e^3 = z_2, \qquad e^2 \wedge e^3 = z_3$$

is uniquely determined. [*Hint:* Write arbitrary elements of V in terms of the unit vectors and expand.]

Compare (c) with the formulas for the cross product given in Chapter I. Observe that the cross product satisfies AP 1 and AP 2. A product satisfying these conditions is called an *alternating product*.

3. Let V, V' be vector spaces, and consider a product as described in Exercise 2, satisfying conditions AP 1, and AP 2.

(a) Assume that dim $V = 2$. Show that the set of all elements $v \wedge w$ with v, w in V is a subspace of V', of dimension 0 or 1.

(b) Assume that dim $V = 3$. Let U' be the subspace of V' generated by all elements $v \wedge w$ with v, w in V. Show that U' has dimension $\leqq 3$.

§7. DETERMINANT OF A TRANSPOSE

Theorem 6. *Let A be a square matrix. Then* $\mathrm{Det}(A) = \mathrm{Det}({}^t A)$.

Proof. In Theorem 5, we had

(*) $$\mathrm{Det}(A) = \sum_\sigma \epsilon(\sigma) a_{\sigma(1),1} \cdots a_{\sigma(n),n}.$$

Let σ be a permutation of $\{1, \ldots, n\}$. If $\sigma(j) = k$, then $\sigma^{-1}(k) = j$. We can therefore write

$$a_{\sigma(j),j} = a_{k,\sigma^{-1}(k)}.$$

In a product

$$a_{\sigma(1),1} \cdots a_{\sigma(n),n}$$

each integer k from 1 to n occurs precisely once among the integers $\sigma(1), \ldots, \sigma(n)$. Hence this product can be written

$$a_{1,\sigma^{-1}(1)} \cdots a_{n,\sigma^{-1}(n)},$$

and our sum (*) is equal to

$$\sum_\sigma \epsilon(\sigma^{-1}) a_{1,\sigma^{-1}(1)} \cdots a_{n,\sigma^{-1}(n)},$$

because $\epsilon(\sigma) = \epsilon(\sigma^{-1})$. In this sum, each term corresponds to a permutation σ. However, as σ ranges over all permutations, so does σ^{-1} because a permutation determines its inverse uniquely. Hence our sum is equal to

$$(**) \qquad \sum_\sigma \epsilon(\sigma)a_{1,\sigma(1)} \cdots a_{n,\sigma(n)}.$$

The sum (**) is precisely the sum giving the expanded form of the determinant of the transpose of A. Hence we have proved what we wanted.

§8. DETERMINANT OF A PRODUCT

We shall prove the important rule:

Theorem 7. *Let A, B be two $n \times n$ matrices. Then*

$$\text{Det}(AB) = \text{Det}(A)\,\text{Det}(B).$$

The determinant of a product is equal to the product of the determinants.

Proof. Let $A = (a_{ij})$ and $B = (b_{jk})$:

$$\begin{pmatrix} a_{11} & \cdots & a_{1n} \\ \vdots & & \vdots \\ a_{n1} & \cdots & a_{nn} \end{pmatrix} \begin{pmatrix} b_{11} & \cdots & b_{1k} & \cdots & b_{1n} \\ \vdots & & \vdots & & \vdots \\ b_{n1} & \cdots & b_{nk} & \cdots & b_{nn} \end{pmatrix}.$$

Let $AB = C$, and let C^k be the k-th column of C. Then by definition,

$$C^k = b_{1k}A^1 + \cdots + b_{nk}A^n.$$

Thus

$$\begin{aligned} D(AB) &= D(C^1, \ldots, C^n) \\ &= D(b_{11}A^1 + \cdots + b_{n1}A^n, \ldots, b_{1n}A^1 + \cdots + b_{nn}A^n). \end{aligned}$$

If we expand this out using the Lemma before Theorem 5, we find a sum

$$\begin{aligned} \sum_\sigma D(b_{\sigma(1),1}A^{\sigma(1)}, \ldots, b_{\sigma(n),n}A^{\sigma(n)}) \\ = \sum_\sigma b_{\sigma(1),1} \cdots b_{\sigma(n),n}D(A^{\sigma(1)}, \ldots, A^{\sigma(n)}) \\ = \sum_\sigma \epsilon(\sigma)b_{\sigma(1),1} \cdots b_{\sigma(n),n}D(A^1, \ldots, A^n). \end{aligned}$$

According to the formula for determinants which we found, this is equal to $D(B)D(A)$, as was to be shown.

Corollary. *Let A be an invertible $n \times n$ matrix. Then*

$$\text{Det}(A^{-1}) = \text{Det}(A)^{-1}.$$

Proof. We have $1 = D(I) = D(AA^{-1}) = D(A)D(A^{-1})$. This proves what we wanted.

§9. INVERSE OF A MATRIX

Let A be an $n \times n$ matrix. If B is a matrix such that $AB = I$ and $BA = I$ ($I =$ unit $n \times n$ matrix), then we called B an *inverse* of A, and we write $B = A^{-1}$. If there exists an inverse of A, then it is unique. Indeed, let C be an inverse of A. Then $CA = I$. Multiplying by B on the right, we obtain $CAB = B$. But $CAB = C(AB) = CI = C$. Hence $C = B$. A similar argument works for $AC = I$.

Theorem 8. *Let $A = (a_{ij})$ be an $n \times n$ matrix, and assume that $D(A) \neq 0$. Then A is invertible. Let E^j be the j-th column unit vector, and let*

$$b_{ij} = \frac{D(A^1, \ldots, E^j, \ldots, A^n)}{D(A)},$$

where E^j occurs in the i-th place. Then the matrix $B = (b_{ij})$ is an inverse for A.

Proof. Let $X = (X_{ij})$ be an unknown $n \times n$ matrix. We wish to solve for the components x_{ij}, so that they satisfy $AX = I$. From the definition of products of matrices, this means that for each j, we must solve

$$E^j = x_{1j}A^1 + \cdots + x_{nj}A^n.$$

This is a system of linear equations, which can be solved uniquely by Cramer's rule, and we obtain

$$x_{ij} = \frac{D(A^1, \ldots, E^j, \ldots, A^n)}{D(A)},$$

which is the formula given in the theorem.

We must still prove that $XA = I$. Note that $D({}^tA) \neq 0$. Hence by what we have already proved, we can find a matrix Y such that ${}^tA Y = I$. Taking transposes, we obtain ${}^tYA = I$. Now we have

$$I = {}^tY(AX)A = {}^tYA(XA) = XA,$$

thereby proving what we want, namely that $X = B$ is an inverse for A.

We can write out the components of the matrix B in Theorem 8 as follows:

$$b_{ij} = \frac{\begin{vmatrix} a_{11} & \cdots & 0 & \cdots & a_{1n} \\ \vdots & & \vdots & & \vdots \\ a_{j1} & \cdots & 1 & \cdots & a_{jn} \\ \vdots & & \vdots & & \vdots \\ a_{n1} & \cdots & 0 & \cdots & a_{nn} \end{vmatrix}}{\text{Det}(A)}.$$

If we expand the determinant in the numerator according to the i-th column, then all terms but one are equal to 0, and hence we obtain the numerator of b_{ij} as a subdeterminant of $\mathrm{Det}(A)$. Let A_{ij} be the matrix obtained from A by deleting the i-th row and the j-th column. Then

$$b_{ij} = \frac{(-1)^{i+j}\,\mathrm{Det}(A_{ji})}{\mathrm{Det}(A)}$$

(note the reversal of indices!) and thus we have the formula

$$A^{-1} = \text{transpose of } \left(\frac{(-1)^{i+j}\,\mathrm{Det}(A_{ij})}{\mathrm{Det}(A)}\right).$$

A square matrix whose determinant is $\neq 0$, or equivalently which admits an inverse, is called *non-singular*.

EXERCISES

1. Find the inverses of the matrices in Exercise 1, §4.

2. Using the fact that if A, B are two $n \times n$ matrices then

$$\mathrm{Det}(AB) = \mathrm{Det}(A)\,\mathrm{Det}(B),$$

prove that a matrix A such that $\mathrm{Det}(A) = 0$ does not have an inverse.

3. Write down explicitly the inverse of a 2×2 matrix

$$\begin{pmatrix} a & b \\ c & d \end{pmatrix}.$$

Chapter XIII

Applications to Functions of
Several Variables

Having acquired the language of linear maps and matrices, we shall be able to define the derivative of a mapping, or rather, of a differentiable mapping. The theoretical considerations involved in the proof of the general chain rule of §3 become of course a little abstract. But you should note that it is precisely the availability of the notion of linear mapping which allows us to give a statement of the chain rule, and a proof, which runs exactly parallel to the proof for functions of one variable, as given in the *First Course*. The analysis profits from algebra, and conversely, the algebra of linear mappings finds a neat application which enhances its attractiveness.

§1. THE DERIVATIVE AS A LINEAR MAP

We shall interpret our notion of differentiability given in Chapter III in terms of linear mappings.

Let U be an open set in $\mathbf{R}^n$. Let f be a function defined on U. Let P be a point of U, and assume that f is differentiable at P. Then there is a vector A, and a function g such that for all small vectors H we can write

$$(1) \qquad f(P + H) = f(P) + A \cdot H + \|H\|g(H),$$

and

$$(2) \qquad \lim_{\|H\| \to 0} g(H) = 0.$$

The vector A, expressed in terms of coordinates, is none other than the vector of partial derivatives:

$$A = \operatorname{grad} f(P) = \big(D_1 f(P), \ldots, D_n f(P)\big).$$

We have seen that there is a linear map $L = L_A$ such that

$$L(H) = A \cdot H.$$

Our condition that f is differentiable may therefore be expressed by saying that there is a linear map $L: \mathbf{R}^n \to \mathbf{R}$ and a function g defined for

519

sufficiently small H, such that

(3) $$f(P + H) = f(P) + L(H) + \|H\|g(H)$$

and

$$\lim_{\|H\| \to 0} g(H) = 0.$$

In the case of functions of one variable, we have of course the same kind of formula, namely

$$f(a + h) = f(a) + ch + |h|g(h)$$

where

$$\lim_{h \to 0} g(h) = 0.$$

Here, a, h are numbers, and so is the ordinary derivative c. But the map $L_c: \mathbf{R} \to \mathbf{R}$ such that $L_c(h) = ch$ (multiplication by the number c) is a linear map, so that also in this case, we can write

$$f(a + h) = f(a) + L_c(h) + |h|g(h).$$

Up to now, we did not define the notion of derivative for functions of several variables. We now define the derivative of f at P to be this linear map, which we shall denote by $Df(P)$ or also $f'(P)$. This notation is therefore entirely similar to the notation used for functions of one variable. We could not make the definition before we knew what a linear map is. All the theory developed in Chapters II through VII could be carried out knowing only dot products, and this is the reason we postponed making the general definition of derivative until now.

If L is a linear map from one vector space into another, then it will be useful to omit some parentheses in order to simplify the notation. Thus we shall sometimes write Lv instead of $L(v)$. With this convention, we can write (3) in the form

(4) $$f(P + H) = f(P) + Df(P)H + \|H\|g(H),$$

or also

(5) $$f(P + H) = f(P) + f'(P)H + \|H\|g(H).$$

These ways of expressing differentiability are those which generalize to arbitrary mappings.

Let U be an open set in $\mathbf{R}^n$. Let $F: U \to \mathbf{R}^m$ be a mapping. Let P be a point of U. We shall say that F is *differentiable* at P if there exists a linear map

$$L: \mathbf{R}^n \to \mathbf{R}^m$$

and a mapping G defined for all vectors H sufficiently small, such that we have

$$(6) \qquad F(P + H) = F(P) + LH + \|H\|G(H)$$

and

$$(7) \qquad \lim_{\|H\| \to 0} G(H) = O.$$

If such a linear mapping L exists, then we interpret (6) as saying that L approximates F up to an error term whose magnitude is small, near the point P.

A linear map L satisfying conditions (6) and (7) will be said to be *tangent* to F at P. It is also said to be the best linear approximation to F at P.

Just as before, we define a map ψ defined for small H to be $o(H)$ ("little oh of H") if

$$\lim_{\|H\| \to 0} \frac{\psi(H)}{\|H\|} = O.$$

Then we can write our definition of differentiability in the form

$$F(P + H) = F(P) + L(H) + o(H),$$

where L is a linear map.

Theorem 1. *Suppose that there exist linear maps L, M which are tangent to F at P. Then $L = M$. In other words, if there exists one linear map which is tangent to F at P, then there is only one.*

Proof. Suppose that there are two mappings G_1, G_2 such that for all sufficiently small H, we have

$$F(P + H) = F(P) + LH + \|H\|G_1(H),$$
$$F(P + H) = F(P) + MH + \|H\|G_2(H),$$

and

$$\lim_{\|H\| \to 0} G_1(H) = O, \qquad \lim_{\|H\| \to 0} G_2(H) = O.$$

We must show that for any vector Y we have $LY = MY$. Let t range over small positive numbers. Then tY is small, and $P + tY$ lies in U. Thus $F(P + tY)$ is defined. By hypothesis, we have

$$F(P + tY) = F(P) + L(tY) + \|tY\|G_1(tY),$$
$$F(P + tY) = F(P) + M(tY) + \|tY\|G_2(tY).$$

Subtracting, we obtain

$$O = L(tY) - M(tY) + \|tY\|[G_1(tY) - G_2(tY)].$$

Let $G = G_1 - G_2$. Since L, M are linear, we can write $L(tY) = tL(Y)$ and $M(tY) = tM(Y)$. Consequently, we obtain

$$tM(Y) - tL(Y) = t\| Y\|G(tY).$$

Take $t \neq 0$. Dividing by t yields

$$M(Y) - L(Y) = \| Y\|G(tY).$$

As t approaches 0, $G(tY)$ approaches O also. Hence the right-hand side of this last equation approaches O. But $M(Y) - L(Y)$ is a fixed vector. The only way this is possible is that $M(Y) - L(Y) = O$, in other words, $M(Y) = L(Y)$, as was to be shown.

If there exists a linear map tangent to F at P, we shall denote this linear map by $F'(P)$, or $DF(P)$ and call it the *derivative* of F at P. We may therefore write

$$F(P + H) = F(P) + F'(P)H + \|H\|G(H)$$

instead of (6).

In the next section, we shall see how the linear map $F'(P)$ can be computed, or rather how its matrix can be computed when we deal with vectors as n-tuples.

EXERCISES

1. Let $f: \mathbf{R} \to \mathbf{R}$ be a function, and let a be a number. Assume that there exists a linear map L tangent to f at a. Show that

$$L(1) = \lim_{h \to 0} \frac{f(a + h) - f(a)}{h}.$$

2. Conversely, assume that the limit

$$\lim_{h \to 0} \frac{f(a + h) - f(a)}{h}$$

exists and is equal to a number b. Let L_b be the linear map such that $L_b(x) = bx$ for all numbers x. Show that L_b is tangent to f at a. It is customary to identify the number b and the linear map L_b, and to call either one the derivative of f at a.

3. Let $L: \mathbf{R} \to V$ be a linear map from the reals into some vector space V. Show that there is some element v in V such that $L(x) = xv$ for all numbers x.

4. Going back to Chapter II, let $X(t)$ be a curve, defined for all numbers t, say. Discuss in a manner analogous to Exercises 1 and 2 the derivative dX/dt, and the linear map $L_t: \mathbf{R} \to \mathbf{R}^n$ which is tangent to X at t.

§2. THE JACOBIAN MATRIX

Throughout this section, all our vectors will be vertical vectors. We let $D_1, \ldots, D_n$ be the usual partial derivatives. Thus $D_i = \partial/\partial x_i$.

Let $F: \mathbf{R}^n \to \mathbf{R}^m$ be a mapping. We can represent F by coordinate functions. In other words, there exist functions $f_1, \ldots, f_m$ such that

$$F(X) = \begin{pmatrix} f_1(X) \\ f_2(X) \\ \vdots \\ f_m(X) \end{pmatrix} = {}^t(f_1(X), \ldots, f_m(X)).$$

To simplify the typography, we shall sometimes write a vertical vector as the transpose of a horizontal vector, as we have just done.

We view X as a column vector, $X = {}^t(x_1, \ldots, x_n)$.

Let us assume that the partial derivatives of each function f_i $(i = 1, \ldots, m)$ exist. We can then form the matrix of partial derivatives:

$$\left(\frac{\partial f_i}{\partial x_j} \right) = \begin{pmatrix} \dfrac{\partial f_1}{\partial x_1} & \dfrac{\partial f_1}{\partial x_2} & \cdots & \dfrac{\partial f_1}{\partial x_n} \\ \dfrac{\partial f_2}{\partial x_1} & \dfrac{\partial f_2}{\partial x_2} & \cdots & \dfrac{\partial f_2}{\partial x_n} \\ \vdots & \vdots & & \vdots \\ \dfrac{\partial f_m}{\partial x_1} & \dfrac{\partial f_m}{\partial x_2} & \cdots & \dfrac{\partial f_m}{\partial x_n} \end{pmatrix} = \begin{matrix} D_1 f_1(X) & \cdots & D_n f_1(X) \\ \vdots & & \vdots \\ D_1 f_m(X) & \cdots & D_n f_m(X) \end{matrix}$$

$i = 1, \ldots, m$ and $j = 1, \ldots, n$. This matrix is called the *Jacobian* matrix of F, and is denoted by $J_F(X)$.

In the case of two variables (x, y), say F is given by functions (f, g), so that

$$F(x, y) = (f(x, y), g(x, y)),$$

then Jacobian matrix is

$$J_F(x, y) = \begin{pmatrix} \dfrac{\partial f}{\partial x} & \dfrac{\partial f}{\partial y} \\ \dfrac{\partial g}{\partial x} & \dfrac{\partial g}{\partial y} \end{pmatrix}.$$

(As we have done just now, we sometimes write the vectors horizontally, although to be strictly correct, they should be written vertically.)

Example 1. Let $F: \mathbf{R}^2 \to \mathbf{R}^2$ be the mapping defined by

$$F(x, y) = \begin{pmatrix} x^2 + y^2 \\ e^{xy} \end{pmatrix} = \begin{pmatrix} f(x, y) \\ g(x, y) \end{pmatrix}.$$

Find the Jacobian matrix $J_F(P)$ for $P = (1, 1)$.

The Jacobian matrix at an arbitrary point (x, y) is

$$\begin{pmatrix} \dfrac{\partial f}{\partial x} & \dfrac{\partial f}{\partial y} \\[2mm] \dfrac{\partial g}{\partial x} & \dfrac{\partial g}{\partial y} \end{pmatrix} = \begin{pmatrix} 2x & 2y \\ ye^x & xe^y \end{pmatrix}.$$

Hence when $x = 1, y = 1$, we find:

$$J_F(1, 1) = \begin{pmatrix} 2 & 2 \\ e & e \end{pmatrix}.$$

Example 2. Let $F: \mathbf{R}^2 \to \mathbf{R}^3$ be the mapping defined by

$$F(x, y) = \begin{pmatrix} xy \\ \sin x \\ x^2 y \end{pmatrix}.$$

Find $J_F(P)$ at the point $P = (\pi, \pi/2)$.

The Jacobian matrix at an arbitrary point (x, y) is

$$\begin{pmatrix} y & x \\ \cos x & 0 \\ 2xy & x^2 \end{pmatrix}.$$

Hence

$$J_F\left(\pi, \frac{\pi}{2}\right) = \begin{pmatrix} \pi/2 & \pi \\ -1 & 0 \\ \pi^2 & \pi^2 \end{pmatrix}.$$

Theorem 2. *Let U be an open set in $\mathbf{R}^n$. Let $F: U \to \mathbf{R}^m$ be a mapping, having coordinate functions $f_1, \ldots, f_m$. Assume that each function f_i is differentiable at a point X of U. Then F is differentiable at X, and the matrix representing the linear map $DF(X) = F'(X)$ is the Jacobian matrix $J_F(X)$.*

Proof. For each integer i between 1 and n, there is a function g_i such that

$$\lim_{\|H\| \to 0} g_i(H) = 0,$$

and such that we can write

$$f_i(X + H) = f_i(X) + \operatorname{grad} f_i (X) \cdot H + \|H\| g_i(H).$$

We view X and $F(X)$ as vertical vectors. By definition, we can then write

$$F(X + H) = {}^t\big(f_1(X + H), \ldots, f_m(X + H)\big).$$

Hence

$$F(X + H) = \begin{pmatrix} f_1(X) \\ \vdots \\ f_m(X) \end{pmatrix} + \begin{pmatrix} \text{grad } f_1\,(X) \cdot H \\ \vdots \\ \text{grad } f_m\,(X) \cdot H \end{pmatrix} + \|H\| \begin{pmatrix} g_1(H) \\ \vdots \\ g_m(H) \end{pmatrix}.$$

The term in the middle, involving the gradients, is precisely equal to the product of the Jacobian matrix, times H, i.e. to

$$J_F(X)H.$$

Let $G(H) = {}^t(g_1(H), \ldots, g_m(H))$ be the vector on the right. Then

$$F(X + H) = F(X) + J_F(X)H + \|H\|G(H).$$

As $\|H\|$ approaches 0, each coordinate of $G(H)$ approaches 0. Hence $G(H)$ approaches O; in other words,

$$\lim_{\|H\| \to 0} G(H) = O.$$

Hence the linear map represented by the matrix $J_F(X)$ is tangent to F at X. Since such a linear map is unique, we have proved our theorem.

Let U be open in $\mathbf{R}^n$ and $F: U \to \mathbf{R}^n$ be a differentiable map into the same dimensional space. Then the Jacobian matrix $J_F(X)$ is a square matrix, and its determinant is called the *Jacobian determinant* of F at X. We denote it by

$$\Delta_F(X).$$

Example 3. Let F be as in Example 2, $F(x, y) = (x^2 + y^2, e^{xy})$. Then the Jacobian determinant is equal to

$$\Delta_F(x, y) = \begin{vmatrix} 2x & 2y \\ ye^x & xe^y \end{vmatrix} = 2x^2e^y - 2y^2e^x.$$

In particular,

$$\Delta_F(1, 1) = 2e - 2e = 0,$$
$$\Delta_F(1, 2) = 2e^2 - 8e.$$

Example 4. An important map is given by the polar coordinates, $F: \mathbf{R}^2 \to \mathbf{R}^2$ such that $F(r, \theta) = (r \cos \theta, r \sin \theta)$. We can view the map as defined on all of $\mathbf{R}^2$, although when selecting polar coordinates, we take $r > 0$. We see that F maps a rectangle into a circular sector (Fig. 1).

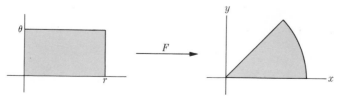

Figure 1

EXERCISES

1. In each of the following cases, compute the Jacobian matrix of F.

   (a) $F(x, y) = (x + y, x^2 y)$ (b) $F(x, y) = (\sin x, \cos xy)$
   (c) $F(x, y) = (e^{xy}, \log x)$ (d) $F(x, y, z) = (xz, xy, yz)$
   (e) $F(x, y, z) = (xyz, x^2 z)$ (f) $F(x, y, z) = (\sin xyz, xz)$

2. Find the Jacobian matrix of the mappings in Exercise 1 evaluated at the following points.

   (a) $(1, 2)$ (b) $(\pi, \pi/2)$ (c) $(1, 4)$
   (d) $(1, 1, -1)$ (e) $(2, -1, -1)$ (f) $(\pi, 2, 4)$

3. Let $L: \mathbf{R}^n \to \mathbf{R}^m$ be a linear map. Show that for each point X of $\mathbf{R}^n$ we have $L'(X) = L$.

4. Find the Jacobian matrix of the following maps.

   (a) $F(x, y) = (xy, x^2)$ (b) $F(x, y, z) = (\cos xy, \sin xy, xz)$

5. Find the Jacobian determinant of the map in Exercise 1(a). Determine all points where the Jacobian determinant is equal to 0.

6. Find the Jacobian determinant of the map in Exercise 1(b).

7. Let $F: \mathbf{R}^2 \to \mathbf{R}^2$ be the map defined by

$$F(r, \theta) = (r \cos \theta, r \sin \theta),$$

in other words the polar coordinates map

$$x = r \cos \theta, \qquad y = r \sin \theta.$$

Find the Jacobian matrix and Jacobian determinant of this mapping. Determine all points (r, θ) where the Jacobian determinant vanishes.

8. Let $F: \mathbf{R}^3 \to \mathbf{R}^3$ be the mapping defined by

$$F(r, \varphi, \theta) = (r \sin \varphi \cos \theta, r \sin \varphi \sin \theta, r \cos \varphi)$$

or in other words

$$x = r \sin \varphi \cos \theta, \qquad y = r \sin \varphi \sin \theta, \qquad z = r \cos \varphi.$$

Find the Jacobian matrix and Jacobian determinant of this mapping.

9. Find the Jacobian matrix and determinant of the map

$$F(r, \theta) = (e^r \cos \theta, e^r \sin \theta).$$

Show that the Jacobian determinant is never 0. Show that there exist two distinct points (r_1, θ_1) and (r_2, θ_2) such that

$$F(r_1, \theta_1) = F(r_2, \theta_2).$$

§3. THE CHAIN RULE

In the *First Course*, we proved a chain rule for composite functions. Earlier in this book, a chain rule was given for a composite of a function and a map defined for real numbers, but having values in $\mathbf{R}^n$. In this section, we give a general formulation of the chain rule for arbitrary compositions of mappings.

Let U be an open set in $\mathbf{R}^n$, and let V be an open set in $\mathbf{R}^m$. Let $F: U \to \mathbf{R}^m$ be a mapping, and assume that all values of F are contained in V. Let $G: V \to \mathbf{R}^s$ be a mapping. Then we can form the composite mapping $G \circ F$ from U into $\mathbf{R}^s$.

Let X be a point of U. Then $F(X)$ is a point of V by assumption. Let us assume that F is differentiable at X, and that G is differentiable at $F(X)$. We know that $F'(X)$ is a linear map from $\mathbf{R}^n$ into $\mathbf{R}^m$, and $G'\big(F(X)\big)$ is a linear map from $\mathbf{R}^m$ into $\mathbf{R}^s$. Thus we may compose these two linear maps to give a linear map $G'\big(F(X)\big) \circ F'(X)$ from $\mathbf{R}^n$ into $\mathbf{R}^s$.

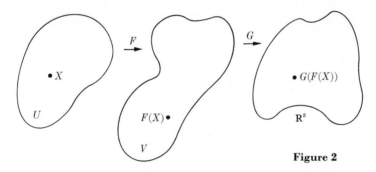

Figure 2

The next theorem tells us what the derivative of $G \circ F$ is in terms of the derivative of F at X, and the derivative of G at $F(X)$. Please observe how the statement and proof of the theorem will be entirely parallel to the statement and proof of the theorem for the chain rule in the *First Course*.

Theorem 3. *Let U be an open set in $\mathbf{R}^n$, let V be an open set in $\mathbf{R}^m$. Let $F: U \to \mathbf{R}^m$ be a mapping such that all values of F are contained in V. Let $G: V \to \mathbf{R}^s$ be a mapping. Let X be a point of U such that F is differentiable at X. Assume that G is differentiable at $F(X)$. Then the composite mapping $G \circ F$ is differentiable at X, and its derivative is given by*

$$(G \circ F)'(X) = G'\big(F(X)\big) \circ F'(X).$$

Proof. By definition of differentiability, there exists a mapping Φ_1 such that

$$\lim_{\|H\| \to 0} \Phi_1(H) = O$$

and

$$F(X + H) = F(X) + F'(X)H + \|H\|\Phi_1(H).$$

Similarly, there exists a mapping Φ_2 such that

$$\lim_{\|K\| \to 0} \Phi_2(K) = O,$$

and
$$G(Y + K) = G(Y) + G'(Y)K + \|K\|\Phi_2(K).$$

We let $K = K(H)$ be
$$K = F(X + H) - F(X) = F'(X)H + \|H\|\Phi_1(H).$$

Then
$$G(F(X + H)) = G(F(X) + K)$$
$$= G(F(X)) + G'(F(X))K + o(K).$$

Using the fact that $G'(F(X))$ is linear, and
$$K = F(X + H) - F(X) = F'(X)H + \|H\|\Phi_1(H),$$

we can write
$$(G \circ F)(X + H) = (G \circ F)(X) + G'(F(X))F'(X)H$$
$$+ \|H\|G'(F(X))\Phi_1(H) + o(K).$$

Using simple estimates which we do not give in detail, we conclude that
$$(G \circ F)(X + H) = (G \circ F)(X) + G'(F(X))F'(X)H + o(H).$$

This proves that the linear map
$$G'(F(X))F'(X)$$

is tangent to $G \circ F$ at X. It must therefore be equal to $(G \circ F)'(X)$, as was to be shown.

§4. INVERSE MAPPINGS AND IMPLICIT FUNCTIONS

Let U be open in $\mathbf{R}^n$ and let $F: U \to \mathbf{R}^n$ be a map, given by coordinate functions:
$$F(X) = (f_1(X), \ldots, f_n(X)).$$

If all the partial derivatives of all functions f_i exist and are continuous, we say that F is a C^1-*map*. We say that F is C^1-*invertible* on U if the image $F(U)$ is an open set V, and if there exists a C^1-map $G: V \to U$ such that $G \circ F$ and $F \circ G$ are the respective identity mappings on U and V.

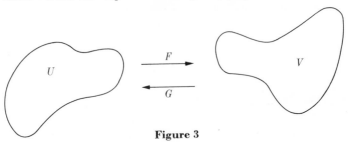

Figure 3

Example 1. Let A be a fixed vector, and let $F: \mathbf{R}^n \to \mathbf{R}^n$ be the translation by A, namely $F(X) = X + A$. Then F is C^1-invertible, its inverse being translation by $-A$.

Example 2. Let U be the subset of $\mathbf{R}^2$ consisting of all pairs (r, θ) with $r > 0$ and $0 < \theta < \pi$. Let

$$F(r, \theta) = (r \cos \theta, r \sin \theta).$$

Let $x = r \cos \theta$ and $y = r \sin \theta$. Then the image of U is the upper half-plane consisting of all (x, y) such that $y > 0$, and arbitrary x (Fig. 4).

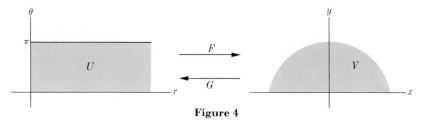

Figure 4

We can solve for the inverse map G, namely:

$$r = \sqrt{x^2 + y^2} \qquad \text{and} \qquad \theta = \arccos \frac{x}{r}$$

so that

$$G(x, y) = \left(\sqrt{x^2 + y^2}, \arccos \frac{x}{r} \right).$$

In many applications, a map is not necessarily invertible, but has still a useful property locally. Let P be a point of U. We say that F is *locally C^1-invertible at P* if there exists an open set U_1 contained in U and containing P such that F is C^1-invertible on U_1.

Example 3. If we view $F(r, \theta) = (r \cos \theta, r \sin \theta)$ as defined on all of $\mathbf{R}^2$, then F is not C^1-invertible on all of $\mathbf{R}^2$, but given any point, it is locally invertible at that point. One could see this by giving an explicit inverse map as we did in Example 1. At any rate, from Example 1, we see that F is C^1-invertible on the set $r > 0$ and $0 < \theta < \pi$.

In most cases, it is not possible to define an inverse map by explicit formulas. However, there is a very important theorem which allows us to conclude that a map is locally invertible at a point.

Inverse mapping theorem. *Let $F: U \to \mathbf{R}^n$ be a C^1-map. Let P be a point of U. If the Jacobian determinant $\Delta_F(P)$ is not equal to 0, then F is locally C^1-invertible at P.*

A proof of this theorem is too involved to be given in this book. However, we make the following comment. The fact that the determinant $\Delta_F(P)$ is not 0 implies (and in fact is equivalent with) the fact that the

Jacobian matrix is invertible, and the Jacobian matrix represents the linear map $F'(P)$. Thus the inverse mapping theorem asserts that if the derivative $F'(P)$ is invertible, then the map F itself is locally invertible at P. Since it is usually very easy to determine whether the Jacobian determinant vanishes or not, we see that the inverse mapping theorem gives us a simple criterion for local invertibility.

Example 4. Consider the case of one variable, $y = f(x)$. In the *First Course*, we proved that if $f'(x_0) \neq 0$ at a point x_0, then there is an inverse function defined near $y_0 = f(x_0)$. Indeed, say $f'(x_0) > 0$. By continuity, assuming that f' is continuous (i.e. f is C^1), we know that $f'(x) > 0$ for x close to x_0. Hence f is strictly increasing, and an inverse function exists near x_0. In fact, we determined the derivative. If g is the inverse function, then we proved that

$$g'(y_0) = f'(x_0)^{-1}.$$

Example 5. The formula for the derivative of the inverse function in the case of one variable can be generalized to the case of the inverse mapping theorem. Suppose that the map $F: U \to V$ has a C^1-inverse $G: V \to U$. Let X be a point of U. Then $G \circ F = I$ is the identity, and since I is linear, we see directly from the definition of the derivative that $I'(X) = I$. Using the chain rule, we find that

$$I = (G \circ F)'(X) = G'(F(X)) \circ F'(X)$$

for all X in U. In particular, this means that if $Y = F(X)$, then

$$\boxed{G'(Y) = F'(X)^{-1}}$$

where the inverse in this last expression is to be understood as the inverse of the linear map $F'(X)$. Thus we have generalized the formula for the derivative of an inverse function.

Example 6. Let $F(x, y) = (e^x \cos y, e^x \sin y)$. Show that F is locally invertible at every point.

We find that

$$J_F(x, y) = \begin{pmatrix} e^x \cos y & -e^x \sin y \\ e^x \sin y & e^x \cos y \end{pmatrix}, \quad \text{whence} \quad \Delta_F(x, y) = e^x \neq 0.$$

Since the Jacobian determinant is not 0, it follows that F is locally invertible at (x, y) for all x, y.

Example 7. Let U be open in $\mathbf{R}^2$ and let $f: U \to \mathbf{R}$ be a C^1-function. Let (a, b) be a point of U. Assume that $D_2 f(a, b) \neq 0$. Then the map F

given by

$$(x, y) \mapsto F(x, y) = (x, f(x, y))$$

is locally invertible at (a, b).

Proof. All we have to do is compute the Jacobian matrix and determinant. We have

$$J_F(x, y) = \begin{pmatrix} 1 & 0 \\ \dfrac{\partial f}{\partial x} & \dfrac{\partial f}{\partial y} \end{pmatrix}$$

so that

$$J_F(a, b) = \begin{pmatrix} 1 & 0 \\ D_1 f(a, b) & D_2 f(a, b) \end{pmatrix}$$

and hence

$$\Delta_F(a, b) = D_2 f(a, b).$$

By assumption, this is not 0, and the inverse mapping theorem implies what we want.

The result of Example 7 can be used to discuss implicit functions. Again let $f: U \to \mathbf{R}$ be as in Example 7, and assume that $f(a, b) = c$. We ask whether there is some differentiable function $y = \varphi(x)$ defined near $x = a$ such that $\varphi(a) = b$ and

$$f(x, \varphi(x)) = c$$

for all x near a. If such a function φ exists, then we say that $y = \varphi(x)$ is the *function determined implicitly by f.*

Theorem 4 **(Implicit function theorem).** *Let U be open in $\mathbf{R}^2$ and let $f: U \to \mathbf{R}$ be a C^1-function. Let (a, b) be a point of U, and let $f(a, b) = c$. Assume that $D_2 f(a, b) \neq 0$. Then there exists an implicit function $y = \varphi(x)$ which is C^1 in some interval containing a, and such that $\varphi(a) = b$.*

Proof. We apply Example 7 and use the notation of that exercise. Thus we let

$$F(x, y) = (x, f(x, y)).$$

We know that $F(a, b) = (a, c)$ and that there exists a C^1-inverse G defined locally near (a, c). The inverse map G has two coordinate functions, and we can write $G(x, z) = (x, g(x, z))$ for some function g. Thus we put $y = g(x, z)$, and $z = f(x, y)$. We define

$$\varphi(x) = g(x, c).$$

Then on the one hand,

$$F(x, \varphi(x)) = F(x, g(x, c)) = F(G(x, c)) = (x, c),$$

and on the other hand,

$$F(x, \varphi(x)) = (x, f(x, \varphi(x))).$$

This proves that $f(x, \varphi(x)) = c$. Furthermore, by definition of an inverse map, $G(a, c) = (a, b)$ so that $\varphi(a) = b$. This proves the implicit function theorem.

Example 8. Let $f(x, y) = x^2 + y^2$ and let $(a, b) = (1, 1)$. Then $c = f(1, 1) = 2$. We have $D_2 f(x, y) = 2y$ so that

$$D_2 f(1, 1) = 2 \neq 0,$$

so the implicit function $y = \varphi(x)$ near $x = 1$ exists. In this case, we can of course solve explicitly for y, namely

$$y = \sqrt{2 - x^2}.$$

Example 9. We take $f(x, y) = x^2 + y^2$ as in Example 8, and $(a, b) = (-1, -1)$. Then again $c = f(-1, -1) = 2$, and

$$D_2 f(-1, -1) = -2 \neq 0.$$

In this case we can still solve for y in terms of x, namely

$$y = -\sqrt{2 - x^2}.$$

In general, the equation $f(x, y) = c$ defines some curve as in the following picture.

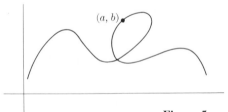

Figure 5

Near the point (a, b) as indicated in the picture, we see that there is an implicit function:

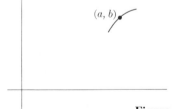

Figure 6

but that one could not define the implicit function for all x, only for those x near a.

Example 10. Let $f(x, y) = x^2y + 3y^3x^4 - 4$.   Take $(a, b) = (1, 1)$ so that $f(a, b) = 0$. Then $D_2f(x, y) = x^2 + 9y^2x^4$ and

$$D_2f(1, 1) = 10 \neq 0.$$

Hence the implicit function $y = \varphi(x)$ exists, but there is no simple way to solve for it. We can also determine the derivative $\varphi'(1)$. Indeed, differentiating the equation $f(x, y) = 0$, knowing that $y = \varphi(x)$ is a differentiable function, we find

$$2xy + x^2y' + 12y^3x^3 + 9y^2y'x^4 = 0,$$

whence we can solve for $y' = \varphi'(x)$, namely

$$\varphi'(x) = y' = -\frac{2xy + 12y^3x^3}{x^2 + 9y^2x^4}.$$

Hence

$$\varphi'(1) = -\frac{2 + 12}{1 + 9} = -\frac{7}{5}.$$

In Exercise 4 we give the general formula for an arbitrary function f.

Example 11. In general, given any function $f(x, y) = 0$ and $y = \varphi(x)$ we can find $\varphi'(x)$ by differentiating in the usual way. For instance, suppose

$$x^3 + 4y \sin(xy) = 0.$$

Then taking the derivative with respect to x, we find

$$3x^2 + 4y' \sin(xy) + 4y \cos(xy)(y + xy').$$

We then solve for y' as

$$y' = -\frac{4y^2 \cos(xy) + 3x^2}{4 \sin(xy) + 4xy \cos(xy)}$$

whenever $4 \sin(xy) + 4xy \cos(xy) \neq 0$. Similarly, we can solve for y'' by differentiating either of the last two expressions. In the present case, this gets complicated.

EXERCISES

1. Determine whether the following mappings are locally C^1-invertible at the given point.
   (a) $F(x, y) = (x^2 - y^2, 2xy)$ at $(x, y) \neq (0, 0)$
   (b) $F(x, y) = (x^3y + 1, x^2 + y^2)$ at $(1, 2)$
   (c) $F(x, y) = (x + y, y^{1/4})$ at $(1, 16)$
   (d) $F(x, y) = \left(\frac{x}{x^2 + y^2}, \frac{y}{x^2 + y^2}\right)$ at $(x, y) \neq (0, 0)$
   (e) $F(x, y) = (x + x^2 + y, x^2 + y^2)$ at $(x, y) = (5, 8)$

2. Determine whether the mappings of Exercises 1, 2 of §2 are locally C^1-invertible at the indicated point.

3. Show that the map defined by $F(x, y) = (e^x \cos y, e^x \sin y)$ is not invertible on all of $\mathbf{R}^2$, even though it is locally invertible everywhere.

4. Let $y = \varphi(x)$ be an implicit function satisfying $f(x, \varphi(x)) = 0$, both f, φ being C^1. Show that

$$\varphi'(x) = -\frac{D_1 f(x, \varphi(x))}{D_2 f(x, \varphi(x))}$$

wherever $D_2 f(x, \varphi(x)) \neq 0$.

5. Find an expression for $\varphi''(x)$ by differentiating the preceding expression for $\varphi'(x)$.

6. Let $f(x, y) = (x - 2)^3 y + xe^{y-1}$. Is $D_2 f(a, b) \neq 0$ at the following points (a, b)?

(a) $(1, 1)$ (b) $(0, 0)$ (c) $(2, 1)$

7. Let f be a C^1-function of 3 variables (x, y, z) defined on an open set U of $\mathbf{R}^3$. Let (a, b, c) be a point of U, and assume $f(a, b, c) = 0$, $D_3 f(a, b, c) \neq 0$. Show that there exists a C^1-function $\varphi(x, y)$ defined near (a, b) such that

$$f(x, y, \varphi(x, y)) = 0 \quad \text{and} \quad \varphi(a, b) = c.$$

We call φ the implicit function $z = \varphi(x, y)$ determined by f at (a, b).

8. In Exercise 7, show that

$$D_1\varphi(a, b) = -\frac{D_1 f(a, b, c)}{D_3 f(a, b, c)} \quad \text{and } D_2 \varphi(a,b) = \frac{-D_2 f}{D_3 f(a}$$

9. For each of the following functions f, show that $f(x, y) = 0$ defines an implicit function $y = \varphi(x)$ at the given point (a, b), and find $\varphi'(a)$.

(a) $f(x, y) = x^2 - xy + y^2 - 3$ at $(1, 2)$
(b) $f(x, y) = x \cos xy$ at $(1, \pi/2)$
(c) $f(x, y) = 2e^{x+y} - x + y$ at $(1, -1)$
(d) $f(x, y) = xe^y - y + 1$ at $(-1, 0)$
(e) $f(x, y) = x + y + x \sin y$ at $(0, 0)$
(f) $f(x, y) = x^5 + y^5 + xy + 4$ at $(2, -2)$

10. For each of the following functions $f(x, y, z)$, show that $f(x, y, z) = 0$ defines an implicit function $z = \varphi(x, y)$ at the given point (a, b, c) and find $D_1\varphi(a, b)$ and $D_2\varphi(a, b)$.

(a) $f(x, y, z) = x + y + z + \cos xyz$ at $(0, 0, -1)$
(b) $f(x, y, z) = z^3 - z - xy \sin z$ at $(0, 0, 0)$
(c) $f(x, y, z) = x^3 + y^3 + z^3 - 3xyz - 4$ at $(1, 1, 2)$
(d) $f(x, y, z) = x + y + z - e^{xyz}$ at $(0, \frac{1}{2}, \frac{1}{2})$

11. Let $f(x, y, z) = x^3 - 2y^2 + z^2$. Show that $f(x, y, z) = 0$ defines an implicit function $x = \varphi(y, z)$ at the point $(1, 1, 1)$. Find $D_1\varphi$ and $D_2\varphi$ at the point $(1, 1)$.

12. In Exercise 10, show that $f(x, y, z) = 0$ also determines y as an implicit function of (x, z) and z as an implicit function of (x, y) at the given point. Find the partial derivatives of these implicit functions at the given point.

13. Show that the equation $x^2/4 + y^2 + z^2/9 = 0$ defines an implicit function $z = \varphi(x, y)$ at the point $(1, \sqrt{11}/6, 2)$, and an implicit function $y = \psi(x, z)$ at this point. Find the first partial derivatives of these functions at the given point.

Chapter XIV

Multiple Integrals

When studying functions of one variable, it was possible to give essentially complete proofs for the existence of an integral of a continuous function over an interval. The investigation of the integral involved lower sums and upper sums.

In order to develop a theory of integration for functions of several variables, it becomes necessary to have techniques whose degree of sophistication is somewhat greater than that which is available to us. Hence we shall only state results, and omit most of the proofs, except in special cases. These results will allow us to compute multiple integrals.

We shall also list various formulas giving double and triple integrals in terms of polar coordinates, and we give a geometric argument to make them plausible. Here again, the general formula for changing variables in a multiple integral can be handled theoretically (and elegantly) only when much more machinery is available than we have at present. The proofs properly belong to an advanced calculus course. (Cf. *Analysis I.*)

§1. DOUBLE INTEGRALS

We begin by discussing the analogue of upper and lower sums associated with partitions.

Let R be a region of the plane (Fig. 1), and let f be a function defined on R. We shall say that f is *bounded* if there exists a number M such that $|f(X)| \leq M$ for all X in R.

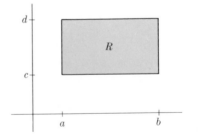

Figure 1

Let a, b be two numbers with $a \leq b$, and let c, d be two numbers with $c \leq d$. We consider the closed interval $[a, b]$ on the x-axis and the closed interval $[c, d]$ on the y-axis. These determine a rectangle R in the plane, consisting of all pairs of points (x, y) with $a \leq x \leq b$ and $c \leq y \leq d$.

536

The rectangle R above will be denoted by $[a, b] \times [c, d]$.

Let I denote the interval $[a, b]$. By a partition P_I of I we mean a sequence of numbers

$$x_1 = a \le x_2 \le \cdots \le x_m = b$$

which we also write as $P_I = (x_1, \ldots, x_m)$. Similarly, by a partition P_J of the interval $J = [c, d]$ we mean a sequence of numbers

$$y_1 = c \le y_2 \le \cdots \le y_n = d$$

which we write as $P_J = (y_1, \ldots, y_n)$.

Each pair of small intervals $[x_i, x_{i+1}]$ and $[y_j, y_{j+1}]$ determines a rectangle

$$S_{ij} = [x_i, x_{i+1}] \times [y_j, y_{j+1}].$$

(Cf. Fig. 2(a).) We denote symbolically by $P = P_I \times P_J$ the partition of R into rectangles S_{ij} and we call such S_{ij} a *subrectangle* of the *partition* (Fig. 2(b)).

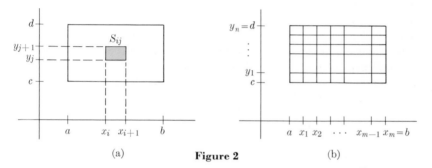

(a)   **Figure 2**   (b)

Let S be a set and f a function on S (with values which are real, as usual). Assume that f is bounded. By

$$\sup{}_S f = \sup_{v \in S} f(v)$$

we mean the least upper bound of all values $f(v)$ for v in S. We take it as a known property of the real numbers that any bounded set of numbers has a least upper bound, and also a greatest lower bound. Similarly, we denote by

$$\inf{}_S f = \inf_{v \in S} f(v)$$

the greatest lower bound of all values of f on S.

If R is a rectangle as above, we define its 2-dimensional volume (that is, its area) to be the obvious thing, namely

$$\text{Vol}(R) = (d - c)(b - a).$$

Thus the volume of each subrectangle S_{ij} is $(y_{j+1} - y_j)(x_{i+1} - x_i)$.

We then form sums which are analogous to the lower and upper sums used to define the integral of functions of one variable. If P denotes the partition as above, and f is a bounded function on R, we define:

$$L(P, f) = \sum_S (\inf_S f) \, \mathrm{Vol}(S),$$

$$U(P, f) = \sum_S (\sup_S f) \, \mathrm{Vol}(S).$$

The symbol $\sum_S$ means that we must take the sum over all subrectangles of the partition. In terms of the indices i, j, we can rewrite say the lower sum as

$$L(P, f) = \sum_{i=1}^m \sum_{j=1}^n (\inf_{S_{ij}} f)(y_{j+1} - y_j)(x_{i+1} - x_i)$$

and similarly for the upper sum.

Just as in the case of functions of one variable, we can then take refinements of partitions. If P_I' is a partition of I, we say that P_I' is a refinement of P_I if every number of P_I is among the numbers of P_I'. If P_J' is a refinement of P_J, then we call $P_I' \times P_J' = P'$ a refinement of P.

We omit the proof of the following lemma, which is entirely similar to the one variable case.

Lemma. *If P' is a refinement of P, then*

$$L(P,f) \le L(P',f) \le U(P',f) \le U(P,f).$$

In other words, the lower sums increase under refinements of the partition, while the upper sums decrease.

We define f to be *integrable* on R if there exists a unique number which is greater than or equal to every lower sum, and less than or equal to every upper sum. Formulated in another way, we can say that f is integrable on R if and only if the least upper bound of all lower sums is equal to the greatest lower bound of all upper sums. If this number exists, we call it the *integral* of f, and denote it by

$$\int_R f \quad \text{or} \quad \iint_R f(x, y) \, dy \, dx.$$

We can interpret the integral as a volume under certain conditions. Namely, suppose that $f(x, y) \ge 0$ for all (x, y) in R. The value $f(x, y)$ may be viewed as a height above the point (x, y), and we may consider the integral of f as the volume of the 3-dimensional region lying above the rectangle R and bounded from above by the graph of f (Fig. 3).

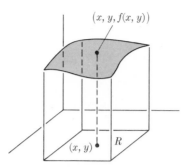

Figure 3

Each term

$$(\inf_S f)\, \text{Vol}(S)$$

is the volume of a rectangular box whose base is the rectangle S in the (x, y)-plane, and whose height is $\inf_S f$. The volume of such a box is precisely $(\inf_S f)\, \text{Vol}(S)$, where, as we said above, $\text{Vol}(S)$ is the 2-dimensional volume of S, that is its area. This box lies below the 3-dimensional region bounded from above by the graph of f. Similarly, the term

$$(\sup_S f)\, \text{Vol}(S)$$

is the volume of a box whose base is S and whose height is $\sup_S f$. This box lies above the above region. This makes our interpretation of the integral as volume clear.

Also, as in one variable, a positive function on a region may be viewed as a density of mass, and thus if $f \geqq 0$ on R, then we also interpret

$$\iint_R f(x, y)\, dy\, dx$$

as the *mass* of R.

Theorem 1. *Assume that f, g are bounded functions on the rectangle R, and are integrable. Then $f + g$ is integrable. If k is a number, then kf is integrable. We have:*

$$\int_R (f + g) = \int_R f + \int_R g \quad \text{and} \quad \int_R (kf) = k \int_R f.$$

In other words, integrable functions form a vector space, and the integral is a linear map on this vector space.

Proof. Let P be a partition of R and let S be a subrectangle of the partition. For any point v in S we have

$$\inf_S f \leqq f(v) \quad \text{and} \quad \inf_S g \leqq g(v),$$

whence

$$\inf_S f + \inf_S g \leqq f(v) + g(v).$$

Thus $\inf_S f + \inf_S g$ is a lower bound for all values $f(v) + g(v)$. Hence by definition of a greatest lower bound, we obtain the inequality

$$\inf_S f + \inf_S g \leq \inf_{v \in S} (f(v) + g(v)) = \inf_S (f + g).$$

Consequently we get

$$\begin{aligned}
L(P, f) + L(P, g) &= \sum_S (\inf_S f) \operatorname{Vol}(S) + \sum_S (\inf_S g) \operatorname{Vol}(S) \\
&= \sum_S (\inf_S f + \inf_S g) \operatorname{Vol}(S) \\
&\leq \sum_S \inf_S (f + g) \operatorname{Vol}(S) \\
&= L(P, f + g).
\end{aligned}$$

By a similar argument, we find that

$$L(P, f) + L(P, g) \leq L(P, f + g) \leq U(P, f + g) \leq U(P, f) + U(P, g).$$

Since $L(P, f)$ and $U(P, f)$ are arbitrarily close together for suitable partitions, and $L(P, g)$, $U(P, g)$ are arbitrarily close together for suitable partitions, we see by the usual squeezing process of limits that $L(P, f + g)$ and $U(P, f + g)$ are arbitrarily close together for suitable partitions. This proves that $f + g$ is integrable.

As for the constant k, we note that

$$\inf_S (kf) = \inf_{v \in S} (kf(v)) = k \cdot \inf_{v \in S} f(v).$$

Hence k comes out as a factor in each term of the lower sum, and similarly for the upper sum, so that

$$kL(P, f) = L(P, kf) \leq U(P, kf) = kU(P, f).$$

From this our second assertion follows.

Theorem 2. *If f, g are integrable on R, and $f \leq g$, then*

$$\int_R f \leq \int_R g.$$

Proof. We have for each subrectangle S of a partition P:

$$\inf_S f \leq f(v) \leq g(v)$$

for all v in S. Hence $\inf_S f$ is a lower bound for the values of g on S, and hence

$$\inf_S f \leq \inf_S g.$$

Consequently

$$L(P, f) = \sum_S (\inf_S f) \operatorname{Vol}(S) \leq \sum_S (\inf_S g) \operatorname{Vol}(S) = L(P, g) \leq \int_R g.$$

Since $\int_R g$ is an upper bound for $L(P, f)$ it follows that the least upper bound of all lower sums for f is $\leqq \int_R g$, in other words

$$\int_R f \leqq \int_R g,$$

as was to be shown.

We need some criterion for functions to be integrable. The next theorem gives such a criterion, and we shall state it without proof. We need some terminology.

Let s, t be numbers with $s \leqq t$. Let f be a function defined on the closed interval $[s, t]$. If f is differentiable, and if its derivative is continuous, we shall say that f is *smooth*. Let f, g be two functions defined on $[s, t]$. If both f and g are smooth, then the set of points $(f(x), g(x))$ as x ranges over the interval will be called a *smooth curve*. [In preceding chapters we had considered curves arising possibly from open intervals, but for this chapter, we change our meaning and deal only with closed intervals. If the interval consists of a single point, we *define* any function of that point to be differentiable, and we agree to say that its derivative is 0. If $s < t$, then at the end points, the derivative is meant to be the right or left derivative respectively.]

Any curve which the reader draws will consist of a finite number of smooth curves. For instance, a line segment is a smooth curve. We draw a finite number of smooth curves in the next picture.

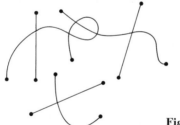

Figure 4

Let A be a region in the plane. We say as usual that A is *bounded* if there exists a number M such that $\|X\| \leq M$ for all points X in A. Any bounded region is contained in some rectangle.

The set of boundary points of a region A will be called the *boundary* of A. We shall say that the boundary of A is *smooth* if it consists of a finite number of smooth curves.

Let A be a region in the plane, and let f be a function defined on A. As usual, we say that f is *continuous* at a point P of A if

$$\lim_{X \to P} f(X) = f(P).$$

We say that f is continuous on A if it is continuous at every point of A.

Theorem 3. *Let R be a rectangle, and let f be a function defined on R, bounded and continuous except possibly at the points lying on a finite number of smooth curves. Then f is integrable on R.*

This is the promised criterion. Since most functions which arise in practice are of the type described in Theorem 3, we see that most functions are integrable.

Theorem 3 also allows us to integrate on more general sets than rectangles. Let A be a region in the plane, contained in a rectangle R (Fig. 5). Let f be a function defined on A. We denote by f_A the function which has the same values as f at points of A, and such that $f_A(Q) = 0$ if Q is a point not in A. Then f_A is defined on the rectangle R, and we define

$$\int_A f = \int_R f_A$$

provided that f_A is integrable. By Theorem 3, we note that if the boundary of A is smooth, and if f is continuous on A, then f_A is continuous except at all points lying on the boundary of A, and hence f_A is integrable.

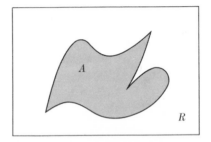

Figure 5

We now have one more property of the integral, corresponding to linearity for regions.

Theorem 4. *Let A be a bounded region in the plane, expressed as a union of two regions A_1 and A_2 having no points in common except possibly boundary points. Assume that the boundaries of A, A_1, A_2 are smooth. If f is a function defined on A and continuous except at a finite number of smooth curves, then*

$$\int_A f = \int_{A_1} f + \int_{A_2} f.$$

The proof of Theorem 4 is left as an exercise with hints (Exercise 3).

In the next section, we shall determine an effective way for computing integrals. Theorem 4 can be used in conjunction with these ways to make such computations easier. Indeed, a region can sometimes be decomposed into other regions A_1, A_2 over which it is easier to find the integral separately. Examples of this will be given later.

EXERCISES

1. Let f be a bounded function on a rectangle R, and assume that f is integrable. Let M be a number such that $|f(v)| \leq M$ for all v in R. Show that

$$\left| \int_R f \right| \leq M \operatorname{Vol}(R).$$

2. Let ψ denote the constant function taking the value 1 for all points of the plane. If A is a region in the plane, denote by ψ_A the function taking the value 1 at points of A, and the value 0 at points not in A. If A is the union of two sets A_1, A_2 which have no point in common, show that

$$\psi_A = \psi_{A_1} + \psi_{A_2}.$$

In this case, show how to deduce Theorem 4 from Theorem 1. [*Hint:* Show that $f_A = \psi_A f$.] Generalize to the union of three disjoint sets.

3. (a) Let A be the union of two sets A_1, A_2. Show that A is the union of the sets (Fig. 6)

$$A_1 - (A_1 \cap A_2), \qquad (A_1 \cap A_2), \qquad A_2 - (A_1 \cap A_2),$$

and that no two of these sets have elements in common. Here we use the following notation: If A, B are sets, then $A - B$ denotes the set of elements of A which are not elements of B.

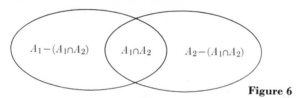

Figure 6

(b) Let A be the union of two sets A_1, A_2. Assuming that all functions occurring in the following formula are integrable, prove the formula:

$$\int_A f = \int_{A_1} f + \int_{A_2} f - \int_{A_1 \cap A_2} f.$$

§2. REPEATED INTEGRALS

To compute the integral we shall investigate double integrals.

Let f be a function defined on our rectangle. For each x in the interval $[a, b]$ we have a function f_x of y given by $f_x(y) = f(x, y)$, and this function f_x is defined on the interval $[c, d]$. Assume that for each x the function f_x is integrable over this interval (in the old sense of the word, for functions of one variable). We may then form the integral

$$\int_c^d f_x(y)\, dy = \int_c^d f(x, y)\, dy.$$

The expression we obtain depends on the particular value of x chosen in the interval $[a, b]$, and is thus a function of x. Assume that this function is integrable over the interval $[a, b]$. We can then take the integral

$$\int_a^b \left[\int_c^d f(x, y) \, dy \right] dx, \qquad \text{also written} \qquad \int_a^b \int_c^d f(x, y) \, dy \, dx,$$

which is called the *repeated integral* of f.

Example 1. Let $f(x, y) = x^2 y$. Find the repeated integral of f over the rectangle determined by the intervals $[1, 2]$ on the x-axis and $[-3, 4]$ on the y-axis.

We must find the repeated integral

$$\int_1^2 \int_{-3}^4 f(x, y) \, dy \, dx.$$

To do this, we first compute the integral with respect to y, namely

$$\int_{-3}^4 x^2 y \, dy.$$

For a fixed value of x, we can take x^2 out of the integral, and hence this inner integral is equal to

$$x^2 \int_{-3}^4 y \, dy = x^2 \frac{y^2}{2} \Big|_{-3}^4 = \frac{7x^2}{2} .$$

We then integrate with respect to x, namely

$$\int_1^2 \frac{7x^2}{2} \, dx = \frac{49}{6} .$$

Thus the integral of f over the rectangle is equal to $\frac{49}{6}$.

The repeated integral is useful in computing a double integral because of the following theorem, which will be proved after discussing some examples.

Theorem 5. *Let R be a rectangle $[a, b] \times [c, d]$, and let f be integrable on R. Assume that for each x in $[a, b]$ the function f_x given by*

$$f_x(y) = f(x, y)$$

is integrable on $[c, d]$. Then the function

$$x \mapsto \int_c^d f(x, y) \, dy$$

is integrable on $[a, b]$, and

$$\int_R f = \int_a^b \left[\int_c^d f(x, y) \, dy \right] dx.$$

Geometrically speaking, the inner integral for a fixed value of x gives the area of a cross section as indicated in the following figure. Then integrating such areas yields the volume of the 3-dimensional figure bounded below by the rectangle R, and above by the graph of f.

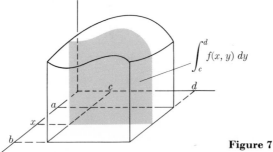

Figure 7

The following situation will arise frequently in practice.

Let g_1, g_2 be two smooth functions on a closed interval $[a, b]$ ($a \leq b$) such that $g_1(x) \leq g_2(x)$ for all x in that interval. Let c, d be numbers such that

$$c < g_1(x) \leq g_2(x) < d$$

for all x in the interval $[a, b]$. Then g_1, g_2 determine a region A lying between $x = a$, $x = b$, and the two curves $y = g_1(x)$ and $y = g_2(x)$. (Cf. Fig. 8.)

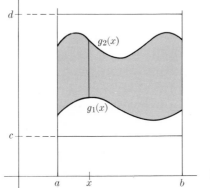

Figure 8

Let f be a function which is continuous on the region A, and define f on the rectangle $[a, b] \times [c, d]$ to be equal to 0 at any point of the rectangle not lying in the region A. For any value x in the interval $[a, b]$ the integral

$$\int_c^d f(x, y)\, dy$$

can be written as a sum:

$$\int_c^{g_1(x)} f(x, y)\, dy + \int_{g_1(x)}^{g_2(x)} f(x, y)\, dy + \int_{g_2(x)}^d f(x, y)\, dy.$$

Since $f(x, y) = 0$ whenever $c \leq y < g_1(x)$ and $g_2(x) < y \leq d$, it follows that the two extreme integrals are equal to 0. Thus the repeated integral of f over the rectangle is in fact equal to the repeated integral

$$\int_a^b \left[\int_{g_1(x)}^{g_2(x)} f(x, y)\, dy \right] dx.$$

Regions of the type described by two functions g_1, g_2 as above are the most common type of regions with which we deal.

From Theorem 5 and the preceding discussion, we obtain:

Corollary. *Let g_1, g_2 be two smooth functions defined on a closed interval $[a, b]$ $(a \leq b)$ such that $g_1(x) \leq g_2(x)$ for all x in that interval. Let f be a continuous function on the region A lying between $x = a$, $x = b$, and the two curves $y = g_1(x)$ and $y = g_2(x)$. Then*

$$\int_A f = \int_a^b \left[\int_{g_1(x)}^{g_2(x)} f(x, y)\, dy \right] dx;$$

in other words, the double integral is equal to the repeated integral.

We shall give the proof of Theorem 5 below. Before doing that, we first give examples showing how to apply Theorem 5, or rather its corollary.

Example 2. Let $f(x, y) = x^2 + y^2$. Find the integral of f over the region A bounded by the straight line $y = x$ and the parabola $y = x^2$ (Fig. 9).

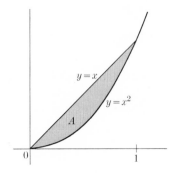

Figure 9

In this case, we have $g_1(x) = x^2$ and $g_2(x) = x$. Thus our integral is equal to

$$\int_0^1 \left[\int_{x^2}^x (x^2 + y^2)\, dy \right] dx.$$

Now the inner integral is given by

$$\int_{x^2}^x (x^2 + y^2)\, dy = x^2 y + \left. \frac{y^3}{3} \right|_{x^2}^x$$

$$= x^3 + \frac{x^3}{3} - x^4 - \frac{x^6}{3}.$$

Hence the repeated integral is equal to

$$\int_A f = \int_0^1 \left(x^3 + \frac{x^3}{3} - x^4 - \frac{x^6}{3} \right) dx = \frac{x^4}{4} + \frac{x^4}{12} - \frac{x^5}{5} - \left. \frac{x^7}{21} \right|_0^1$$

$$= \frac{1}{4} + \frac{1}{12} - \frac{1}{5} - \frac{1}{21}.$$

(We don't need to simplify the number on the right.)

Given a region A, it is frequently possible to break it up into smaller regions having only boundary points in common, and such that each smaller region is of the type we have just described. In that case, to compute the integral of a function over S, we can apply Property 3.

Example 3. Let $f(x, y) = 2xy$. Find the integral of f over the triangle bounded by the lines $y = 0$, $y = x$, and the line $x + y = 2$.

The region is as shown in Fig. 10.

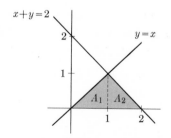

Figure 10

We break up our region into the portion from 0 to 1 and the portion from 1 to 2. These correspond to the small triangles A_1, A_2, as indicated in the picture. Then

$$\int_{A_1} f = \int_0^1 \left[\int_0^x 2xy\, dy \right] dx \qquad \text{and} \qquad \int_{A_2} f = \int_1^2 \left[\int_0^{2-x} 2xy\, dy \right] dx.$$

There is no difficulty in evaluating these integrals, and we leave them to you.

Finally, we define the *area* of a region A to be the integral of the function 1 over A, i.e.

$$\mathrm{Vol}(A) = \iint_A 1 \, dy \, dx.$$

Example 4. Find the area of the region bounded by the straight line $y = x$ and the curve $y = x^2$.

The region has been sketched in Example 2. By definition,

$$\mathrm{Vol}(A) = \int_0^1 \int_{x^2}^{x} dy \, dx = \int_0^1 (x - x^2) \, dx$$

$$= \frac{x^2}{2} - \frac{x^3}{3}\Big|_0^1 = \frac{1}{2} - \frac{1}{3} = \frac{1}{6}.$$

We also observe that the same arguments as before apply if we interchange the role of x and y. Thus for the rectangle R we also have

$$\int_R f(x, y) \, dy \, dx = \int_R f(x, y) \, dx \, dy = \int_c^d \left[\int_a^b f(x, y) \, dx \right] dy.$$

The same goes for a region described by functions

$$x = g_1(y)$$

and

$$x = g_2(y)$$

with $g_1 \leq g_2$ between $y = c$ and $y = d$.

If A is a region in the plane bounded by a finite number of smooth curves, and f is a function on A such that $f(x) \geq 0$ for $x \in A$, then we can interpret f as a density function, and we also call the integral $\int_A f$ the *mass* of A.

Example 5. Find the integral of the function $f(x, y) = x^2 y^2$ over the region bounded by the lines $y = 1$, $y = 2$ and $x = y$ (Fig. 11).

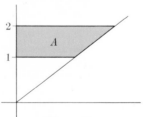

Figure 11

We have to compute the integral as prescribed, namely:

$$\int_1^2 \left[\int_0^y x^2 y^2 \, dx \right] dy = \int_1^2 y^2 \frac{x^3}{3} \Big|_0^y \, dy = \int_1^2 \frac{y^5}{3} \, dy = \frac{7}{2}.$$

We can also say that the preceding integral, namely $7/2$, is the mass of A corresponding to the density given by the function f. Of course the units of mass are those determined by the units of density.

We now give the proof of Theorem 5. We let R be the product of the intervals I, J so $R = I \times J$. We consider a partition $P = P_I \times P_J$ of R, where P_I, P_J are partitions of the intervals I, J respectively. Each sub-rectangle of P can then be written as

$$S = S_I \times S_J,$$

where S_I is a subinterval of I and S_J a subinterval of J. Then

$$\text{Vol}(S) = l(S_J)l(S_I),$$

where l denotes the length of an interval.

We denote the function

$$x \mapsto \int_c^d f(x, y) \, dy$$

by $\int_J f$, so that the value of this function at x is

$$\int_J f_x = \int_c^d f(x, y) \, dy.$$

We have:

$$L(P_I \times P_J, f) = \sum_S (\inf_S f) \, \text{Vol}(S)$$

$$= \sum_{S_I} \sum_{S_J} (\inf_{S_I \times S_J} f) \, \text{Vol}(S_I \times S_J)$$

(*) $$= \sum_{S_I} \left[\sum_{S_J} \left(\inf_{(x,y) \in S_I \times S_J} f(x, y) \right) l(S_J) \right] l(S_I).$$

For any x in I we have

$$\sum_{S_J} \left(\inf_{(x,y) \in S_I \times S_J} f(x, y) \right) l(S_J) \leq \sum_{S_J} \inf_{y \in S_J} f(x, y) l(S_J)$$

$$= L(P_J, f_x)$$

$$\leq \int_J f_x,$$

because each term in the expression on the left involves an inf over all (x, y) rather than only over y, and thus contributes less to the sum. Thus the expression on the left is a lower bound for the expression on the right. From this we conclude that the expression on the left is $\leq \inf_{x \in S_I} \int_J f_x$, and hence by (*)

$$L(P, f) = L(P_I \times P_J, f) \leq \sum_{S_I} \left(\inf_{x \in S_I} \int_J f_x \right) l(S_I)$$
$$= L\left(P_I, \int_J f\right)$$
$$\leq U\left(P_I, \int_J f\right).$$

By similar arguments applied to upper sums instead of lower sums, we conclude that

$$L(P, f) \leq L\left(P_I, \int_J f\right) \leq U\left(P_I, \int_J f\right) \leq U(P_I \times P_J, f) = U(P, f).$$

Since f is assumed to be integrable, it follows that for suitable partitions, $L(P,f)$ and $U(P,f)$ are arbitrarily close together. Thus the lower sums for the function $\int_J f$ and the upper sums for this function are arbitrarily close for suitable partitions P. This implies that the function $\int_J f$ is integrable, and the fact that these lower sums and upper sums are squeezed between $L(P,f)$ and $U(P,f)$ shows that the double integral is equal to the repeated integral, as desired.

EXERCISES

1. Find the value of the following repeated integrals.

(a) $\int_0^2 \int_1^3 (x + y) \, dx \, dy$ (b) $\int_0^2 \int_1^{x^2} y \, dy \, dx$ (c) $\int_0^1 \int_{y^2}^y \sqrt{x} \, dx \, dy$

(d) $\int_0^\pi \int_0^x x \sin y \, dy \, dx$ (e) $\int_1^2 \int_y^{y^2} dx \, dy$ (f) $\int_0^\pi \int_0^{\sin x} y \, dy \, dx$

2. Sketch the regions described by the following inequalities.
   (a) $|x| \leq 1, -1 \leq y \leq 2$ (b) $|x| \leq 3, |y| \leq 4$
   (c) $x + y \leq 1, x \geq 0, y \geq 0$ (d) $0 \leq y \leq |x|, 0 \leq x \leq 5$
   (e) $0 \leq x \leq y, 0 \leq y \leq 5$ (f) $|x| + |y| \leq 1$

3. Find the integral of the following functions.
   (a) $x \cos(x + y)$ over the triangle whose vertices are $(0, 0)$, $(\pi, 0)$, and (π, π).
   (b) e^{x+y} over the region defined by $|x| + |y| \leq 1$.
   (c) $x^2 - y^2$ over the region bounded by the curve $y = \sin x$ between 0 and π.
   (d) $x^2 + y$ over the triangle whose vertices are $(-\frac{1}{2}, \frac{1}{2})$, $(1, 2)$, $(1, -1)$.

4. Find the numerical answer in Example 2.

5. Let a be a number > 0. Show that the area of the region consisting of all points (x, y) such that $|x| + |y| \leq a$, is $(2a)^2/2!$.

6. Find the following integrals and sketch the region of integration in each case.

(a) $\int_1^2 \int_{x^2}^{x^3} x \, dy \, dx$

(b) $\int_1^{-1} \int_x^{2x} e^{x+y} \, dy \, dx$

(c) $\int_0^2 \int_1^3 |x - 2| \sin y \, dx \, dy$

(d) $\int_0^{\pi/2} \int_{-y}^y \sin x \, dx \, dy$

(e) $\int_{-1}^1 \int_0^{|x|} dy \, dx$

(f) $\int_0^{\pi/2} \int_0^{\cos y} x \sin y \, dx \, dy$

7. Sketch the region defined by $x \geq 0$, $x^2 + y^2 \leq 2$, and $x^2 + y^2 \geq 1$. Determine the integral of $f(x, y) = x^2$ over this region.

8. Integrate the function f over the indicated region.

(a) $f(x, y) = 1/(x + y)$ over the region bounded by the lines $y = x$, $x = 1$, $x = 2$, $y = 0$.

(b) $f(x, y) = x^2 - y^2$ over the region defined by the inequalities

$$0 \leq x \leq 1 \quad \text{and} \quad x^2 - y^2 \geq 0.$$

(c) $f(x, y) = x \sin xy$ over the rectangle $0 \leq x \leq \pi$ and $0 \leq y \leq 1$.

(d) $f(x, y) = x^2 - y^2$ over the triangle whose vertices are $(-1, 1)$, $(0, 0)$, $(1, 1)$.

(e) $f(x, y) = 1/(x + y + 1)$ over the square $0 \leq x \leq 1, 0 \leq y \leq 1$.

9. In the proof of Theorem 5, write out in detail the proof of the inequality

$$U\left(P_I, \int_J f\right) \leq U(P, f).$$

10. We recall that a translation $T: \mathbf{R}^2 \to \mathbf{R}^2$ is a map of the type $T(X) = X + w$ for some vector w. It is a geometric property of area that the area of a region does not change under translation. We shall now sketch a proof for the area given by an integral.

(a) Let g be a function of one variable, and t a number. Show that

$$\int_{c+s}^{d+s} g(y - s) \, dy = \int_c^d g(y) \, dy.$$

(b) If s, t are numbers, show that

$$\int_{a+t}^{b+t} \int_{c+s}^{d+s} f(x - t, y - s) \, dy \, dx = \int_a^b \int_c^d f(x, y) \, dy \, dx.$$

(Assume all functions occurring here to be integrable.)

(c) Let ψ_A be the characteristic function of a region A, that is the function such that $\psi_A(v) = 1$ if v is in A and $\psi_A(v) = 0$ if v is not in A. Let w be a vector in $\mathbf{R}^2$. Show that the characteristic function of the translation $A + w$ is the function ψ such that $\psi(v) = \psi_A(v - w)$.

(d) Conclude that

$$\int_A \psi_A = \int_{A+w} \psi_{A+w}.$$

§3. POLAR COORDINATES

It is frequently more convenient to describe a region by means of polar coordinates than with the "rectangular" coordinates of the preceding section. Such a region can then be described as the image of a simpler region as follows.

Let a, b be numbers with $0 \leq a \leq b \leq 2\pi$. Let c, d be two numbers with $0 \leq c \leq d$. Then the inequalities

$$a \leq \theta \leq b \quad \text{and} \quad c \leq r \leq d$$

describe a rectangle in the (r, θ)-plane. Under the map

$$G: \mathbf{R}^2 \to \mathbf{R}^2$$

given by $G(r, \theta) = (r \cos \theta, r \sin \theta)$, i.e.

$$x = r \cos \theta, \qquad y = r \sin \theta,$$

this rectangle goes into a circular region as shown in the next picture.

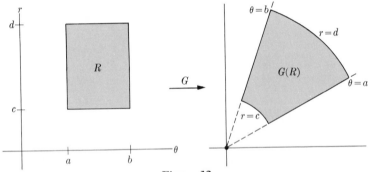

Figure 12

The preceding map G is called the *polar coordinate* map.

Consider partitions

$$a = \theta_1 \leq \theta_2 \leq \cdots \leq \theta_n = b, \qquad c = r_1 \leq r_2 \leq \cdots \leq r_m = d$$

of the two intervals $[a, b]$ and $[c, d]$. Each pair of intervals $[\theta_i, \theta_{i+1}]$ and $[r_j, r_{j+1}]$ determines a small region as shown in the following figure.

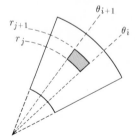

Figure 13

The area of such a region is equal to the difference between the area of the sector having angle $\theta_{i+1} - \theta_i$ and radius r_{j+1}, and the area of the sector having the same angle but radius r_j. The area of a sector having angle θ and radius r is equal to

$$\frac{\theta}{2\pi} \pi r^2 = \frac{\theta r^2}{2}.$$

Consequently the difference mentioned above is equal to

$$\frac{(\theta_{i+1} - \theta_i)r_{j+1}^2}{2} - \frac{(\theta_{i+1} - \theta_i)r_j^2}{2} = (\theta_{i+1} - \theta_i)\frac{(r_{j+1} + r_j)}{2}(r_{j+1} - r_j).$$

We note that

$$r_j \leqq \frac{r_{j+1} + r_j}{2} \leqq r_{j+1}.$$

If f is a function on the (x, y)-plane, it determines a function of (r, θ) by the formula

$$f^*(r, \theta) = f(r \cos \theta, r \sin \theta).$$

Let

$$\varphi(r, \theta) = f^*(r, \theta)r.$$

Then

$$\sum_{j=1}^{m} \sum_{i=1}^{n} f^*(r_j, \theta_i)r_j(r_{j+1} - r_j)(\theta_{i+1} - \theta_i)$$

is a Riemann sum for the function φ on the product $[a, b] \times [c, d]$. Consequently the following theorem is now very plausible.

Theorem 6. *Let $R = [a, b] \times [c, d]$ be as above, and let G be the polar coordinate map. Let f be bounded and continuous on $G(R)$, except possibly at a finite number of smooth curves. Let f^* be the corresponding function of (r, θ). Then*

$$\iint_R f^*(r, \theta)r \, dr \, d\theta = \iint_{G(R)} f(x, y) \, dy \, dx.$$

In the next section, we shall state another theorem which gives another justification for this change of variables formula. We do not prove any of these statements in this course, since the rigorous proofs depend on more developed techniques.

As with rectangular coordinates, we can deal with more general regions. Let g_1, g_2 be two smooth functions defined on the interval $[a, b]$ and assume

$$0 \leqq g_1(\theta) \leqq g_2(\theta)$$

for all θ in that interval. Let A be the region consisting of all points (θ, r) such that $a \leq \theta \leq b$ and $g_1(\theta) \leq r \leq g_2(\theta)$. We can select two numbers $c, d \geq 0$ such that

$$c \leq g_1(\theta) \leq g_2(\theta) \leq d$$

for all θ in the interval $[c, d]$. Let f be continuous on $G(A)$ and extend f to the circular sector of radius d between $\theta = a$ and $\theta = b$ by giving it the value 0 outside $G(A)$. *Then the integral of Theorem 6 taken over this sector is equal to the repeated integral*

$$\int_a^b \int_{g_1(\theta)}^{g_2(\theta)} f^*(\theta, r) r \, dr \, d\theta.$$

The following picture shows a typical region $G(A)$ under consideration. The important thing to remember about the formula of Theorem 6 is the appearance of an extra r inside the integral.

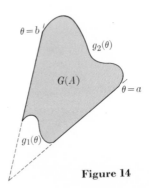

Figure 14

We also remark that a region could be described by taking θ as a function of r, and letting r vary between two constant values. In view of Theorem 5, we can evaluate the double integral of Theorem 6 by repeated integration first with respect to θ and then with respect to r.

In dealing with polar coordinates, it is useful to remember the equation of a circle. Let $a > 0$. Then

$$r = a \cos \theta, \qquad -\pi/2 \leq \theta \leq \pi/2,$$

is the equation of a circle of radius $a/2$ and center $(a/2, 0)$. Similarly,

$$r = a \sin \theta, \qquad 0 \leq \theta \leq \pi,$$

is the equation of a circle of radius $a/2$ and center $(0, a/2)$. You can easily show this, as an exercise, using the relations

$$r = \sqrt{x^2 + y^2}, \qquad x = r \cos \theta, \qquad y = r \sin \theta.$$

(*Note.* The coordinates of the center above are given in rectangular coordinates.)

Example. Find the integral of the function $f(x, y) = x^2$ over the region enclosed by the curve given in polar coordinates by the equation

$$r = (1 - \cos \theta).$$

The function of the polar coordinates (r, θ) corresponding to f is given by

$$f^* (r, \theta) = r^2 \cos^2 \theta.$$

The region in the polar coordinate space is described by the inequalities

$$0 \leq r \leq 1 - \cos \theta \qquad \text{and} \qquad 0 \leq \theta \leq 2\pi.$$

This region in the (x, y)-plane looks like this:

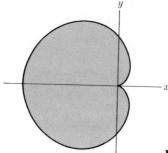

Figure 15

The desired integral is therefore the integral

$$\int_0^{2\pi} \int_0^{1-\cos \theta} r^3 \cos^2 \theta \, dr \, d\theta.$$

We integrate first with respect to r, which is easy, and see that our integral is equal to

$$\int_0^{2\pi} \tfrac{1}{4}(1 - \cos \theta)^4 \cos^2 \theta \, d\theta.$$

The evaluation of this integral is done by techniques of the first course in calculus. We expand out the expression of the fourth power, and get a sum of terms involving $\cos^k \theta$ for $k = 0, \ldots, 6$. The reader should know how to integrate powers of the cosine, using repeatedly the formula

$$\cos^2 \theta = \frac{1 + \cos 2\theta}{2},$$

or using the recursion formula in terms of lower powers. No matter what method the reader uses, he will find the final answer to be

$$\frac{49\pi}{32}.$$

EXERCISES

1. By changing to polar coordinates, find the integral of $e^{x^2+y^2}$ over the region consisting of the points (x, y) such that $x^2 + y^2 \leq 1$.

2. Find the volume of the region lying over the disc $x^2 + (y - 1)^2 \leq 1$ and bounded from above by the function $z = x^2 + y^2$.

3. Find the integral of $e^{-(x^2+y^2)}$ over the circular disc bounded by

$$x^2 + y^2 = a^2, \qquad a > 0.$$

4. What is

$$\int_{-\infty}^{\infty} \int_{-\infty}^{\infty} e^{-(x^2+y^2)} \, dx \, dy?$$

5. Find the mass of a square plate of side a if the density is proportional to the square of the distance from a vertex.

6. Find the mass of a circular disk of radius a if the density is proportional to the square of the distance from a point on the circumference.

7. Find the mass of a plate bounded by one arch of the curve $y = \sin x$, and the x-axis, if the density is proportional to the distance from the x-axis.

Evaluate the following integrals. Take $a > 0$.

8. $\displaystyle\int_{-a}^{a} \int_{-\sqrt{a^2-x^2}}^{\sqrt{a^2-x^2}} dy \, dx$ 9. $\displaystyle\int_{0}^{a} \int_{0}^{\sqrt{a^2-y^2}} (x^2 + y^2) \, dx \, dy$

10. $\displaystyle\int_{0}^{a/\sqrt{2}} \int_{y}^{\sqrt{a^2-y^2}} x \, dx \, dy$

11. Find the area inside the curve $r = a(1 + \cos \theta)$ and outside the circle $r = a$.

12. The base of a solid is the area of Exercise 11 and the top is given by the function $f(x, y) = x$. Find the volume.

13. Find the area enclosed by the curve $r^2 = 2a^2 \cos 2\theta$.

14. The base of a solid is the area of Exercise 13, and the top is bounded by the function (in terms of polar coordinates) $f(r, \theta) = \sqrt{2a^2 - r^2}$. Find the volume.

15. Find the integral of the function

$$f(x, y) = \frac{1}{(x^2 + y^2 + 1)^{3/2}}$$

over the disc of radius a centered at the origin. Letting a tend to infinity, show that

$$\int_{-\infty}^{-\infty} \int_{-\infty}^{-\infty} f(x, y)\, dy\, dx = 2\pi.$$

16. Answer the same question for the function

$$f(x, y) = \frac{1}{(x^2 + y^2 + 2)^2}.$$

17. Find the integral of the function

$$f(x, y) = \frac{1}{(x^2 + y^2)^3}$$

over the region between the two circles of radius 2 and radius 3, centered at the origin.

18. (a) Find the integral of the function $f(x, y) = x$ over the region given in polar coordinates by $x = 1 - \cos\theta$.
    (b) Let a be a number > 0. Find the ingegral of the function $f(x, y) = x^2$ over the region given in polar coordinates by $v = a(1 - \cos\theta)$.

§4. DETERMINANTS AS AREA

It is remarkable that the determinant has an interpretation as a volume. We discuss the 2-dimensional case, and thus speak of area, although we continue to write Vol for the area of a 2-dimensional figure.

Consider the parallelogram spanned by two vectors v, w.

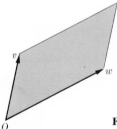

Figure 16

We view v, w as column vectors, and can thus form their determinant $D(v, w)$. This determinant may be positive or negative since

$$D(v, w) = -D(w, v).$$

Thus the determinant itself cannot be the area of this parallelogram, since area is always $\geqq 0$. However, we shall prove:

Theorem 7. *The area of the parallelogram spanned by v, w is equal to the absolute value of the determinant, namely $|D(v, w)|$.*

To prove Theorem 7, we introduced the notion of oriented area. Let $P(v, w)$ be the parallelogram spanned by v and w. We denote by $\text{Vol}_0(v, w)$ the area of $P(v, w)$ if the determinant $D(v, w)$ is $\geqq 0$, and minus the area of $P(v, w)$ if the determinant $D(v, w)$ is < 0. Thus at least $\text{Vol}_0(v, w)$ has the same sign as the determinant, and we call $\text{Vol}_0(v, w)$ the *oriented area*. We denote by $\text{Vol}(v, w)$ the area of the parallelogram spanned by v, w. Hence $\text{Vol}_0(v, w) = \pm \text{Vol}(v, w)$.

To prove Theorem 7, it will suffice to prove:

The oriented area is equal to the determinant. In other words,

$$\text{Vol}_0(v, w) = D(v, w).$$

Now to prove this, it will suffice to prove that Vol_0 satisfies the three properties characteristic of a determinant, namely:

1. Vol_0 is linear in each variable v and w.
2. $\text{Vol}_0(v, v) = 0$ for all v.
3. $\text{Vol}_0(e_1, e_2) = 1$ if e_1, e_2 are the standard unit vectors.

We know that these three properties characterize determinants, and this was proved in the section of uniqueness in Chapter XII. For the convenience of the reader, we repeat the argument here very briefly. We assume that we have a function g satisfying these three properties (with g replacing Vol_0). Then for any vectors

$$v = ae_1 + ce_2 \quad \text{and} \quad w = be_1 + de_2$$

we have

$$g(ae_1 + ce_2, be_1 + de_2) = abg(e_1, e_1) + adg(e_1, e_2) \\ + cbg(e_2, e_1) + cdg(e_2, e_2).$$

The first and fourth term are equal to 0. By Exercise 1,

$$g(e_2, e_1) = -g(e_1, e_2)$$

and hence

$$g(v, w) = (ad - bc)g(e_1, e_2) = ad - bc.$$

This proves what we wanted.

Consider now Vol_0. The last two properties are obvious. Indeed, the parallelogram spanned by v, w is simply a line segment, and its 2-dimensional area is therefore equal to 0. Thus property 2 is satisfied. As for the third property, the parallelogram spanned by the unit vectors e_1, e_2 is simply the unit square, whose area is 1. Hence in this case we have $\text{Vol}_0(e_1, e_2) = 1$.

The harder property is the first. If the reader has not already done so, he should now read the geometric applications, §5 of Chapter X, before reading the rest of this proof, which we shall base on geometric considerations concerning area.

We shall need a lemma.

Lemma 1. *If v, w are linearly dependent, then $\text{Vol}_0(v, w) = 0$.*

Proof. Suppose that we can write

$$av + bw = 0$$

with a or $b \neq 0$. Say $a \neq 0$. Then

$$v = -\frac{b}{a}w = cw$$

Figure 17

so that v, w lie on the same straight line, and the parallelogram spanned by v, w is a line segment (Fig. 17). Hence $\text{Vol}_0(v, w) = 0$, thus proving the lemma.

We also know that when v, w are linearly dependent, then $D(v, w) = 0$, so in this trivial case, our theorem is proved. In the subsequent lemmas, we assume that v, w are linearly independent.

Lemma 2. *Assume that v, w are linearly independent, and let n be a positive integer. Then*

$$\text{Vol}(nv, w) = n \, \text{Vol}(v, w).$$

Proof. The parallelogram spanned by nv and w consists of n parallelograms as shown in the following picture.

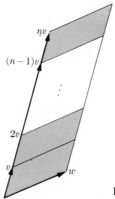

Figure 18

These n parallelograms are simply the translations of $P(v, w)$ by $v, 2v, \ldots, (n-1)v$, and each translation of $P(v, w)$ has the same area as $P(v, w)$. These translations have only line segments in common, and hence

$$\text{Vol}(nv, w) = n\,\text{Vol}(v, w)$$

as desired.

Corollary. *Assume that v, w are linearly independent and let n be a positive integer. Then*

$$\text{Vol}\left(\frac{1}{n}v, w\right) = \frac{1}{n}\,\text{Vol}(v, w).$$

If m, n are positive integers, then

$$\text{Vol}\left(\frac{m}{n}v, w\right) = \frac{m}{n}\,\text{Vol}(v, w).$$

Proof. Let $v_1 = (1/n)v$. By the lemma, we know that

$$\text{Vol}(nv_1, w) = n\,\text{Vol}(v_1, w).$$

This is merely a reformulation of our first assertion, since $nv_1 = v$. As for the second assertion, we write $m/n = m \cdot 1/n$ and apply the proved statements successively:

$$\text{Vol}\left(m \cdot \frac{1}{n}v, w\right) = m\,\text{Vol}\left(\frac{1}{n}v, w\right)$$

$$= m \cdot \frac{1}{n}\,\text{Vol}(v, w)$$

$$= \frac{m}{n}\,\text{Vol}(v, w).$$

Lemma 3. $\text{Vol}(-v, w) = \text{Vol}(v, w).$

Proof. The parallelogram spanned by $-v$ and w is a translation by $-v$ of the parallelogram $P(v, w)$. Hence $P(v, w)$ and $P(-v, w)$ have the same area. (Cf. Fig. 19.)

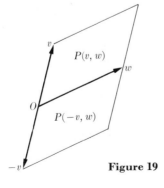

Figure 19

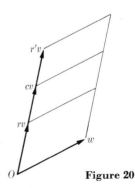

Figure 20

Lemma 4. *If c is any real number > 0, then*

$$\text{Vol}(cv, w) = c\,\text{Vol}(v, w).$$

Proof. Let r, r' be rational numbers such that $0 < r < c < r'$ (Fig. 20). Then

$$P(rv, w) \subset P(cv, w) \subset P(r'v, w).$$

Hence by Lemma 2,

$$
\begin{aligned}
r\,\text{Vol}(v, w) &= \text{Vol}(rv, w) \\
&\leqq \text{Vol}(cv, w) \\
&\leqq \text{Vol}(r'v, w) \\
&= r'\,\text{Vol}(v, w).
\end{aligned}
$$

Letting r and r' approach c as a limit, we find that

$$\text{Vol}(cv, w) = c\,\text{Vol}(v, w),$$

as was to be shown.

From Lemmas 3 and 4 we can now prove that

$$\boxed{\text{Vol}_0(cv, w) = c\,\text{Vol}_0(v, w)}$$

for any real number c, and any vectors v, w. Indeed, if v, w are linearly dependent, then both sides are equal to 0. If v, w are linearly independent, we use the definition of Vol_0 and Lemmas 3, 4. Say $D(v, w) > 0$ and c is negative, $c = -d$. Then $D(cv, w) \leqq 0$ and consequently

$$
\begin{aligned}
\text{Vol}_0(cv, w) = -\text{Vol}(cv, w) &= -\text{Vol}(-dv, w) \\
&= -\text{Vol}(dv, w) \\
&= -d\,\text{Vol}(v, w) \\
&= c\,\text{Vol}(v, w) = c\,\text{Vol}_0(v, w).
\end{aligned}
$$

A similar argument works when $D(v, w) \leqq 0$. We have therefore proved one of the conditions of linearity of the function Vol_0. The analogous property of course works on the other side, namely

$$\boxed{\text{Vol}_0(v, cw) = c\,\text{Vol}_0(v, w).}$$

For the other condition, we again have a lemma.

Lemma 5. *Assume that v, w are linearly independent. Then*

$$\text{Vol}(v + w, w) = \text{Vol}(v, w).$$

Proof. We have to prove that the parallelogram spanned by v, w has the same area as the parallelogram spanned by $v + w$, w.

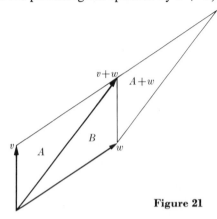

Figure 21

The parallelogram spanned by v, w consists of two triangles A and B as shown in the picture. The parallelogram spanned by $v + w$ and w consists of the triangles B and the translation of A by w. Since A and $A + w$ have the same area, we get:

$$\text{Vol}(v, w) = \text{Vol}(A) + \text{Vol}(B) = \text{Vol}(A + w) + \text{Vol}(B) = \text{Vol}(v + w, w),$$

as was to be shown.

We are now in a position to deal with the second property of linearity. Let w be a fixed non-zero vector in the plane, and let v be a vector such that $\{v, w\}$ is a basis of the plane. We shall prove that for any numbers c, d we have

(1) $$\text{Vol}_0(cv + dw, w) = c\,\text{Vol}_0(v, w).$$

Indeed, if $d = 0$, this is nothing but what we have shown previously. If $d \neq 0$, then again by what has been shown previously,

$$d\,\text{Vol}_0(cv + dw, w) = \text{Vol}_0(cv + dw, dw) = c\,\text{Vol}_0(v, dw) = cd\,\text{Vol}_0(v, w).$$

Canceling d yields relation (1).

From this last formula, the linearity now follows. Indeed, if

$$v_1 = c_1 v + d_1 w \qquad \text{and} \qquad v_2 = c_2 v + d_2 w,$$

then

$$\begin{aligned}
\text{Vol}_0(v_1 + v_2, w) &= \text{Vol}_0((c_1 + c_2)v + (d_1 + d_2)w, w) \\
&= (c_1 + c_2)\,\text{Vol}_0(v, w) \\
&= c_1\,\text{Vol}_0(v, w) + c_2\,\text{Vol}_0(v, w) \\
&= \text{Vol}_0(v_1, w) + \text{Vol}_0(v_2, w).
\end{aligned}$$

This concludes the proof of the fact that

$$\text{Vol}_0(v, w) = D(v, w),$$

and hence of Theorem 7.

Remark 1. The proof given above is slightly long, but each step is quite simple. Furthermore, when one wishes to generalize the proof to higher dimensional space (even 3-space), one can give an entirely similar proof. The reason for this is that the conditions characterizing a determinant involve only two coordinates at a time and thus always take place in some two dimensional plane. Keeping all but two coordinates fixed, the above proof then can be extended at once. Thus for instance in 3-space, let us denote by $P(u, v, w)$ the box spanned by vectors u, v, w (Fig. 22), namely all combinations

$$t_1 u + t_2 v + t_3 w \qquad \text{with} \qquad 0 \leq t_i \leq 1.$$

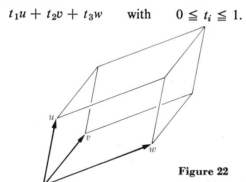

Figure 22

Let $\text{Vol}(u, v, w)$ be the volume of this box. Then

$$\text{Vol}(u, v, w) = |D(u, v, w)|$$

is again the absolute value of the determinant.

Remark 2. We have used geometric properties of area to carry out the above proof. One can lay foundations for all this purely analytically. If the reader is interested, cf. my book *Analysis I*.

We interpret Theorem 7 in terms of linear maps. Given vectors v, w in the plane, we know that there exists a unique linear map

$$L: \mathbf{R}^2 \to \mathbf{R}^2$$

such that $L(e_1) = v$ and $L(e_2) = w$. In fact, if

$$v = a e_1 + c e_2, \qquad w = b e_1 + d e_2,$$

then the matrix associated with the linear map is

$$\begin{pmatrix} a & b \\ c & d \end{pmatrix}.$$

Furthermore, if we denote by C the unit cube spanned by e_1, e_2, and by P the parallelogram spanned by v, w, then P is the image under L of C, that is $L(C) = P$. Indeed, as we have seen, for $0 \leq t_i \leq 1$ we have

$$L(t_1 e_1 + t_2 e_2) = t_1 L(e_1) + t_2 L(e_2) = t_1 v + t_2 w.$$

If we define the determinant of a linear map to be the determinant of its associated matrix, we conclude that

(*)   (Area of P) $= |\text{Det}(L)|$.

To take a numerical example, the area of the parallelogram spanned by the vectors $(2, 1)$ and $(3, -1)$ (Fig. 23) is equal to the absolute value of

$$\begin{vmatrix} 2 & 1 \\ 3 & -1 \end{vmatrix} = -5$$

and hence is equal to 5.

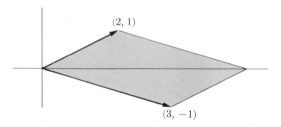

(2, 1)

(3, −1)   **Figure 23**

Theorem 8. *Let P be a parallelogram spanned by two vectors. Let $L: \mathbf{R}^2 \to \mathbf{R}^2$ be a linear map. Then*

$$\text{Area of } L(P) = |\text{Det } L| \ (\text{Area of } P).$$

Proof. Suppose that P is spanned by two vectors v, w. Then $L(P)$ is spanned by $L(v)$ and $L(w)$. (Cf. Fig. 24.) There is a linear map $L_1: \mathbf{R}^2 \to \mathbf{R}^2$ such that

$$L_1(e_1) = v \qquad \text{and} \qquad L_1(e_2) = w.$$

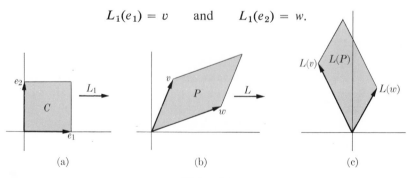

(a)   (b)   (c)

Figure 24

Then $P = L_1(C)$, where C is the unit cube, and

$$L(P) = L(L_1(C)) = (L \circ L_1)(C).$$

By what we proved above in (*), we obtain

$$\text{Vol } L(P) = |\text{Det}(L \circ L_1)| = |\text{Det}(L)\,\text{Det}(L_1)| = |\text{Det}(L)|\,\text{Vol}(P),$$

thus proving our assertion.

Corollary. *For any rectangle R and any linear map $L: \mathbf{R}^2 \to \mathbf{R}^2$ we have*

$$\text{Vol } L(R) = |\text{Det}(L)|\,\text{Vol}(R).$$

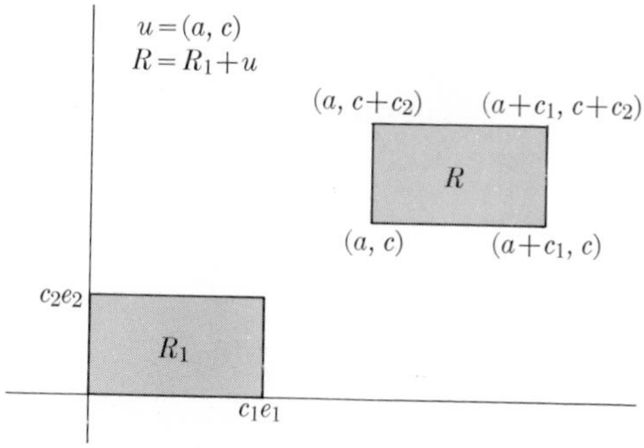

Figure 25

Proof. Let c_1, c_2 be the lengths of the sides of R. Let R_1 be the rectangle spanned by $c_1 e_1$ and $c_2 e_2$. Then R is the translation of R_1 by some vector, say $R = R_1 + u$. Then

$$L(R) = L(R_1 + u) = L(R_1) + L(u)$$

is the translation of $L(R_1)$ by $L(u)$. (Cf. Fig. 25.) Since area does not change under translation, we need only apply Theorem 8 to conclude the proof.

EXERCISE

1. If g satisfies the first two axioms of a determinant, prove that

$$g(v, w) = -g(w, v)$$

for all vectors v, w. This fact was used in the uniqueness proof. [*Hint:* Expand $g(v + w, v + w) = 0$.]

§5. CHANGE OF VARIABLES FORMULA

Let R be a rectangle in $\mathbf{R}^2$ and suppose that R is contained in some open set U. Let

$$G: U \to \mathbf{R}^2$$

be a C^1-map. If G has two coordinate functions,

$$G(u, v) = (g_1(u, v), g_2(u, v)),$$

this means that the partial derivatives of g_1, g_2 exist and are continuous. We let $G(u, v) = (x, y)$, so that

$$x = g_1(u, v) \quad \text{and} \quad y = g_2(u, v).$$

Then the Jacobian determinant of the map G is by definition

$$\Delta_G(u, v) = \begin{vmatrix} \dfrac{\partial g_1}{\partial u} & \dfrac{\partial g_1}{\partial v} \\[2ex] \dfrac{\partial g_2}{\partial u} & \dfrac{\partial g_2}{\partial v} \end{vmatrix}.$$

This determinant is nothing but the determinant of the linear map $G'(u, v)$, which is the tangent linear map to G at (u, v).

Theorem 9. *Assume that G is C^1-invertible on the interior of the rectangle R. Let f be a function on $G(R)$ which is continuous except on a finite number of smooth curves. Then*

$$\int_R (f \circ G)|\Delta_G| = \int_{G(R)} f$$

or in terms of coordinates,

$$\iint_R f(G(u, v))|\Delta_G(u, v)| \, du \, dv = \iint_{G(R)} f(x, y) \, dy \, dx.$$

The proof of Theorem 9 is not easy to establish rigorously, depending on ϵ and δ arguments. However, we can make it plausible in view of Theorem 8.

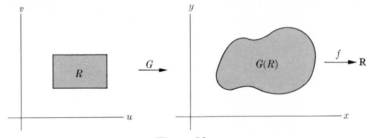

Figure 26

Indeed, suppose first that f is a constant function, say $f(x, y) = 1$ for all (x, y). Then the integral on the right, over $G(R)$, is simply the area of $G(R)$, and our formula reduces to

$$\int_R |\Delta_G| = \int_{G(R)} 1.$$

As we pointed out before, Δ_G is the determinant of the approximating linear map to G. If G is itself linear, then $G'(u, v) = G$ for all u, v and in this case, our formula reduces to Theorem 8, or rather its corollary. In the general case, one has to show that when one approximates G by its tangent linear map, which depends on (u, v), and then integrates $|\Delta_G|$ one still obtains the same result. Cf. for instance my *Analysis I* for a complete proof. A special case will be proved in the next chapter.

When f is not a constant function, one still has the problem of reducing this case to the case of constant functions. This is done by taking a partition of R into small rectangles S, and then approximating f on each $G(S)$ by a constant function. Again, the details are out of the bounds of this book.

We shall now see how we recover the integral in terms of polar coordinates from the general Theorem 9.

Example 1. Let $x = r \cos \theta$ and $y = r \sin \theta$, $r \geq 0$. Then in this case, we have computed previously the determinant, which is

$$\Delta_G(r, \theta) = r.$$

Thus we find again the formula

$$\iint_R f(r \cos \theta, r \sin \theta) r \, dr \, d\theta = \iint_{G(R)} f(x, y) \, dy \, dx.$$

Of course, we have to take a rectangle for which the map

$$G(r, \theta) = (r \cos \theta, r \sin \theta)$$

is invertible on the interior of the rectangle. For instance, we can take

$$0 \leq r_1 \leq r \leq r_2 \qquad \text{and} \qquad 0 \leq \theta_1 \leq \theta \leq \theta_2 \leq 2\pi.$$

The image of the rectangle R is the portion $G(R)$ of the sector as shown in Fig. 27.

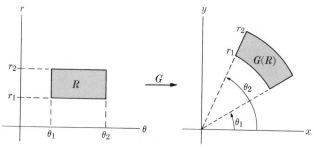

Figure 27

The analogue of Theorem 9 also holds for arbitrary regions A instead of rectangles, provided the boundary consists of a finite number of smooth curves. Thus the general formula states that

$$\int_A (f \circ G)|\Delta_G| = \int_{G(A)} f.$$

Example 2. Let A be the triangle whose vertices are $(1, 2)$, $(3, -1)$, and $(0, 0)$. Find the area of this triangle.

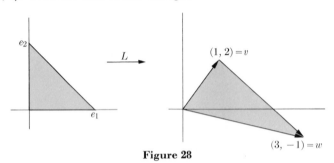

Figure 28

This triangle is the image of the triangle spanned by 0, e_1, e_2 under a linear map, namely the linear map L such that

$$L(e_1) = (1, 2)$$

and

$$L(e_2) = (3, -1).$$

It is verified at once that $|\text{Det}(L)| = 7$. Since the area of the triangle spanned by 0, e_1, e_2 is $\frac{1}{2}$, it follows that the desired area is equal to $\frac{7}{2}$.

Example 3. Let $(x, y) = G(u, v) = (e^u \cos v, e^u \sin v)$. Let R be the rectangle in the (u, v)-space defined by the inequalities $0 \leq u \leq 1$ and $0 \leq v \leq \pi$. It is not difficult to show that G satisfies the hypotheses of Theorem 9, but we shall assume this. The Jacobian matrix of G is given by

$$\begin{pmatrix} e^u \cos v & -e^u \sin v \\ e^u \sin v & e^u \cos v \end{pmatrix}$$

so that its Jacobian determinant is equal to

$$\Delta_G(u, v) = e^{2u}.$$

Let $f(x, y) = x^2$. Then $f^*(u, v) = e^{2u} \cos^2 v$. According to Theorem 9, the integral of f over $G(R)$ is given by the integral

$$\int_0^1 \int_0^\pi e^{4u} \cos^2 v \, du \, dv$$

$$\int \left(\tfrac{1}{4} e^{-1}\right) \cos^2 v$$

which can be evaluated very simply by integrating e^{4u} with respect to u and $\cos^2 v$ with respect to v, and taking the product. The final answer is then equal to

$$\left(\frac{e^4 - 1}{4}\right)\left(\tfrac{1}{2}\pi.\right)$$

EXERCISES

In the following exercises, you may assume that the map G satisfies the hypotheses of Theorem 9.

1. Let $(x, y) = G(u, v) = (u^2 - v^2, 2uv)$. Let A be the region defined by $u^2 + v^2 \leq 1$ and $0 \leq u, 0 \leq v$. Find the integral of the function

$$f(x, y) = 1/(x^2 + y^2)^{1/2}$$

over $G(A)$.

2. (a) Let $(x, y) = G(u, v)$ be the same map as in Exercise 1. Let A be the square $0 \leq u \leq 2$ and $0 \leq v \leq 2$. Find the area of $G(A)$.
   (b) Find the integral of $f(x, y) = x$ over $G(A)$.

3. (a) Let R be the rectangle whose corners are $(1, 2)$, $(1, 5)$, $(3, 2)$, and $(3, 5)$. Let G be the linear map represented by the matrix

$$\begin{pmatrix} 2 & 1 \\ -1 & 3 \end{pmatrix}.$$

   Find the area of $G(R)$.

   (b) Same question if G is represented by the matrix $\begin{pmatrix} 3 & 2 \\ 1 & -6 \end{pmatrix}.$

4. Let $(x, y) = G(u, v) = (u + v, u^2 - v)$. Let A be the region in the first quadrant bounded by the axes and the line $u + v = 2$. Find the integral of the function $f(x, y) = 1/\sqrt{1 + 4x + 4y}$ over $G(A)$.

5. Let $(x, y) = G(u, v) = (au, bv)$ where a, b are numbers > 0. For any region A, show that $\mathrm{Vol}\, G(A) = ab\, \mathrm{Vol}(A)$.

6. Compute the area enclosed by the ellipse, defined by

$$\frac{x^2}{a^2} + \frac{y^2}{b^2} \leq 1.$$

   Take $a, b > 0$.

7. Let $(x, y) = G(u, v) = (u, v(1 + u^2))$. Let R be the rectangle $0 \leq u \leq 3$ and $0 \leq v \leq 2$. Find the integral of $f(x, y) = x$ over $G(R)$.

8. Let G be the linear map represented by the matrix

$$\begin{pmatrix} 3 & 0 \\ 1 & 5 \end{pmatrix}.$$

If A is the interior of a circle of radius 10, what is the area of $G(A)$?

9. Let G be the linear map of Exercise 8, and let A be the ellipse defined as in Exercise 6. What is the area of $G(A)$?

10. Let T be the triangle bounded by the x-axis, the y-axis, and the line $x + y = 1$. Let φ be a continuous function of one variable on the interval $[0, 1]$. Let m, n be positive integers. Show that

$$\iint_T \varphi(x + y)x^m y^n \, dy \, dx = c_{m,n} \int_0^1 \varphi(t)t^{m+n+1} \, dt,$$

where $c_{m,n}$ is the constant given by the integral $\int_0^1 (1 - t)^m t^n \, dt$. [*Hint:* Let $x = u - v$ and $y = v$.]

11. Let B be the region bounded by the ellipse $x^2/a^2 + y^2/b^2 = 1$. Find the integral

$$\iint_B y \, dy \, dx.$$

§6. TRIPLE INTEGRALS

The entire discussion concerning 2-dimensional integrals generalizes to higher dimensions. We discuss briefly the 3-dimensional case.

A 3-dimensional rectangle (rectangular parallelepiped) can be written as a product of three intervals:

$$R = [a_1, b_1] \times [a_2, b_2] \times [a_3, b_3].$$

A partition P of R is then determined by partitions P_1, P_2, P_3 of the three intervals respectively, and partitions R into 3-dimensional subrectangles, which we denote again by S.

If f is a bounded function on R, we may then form upper and lower sums. Indeed, we define the volume of the rectangle R above to be the 3-dimensional volume

$$\text{Vol}(R) = (b_3 - a_3)(b_2 - a_2)(b_1 - a_1)$$

and similarly for the subrectangles of the partition. Then we have

$$L(P, f) = \sum_S (\inf_S f)\,\text{Vol}(S),$$

$$U(P, f) = \sum_S (\sup_S f)\,\text{Vol}(S).$$

A refinement P' of P is determined by refinements P_1', P_2', P_3' of P_1, P_2, P_3 respectively, and the Lemma of §1 extends to this case.

Again, we say that f is integrable if the least upper bound of the lower sums is equal to the greatest lower bound of the upper sums, and if this is the case, we define it to be the integral of f over R, written

$$\int_R f = \iiint_R f(x, y, z) \, dz \, dy \, dx$$

if the variables are x, y, z.

If $f \geqq 0$, then we interpret this integral as the 4-dimensional volume of the 4-dimensional region lying in 4-space, bounded from below by R, and from above by the graph of f. Of course, we cannot draw this figure because it is in 4-space, but the terminology goes right over.

Theorem 1 and Theorem 2 are again valid, that is the integral is linear, and satisfies the usual inequality.

The criterion of Theorem 3 for a function to be integrable also has an analogue. In this case, however, we have to parametrize the boundary of a 3-dimensional region by 2-dimensional smooth pieces of surfaces. Thus let T be a 2-dimensional rectangle, and let

$$F: \mathbf{T} \to \mathbf{R}^3$$

be a map. If F is of class C^1 we shall say that F is smooth, and we call the image of F a smooth surface (Fig. 29).

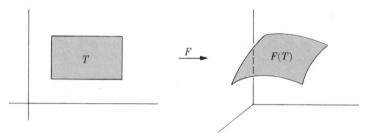

Figure 29

The analogue of Theorem 3 is then: *Let R be a 3-dimensional rectangle, and let f be a function defined on R, bounded and continuous except possibly at the points lying on a finite number of smooth surfaces. Then f is integrable on R.*

Again we can integrate over a more general region than a rectangle, provided such a region A has a boundary which is contained in a finite number of smooth surfaces. Then Theorem 4 holds. If A denotes a 3-dimensional region and f is a function on A, we denote the integral of f over A by

$$\int_A f \quad \text{or} \quad \iiint_A f(x, y, z) \, dz \, dy \, dx.$$

If we view A as a solid piece of material, and f is interpreted as a density distribution over A, then the integral of f over A may be interpreted as the *mass* of A.

To compute multiple integrals in the 3-dimensional case, we have the same situation as in the 2-dimensional case.

The theorem concerning the relation with repeated integrals holds, so that if R is the rectangle given by

$$R = [a_1, b_1] \times [a, b_{22}] \times [a_3, b_3],$$

then
$$\int_R f = \int_{a_1}^{b_1}\left[\int_{a_2}^{b_2}\left(\int_{a_3}^{b_3} f(x, y, z)\, dz\right) dy\right] dx.$$

Of course, the repeated integral can be evaluated in any order.

Example 1. Find the integral of the function $f(x, y, z) = \sin x$ over the rectangle $0 \leq x \leq \pi$, $2 \leq y \leq 3$, and $-1 \leq z \leq 1$.

The integral is equal to

$$\int_0^\pi \int_2^3 \int_{-1}^1 \sin x \, dz \, dy \, dx.$$

If we first integrate with respect to z, we get $z|_{-1}^1 = 2$. Next with respect to y, we get $y|_2^3 = 1$. We are then reduced to the integral

$$\int_0^\pi 2 \sin x \, dx = -2 \cos x \Big|_0^\pi = -2(\cos \pi - \cos 0) = 4.$$

We also have the integral over regions determined by inequalities.

Case 1. Rectangular coordinates. Let a, b be numbers, $a \leq b$. Let g_1, g_2 be two smooth functions defined on the interval $[a, b]$ such that

$$g_1(x) \leq g_2(x),$$

and let $h_1(x, y) \leq h_2(x, y)$ be two smooth functions defined on the region consisting of all points (x, y) such that

$$a \leq x \leq b \quad \text{and} \quad g_1(x) \leq y \leq g_2(x).$$

Let A be the set of points (x, y, z) such that

$$a \leq x \leq b, \quad g_1(x) \leq y \leq g_2(x), \quad \text{and} \quad h_1(x, y) \leq z \leq h_2(x, y).$$

Let f be continuous on A. Then

$$\int_A f = \int_a^b \left[\int_{g_1(x)}^{g_2(x)} \left(\int_{h_1(x,y)}^{h_2(x,y)} f(x, y, z)\, dz \right) dy \right] dx.$$

For simplicity, the integral on the right will also be written without the brackets.

For example, consider the tetrahedron T spanned by 0 and the three unit vectors (Fig. 30).

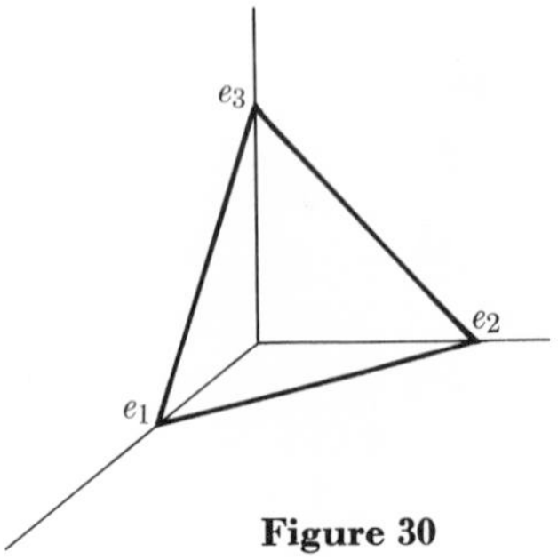

Figure 30

This tetrahedron is described by the inequalities:

$$0 \leq x \leq 1, \qquad 0 \leq y \leq 1 - x, \qquad 0 \leq z \leq 1 - x - y.$$

Hence if f is a function on the tetrahedron, its integral over T is given by

$$\int_T f = \int_0^1 \int_0^{1-x} \int_0^{1-x-y} f(x, y, z) \, dz \, dy \, dx.$$

There is no difficulty in evaluating these integrals, which we leave to the reader [Exercise 17(a)].

Before discussing the other two cases, namely cylindrical and spherical coordinates, we point out that the change of variables formula is valid in three dimensions. We can state it as follows.

Change of variables formula. *Let A be a bounded region in $\mathbf{R}^3$ whose boundary consists of a finite number of smooth surfaces. Let A be contained in some open set U, and let*

$$G: U \to \mathbf{R}^3$$

be a C^1-map, which we assume to be C^1-invertible on the interior of A. Let f be a function on $G(A)$, continuous except on a finite number of smooth surfaces. Then

$$\int_A (f \circ G)|\Delta_G| = \int_{G(A)} f.$$

In the 3-dimensional case, the Jacobian matrix of G at every point is then a 3×3 matrix.

Example 2. Let R be the 3-dimensional rectangle spanned by the three unit vectors e_1, e_2, e_3. Let v_1, v_2, v_3 be three vectors in 3-space, and let

$$G: \mathbf{R}^3 \to \mathbf{R}^3$$

be the linear map such that $G(e_i) = v_i$. Then $G(R)$ is a parallelotope (not necessarily rectangular). (Cf. Fig. 31.)

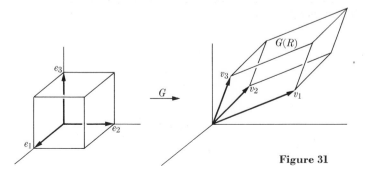

Figure 31

The volume of the unit cube is equal to 1. Hence the volume of $G(R)$ is equal to $|\text{Det}(G)|$.

For instance, if

$$v_1 = (3, 1, 2),$$
$$v_2 = (1, -1, 4),$$
$$v_3 = (2, 1, 0),$$

then

$$\text{Det}(G) = \begin{vmatrix} 3 & 1 & 2 \\ 1 & -1 & 4 \\ 2 & 1 & 0 \end{vmatrix} = -4$$

so the volume of $G(R)$ is equal to 4.

Case 2. Cylindrical coordinates. We consider the map given by

$$G(r, \theta, z) = (r \cos \theta, r \sin \theta, z).$$

Then the Jacobian determinant of G is equal to r, so that if a region is described by cylindrical coordinates in 3-space, the integral is given by

$$\iiint_A f(r \cos \theta, r \sin \theta, z) r \, dz \, dr \, d\theta = \iiint_{G(A)} f(x, y, z) \, dz \, dy \, dx.$$

Example 3. The image of a box B defined by the inequalities:

$$0 \leq \theta_1 \leq \theta \leq \theta_2 \leq 2\pi, \quad 0 \leq r_1 \leq r \leq r_2, \quad \text{and} \quad z_1 \leq z \leq z_2,$$

under the map G is shown in the following picture.

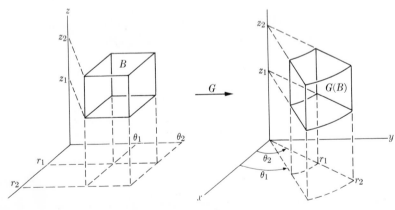

Figure 32

Hence the volume of $G(B)$ is equal to

$$\int_{\theta_1}^{\theta_2} \int_{r_1}^{r_2} \int_{z_1}^{z_2} r \, dz \, dr \, d\theta = (z_2 - z_1) \left(\frac{r_2^2 - r_1^2}{2} \right) (\theta_2 - \theta_1).$$

A region may be described by inequalities given by functions. For instance, *let A be the region in the* (θ, r, z)*-space consisting of all points* (θ, r, z) *satisfying conditions:*

$$a \leqq \theta \leqq b, \quad (b \leqq a + 2\pi),$$
$$0 \leqq g_1(\theta) \leqq r \leqq g_2(\theta),$$

with smooth functions g_1, g_2 *defined on the interval* $[a, b]$*, and*

$$h_1(\theta, r) \leqq z \leqq h_2(\theta, r),$$

with smooth functions h_1, h_2 *defined on the 2-dimensional region bounded by* $\theta = a$, $\theta = b$, *and* g_1, g_2, *i.e. the region consisting of all points* (θ, r) *satisfying the above inequalities. Let G be the map of cylindrical coordinates given above. Let f be a continuous function on the region* $G(A)$ *in the* (x, y, z)*-space. Let*

$$f^*(\theta, r, z) = f(r \cos \theta, r \sin \theta, z).$$

Then

$$\int_{G(A)} f = \int_a^b \int_{g_1(\theta)}^{g_2(\theta)} \int_{h_1(\theta, r)}^{h_2(\theta, r)} f^*(\theta, r, z) r \, dz \, dr \, d\theta.$$

The function which we denote by f^* may be viewed as the function f in terms of the cylindrical coordinates.

Example 4. Find the mass of a solid bounded by the polar coordinates $\pi/3 \leqq \theta \leqq 2\pi/3$ and $r = \cos \theta$ and by $z = 0$, $z = r$, if the density is given by the function

$$f^*(r, \theta, z) = 3r.$$

The mass is given by the integral

$$\int_{\pi/3}^{2\pi/3} \int_0^{\cos \theta} \int_0^r 3r \cdot r \, dz \, dr \, d\theta.$$

integrating the inner integral with respect to z yields $3r^2 r = 3r^3$. Integrating with respect to r between 0 and $\cos \theta$ yields

$$\left. \frac{3r^4}{4} \right|_0^{\cos \theta} = \frac{3 \cos^4 \theta}{4}.$$

Finally we integrate with respect to θ, using elementary techniques of integration: $\cos^2 \theta = (1 + \cos 2\theta)/2$ so that

$$\cos^4 \theta = \tfrac{1}{4}(1 + 2 \cos 2\theta + \cos^2 2\theta)$$
$$= \frac{1}{4}\left(1 + 2 \cos 2\theta + \frac{1 + \cos 4\theta}{2}\right).$$

We can now integrate this between the given limits, and we find

$$\frac{3}{4}\int_{\pi/3}^{2\pi/3} \cos^4 \theta \, d\theta = \frac{3}{16}\left(\frac{\pi}{3} - \sqrt{3} + \frac{\pi}{6} + \frac{\sqrt{3}}{8}\right).$$

Note. In Example 4, the function is already given in terms of (r, θ, z). It corresponds to the function $f(x, y, z) = 3\sqrt{x^2 + y^2}$. Indeed, taking $f(r \cos \theta, r \sin \theta, z)$ yields $3r$.

Case 3. Spherical coordinates. We consider the mapping $G: \mathbf{R}^3 \to \mathbf{R}^3$ given by $G(\rho, \theta, \varphi) = (\rho \sin \varphi \cos \theta, \rho \sin \varphi \sin \theta, \rho \cos \varphi)$, so that we let

$$x = \rho \sin \varphi \cos \theta, \qquad y = \rho \sin \varphi \sin \theta, \qquad z = \rho \cos \varphi.$$

Then the Jacobian determinant is given by

$$\Delta_G(\rho, \theta, \varphi) = \rho^2 \sin \varphi.$$

We consider the region in the (ρ, θ, φ)-coordinates described by

$$0 \leq \rho, \qquad 0 \leq \varphi \leq \pi, \qquad 0 \leq \theta \leq 2\pi.$$

Then G is invertible in the interior of this region. Indeed, G gives us the spherical coordinates of a point (x, y, z) as shown in the following picture.

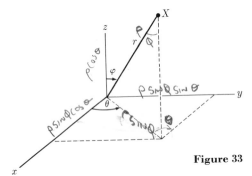

Figure 33

In fact, we have

$$\rho = \sqrt{x^2 + y^2 + z^2}.$$

We denote this by ρ to distinguish it from the polar coordinate r in the (x, y)-plane. We see that

$$x^2 + y^2 = \rho^2 - z^2 = \rho^2 \sin^2 \varphi$$

so that the polar r is given by

$$r = \sqrt{x^2 + y^2} = \rho \sin \varphi.$$

In taking the square root, we do not need to use the absolute value $|\sin \varphi|$ because we take $0 \leq \varphi \leq \pi$ so that $\sin \varphi \geq 0$ for our values of φ.

In the present case, the change of variables formula yields:

$$\iiint\limits_{A} f(G(\rho, \theta, \varphi))\rho^2 \sin \varphi \, d\rho \, d\varphi \, d\theta = \iiint\limits_{G(A)} f(x, y, z) \, dz \, dy \, dx.$$

For instance, let R be the 3-dimensional rectangle in the (ρ, θ, φ)-space described by the inequalities:

$$\theta_1 \leqq \theta \leqq \theta_2, \qquad (\theta_2 \leqq \theta_1 + 2\pi),$$
$$0 \leqq \rho_1 \leqq \rho \leqq \rho_2,$$
$$0 \leqq \varphi_1 \leqq \varphi \leqq \varphi_2 \leqq \pi.$$

The image of R under the map G is then an elementary spherical region as shown in the next picture.

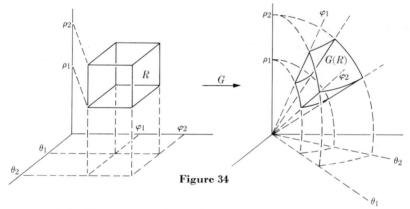

Figure 34

Example 5. The volume of the elementary spherical region $G(R)$ just described is equal to the integral

$$\int_{\theta_1}^{\theta_2} \int_{\varphi_1}^{\varphi_2} \int_{\rho_1}^{\rho_2} \rho^2 \sin \varphi \, d\rho \, d\varphi \, d\theta = \left(\frac{\rho_2^3}{3} - \frac{\rho_1^3}{3}\right)(\cos \varphi_1 - \cos \varphi_2)(\theta_2 - \theta_1).$$

In this case, the repeated 3-fold integral splits into separate integrals with respect to ρ, φ, θ independently. These integrals are of course very simple to evaluate, as we have done above. In this case, the limits of integration are constant.

Example 6. Find the mass of a solid body S determined by the inequalities of spherical coordinates:

$$0 \leqq \theta \leqq \frac{\pi}{2}, \qquad \frac{\pi}{4} \leqq \varphi \leqq \arctan 2, \qquad 0 \leqq \rho \leqq \sqrt{6},$$

if the density, given as a function of the spherical coordinates (θ, φ, ρ), is equal to $1/\rho$.

To find the mass, we have to integrate the given function over the region. The integral is given by

$$\int_0^{\pi/2} \int_{\pi/4}^{\arctan 2} \int_0^{\sqrt{6}} \frac{1}{\rho} \rho^2 \sin \varphi \, d\rho \, d\varphi \, d\theta.$$

Performing the repeated integral, we obtain

$$\frac{3\pi}{2} \left(\frac{1}{\sqrt{2}} - \frac{1}{\sqrt{5}} \right).$$

We note that in the present example, the limits of integration are constants, and hence the repeated integral is equal to a product of the integrals

$$\int_0^{\pi/2} d\theta \cdot \int_{\pi/4}^{\arctan 2} \sin \varphi \, d\varphi \cdot \int_0^{\sqrt{6}} \rho \, d\rho.$$

Each integration can be performed separately. Of course, this does not hold when the limits of integration are non-constant functions.

As before, we have a similar integral when the boundaries of integration are not constant. We state the result:

Let a, b be numbers such that $0 \leq b - a \leq 2\pi$. Let $g_1(\theta)$, $g_2(\theta)$ be smooth functions of θ, defined on the interval $a \leq \theta \leq b$ such that

$$0 \leq g_1(\theta) \leq g_2(\theta) \leq \pi.$$

Let h_1, h_2 be functions of two variables, defined and smooth on the region consisting of all points (θ, φ) such that

$$a \leq \theta \leq b,$$
$$g_1(\theta) \leq \varphi \leq g_2(\theta)$$

and such that $0 \leq h_1(\theta, \varphi) \leq h_2(\theta, \varphi)$ for all (θ, φ) in this region. Let A be the 3-dimensional region in the (θ, φ, ρ)-space consisting of all points such that

$$a \leq \theta \leq b,$$
$$g_1(\theta) \leq \varphi \leq g_2(\theta),$$
$$h_1(\theta, \varphi) \leq \rho \leq h_2(\theta, \varphi).$$

Let G be the spherical coordinate map, and let f be a continuous function on $G(A)$. Let $f^*(\theta, \varphi, \rho) = f(G(\theta, \varphi, \rho))$. Then

$$\int_{G(A)} f = \int_a^b \int_{g_1(\theta)}^{g_2(\theta)} \int_{h_1(\theta,\varphi)}^{h_2(\theta,\varphi)} f^*(\theta, \varphi, \rho)\rho^2 \sin \varphi \, d\rho \, d\varphi \, d\theta.$$

Example 7. Find the volume above the cone $z^2 = x^2 + y^2$ and inside the sphere $x^2 + y^2 + z^2 = z$ (Fig. 35).

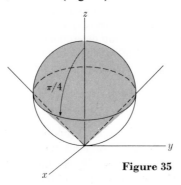

Figure 35

The equation for the sphere in spherical coordinates is obtained by the values

$$\rho^2 = x^2 + y^2 + z^2$$

and

$$z = \rho \cos \varphi.$$

Thus the sphere is given by the equation

$$\rho = \cos \varphi.$$

The cone is given by $\cos^2 \varphi = \sin^2 \varphi$, and since $0 \le \varphi \le \pi$ this is the same as $\varphi = \pi/4$. Thus the region of integration is the image under the spherical coordinate map of the region A described by the inequalities:

$$0 \le \theta \le 2\pi, \qquad 0 \le \varphi \le \pi/4, \qquad 0 \le \rho \le \cos \varphi.$$

Hence our volume is equal to the integral

$$\int_{G(A)} 1 = \int_0^{2\pi} \int_0^{\pi/4} \int_0^{\cos \varphi} \rho^2 \sin \varphi \, d\rho \, d\varphi \, d\theta.$$

The inside integral with respect to ρ is equal to

$$(\sin \varphi) \left.\frac{\rho^3}{3}\right|_0^{\cos \varphi} = \frac{1}{3} \cos^3 \varphi \sin \varphi.$$

This is now easily integrated with respect to φ, and yields

$$\frac{1}{3} \left.\frac{-\cos^4 \varphi}{4}\right|_0^{\pi/4} = \frac{1}{12} \left(-\frac{1}{4} + 1 \right) = \frac{3}{48}.$$

Finally, we integrate with respect to θ, and the final answer is therefore equal to

$$\tfrac{3}{48} \cdot 2\pi = \tfrac{1}{8}\pi.$$

EXERCISES

1. (a) Let $G: \mathbf{R}^3 \to \mathbf{R}^3$ be the map which sends spherical coordinates (θ, φ, ρ) into cylindrical coordinates (θ, r, z). Write down the Jacobian matrix for this map, and its Jacobian determinant.

   (b) Write down the change of variables formula for this case.

   (c) Evaluate the volume of the region given in cylindrical coordinates by

$$0 \leq \theta_1 \leq \theta \leq \theta_2 \leq 2\pi,$$

$$0 \leq r \leq \rho_1 \sin \varphi_1, \qquad r \cot \varphi_1 \leq z \leq \sqrt{\rho_1^2 - r^2}$$

   by an integral taken directly in terms of cylindrical coordinates, and then by using the change of variables formula and integrating in terms of the spherical coordinates. By what inequalities is the region described in terms of the spherical coordinates?

2. Find the integral

$$\int_0^\pi \int_0^{\sin \theta} \int_0^{\rho \cos \theta} \rho^2 \, dz \, d\rho \, d\theta.$$

3. Find the mass of a spherical ball of radius $a > 0$ if the density at any point is equal to a constant k times the distance of that point to the center.

4. Find the mass of a spherical shell of inside radius a and outside radius b if the density at any point is inversely proportional to the distance from the center.

5. Find the integral of the function

$$f(x, y, z) = x^2$$

over that portion of the cylinder

$$x^2 + y^2 = a^2$$

lying between the planes

$$z = 0 \qquad \text{and} \qquad z = b > 0.$$

6. Find the mass of a sphere of radius a if the density at any point is proportional to the distance from a fixed plane passing through a diameter.

7. Find the volume of the region bounded by the cylinder $y = \cos x$, and the planes

$$z = y, \qquad x = 0, \qquad x = \pi/2, \qquad \text{and} \qquad z = 0.$$

8. Find the volume of the region bounded above by the sphere

$$x^2 + y^2 + z^2 = 1$$

and below by the surface

$$z = x^2 + y^2.$$

9. Find the volume of that portion of the sphere $x^2 + y^2 + z^2 = a^2$, which is inside the cylinder $r = a \sin \theta$, using cylindrical coordinates.

10. Find the volume above the cone $z^2 = x^2 + y^2$ and inside the sphere $\rho = 2a \cos \varphi$ (spherical coordinates). [Draw a picture. What is the center of the sphere? What is the equation of the cone in spherical coordinates?]

11. Find the volumes of the following regions, in 3-space.

 (a) Bounded above by the plane $z = 1$, and below by the top half of $z^2 = x^2 + y^2$.

 (b) Bounded above and below by $z^2 = x^2 + y^2$, and on the sides by $x^2 + y^2 + z^2 = 1$.

 (c) Bounded above by $z = x^2 + y^2$, below by $z = 0$, and on the sides by $x^2 + y^2 = 1$.

 (d) Bounded above by $z = x$, and below by $z = x^2 + y^2$.

12. Find the integral of the following functions over the indicated region, in 3-space.

 (a) $f(x, y, z) = x^2$ over the tetrahedron bounded by the plane

$$12x + 20y + 15z = 60,$$

 and the coordinate planes.

 (b) $f(x, y, z) = y$ over the tetrahedron as in (a).

 (c) $f(x, y, z) = 7yz$ over the region on the positive side of the (x, z)-plane, bounded by the planes $y = 0$, $z = 0$, and $z = a$ (for some positive number a), and the cylinder $x^2 + y^2 = b^2$ ($b > 0$).

13. Find the volume inside the sphere

$$x^2 + y^2 + z^2 = 1.$$

14. Let A be a region in $\mathbf{R}^3$ and assume that its volume is equal to k. Let $G: \mathbf{R}^3 \to \mathbf{R}^3$ be the map such that $G(x, y, z) = (ax, by, cz)$, where a, b, c are positive numbers. What is the volume of $G(A)$?

15. What is the volume of the ellipsoid

$$\frac{x^2}{a^2} + \frac{y^2}{b^2} + \frac{z^2}{c^2} \leq 1.$$

16. Find the volume of the image of the solid which is the image of a ball of radius a under the linear map represented by the matrix

$$\begin{pmatrix} 1 & -1 & 1 \\ 0 & 2 & 5 \\ 0 & 0 & 7 \end{pmatrix}.$$

17. (a) Find the volume of the tetrahedron A determined by the inequalities

$$0 \leq x, \quad 0 \leq y, \quad 0 \leq z \quad \text{and} \quad x + y + z \leq 1.$$

 (b) This tetrahedron can also be written in the form

$$t_1 e_1 + t_2 e_2 + t_3 e_3 \quad \text{with} \quad t_1 + t_2 + t_3 \leq 1, \quad 0 \leq t_i.$$

If w_1, w_2, w_3 are linearly independent vectors in 3-space, and L is the linear map such that $L(e_i) = w_i$, show that $L(A)$ is described by similar inequalities. We call it the tetrahedron spanned by 0, w_1, w_2, w_3.

(c) Determine the volume of the tetrahedron spanned by the origin and the three vectors $(1, 1, 2)$, $(2, 0, -1)$, $(3, 1, 2)$.

(d) Using the fact that the volume of a region does not change under translation, determine the volume of the tetrahedron spanned by the four points $(1, 1, 1)$, $(2, 2, 3)$, $(3, 1, 0)$, and $(4, 2, 3)$.

18. (a) Determine the volume of the tetrahedron spanned by the four points $(2, 1, 0)$, $(3, -1, 1)$, $(-1, 1, 2)$, $(0, 0, 1)$.

(b) Same question for the four points $(3, 1, 2)$, $(2, 0, 0)$, $(4, 1, 5)$, $(5, -1, 1)$.

Chapter XV

Green's Theorem

§1. STATEMENT OF THE THEOREM

In this chapter, we shall change slightly our notation concerning curve integrals.

Suppose we are given a vector field on some open set U in the plane. Then this vector field has two components, i.e. we can write

$$F(x, y) = (P(x, y), Q(x, y)),$$

where P, Q are functions of two variables (x, y). In everything that follows, we assume that all functions we deal with are C^1, i.e. that these functions have continuous partial derivatives.

Let $C: [a, b] \to U$ be a curve. We shall use a new notation for the integral of F over C, namely we write

$$\int_C F = \int_a^b F(C(t)) \cdot C'(t)\, dt = \int_C P(x, y)\, dx + Q(x, y)\, dy$$

or abbreviate this as

$$\int_C P\, dx + Q\, dy.$$

This is reasonable since the curve gives

$$x = x(t)$$

and

$$y = y(t)$$

as functions of t, and

$$F(C(t)) \cdot \frac{dC}{dt} = P(x, y)\frac{dx}{dt} + Q(x, y)\frac{dy}{dt}.$$

Green's theorem. *Let P, Q be C^1-functions on a region A, which is the interior of a closed piecewise C^1-path C, parametrized counterclockwise. Then*

$$\int_C P\, dx + Q\, dy = \iint_A \left(\frac{\partial Q}{\partial x} - \frac{\partial P}{\partial y} \right) dy\, dx.$$

583

The region and its boundary may look as follows:

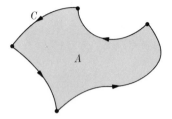

Figure 1

It is difficult to prove Green's theorem in general, partly because it is difficult to make rigorous the notion of "interior" of a path, and also the notion of counterclockwise. In practice, for any specifically given region, it is always easy, however. That it may be difficult in general is already suggested by drawing a somewhat less simple region as follows:

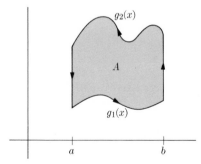

Figure 2

We shall therefore prove Green's theorem only in special cases, where we can give the region and the parametrization of its boundary explicitly.

Case 1. Suppose that the region A is given by the inequalities

$$a \leq x \leq b \quad \text{and} \quad g_1(x) \leq y \leq g_2(x)$$

in the same manner as we studied before in Chapter XIV, §2.

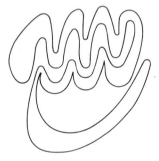

Figure 3

The boundary of A then consists of four pieces, the two vertical segments, and the pieces parametrized by the maps:

$$\gamma_1: t \mapsto (t, g_1(t)), \qquad\qquad a \leq t \leq b,$$
$$\gamma_2: t \mapsto (t, g_2(t)), \qquad\qquad a \leq t \leq b.$$

Then we can prove one-half of Green's theorem, namely

$$\int_C P \, dx = \iint_A -\frac{\partial P}{\partial y} \, dy \, dx.$$

Proof. We have

$$\iint_A \frac{\partial P}{\partial y} \, dy \, dx = \int_a^b \int_{g_1(x)}^{g_2(x)} D_2 P(x, y) \, dy \, dx$$

$$= \int_a^b \left(P(x, y) \Big|_{g_1(x)}^{g_2(x)} \right) dx$$

$$= \int_a^b [P(x, g_2(x)) - P(x, g_1(x))] \, dx$$

$$= \int_{\gamma_2} P \, dx - \int_{\gamma_1} P \, dx.$$

However, the boundary of A, oriented counterclockwise, consists of four pieces,

$$\gamma_1, \gamma_2^-, \gamma_3, \gamma_4,$$

where γ_2^- is the opposite curve to γ_2, and γ_3, γ_4 are the vertical segments. One sees at once that the integrals

$$\int_{\gamma_3} P \, dx \qquad \text{and} \qquad \int_{\gamma_4} P \, dx$$

are equal to 0, and thus we obtain the formula in this case.

Case 2. Suppose that the region is given by similar inequalities as in Case 1, but with respect to the y-axis. In other words, the region A is defined by inequalities

$$c \leq y \leq d \qquad \text{and} \qquad g_1(y) \leq x \leq g_2(y).$$

Then we prove the other half of Green's theorem, namely

$$\iint_A \frac{\partial Q}{\partial x} \, dy \, dx = \int_C Q \, dy.$$

Proof. We take the integral with respect to x first:

$$\iint_A \frac{\partial Q}{\partial x}\, dx\, dy = \int_c^d \left[\int_{g_1(y)}^{g_2(y)} D_1 Q(x, y)\, dx \right] dy$$

$$= \int_c^d [Q(g_2(y), y) - Q(g_1(y), y)]\, dy.$$

In this case, the integral of $Q\, dy$ over the horizontal segments is equal to 0, and hence our formula is proved.

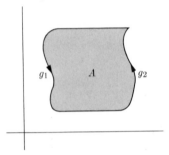

Figure 4

In particular, if a region is of a type satisfying both the preceding conditions, then the full theorem follows. Examples of such regions are rectangles and triangles and interiors of circles:

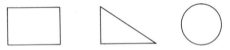

Figure 5

We have therefore proved Green's theorem in these cases.

Frequently, a region can be decomposed into regions of the preceding types. We draw a picture to illustrate this, namely the annulus lying between two circles.

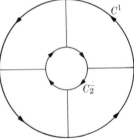

Figure 6

By drawing four line segments as shown, we decompose this annulus into four regions, and it would thus suffice to prove Green's theorem for each one of these four regions. None of them yet satisfies the desired hypotheses, but one more decomposition will do for each region, as shown in the next picture.

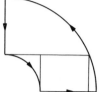

Figure 7

Consequently if we denote by C_1 the outside circle taken counterclockwise, and by C_2 the inside circle taken counterclockwise, if we let $C = \{C_1, C_2^-\}$, and if A is the region between C_1 and C_2, then

$$\iint_A \left(\frac{\partial Q}{\partial x} - \frac{\partial P}{\partial y} \right) dy \, dx = \int_C P \, dx + Q \, dy$$

$$= \int_{C_1} P \, dx + Q \, dy - \int_{C_2} P \, dx + Q \, dy.$$

Example 1. Let A be the region between two concentric circles C_1, C_2 as shown, both with counterclockwise orientation (Fig. 8).

Figure 8

Let F be a vector field on A, $F = \text{grad } \varphi$ for some function φ. Show that the integral of F over C_1 is equal to the integral of F over C_2. (As usual, assume all functions to be differentiable as needed.)

We can write

$$F(x, y) = \left(\frac{\partial \varphi}{\partial x}, \frac{\partial \varphi}{\partial y} \right)$$

so that $P = \partial \varphi / \partial x$ and $Q = \partial \varphi / \partial y$. Then $\partial Q / \partial x = \partial P / \partial y$ so that in Green's theorem we have

$$\iint_A \left(\frac{\partial Q}{\partial x} - \frac{\partial P}{\partial y} \right) dy \, dx = 0.$$

By the remark made previously, this implies that

$$\int_{C_1} P\, dx + Q\, dy = \int_{C_2} P\, dx + Q\, dy,$$

as was to be shown.

Example 2. Find the integral of the vector field

$$F(x, y) = (y + 3x, 2y - x)$$

counterclockwise around the ellipse $4x^2 + y^2 = 4$.

Let $P(x, y) = y + 3x$ and $Q(x, y) = 2y - x$. Then $\partial Q/\partial x = -1$ and $\partial P/\partial y = -1$. By Green's theorem, we get

$$\int_C P\, dx + Q\, dy = \iint_A (-2)\, dy\, dx = -2\operatorname{Vol}(A),$$

where $\operatorname{Vol}(A)$ is the area of the ellipse, which is known to be 2π ($= \pi ab$ when the ellipse is in the form $x^2/a^2 + y^2/b^2 = 1$).

EXERCISES

1. Use Green's theorem to find the integral $\int_C y^2\, dx + x\, dy$ when C is the following curve (taken counterclockwise).
   (a) The square with vertices $(0, 0)$, $(2, 0)$, $(2, 2)$, $(0, 2)$.
   (b) The square with vertices $(\pm 1, \pm 1)$.
   (c) The circle of radius 2 centered at the origin.
   (d) The circle of radius 1 centered at the origin.
   (e) The square with vertices $(\pm 2, 0)$, $(0, \pm 2)$.
   (f) The ellipse $x^2/a^2 + y^2/b^2 = 1$.

2. Let A be a region, which is the interior of a closed curve C oriented counterclockwise. Show that the area of A is given by

$$\operatorname{Vol}(A) = \tfrac{1}{2}\int_C - y\, dx + x\, dy = \int_C x\, dy.$$

3. Let C_1 be the curve bounded by the parabola
$$y^2 = 2(x + 2)$$
and the line
$$x = 2$$
as shown in Fig. 9. Find the integral

$$\int_{C_1} \frac{-y}{x^2 + y^2}\, dx + \frac{x}{x^2 + y^2}\, dy.$$

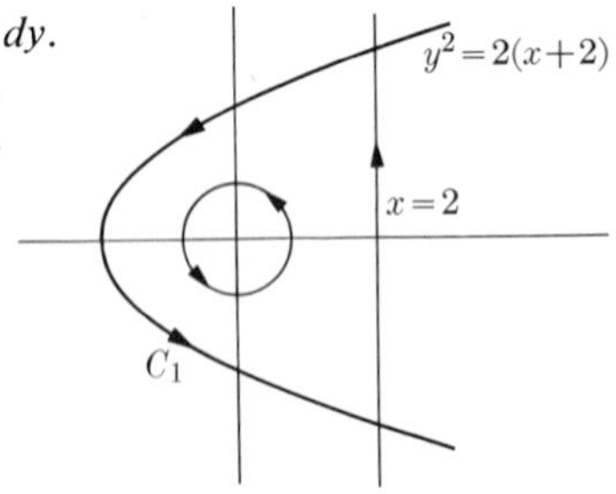

Figure 9

[*Hint:* Reduce this to an integral over the circle of radius 1.]

4. Assume that the function f satisfies Laplace's equation,

$$\frac{\partial^2 f}{\partial x^2} + \frac{\partial^2 f}{\partial y^2} = 0,$$

on a region A which is the interior of a curve C, oriented counterclockwise. Show that

$$\int_C \frac{\partial f}{\partial y} dx - \frac{\partial f}{\partial x} dy = 0.$$

5. If $F = (Q, P)$ is a vector field, we recall that its divergence is defined to be $\text{div } F = \partial Q/\partial x + \partial P/\partial y$. If C is a curve, we say that C is parametrized by arc length if $\|C'(s)\| = 1$ (we then use s as the parameter). Let

$$C(s) = (g_1(s), g_2(s))$$

be parametrized by arc length. Define the unit normal vector at s to be the vector

$$N(s) = (g_2'(s), -g_1'(s)).$$

Verify that this is a unit vector. Show that if F is a vector field on a region A, which is the interior of the closed curve C, oriented counterclockwise, and parametrized by arc length, then

$$\iint_A (\text{div } F) \, dy \, dx = \int_C F \cdot N \, ds.$$

6. Let $C: [a, b] \rightarrow U$ be a C^1-curve in an open set U of the plane. If f is a function on U (assumed to be differentiable as needed), we define

$$\int_C f = \int_a^b f(C(t))\|C'(t)\| \, dt$$

$$= \int_a^b f(C(t)) \sqrt{\left(\frac{dx}{dt}\right)^2 + \left(\frac{dy}{dt}\right)^2} \, dt.$$

For $r > 0$, let $x = r \cos \theta$ and $y = r \sin \theta$. Let φ be the function of r defined by

$$\varphi(r) = \frac{1}{2\pi r} \int_{C_r} f = \frac{1}{2\pi r} \int_0^{2\pi} f(r \cos \theta, r \sin \theta) r \, d\theta.$$

where C_r is the circle of radius r, parametrized as above. Assume that f satisfies Laplace's equation

$$\frac{\partial^2 f}{\partial x^2} + \frac{\partial^2 f}{\partial y^2} = 0.$$

Show that $\varphi(r)$ does not depend on r and in fact

$$f(0, 0) = \frac{1}{2\pi r} \int_{C_r} f.$$

[*Hint:* First take $\varphi'(r)$ and differentiate under the integral, with respect to r. Let D_r be the disc of radius r which is the interior of C_r. Using Exercise 5, you will find that

$$\varphi'(r) = \frac{1}{2\pi r} \iint\limits_{D_r} \operatorname{div} \operatorname{grad} f(x, y)\, dy\, dx$$

$$= \frac{1}{2\pi r} \iint\limits_{D_r} \left(\frac{\partial^2 f}{\partial x^2} + \frac{\partial^2 f}{\partial y^2} \right) dy\, dx$$

$$= 0.$$

Taking the limit as $r \to 0$, prove the desired assertion.]

§2. APPLICATION TO THE CHANGE OF VARIABLES FORMULA

When a region A is the interior of a closed path, then we can use Green's theorem to prove the change of variables formula in special cases. Indeed, Green's theorem reduces a double integral to an integral over a curve, and change of variables formulas for curves are easier to establish than for 2-dimensional areas. Thus we begin by looking at a special case of a change of variables formula for curves.

Let $C: [a, b] \to U$ be a C^1-curve in an open set of $\mathbf{R}^2$. Let $G: U \to \mathbf{R}^2$ be a C^2-map, given by coordinate functions,

$$G(u, v) = (x, y) = \big(f(u, v), g(u, v) \big).$$

Then the composite $G \circ C$ is a curve. If $C(t) = \big(\alpha(t), \beta(t) \big)$, then

$$G \circ C(t) = G\big(C(t) \big) = \big(f(\alpha(t), \beta(t)), g(\alpha(t), \beta(t)) \big).$$

Example 1. Let $G(u, v) = (u, -v)$ be the reflection along the horizontal axis. If $C(t) = (\cos t, \sin t)$, then

$$G \circ C(t) = (\cos t, -\sin t).$$

Thus $G \circ C$ again parametrizes the circle, but observe that the orientation of $G \circ C$ is opposite to that of C, i.e. it is clockwise!

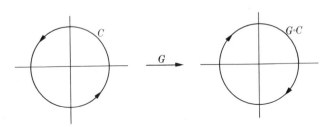

Figure 10

The reason for this reversal of orientation is that the Jacobian determinant of G is negative, namely it is the determinant of

$$\begin{pmatrix} 1 & 0 \\ 0 & -1 \end{pmatrix}.$$

Thus a map G is said to *preserve orientation* if $\Delta_G(u, v) > 0$ for all (u, v) in the domain of definition of G. For simplicity, we only consider such maps G.

Green's theorem leads us to consider the integral

$$\int_{G \circ C} x \, dy.$$

By definition and the chain rule, we have

$$\int_{G \circ C} x \, dy = \int_a^b f(C(t)) \left(\frac{\partial y}{\partial u} \frac{du}{dt} + \frac{\partial y}{\partial v} \frac{dv}{dt} \right) dt$$

$$= \int_C f(u, v) \frac{\partial y}{\partial u} \, du + g(u, v) \frac{\partial y}{\partial v} \, dv.$$

This is true for any C^1-curve as above. Hence it remains true for any piecewise C^1-path, consisting of a finite number of curves.

We are now ready to state and prove the change of variables formula in the case to which Green's theorem applies.

Let U be open in $\mathbf{R}^2$, and let A be a region which is the interior of a closed path C (piecewise C^1 as usual) contained in U. Let

$$G: U \to \mathbf{R}^2$$

be a C^2-map, which is C^1-invertible on U and such that $\Delta_G > 0$. Then $G(A)$ is a region which is the interior of the path $G \circ C$. We then have

$$\iint_{G(A)} dy \, dx = \iint_A \Delta_G(u, v) \, du \, dv.$$

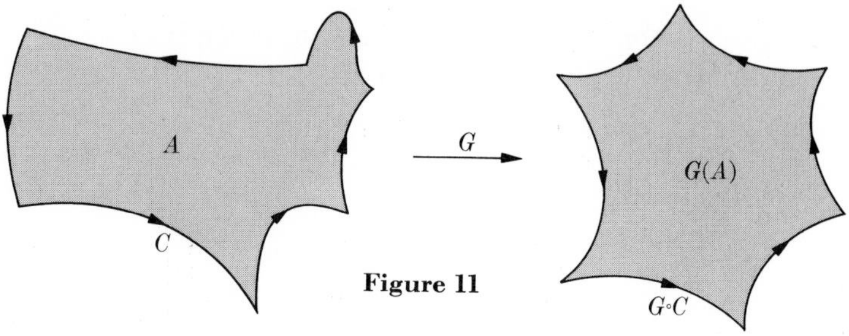

Figure 11

Proof. Let $G(u, v) = (f(u, v), g(u, v))$ be expressed by its coordinates. We have, using Green's theorem:

$$\iint_{G(A)} dy\, dx = \int_{G \circ C} x\, dy = \int_C f\frac{\partial g}{\partial u}\, du + f\frac{\partial g}{\partial v}\, dv$$

$$= \iint_A \left[\frac{\partial}{\partial u}\left(f\frac{\partial g}{\partial v}\right) - \frac{\partial}{\partial v}\left(f\frac{\partial g}{\partial u}\right)\right] du\, dv$$

$$= \iint_A \left[\frac{\partial f}{\partial u}\frac{\partial g}{\partial v} + f\frac{\partial g}{\partial u\, \partial v} - f\frac{\partial g}{\partial u\, \partial v} - \frac{\partial f}{\partial v}\frac{\partial g}{\partial u}\right] du\, dv$$

$$= \iint_A \left[\frac{\partial f}{\partial u}\frac{\partial g}{\partial v} - \frac{\partial g}{\partial u}\frac{\partial f}{\partial v}\right] du\, dv$$

$$= \iint_A \Delta_G(u, v)\, du\, dv,$$

thus proving what we wanted.

EXERCISES

1. Under the same assumptions as the theorem in this section, assume that $\varphi = \varphi(x, y)$ is a continuous function on $G(A)$, and that we can write $\varphi(x, y) = \partial Q/\partial x$ for some continuous function Q. Prove the more general formula

$$\iint_{G(A)} \varphi(x, y)\, dy\, dx = \iint_A \varphi(G(u, v))\Delta_G(u, v)\, du\, dv.$$

[*Hint:* Let $P = 0$ and follow the same pattern of proof as in the text.]

2. Let $(x, y) = G(u, v)$ as in the text. We suppose that $G: U \to \mathbf{R}^2$, and that F is a vector field on $G(U)$. Then $F \circ G$ is a vector field on U. Let C be a C^1-curve in U. Show that

$$\int_{G \circ C} F = \int_C (F \circ G) \cdot \frac{\partial G}{\partial u}\, du + (F \circ G) \cdot \frac{\partial G}{\partial v}\, dv.$$

[Let $F(x, y) = (P(x, y), Q(x, y))$ and apply the definitions.]

Chapter XVI

Orthogonality and Fourier Series

This chapter can be read immediately after Chapter XII.

§1. SCALAR PRODUCTS

Let V be a vector space. A *scalar product* on V is an association which to any pair of elements (v, w) of V associates a number, denoted by $\langle v, w \rangle$, satisfying the following properties:

SP 1. *We have* $\langle v, w \rangle = \langle w, v \rangle$ *for all* v, w *in* V.

SP 2. *If* u, v, w *are elements of* V, *then*

$$\langle u, v + w \rangle = \langle u, v \rangle + \langle u, w \rangle.$$

SP 3. *If* x *is a number, then*

$$\langle xu, v \rangle = x\langle u, v \rangle = \langle u, xv \rangle.$$

We shall also assume that the scalar product satisfies the condition:

SP 4. *For all* v *in* V *we have* $\langle v, v \rangle \geqq 0$.

This is slightly weaker than the corresponding condition for the dot product. If in addition to this we have $\langle v, v \rangle > 0$ whenever $v \neq O$, then we say that the scalar product is *positive definite*. The reason for considering the slightly more general case is that we need it for later application to Fourier series. Cf. §4.

Example 1. Let $V = \mathbf{R}^n$, and define

$$\langle X, Y \rangle = X \cdot Y$$

for elements X, Y of $\mathbf{R}^n$. Then this is a positive definite scalar product.

Example 2. Let V be the space of continuous real-valued functions on the interval $[-\pi, \pi]$. If f, g are in V, we define

$$\langle f, g \rangle = \int_{-\pi}^{\pi} f(t)g(t)\, dt.$$

593

Simple properties of the integral show that this is a scalar product, which is in fact positive definite.

Later in this chapter, we shall study the second example, which gives rise to the theory of Fourier series. At first, we discuss only general properties of scalar products. The notation $\langle\ ,\ \rangle$ is used because in dealing with vector spaces of functions, a dot $f \cdot g$ may be confused with the ordinary product of functions.

As in the case of the dot product, we define elements v, w of V to be *orthogonal*, or *perpendicular*, and write $v \perp w$, if $\langle v, w \rangle = 0$. If S is a subset of V, we denote by $S^{\perp}$ the set of all elements w in V which are perpendicular to all elements of S, i.e. such that $\langle w, v \rangle = 0$ for all v in S. Then using SP 1, SP 2, and SP 3, one verifies at once that S is a subspace of V, called the *orthogonal space* of S. If w is perpendicular to S, we also write $w \perp S$. Let U be the subspace of V generated by the elements of S. If w is perpendicular to S, and if v_1, v_2 are in S, then

$$\langle w, v_1 + v_2 \rangle = \langle w, v_1 \rangle + \langle w, v_2 \rangle = 0.$$

If c is a number, then

$$\langle w, cv_1 \rangle = c\langle w, v_1 \rangle = 0.$$

Hence w is perpendicular to linear combinations of elements of S, and hence w is perpendicular to U.

Example 3. Let (a_{ij}) be an $m \times n$ matrix, and let $A_1, \ldots, A_m$ be its row vectors. Let $X = (x_1, \ldots, x_n)$ as usual. The system of homogeneous linear equations

$$
\begin{array}{ccc}
a_{11}x_1 + \cdots + a_{1n}x_n = 0 \\
\vdots \qquad \vdots \qquad \vdots \\
a_{m1}x_1 + \cdots + a_{mn}x_n = 0
\end{array}
$$

(**)

can also be written in abbreviated form using the dot product, as

$$A_1 \cdot X = 0, \quad \ldots, \quad A_m \cdot X = 0.$$

The set of solutions X of this homogeneous system is therefore the set of all vectors perpendicular to $A_1, \ldots, A_m$. It is therefore the subspace of $\mathbf{R}^n$ which is the orthogonal subspace to the space generated by $A_1, \ldots, A_m$. If U is the space of solutions, and if W denotes the space generated by $A_1, \ldots, A_m$, we have

$$U = W^{\perp}.$$

We call dim U the *dimension of the space of solutions of the system of linear equations*.

We return to the general case. Since we do not yet assume positive definiteness, it may happen that there is some element w in V such that $w \neq O$ but $\langle w, w \rangle = 0$. If such an element exists, then it must satisfy a much stronger orthogonality property:

Theorem 1. *Let w be such that $\langle w, w \rangle = 0$. Then $\langle w, v \rangle = 0$ for all elements v in V.*

Proof. Let t be a number $\neq 0$. Then:

$$0 \leq \langle v + tw, v + tw \rangle = \langle v, v \rangle + 2t\langle v, w \rangle + t^2\langle w, w \rangle$$
$$= \langle v, v \rangle + 2t\langle v, w \rangle.$$

If $\langle v, w \rangle \neq 0$ we selected t very large of opposite sign to $\langle v, w \rangle$. Then $\langle v, v \rangle + 2t\langle v, w \rangle$ is negative, a contradiction. Hence $\langle v, w \rangle = 0$, as was to be shown.

Let V_0 be the set of all elements w in V which are perpendicular to all of V. Then V_0 is a subspace, and from Theorem 1, we conclude that if w is an element of V such that $\langle w, w \rangle = 0$, then w lies in V_0.

As in Chapter I, we can now define what we call the *length* or *norm* by

$$\|v\| = \sqrt{\langle v, v \rangle}.$$

We can take the square root because of our assumption that $\langle v, v \rangle \geq 0$. We have $\|v\| = 0$ if and only if v is an element of V_0. We can prove the *Schwarz inequality* as in Chapter I.

Theorem 2. *For all v, w in V we have*

$$|\langle v, w \rangle| \leq \|v\| \, \|w\|.$$

Proof. The proof given in Chapter I is valid now because it was given without coordinates. However, we repeat it in full. Let $a = \langle w, w \rangle$ and $b = -\langle v, w \rangle$. Then:

$$0 \leq \langle av + bw, av + bw \rangle$$
$$= a^2\langle v, v \rangle + 2ab\langle v, w \rangle + b^2\langle w, w \rangle$$
$$= \|w\|^4\|v\|^2 - 2\|w\|^2\langle v, w \rangle^2 + \|w\|^2\langle v, w \rangle^2$$
$$= \|w\|^4\|v\|^2 - \|w\|^2\langle v, w \rangle^2.$$

If $\|w\| = 0$, then our inequality is obvious. If $\|w\| \neq 0$, then we can divide by $\|w\|^2$ and transposing one term we find that

$$\langle v, w \rangle^2 \leq \|v\|^2\|w\|^2.$$

Taking the square root proves our theorem.

Theorem 3. *The function $v \mapsto \|v\|$ satisfies the properties:*

SN 1. *We have $\|v\| \geq 0$, and $\|v\| = 0$ if and only if v is in V_0.*

SN 2. *For every number c, we have $\|cv\| = |c|\, \|v\|$.*

SN 3. *For v, w in V we have $\|v + w\| \leq \|v\| + \|w\|$.*

Proof. The first assertion follows from Theorem 1. The second is left to the reader. The third is proved with the Schwarz inequality. It suffices to prove that

$$\|v + w\|^2 \leq (\|v\| + \|w\|)^2.$$

To do this, we have

$$\|v + w\|^2 = \langle v + w, v + w \rangle = \langle v, v \rangle + 2\langle v, w \rangle + \langle w, w \rangle$$
$$\leq \|v\|^2 + 2\|v\|\, \|w\| + \|w\|^2$$
$$= (\|v\| + \|w\|)^2,$$

as was to be shown.

An element of V is said to be a *unit vector* if $\|v\| = 1$. If $\|v\| \neq 0$, then $v/\|v\|$ is a unit vector.

The three properties of Theorem 3 are those of a norm, except for the weakened version SN 1 where we use V_0. When this weak version holds, we then call a function $v \mapsto \|v\|$ satisfying these three properties a *seminorm*.

The following two identities follow directly from the definition of the length.

The Pythagoras theorem. *If v, w are perpendicular, then*

$$\|v + w\|^2 = \|v\|^2 + \|w\|^2.$$

The parallelogram law. *For any v, w we have*

$$\|v + w\|^2 + \|v - w\|^2 = 2\|v\|^2 + 2\|w\|^2.$$

The proofs are trivial. We give the first, and leave the second as an exercise. For the first, we have

$$\|v + w\|^2 = \langle v + w, v + w \rangle = \langle v, v \rangle + 2\langle v, w \rangle + \langle w, w \rangle$$
$$= \|v\|^2 + \|w\|^2.$$

Let w be an element of V such that $\|w\| \neq 0$. For any v there exists a unique number c such that $v - cw$ is perpendicular to w. Indeed, for $v - cw$ to be perpendicular to w we must have

$$\langle v - cw, w \rangle = 0,$$

whence $\langle v, w \rangle - \langle cw, w \rangle = 0$ and $\langle v, w \rangle = c\langle w, w \rangle$. Thus

$$c = \frac{\langle v, w \rangle}{\langle w, w \rangle}.$$

Conversely, letting c have this value shows that $v - cw$ is perpendicular to w. We call c the *Fourier coefficient* of v with respect to w.

Example 4. Let V be the space of continuous functions on $[-\pi, \pi]$. Let f be the function given by $f(x) = \sin kx$, where k is some integer $\neq 0$. Then

$$\|f\| = \sqrt{\langle f, f \rangle} = \left(\int_{-\pi}^{\pi} \sin^2 kx \, dx \right)^{1/2}$$

$$= \sqrt{\pi}.$$

If g is any continuous function on $[-\pi, \pi]$, then the Fourier coefficient of g with respect to f is

$$\frac{\langle g, f \rangle}{\langle f, f \rangle} = \frac{1}{\pi} \int_{-\pi}^{\pi} g(x) \sin kx \, dx.$$

As with the case of n-space, we define the projection of v along w to be the vector cw, because of our usual picture:

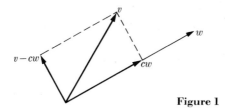

Figure 1

Let $v_1, \ldots, v_n$ be elements of V which are not in V_0, and which are mutually perpendicular, that is $\langle v_i, v_j \rangle = 0$ if $i \neq j$. Let c_i be the Fourier coefficient of v with respect to v_i. Then

$$v - c_1 v_1 - \cdots - c_n v_n$$

is perpendicular to $v_1, \ldots, v_n$. To see this, all we have to do is to take the product with v_j for any j. All the terms involving $\langle v_i, v_j \rangle$ will give 0 if $i \neq j$, and we shall have two remaining terms

$$\langle v, v_j \rangle - c_j \langle v_j, v_j \rangle$$

which cancel. Thus subtracting linear combinations as above orthogonalizes v with respect to $v_1, \ldots, v_n$. The next theorem shows that $c_1 v_1 + \cdots + c_n v_n$ gives the closest approximation to v as a linear combination of $v_1, \ldots, v_n$.

Theorem 4. *Let $v_1, \ldots, v_n$ be vectors which are mutually perpendicular, and such that $\|v_i\| \neq 0$ for all i. Let v be an element of V, and let c_i be the Fourier coefficient of v with respect to v_i. Let $a_1, \ldots, a_n$ be numbers. Then*

$$\left\| v - \sum_{k=1}^{n} c_k v_k \right\| \leq \left\| v - \sum_{k=1}^{n} a_k v_k \right\| .$$

Proof. We know that

$$v - \sum_{k=1}^{n} c_k v_k$$

is perpendicular to each v_i, $i = 1, \ldots, n$. Hence it is perpendicular to any linear combination of $v_1, \ldots, v_n$. Now we have:

$$\|v - \sum a_k v_k\|^2 = \|v - \sum c_k v_k + \sum(c_k - a_k)v_k\|^2$$
$$= \|v - \sum c_k v_k\|^2 + \|\sum(c_k - a_k)v_k\|^2$$

by the Pythagoras theorem. This proves that

$$\|v - \sum c_k v_k\|^2 \leq \|v - \sum a_k v_k\|^2,$$

and thus our theorem is proved.

The next theorem is known as the *Bessel inequality.*

Theorem 5. *If $v_1, \ldots, v_n$ are mutually perpendicular unit vectors, and if c_i is the Fourier coefficient of v with respect to v_i, then*

$$\sum_{i=1}^{n} c_i^2 \leq \|v\|^2.$$

Proof. We have

$$0 \leq \langle v - \sum c_i v_i, v - \sum c_i v_i \rangle$$
$$= \langle v, v \rangle - \sum 2c_i \langle v, v_i \rangle + \sum c_i^2$$
$$= \langle v, v \rangle - \sum c_i^2.$$

From this our inequality follows.

EXERCISES

1. Let V be a vector space with a scalar product. Show that $\langle O, v \rangle = 0$ for all v in V.

2. Assume that the scalar product is positive definite. If $v_1, \ldots, v_n$ are non-zero elements which are mutually perpendicular, show that they are linearly independent.

3. Let M be a square $n \times n$ matrix which is equal to its transpose. If X, Y are column n-vectors, then

$$^tXMY$$

is a 1×1 matrix, which we identify with a number. Show that the map

$$(X, Y) \mapsto {}^tXMY$$

satisfies the three properties SP 1, SP 2, SP 3. Give an example of a 2×2 matrix M such that the fourth property is not satisfied.

§2. ORTHOGONAL BASES

Let V be a vector space with a positive definite scalar product throughout this section. A basis $\{v_1, \ldots, v_n\}$ of V is said to be *orthogonal* if its elements are mutually perpendicular, i.e. if $\langle v_i, v_j \rangle = 0$ whenever $i \neq j$. If in addition each element of the basis has length 1, then the basis is called *orthonormal*.

The standard unit vectors of $\mathbf{R}^n$ form an orthonormal basis of $\mathbf{R}^n$, with respect to the ordinary dot product.

Theorem 6. *Let V be a finite dimensional vector space, with a positive definite scalar product. Let W be a subspace of V, and let $\{w_1, \ldots, w_m\}$ be an orthogonal basis of W. If $W \neq V$, then there exist elements $w_{m+1}, \ldots, w_n$ of V such that $\{w_1, \ldots, w_n\}$ is an orthogonal basis of V.*

Proof. The method of proof is as important as the theorem, and is called the Gram-Schmidt orthogonalization process. We know from Chapter IX that we can find elements $v_{m+1}, \ldots, v_n$ of V such that

$$\{w_1, \ldots, w_m, v_{m+1}, \ldots, v_n\}$$

is a basis of V. Of course, it is not an orthogonal basis. Let W_{m+1} be the space generated by $w_1, \ldots, w_m, w_{m+1}$. We shall first obtain an orthogonal basis of W_{m+1}. The idea is to take v_{m+1} and subtract from it its projection along $w_1, \ldots, w_m$. Thus we let

$$c_1 = \frac{\langle v_{m+1}, w_1 \rangle}{\langle w_1, w_1 \rangle}, \quad \ldots, \quad c_m = \frac{\langle v_{m+1}, w_m \rangle}{\langle w_m, w_m \rangle}.$$

Let

$$w_{m+1} = v_{m+1} - c_1 w_1 - \cdots - c_m w_m.$$

Then w_{m+1} is perpendicular to $w_1, \ldots, w_m$. Furthermore, $w_{m+1} \neq O$ (otherwise v_{m+1} would be linearly dependent on $w_1, \ldots, w_m$), and v_{m+1} lies in the space generated by $w_1, \ldots, w_{m+1}$ because

$$v_{m+1} = w_{m+1} + c_1 w_1 + \cdots + c_m w_m.$$

Hence $\{w_1, \ldots, w_{m+1}\}$ is an orthogonal basis of W_{m+1}. We can now proceed by induction, showing that the space W_{m+s} generated by

$$w_1, \ldots, w_m, v_{m+1}, \ldots, v_{m+s}$$

has an orthogonal basis

$$\{w_1, \ldots, w_{m+1}, \ldots, w_s\}$$

with $s = 1, \ldots, n - m$. This concludes the proof.

Corollary. *Let V be a finite dimensional vector space with a positive definite scalar product. Assume that $V \neq \{O\}$. Then V has an orthogonal basis.*

Proof. By hypothesis, there exists an element v_1 of V such that $v_1 \neq O$. We let W be the subspace generated by v_1, and apply the theorem to get the desired basis.

We summarize the procedure of Theorem 6 once more. Suppose we are given an arbitrary basis $\{v_1, \ldots, v_n\}$ of V. We wish to orthogonalize it. We proceed as follows. We let:

$$v_1' = v_1$$

$$v_2' = v_2 - \frac{\langle v_2, v_1' \rangle}{\langle v_1', v_1' \rangle} v_1'$$

$$v_3' = v_3 - \frac{\langle v_3, v_2' \rangle}{\langle v_2', v_2' \rangle} v_2' - \frac{\langle v_3, v_1' \rangle}{\langle v_1', v_1' \rangle} v_1'$$

$$\vdots$$

$$v_n' = v_n - \frac{\langle v_n, v_{n-1}' \rangle}{\langle v_{n-1}', v_{n-1}' \rangle} v_{n-1}' - \cdots - \frac{\langle v_n, v_1' \rangle}{\langle v_1', v_1' \rangle} v_1'.$$

Then $\{v_1', \ldots, v_n'\}$ is an orthogonal basis.

Given an orthogonal basis, we can always obtain an orthonormal basis by dividing each vector by its length.

Example 1. Find an orthonormal basis for the vector space generated by the vectors $(1, 1, 0, 1)$, $(1, -2, 0, 0)$, and $(1, 0, -1, 2)$.

Let us denote these vectors by A, B, C. Let

$$B' = B - \frac{B \cdot A}{A \cdot A} A.$$

In other words, we subtract from B its projection along A. Then B' is perpendicular to A. We find

$$B' = \tfrac{1}{3}(4, -5, 0, 1).$$

Now we subtract from C its projection along A and B', and thus we let

$$C' = C - \frac{C \cdot A}{A \cdot A} A - \frac{C \cdot B'}{B' \cdot B'} B'.$$

Since A and B' are perpendicular, taking the scalar product of C' with A and B' shows that C' is perpendicular to both A and B'. We find:

$$C' = \tfrac{1}{7}(-4, -2, -1, 6).$$

The vectors A, B', C' are non-zero and mutually perpendicular. They lie in the space generated by A, B, C. Hence they constitute an orthogonal basis for that space. If we wish an orthonormal basis, then we divide these vectors by their length, and thus obtain

$$\frac{A}{\|A\|} = \frac{1}{\sqrt{3}}(1, 1, 0, 1), \qquad \frac{B'}{\|B'\|} = \frac{1}{\sqrt{42}}(4, -5, 0, 1),$$

$$\frac{C'}{\|C'\|} = \frac{1}{\sqrt{57}}(-4, -2, -1, 6),$$

as an orthonormal basis.

Theorem 7. *Let V be a vector space with a scalar product, of dimension n. Let W be a subspace of V of dimension r. Let U be the subspace of V consisting of all elements which are perpendicular to W. Then U has dimension $n - r$. In other words,*

$$\dim W + \dim W^\perp = \dim V.$$

Proof. If W consists of O alone, or if $W = V$, then our assertion is obvious. We therefore assume that $W \neq V$ and that $W \neq \{O\}$. Let $\{w_1, \dots, w_r\}$ be an orthonormal basis of W. By Theorem 6, there exist elements $u_{r+1}, \dots, u_n$ of V such that

$$\{w_1, \dots, w_r, u_{r+1}, \dots, u_n\}$$

is an orthonormal basis of V. We shall prove that $\{u_{r+1}, \dots, u_n\}$ is an orthonormal basis of U.

Let u be an element of U. Then there exist numbers $x_1, \dots, x_n$ such that

$$u = x_1 w_1 + \cdots + x_r w_r + x_{r+1} u_{r+1} + \cdots + x_n u_n.$$

Since u is perpendicular to W, taking the product with any w_i ($i = 1, \dots, r$), we find

$$0 = \langle u, w_i \rangle = x_i \langle w_i, w_i \rangle = x_i.$$

Hence all $x_i = 0$ ($i = 1, \dots, r$). Therefore u is a linear combination of $u_{r+1}, \dots, u_n$.

Conversely, let $u = x_{r+1}u_{r+1} + \cdots + x_n u_n$ be a linear combination of $u_{r+1}, \ldots, u_n$. Taking the product with any w_i yields 0. Hence u is perpendicular to all w_i ($i = 1, \ldots, r$), and hence is perpendicular to W. This proves that $u_{r+1}, \ldots, u_n$ generate U. Since they are mutually perpendicular, and of norm 1, they form an orthonormal basis of U, whose dimension is therefore $n - r$.

Example 2. Consider $\mathbf{R}^3$. Let A, B be two linearly independent vectors in $\mathbf{R}^3$. Then the space of vectors which are perpendicular to both A and B is a 1-dimensional space. If $\{N\}$ is a basis for this space, any other basis for this space is of type $\{tN\}$, where t is a number $\neq 0$.

Again in $\mathbf{R}^3$, let N be a non-zero vector. The space of vectors perpendicular to N is a 2-dimensional space, i.e. a plane, passing through the origin O.

EXERCISES

1. What is the dimension of the subspace of $\mathbf{R}^6$ perpendicular to the two vectors $(1, 1, -2, 3, 4, 5)$ and $(0, 0, 1, 1, 0, 7)$?

2. Find an orthonormal basis for the subspaces of $\mathbf{R}^3$ generated by the following vectors: (a) $(1, 1, -1)$ and $(1, 0, 1)$, (b) $(2, 1, 1)$ and $(1, 3, -1)$.

3. Find an orthonormal basis for the subspace of $\mathbf{R}^4$ generated by the vectors $(1, 2, 1, 0)$ and $(1, 2, 3, 1)$.

4. Find an orthonormal basis for the subspace of $\mathbf{R}^4$ generated by $(1, 1, 0, 0)$, $(1, -1, 1, 1)$, and $(-1, 0, 2, 1)$.

In the next exercises, we consider the vector space of continuous functions on the interval $[0, 1]$. We define the scalar product of two such functions f, g by the rule

$$\langle f, g \rangle = \int_0^1 f(t)g(t)\, dt.$$

5. Let V be the subspace of functions generated by the two functions $f(t) = t$ and $g(t) = t^2$. Find an orthonormal basis for V.

6. Let V be the subspace generated by the three functions 1, t, t^2 (where 1 is the constant function). Find an orthonormal basis for V.

§3. APPLICATION TO LINEAR EQUATIONS

Theorem 7 of the preceding section has an interesting application to the theory of linear equations. We consider such a system:

$$(**) \qquad \begin{matrix} a_{11}x_1 + \cdots + a_{1n}x_n = 0 \\ \vdots \qquad\qquad \vdots \\ a_{m1}x_1 + \cdots + a_{mn}x_n = 0. \end{matrix}$$

We can interpret its space of solutions in three ways:

(a) *It consists of those vectors X giving linear relations*

$$x_1 A^1 + \cdots + x_n A^n = O$$

between the columns of A.

(b) *The solutions form the space orthogonal to the row vectors of the matrix A.*

(c) *The solutions form the kernel of the linear map represented by A, i.e. are the solutions of the equation $AX = O$.*

If $A = (a_{ij})$ is an $m \times n$ matrix, then the columns $A^1, \ldots, A^n$ generate a subspace, whose dimension is called the *column rank* of A. The rows $A_1, \ldots, A_m$ of A generate a subspace whose dimension is called the *row rank* of A. We may also say that the column rank of A is the maximum number of linearly independent columns, and the row rank is the maximum number of linearly independent rows of A.

Theorem 8. *Let $A = (a_{ij})$ be an $m \times n$ matrix. Then the row rank and the column rank of A are equal to the same number r. Furthermore, $n - r$ is the dimension of the space of solutions of the system of linear equations* (**).

Proof. We shall prove all our statements simultaneously. We consider the map

$$L: \mathbf{R}^n \to \mathbf{R}^m$$

given by

$$L(X) = x_1 A^1 + \cdots + x_n A^n.$$

This map is obviously linear. Its image consists of the space generated by the column vectors of A. Its kernel is by definition the space of solutions of the system of linear equations. By Theorem 3 of Chapter X, §3, we obtain

column rank + dim space of solutions = n.

On the other hand, interpreting the space of solutions as the orthogonal space to the row vectors, and using Theorem 7 of the preceding section, we obtain

row rank + dim space of solutions = n.

From this all our assertions follow at once, and Theorem 8 is proved.

Let $b_1, \ldots, b_m$ be numbers, and consider the system of inhomogeneous equations

(*)
$$\begin{aligned} A_1 \cdot X &= b_1 \\ \vdots \quad &\quad \vdots \\ A_m \cdot X &= b_m. \end{aligned}$$

It may happen that this system has no solution at all, i.e. that the equations are inconsistent. For instance, the system

$$2x + 3y - z = 1$$

$$2x + 3y - z = 2$$

has no solution. However, if there is at least one solution, then all solutions are obtainable from this one by adding an arbitrary solution of the associated homogeneous system (**) (cf. Exercise 7). Hence in this case again, we can speak of the dimension of the set of solutions. It is the dimension of the associated homogeneous system.

Example 1. Find the dimension of the set of solutions of the following system of equations, and determine this set in $\mathbf{R}^3$:

$$2x + y + z = 1$$

$$y - z = 0.$$

We see by inspection that there is at least one solution, namely $x = \frac{1}{2}$, $y = z = 0$. The rank of the matrix

$$\begin{pmatrix} 2 & 1 & 1 \\ 0 & 1 & -1 \end{pmatrix}$$

is 2. Hence the dimension of the set of solutions is 1. The vector space of solutions of the homogeneous system has dimension 1, and one solution is easily found to be

$$y = z = 1, \qquad x = -\tfrac{1}{2}.$$

Hence the set of solutions of the inhomogeneous system is the set of all vectors

$$(\tfrac{1}{2}, 0, 0) + t(-\tfrac{1}{2}, 1, 1),$$

where t ranges over all real numbers. We see that our set of solutions is a straight line.

Example 2. Find a basis for the space of solutions of the equation

$$3x - 2y + z = 0.$$

The space of solutions is the space orthogonal to the vector $(3, -2, 1)$ and hence has dimension 2. There are of course many bases for this space. To find one, we first extend $(3, -2, 1) = A$ to a basis of $\mathbf{R}^3$. We do this by selecting vectors B, C such that A, B, C are linearly independent. For instance, take

$$B = (0, 1, 0)$$

and

$$C = (0, 0, 1).$$

The determinant

$$\begin{vmatrix} 3 & -2 & 1 \\ 0 & 1 & 0 \\ 0 & 0 & 1 \end{vmatrix}$$

is not 0, so this choice of vectors will do. Now we must orthogonalize them. Let

$$B' = B - \frac{\langle B, A \rangle}{\langle A, A \rangle} A = (\tfrac{3}{7}, \tfrac{5}{7}, \tfrac{1}{7}),$$

$$C' = C - \frac{\langle C, A \rangle}{\langle A, A \rangle} A - \frac{\langle C, B' \rangle}{\langle B', B' \rangle} B'$$

$$= (0, 0, 1) - \tfrac{1}{14}(3, -2, 1) - \tfrac{1}{35}(3, 5, 1).$$

Then $\{B', C'\}$ is a basis for the space of solutions of the given equation.

EXERCISES

1. Find the rank of the following matrices.

(a) $\begin{pmatrix} 2 & 1 & 3 \\ 7 & 2 & 0 \end{pmatrix}$ (b) $\begin{pmatrix} -1 & 2 & -2 \\ 3 & 4 & -5 \end{pmatrix}$

(c) $\begin{pmatrix} 1 & 2 & 7 \\ 2 & 4 & -1 \end{pmatrix}$ (d) $\begin{pmatrix} 1 & 2 & -3 \\ -1 & -2 & 3 \\ 4 & 8 & -12 \\ 0 & 0 & 0 \end{pmatrix}$

2. Let A, B be two matrices which can be multiplied. Show that rank of $AB \leq$ rank of A, and also rank of $AB \leq$ rank of B.

3. Let A be a triangular matrix

$$\begin{pmatrix} a_{11} & a_{12} & \cdots & a_{1n} \\ 0 & a_{22} & \cdots & a_{2n} \\ \vdots & \vdots & \ddots & \vdots \\ 0 & 0 & \cdots & a_{nn} \end{pmatrix}.$$

Assume that none of the diagonal elements is equal to 0. What is the rank of A?

4. Find the dimension of the space of solutions of the following systems of equations. Also find a basis for this space of solutions.

(a) $2x + y - z = 0$ (b) $x - y + z = 0$
    $\phantom{2x + {}} y + z = 0$

(c) $4x + 7y - \pi z = 0$
$2x - y + z = 0$

(d) $x + y + z = 0$
$x - y = 0$
$y + z = 0$

5. What is the dimension of the space of solutions of the following systems of linear equations?

(a) $2x - 3y + z = 0$
$x + y - z = 0$

(b) $2x + 7y = 0$
$x - 2y + z = 0$

(c) $2x - 3y + z = 0$
$x + y - z = 0$
$3x + 4y = 0$
$5x + y + z = 0$

(d) $x + y + z = 0$
$2x + 2y + 2z = 0$

6. Let A be a non-zero vector in n-space. Let P be a point in n-space. What is the dimension of the set of solutions of the equation

$$X \cdot A = P \cdot A?$$

7. Let $AX = B$ be a system of linear equations, where A is an $m \times n$ matrix, X is an n-vector, and B is an m-vector. Assume that there is one solution $X = X_0$. Show that every solution is of the form $X_0 + Y$, where Y is a solution of the homogeneous system $AY = O$, and conversely any vector of the form $X_0 + Y$ is a solution.

8. If A is an $n \times n$ matrix whose determinant is $\neq 0$, and B is a given vector in n-space, show that the system of linear equations $AX = B$ has a unique solution. If $B = O$, this solution is $X = O$.

§4. FOURIER SERIES

In this section, we consider the special case when the scalar product is given by

$$\langle f, g \rangle = \int_{-\pi}^{\pi} f(x)g(x)\,dx.$$

We observe that the inequalities of Theorem 2, Theorem 3 (the triangle inequality), Theorem 4, and Theorem 5 give inequalities for certain integrals, which look much more complicated when written out in terms of the integral. For instance, the Schwarz inequality now reads

$$\left| \int_{-\pi}^{\pi} f(x)g(x)\,dx \right| \leq \left(\int_{-\pi}^{\pi} f(x)^2\,dx \right)^{1/2} \left(\int_{-\pi}^{\pi} g(x)^2\,dx \right)^{1/2}.$$

One can write out similarly the other inequalities. The advantage of the abstract notation now becomes evident, since it allows us to give a geometric interpretation for such complicated expressions, and allows us to use a simple notation which can be easily understood at once.

In our previous examples, we used continuous functions on the interval $[-\pi, \pi]$. For many applications one has to deal with somewhat more general functions. A convenient class of functions is that of piecewise continuous functions. We say that f is piecewise continuous if it is continuous except at a finite number of points, and if at each such point c the limits

$$\lim_{\substack{h \to 0 \\ h > 0}} f(c - h) \qquad \text{and} \qquad \lim_{\substack{h \to 0 \\ h > 0}} f(c + h)$$

both exist. The graph of a piecewise continuous function then looks like this:

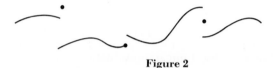

Figure 2

Let V be the set of functions on the interval $[-\pi, \pi]$ which are piecewise continuous. Then V is a vector space, and furthermore, if f, g are piecewise continuous then the ordinary product fg is also piecewise continuous. We can then form the scalar product $\langle f, g \rangle$ since the integral is defined for piecewise continuous functions, and the four properties SP 1 through SP 4 are satisfied. However, the scalar product is not positive definite. A function f which is such that $f(x) = 0$ except at a finite number of points has norm 0. Such functions form precisely the subspace V_0 which we mentioned in §1. Indeed, suppose f is piecewise continuous on $[-\pi, \pi]$ and suppose we have a partition of $[-\pi, \pi]$ into intervals

$$-\pi = a_0 < a_1 < \cdots < a_r = \pi$$

such that f is continuous on each subinterval $[a_i, a_{i+1}]$ except possibly at the end points a_i, $i = 0, \ldots, r - 1$. Suppose that $\|f\| = 0$, so that also $\|f\|^2 = 0 = \langle f, f \rangle$. This means that

$$\int_{-\pi}^{\pi} f(x)^2 \, dx = 0,$$

and the integral is the sum of the integrals over the smaller intervals, so that

$$\sum_{i=0}^{r-1} \int_{a_i}^{a_{i+1}} f(x)^2 \, dx = 0.$$

Each integral satisfies

$$\int_{a_i}^{a_{i+1}} f(x)^2 \, dx \geqq 0$$

and hence each such integral is equal to 0. However, since f is continuous on an interval $[a_i, a_{i+1}]$ except possibly at the end points, we must have $f(x)^2 = 0$ for $a_i < x < a_{i+1}$, whence $f(x) = 0$ for $a_i < x < a_{i+1}$.

Hence $f(x) = 0$ except at a finite number of points.   Conversely, it is clear that if $f(x) = 0$ except at a finite number of points, then $\|f\| = 0$. This gives a description of the space V_0 in the present context.

The space V of piecewise continuous functions on $[-\pi, \pi]$ is not finite dimensional. Instead of dealing with a finite number of orthogonal vectors, we must now deal with an infinite number.

For each positive integer n we consider the functions

$$\varphi_n(x) = \cos nx, \qquad \psi_n(x) = \sin nx,$$

and we also consider the function

$$\varphi_0(x) = 1.$$

It is verified by easy direct integrations that

$$\|\varphi_n\| = \|\psi_n\| = \sqrt{\pi} \qquad \text{if} \qquad n \neq 0,$$

$$\|\varphi_0\| = \sqrt{2\pi}.$$

Hence the Fourier coefficients of a function f with respect to our functions 1, $\cos nx$, $\sin nx$ are equal to:

$$a_0 = \frac{1}{2\pi} \int_{-\pi}^{\pi} f(x)\, dx, \qquad a_n = \frac{1}{\pi} \int_{-\pi}^{\pi} f(x) \cos nx\, dx,$$

$$b_n = \frac{1}{\pi} \int_{-\pi}^{\pi} f(x) \sin nx\, dx.$$

Furthermore, the functions 1, $\cos nx$, $\sin mx$ are easily verified to be mutually orthogonal. In other words, for any pair of distinct functions f, g among 1, $\cos nx$, $\sin mx$ we have $\langle f, g \rangle = 0$. This means:

If $m \neq n$ and $n \geq 0$, then

$$\int_{-\pi}^{\pi} \cos nx \cos mx\, dx = 0, \qquad \int_{-\pi}^{\pi} \sin nx \sin mx = 0;$$

and for any m, n:

$$\int_{-\pi}^{\pi} \cos nx \sin mx\, dx = 0.$$

The verifications of these orthogonalities are mere exercises in elementary calculus. Cf. Exercise 6.

The Fourier series of a function f (piecewise continuous) is defined to be the series

$$a_0 + \sum_{k=1}^{\infty} (a_k \cos kx + b_k \sin kx).$$

The partial sum

$$s_n(x) = a_0 + \sum_{k=1}^{n} (a_k \cos kx + b_k \sin kx)$$

is simply the projection of the function f on the space generated by the functions 1, $\cos kx$, $\sin kx$ for $k = 1, \ldots, n$. In the finite dimensional case, when we have an orthogonal basis $\{v_1, \ldots, v_n\}$ and when c_i is the Fourier coefficient of a vector v, we have

$$v = c_1 v_1 + \cdots + c_n v_n.$$

In the present infinite dimensional case, we write

$$f \sim a_0 + \sum_{k=1}^{\infty} (a_k \cos kx + b_k \sin kx).$$

The sense in which one can replace the sign $\sim$ by an equality depends on various theorems whose proofs go beyond this course. One of these theorems is the following:

Theorem 9. *Assume that the piecewise continuous function f on $[-\pi, \pi]$ is orthogonal to every one of the functions 1, $\cos nx$, $\sin nx$. Then f belongs to V_0, that is $f(x) = 0$ except at a finite number of x. If f is continuous, then $f = 0$.*

Theorem 9 shows at least that a continuous function is entirely determined by its Fourier series. There is another sense, however, in which we would like f to be equal to its Fourier series, namely we would like the values $f(x)$ to be given by

$$f(x) = a_0 + \sum_{k=1}^{\infty} (a_k \cos kx + b_k \sin kx)$$
$$= a_0 + \lim_{n \to \infty} \sum_{k=1}^{n} (a_k \cos kx + b_k \sin kx).$$

It is false in general that if f is merely continuous then $f(x)$ is given by the series. However, it is true under some reasonable conditions, for instance:

Theorem 10. *Let $-\pi < x < \pi$ and assume that f is differentiable in some open interval containing x, and has a continuous derivative in this interval. Then $f(x)$ is equal to the value of the Fourier series.*

Example 1. Find the Fourier series of the function f such that

$$f(x) = 0 \quad \text{if} \quad -\pi < x < 0,$$
$$f(x) = 1 \quad \text{if} \quad 0 < x < \pi.$$

The graph of f is as follows.

Figure 3

Since the Fourier coefficients are determined by an integral, it does not matter how we define f at $-\pi$, 0, or π. We have

$$a_0 = \frac{1}{2\pi} \int_{-\pi}^{\pi} f(x)\, dx = \frac{1}{2\pi} \int_{0}^{\pi} dx = 1,$$

$$a_n = \frac{1}{\pi} \int_{0}^{\pi} \cos nx\, dx = 0,$$

$$b_n = \frac{1}{\pi} \int_{0}^{\pi} \sin nx\, dx = \frac{1}{\pi n} (-\cos nx)\Big|_{0}^{\pi}$$

$$= \begin{cases} 0 & \text{if } n \text{ is even,} \\ \dfrac{2}{\pi n} & \text{if } n \text{ is odd.} \end{cases}$$

Hence the Fourier series of f is:

$$f(x) \sim 1 + \sum_{m=0}^{\infty} \frac{2}{(2m+1)\pi} \sin(2m+1)x.$$

By Theorem 10, we know that $f(x)$ is actually given by the series except at the points $-\pi$, 0, and π.

Example 2. Find the Fourier series of the function f such that $f(x) = -1$ if $-\pi < x < 0$ and $f(x) = x$ if $0 < x < \pi$.
The graph of f is as follows.

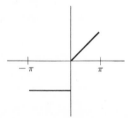

Figure 4

Again we compute the Fourier coefficients. We evaluate the integral over each of the intervals $[-\pi, 0]$ and $[0, \pi]$ since the function is given by different formulas over these intervals. We have

$$a_0 = \frac{1}{2\pi} \int_{-\pi}^{0} (-1) \, dx + \frac{1}{2\pi} \int_{0}^{\pi} x \, dx = \frac{1}{2} + \frac{\pi}{4},$$

$$a_n = \frac{1}{\pi} \int_{-\pi}^{0} (-1) \cos nx \, dx + \frac{1}{\pi} \int_{0}^{\pi} x \cos nx \, dx$$

$$= \begin{cases} 0 & \text{if } n \text{ is even,} \\ -\dfrac{2}{\pi n^2} & \text{if } n \text{ is odd,} \end{cases}$$

$$b_n = \frac{1}{\pi} \int_{-\pi}^{0} (-1) \sin nx \, dx + \frac{1}{\pi} \int_{0}^{\pi} x \sin nx \, dx$$

$$= \begin{cases} -\dfrac{1}{n} & \text{if } n \text{ is even,} \\ \dfrac{2}{\pi n} + \dfrac{1}{n} & \text{if } n \text{ is odd.} \end{cases}$$

Thus we obtain:

$$f(x) = \frac{1}{2} + \frac{\pi}{4} + \sum_{k=1}^{n} (a_k \cos kx + b_k \sin kx).$$

The equality is valid for $-\pi < x < 0$ and $0 < x < \pi$ by Theorem 10.

Example 3. Find the Fourier series of the function $\sin^2 x$.
We have

$$\sin^2 x = \frac{1 - \cos 2x}{2} = \frac{1}{2} - \frac{1}{2} \cos 2x.$$

This is already written as a Fourier series, so the expression on the right is the desired Fourier series.

A function f is said to be *periodic* of period 2π if we have $f(x + 2\pi) = f(x)$ for all x. For such a function, we then have by induction $f(x + 2\pi n) = f(x)$ for all positive integers n. Furthermore, letting $t = x + 2\pi$, we see also that

$$f(t - 2\pi) = f(t)$$

for all t, and hence $f(x - 2\pi n) = f(x)$ for all x and all positive integers n.

Given a piecewise continuous function on the interval $-\pi \leq x < \pi$, we can extend it to a piecewise continuous function which is periodic of period 2π over all of **R**, simply by periodicity.

Example 4. Let $f(x) = x$ on $-\pi \leq x < \pi$. If we extend f by periodicity, then the graph of the extended function looks like this:

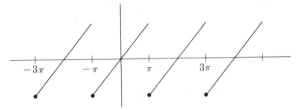

Figure 5

Example 5. Let f be the function on the interval $-\pi \leq x < \pi$ given by:

$$f(x) = 0 \quad \text{if} \quad -\pi \leq x \leq 0,$$
$$f(x) = 1 \quad \text{if} \quad 0 < x < \pi.$$

Then the graph of the function extended by periodicity looks like this:

Figure 6

Example 6. Let f be the function on the interval $-\pi \leq x < \pi$ given by $f(x) = e^x$. Then the graph of the extended function looks like this:

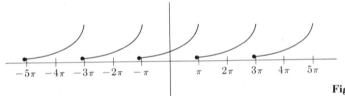

Figure 7

On the other hand, we may also be given a function over the interval $[0, 2\pi]$ and then extend this function by periodicity.

Example 7. Let $f(x) = x$ on the interval $0 \leq x < 2\pi$. The graph of the function extended by periodicity to all of **R** looks like this:

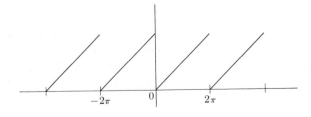

Figure 8

This is different from the function in Example 4, since in the present case, the extended function is never negative. When the function is given on an interval $[0, 2\pi]$, we compute the Fourier coefficients by taking the integral from 0 to 2π. In the present case, we therefore have:

$$a_0 = \frac{1}{2\pi} \int_0^{2\pi} x\, dx = \pi,$$

$$a_n = \frac{1}{\pi} \int_0^{2\pi} x \cos nx\, dx = 0 \qquad \text{for all } n,$$

$$b_n = \frac{1}{\pi} \int_0^{2\pi} x \sin nx\, dx = -\frac{2}{n}.$$

Hence we have, for $0 < x < 2\pi$:

$$x = \pi - 2\left(\sin x + \frac{\sin 2x}{2} + \frac{\sin 3x}{3} + \cdots\right).$$

EXERCISES

1. Write out in full in terms of the integrals the inequality of Theorem 3 (triangle inequality).

2. If f is periodic of period 2π and a, b are numbers, show that

$$\int_a^b f(x)\, dx = \int_{a+2\pi}^{b+2\pi} f(x)\, dx = \int_{a-2\pi}^{b-2\pi} f(x)\, dx.$$

   [*Hint:* Change variables, letting $u = x - 2\pi$, $du = dx$.] Also, prove:

$$\int_{-\pi}^{\pi} f(x + a)\, dx = \int_{-\pi}^{\pi} f(x)\, dx = \int_{-\pi+a}^{\pi+a} f(x)\, dx.$$

   [*Hint:* Split the integral over the bounds $-\pi + a$, $-\pi$, π, $\pi + a$.]

3. Let f be an even function, that is $f(x) = f(-x)$, for all x. Assume that f is periodic of period 2π. Show that all its Fourier coefficients with respect to $\sin nx$ are 0. Let g be an odd function (that is $g(-x) = -g(x)$). Show that all its Fourier coefficients with respect to $\cos nx$ are 0.

4. Compute the Fourier series of the functions, given on the interval $-\pi < x < \pi$ by the following $f(x)$:

   (a) x (b) x^2 (c) $|x|$ (d) $\sin^2 x$
   (e) $|\sin x|$ (f) $|\cos x|$ (g) $\sin^3 x$ (h) $\cos^3 x$

5. Show that the following relations hold:

   (a) For $0 < x < 2\pi$ and $a \neq 0$,

$$\pi e^{ax} = (e^{2a\pi} - 1)\left(\frac{1}{2a} + \sum_{k=1}^{\infty} \frac{a \cos kx - k \sin kx}{k^2 + a^2}\right).$$

(b) For $0 < x < 2\pi$ and a not an integer,

$$\pi \cos ax = \frac{\sin 2a\pi}{2a} + \sum_{k=1}^{\infty} \frac{a \sin 2a\pi \cos kx + k(\cos 2a\pi - 1) \sin kx}{a^2 - k^2}.$$

(c) Letting $x = \pi$ in part (b), conclude that

$$\frac{a\pi}{\sin a\pi} = 1 + 2a^2 \sum_{k=1}^{\infty} \frac{(-1)^k}{a^2 - k^2}.$$

(d) For $0 < x < 2\pi$,

$$\frac{(\pi - x)^2}{4} = \frac{\pi^2}{12} + \sum_{k=1}^{\infty} \frac{\cos kx}{k^2}.$$

6. Prove that the functions 1, $\cos nx$, $\sin mx$ are mutually orthogonal. *Hint:* Use formulas like

$$\sin A \cos B = \tfrac{1}{2}[\sin (A + B) + \sin (A - B)].$$

Chapter XVII

ϵ *and* δ *again*

§1. NORMED VECTOR SPACES

The natural habitat of ϵ and δ is the normed vector space. Let V be a vector space. A *norm* on V is a function, which to each element v of V associates a number, denoted by $\|v\|$, satisfying the following properties:

N 1. *If* $v \neq O$, *then* $\|v\| > 0$, *and* $\|O\| = 0$.

N 2. *If* v *is an element of* V *and* c *is a number, then*

$$\|cv\| = |c| \, \|v\|.$$

N 3. *If* v_1, v_2 *are elements of* V, *then*

$$\|v_1 + v_2\| \leqq \|v_1\| + \|v_2\|.$$

Example 1. If $V = \mathbf{R}^n$ and $\|X\| = \sqrt{X \cdot X}$ is defined as in Chapter I, then $\| \ \|$ is a norm, called the *Euclidean norm*.

Example 2. Let $V = \mathbf{R}^n$, and define the norm of a vector

$$X = (x_1, \ldots, x_n)$$

to be the maximum of the absolute values of the coordinates, that is

$$\|X\| = \max \, (|x_1|, \ldots, |x_n|).$$

It is immediately verified that this is a norm, called the *sup norm*. We carry out this verification in detail. If $\|X\| = 0$, then all $|x_i| = 0$, so $X = O$. Let c be a number. Then

$$
\begin{aligned}
\|cX\| &= \max \, (|cx_1|, \ldots, |cx_n|) \\
&= \max \, (|c| \, |x_1|, \ldots, |c| \, |x_n|) \\
&= |c| \max \, (|x_1|, \ldots, |x_n|) \\
&= |c| \, \|X\|.
\end{aligned}
$$

Example 3. Let V be the space of continuous functions on the interval $[0, 1]$. If f is an element of V, we define

$$\|f\|_1 = \int_0^1 |f(x)| \, dx.$$

615

Elementary properties of the integral show that this is a norm on V, called the L_1-norm.

These three examples should convince the reader that norms are important in their own right, and not only the Euclidean norm which has been used mostly throughout this book.

A *normed vector space* is a vector space V, together with a prescribed norm on it.

We can define the notion of a sphere and a ball in an arbitrary normed vector space V. Indeed, let v_0 be an element of V, and let r be a number > 0. We define the open ball of center v_0 and radius r to be the set of all elements v in V such that

$$\|v - v_0\| < r.$$

Similarly, we define the closed ball by replacing the sign $<$ by $\leq$, and we define the sphere of radius r centered at v_0 to be the set of all elements v in V such that

$$\|v - v_0\| = r.$$

Example 4. Let $V = \mathbf{R}^2$ and let the norm be the sup norm. With respect to this norm, the sphere of radius 3 centered at the origin consists of all points (x, y) such that

$$\max\,(|x|, |y|) = 3.$$

The closed ball of radius 3 consists of all points (x, y) such that

$$\max\,(|x|, |y|) \leq 3.$$

We see that the sphere in this case consists of the perimeter of the square, and the ball consists of the inside and boundary of the square as shown on the following picture.

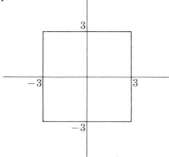

In spite of this slightly unusual interpretation, we shall find the theory of ϵ and δ depending only on the three properties of a norm. In fact, the sup norm in $\mathbf{R}^n$ is frequently the most convenient to deal with for purposes of analysis.

EXERCISES

1. Let $\| \; \|_1$ and $\| \; \|_2$ be norms on a vector space V. Define $\| \; \|_1$ to be equivalent to $\| \; \|_2$ if there exist numbers $C_1, C_2 > 0$ such that

$$C_1\|v\|_1 \leq \|v\|_2 \leq C_2\|v\|_1$$

for all v in V. If $\| \; \|_1$ is equivalent to $\| \; \|_2$ and if $\| \; \|_2$ is equivalent to another norm $\| \; \|_3$, show that $\| \; \|_1$ is equivalent to $\| \; \|_3$.

2. Show that the Euclidean norm on $\mathbf{R}^n$ is equivalent to the sup norm.

3. Let V be the space of continuous functions on $[0, 1]$. If f is an element of V, define

$$\|f\| = \sup |f(x)|$$

where $\sup |f(x)|$ means the least upper bound of all values $|f(x)|$, for x in the interval $[0, 1]$. (a) Show that this is a norm. (b) Show that this norm is not equivalent to the L_1-norm, by showing that there exist functions with arbitrarily large sup norms, but arbitrarily small L_1-norms. [*Hint:* Use a function which has a very narrow peak around 0, and has value 0 otherwise].

4. If $\| \; \|_1$ and $\| \; \|_2$ are norms on a vector space V, show that the function

$$v \mapsto \|v\|_1 + \|v\|_2$$

is also a norm. If c is a number > 0, show that the function

$$v \mapsto c\|v\|_1$$

is a norm.

5. Show that the complex numbers form a normed vector space over the real numbers, the norm being the ordinary absolute value.

6. Let V be a normed vector space. Prove the following inequalities:

$$\|u - v\| \geq \|u\| - \|v\|,$$
$$\|u + v\| \geq \|u\| - \|v\|,$$
$$\|-u\| = \|u\|.$$

Also, if $\|v + w\| \leq c$ for some number c, then $\|v\| \leq c + \|w\|$.

7. If $X = (x_1, \ldots, x_n)$ is a vector in $\mathbf{R}^n$, define

$$\|X\| = |x_1| + \cdots + |x_n|.$$

Show that this is a norm, and that this norm is equivalent to the sup norm.

§2. LIMITS

Let V, W be normed vector spaces. Let S be a subset of V, and let $f: S \to W$ be a mapping of S into W. Let v be an element of V, and w an element of W. We assume that v is *arbitrarily close* to S. By this we mean that given a number $\epsilon > 0$, there exists x in V such that $\|x - v\| < \epsilon$.

We shall say that $f(x)$ approaches the limit w as x approaches v if the following condition is satisfied.

Given $\epsilon > 0$ *there exists* $\delta > 0$ *such that whenever* x *is in* S *and* $\|x - v\| < \delta$ *then* $\|f(x) - w\| < \epsilon$.

We may rephrase this more geometrically by saying that given $\epsilon > 0$, there exists $\delta > 0$ such that whenever x is δ-close to v then $f(x)$ is ϵ-close to w. By δ-close to v we mean that x lies in the open ball of radius δ centered at v.

Since ϵ, δ are always > 0, we usually omit > 0 from the notation.

It is then possible to prove in exactly the same manner as for functions of one variable the various theorems concerning the formal properties of limits. We shall now do this.

Limit of a sum. *Let* f, g *be mappings of* S *into* W. *Assume that*

$$\lim_{x \to v} f(x) = w_1 \qquad and \qquad \lim_{x \to v} g(x) = w_2.$$

Then $\lim_{x \to v} f(x) + g(x)$ *exists and is equal to* $w_1 + w_2$.

Proof. Given ϵ, there exists δ_1 such that whenever x is in S and $\|x - v\| < \delta_1$ we have $\|f(x) - w_1\| < \epsilon/2$, and there exists δ_2 such that whenever x is in S and $\|x - v\| < \delta_2$ then $\|g(x) - w_2\| < \delta/2$. Let δ be the minimum of δ_1 and δ_2. When $\|x - v\| < \delta$ we have

$$
\begin{aligned}
\|f(x) + g(x) - (w_1 + w_2)\| &= \|f(x) - w_1 + g(x) - w_2\| \\
&\leq \|f(x) - w_1\| + \|g(x) - w_2\| \\
&< \epsilon/2 + \epsilon/2 = \epsilon,
\end{aligned}
$$

as was to be shown.

Let U, V, W be normed vector spaces. By a product $U \times V \to W$ we mean a mapping which to each pair of elements (u, v) with u in U and v in V associates an element of W, denoted simply by uv, satisfying the following conditions:

P 1. $(u_1 + u_2)v = u_1v + u_2v$ *and* $u(v_1 + v_2) = uv_1 + uv_2$.

P 2. *If* c *is a number, then* $(cu)v = c(uv) = u(cv)$.

P 3. *We have* $\|uv\| \leq \|u\| \, \|v\|$.

Examples. The ordinary product of numbers satisfies the preceding conditions, taking $U = V = W = \mathbf{R}$.

The dot product satisfies these conditions, the third one being nothing but the Schwarz inequality.

The cross product also satisfies the conditions, taking

$$U = V = W = \mathbf{R}^3.$$

If we view the complex numbers $\mathbf{C}$ as a vector space over the real numbers $\mathbf{R}$, then the product of complex numbers also satisfies these conditions.

Thus we see that our three conditions provide a good abstract set up for the products which we have encountered so far. They also provide the right set up for the theorem concerning limits of products, which runs as follows.

Limit of a product. *Let $U \times V \to W$ be a product. Let S be a subset of a normed vector space. Let $f: S \to U$ and $g: S \to V$ be maps, and let x_0 be arbitrarily close to S. If*

$$\lim_{x \to x_0} f(x) = u \quad \text{and} \quad \lim_{x \to x_0} g(x) = v,$$

then

$$\lim_{x \to x_0} f(x)g(x) = uv.$$

Proof. Given 1, there exists δ_1 such that if $\|x - x_0\| < \delta_1$, then

$$\|g(x) - v\| \leq 1,$$

whence

$$\|g(x)\| \leq 1 + \|v\|.$$

Given ϵ, there exists δ_2 such that if $\|x - x_0\| < \delta_2$, then

$$\|f(x) - u\| < \frac{\epsilon}{2(1 + \|v\|)},$$

and there exists δ_3 such that if $\|x - x_0\| < \delta_3$, then

$$\|g(x) - v\| < \frac{\epsilon}{2(1 + \|u\|)}.$$

Let δ be the minimum of δ_1, δ_2, δ_3. If $\|x - x_0\| < \delta$, then

$$
\begin{aligned}
\|f(x)g(x) - uv\| &= \|f(x)g(x) - ug(x) + ug(x) - uv\| \\
&= \|(f(x) - u)g(x) + u(g(x) - v)\| \\
&\leq \|f(x) - u\|\,\|g(x)\| + \|u\|\,\|g(x) - v\| \\
&< \frac{\epsilon}{2(1 + \|v\|)}(1 + \|v\|) + \|u\|\frac{\epsilon}{2(1 + \|u\|)} \\
&< \epsilon,
\end{aligned}
$$

as was to be shown.

In dealing with vectors, we considered maps into $\mathbf{R}^n$. Such a map F is given by coordinate functions $(f_1, \ldots, f_n)$. Let us use the sup norm on $\mathbf{R}^n$. Then we can prove:

Let V be a normed vector space, and S a subset of V. Let $F: S \to \mathbf{R}^n$ be a mapping, and let $(f_1, \ldots, f_n)$ be its coordinate functions, i.e.

$$F(v) = (f_1(v), \ldots, f_n(v)),$$

where $f_i(v)$ is a number. Let $w = (w_1, \ldots, w_n)$ be an element of $\mathbf{R}^n$. Let v be arbitrarily close to S. Then

$$\lim_{x \to v} F(x) = w$$

if and only if, for every $i = 1, \ldots, n$, we have

$$\lim_{x \to v} f_i(x) = w_i.$$

Proof. Assume first that

$$\lim_{x \to v} F(x) = w.$$

Given ϵ, there exists δ such that if $\|x - v\| < \delta$ then $\|F(x) - w\| < \epsilon$. This means that $|f_i(x) - w_i| < \epsilon$, and hence we conclude that

$$\lim_{x \to v} f_i(x) = w_i$$

for all i.

Conversely, assume that

$$\lim_{x \to v} f_i(x) = w_i \qquad \text{for all } i.$$

Given ϵ, for each i there exists δ_i such that whenever $\|x - v\| < \delta_i$ then $\|f_i(x) - w_i\| < \epsilon$. Let δ be the minimum of all δ_i. Then when $\|x - v\| < \delta$ it follows that $\|F(x) - w\| < \epsilon$, as was to be shown.

In the text, instead of using the sup norm, we used the Euclidean norm. However, Exercise 1 shows that this is irrelevant when dealing with the theory of limits.

Finally, in considering the chain rule for mappings, we needed a theorem for the limit of composite maps, as follows:

Let U, V, W be normed vector spaces. Let S be a subset of U, and T a subset of V. Let

$$f: S \to T \qquad \text{and} \qquad g: T \to W$$

be maps. Let u be arbitrarily close to S and v arbitrarily close to T. Assume that

$$\lim_{x \to u} f(x) = v \qquad \text{and} \qquad \lim_{y \to v} g(y) = w.$$

Then

$$\lim_{x \to u} f(g(x)) = w.$$

Proof. Given ϵ, there exists δ_1 such that whenever $\|y - v\| < \delta_1$ then $\|g(y) - w\| < \epsilon$. With the δ_1 just found being given, there exists δ such that whenever $\|x - u\| < \delta$ then $\|f(x) - v\| < \delta_1$. Hence

$$\|g(f(x)) - w\| < \epsilon,$$

as was to be shown.

As usual, these properties of limits apply to the definition of continuous maps. Let $f: S \to W$ be a map as before. Let v be an element of S. We say that f is *continuous* at v if

$$\lim_{x \to v} f(x) = f(v).$$

Equivalently, this means: Given ϵ, there exists δ such that whenever $\|x - v\| < \delta$ then $\|f(x) - f(v)\| < \epsilon$.

The theorems concerning sums and products of limits now show that the sum and product of continuous functions are continuous. Furthermore, a map into $\mathbf{R}^n$ is continuous if and only if each coordinate function is continuous. Finally, our last statement concerning limits of composite maps shows that a composite of continuous maps is continuous.

It is not our purpose here to develop the theory of ϵ, δ any further, but merely to give an introduction to the basic definitions and properties, to acquaint the reader with them before he deals with them systematically in a course on analysis.

EXERCISES

1. Let S be a subset of a normed vector space V and let $f: S \to W$ be a map into a normed vector space W. Show that if one is given an equivalent norm on V, then the existence of a limit

$$\lim_{x \to v} f(x) = w$$

   with respect to the new norm is equivalent to the existence of the same limit under the other norm. Do the same thing if the norm on W is changed into an equivalent norm. This shows that for limiting purposes, it is irrelevant whether one uses the sup norm or the Euclidean norm on $\mathbf{R}^n$. In fact, the sup norm is often much more convenient.

2. Let V, W be a normed vector space and let S be an open ball centered at 0 in V. Let $f: S \to W$ be a map. We say that f is $o(v)$ for $v \to 0$ if

$$\lim_{v \to 0} \frac{f(v)}{\|v\|} = 0.$$

   Prove the following statements:

   (a) If f_1, f_2 are $o(v)$ for $v \to 0$ then so is $f_1 + f_2$.

(b) If f is $o(v)$ for $v \to 0$ and if g is a bounded function on S (that is there exists a number C such that $|g(v)| \leq C$ for all v in S), then gf is $o(v)$ for $v \to 0$.

By gf we mean of course the map such that $(gf)(v) = g(v)f(v)$.

(c) If f is $o(v)$ for $v \to 0$ and if f_1 is a map such that $\|f_1(v)\| \leq \|f(v)\|$ for all v in S, then f_1 is also $o(v)$ for $v \to 0$.

3. Let V be a normed vector space and let $L: \mathbf{R}^n \to V$ be a linear map. Show that there exists a number $C > 0$ such that for all X in $\mathbf{R}^n$ we have $\|L(X)\| \leq C\|X\|$. [*Hint:* Write $X = x_1 E_1 + \cdots + x_n E_n$ where $E_1, \ldots, E_n$ are the unit vectors. Use the sup norm if you wish.]

4. Show that a linear map as in Exercise 3 is continuous.

Answers to Exercises

Answers to Exercises

First Course

I am much indebted to D. Levine, W. Anscher and M. Brender for the answers to the exercises.

Chapter I, §2

1. $-3 < x < 3$ **2.** $-1 \leq x \leq 0$ **3.** $-\sqrt{3} \leq x \leq -1$ or $1 \leq x \leq \sqrt{3}$
4. $x > 2$ **5.** $-1 < x < 2$ **6.** $x < -1$ or $x > 1$ **7.** $-5 < x < 5$
8. $-1 \leq x \leq 0$ **9.** $x \geq 1$ or $x = 0$ **10.** $x \leq -10$ or $x = 5$
11. $x \leq -10$ or $x = 5$ **12.** $x \geq 1$ or $x = -\frac{1}{2}$ **13.** $x < -4$.

Chapter I, §3

1. $\frac{4}{3}, -\frac{3}{2}$ **2.** $\dfrac{1}{(2x+1)}$ **3.** $0, 2, 108$ **4.** $2z - z^2, 2w - w^2$

5. $x \neq \sqrt{2}$ or $-\sqrt{2}$. $f(5) = \frac{1}{23}$ **6.** All x. $f(27) = 3$
7. (a) 1 (b) 1 (c) -1 (d) -1 **8.** (a) 1 (b) 4 (c) 0 (d) 0
9. (a) -2 (b) -6 (c) $x^2 + 4x - 2$ **10.** $x \geq 0, 2$

Chapter I, §4

1. 8 and 9 **2.** $\frac{1}{5}$ and -1 **3.** $\frac{1}{16}$ and 2 **4.** $\frac{1}{9}$ and $2^{1/3}$ **5.** $\frac{1}{16}$ and $\frac{1}{2}$
6. 9 and 8 **7.** $-\frac{1}{3}$ and -1 **8.** $\frac{1}{4}$ and $\frac{1}{4}$ **9.** 1 and $-\frac{1}{4}$ **10.** $-\frac{1}{512}$ and $\frac{1}{3}$

Chapter II, §1

3. x negative, y positive **4.** x negative, y negative

Chapter II, §3

5. $y = -\frac{8}{3}x - \frac{5}{3}$ **6.** $y = -\frac{3}{2}x + 5$ **7.** $x = \sqrt{2}$

8. $y = \dfrac{9}{\sqrt{3}+3}x + 4 - \dfrac{9\sqrt{3}}{\sqrt{3}+3}$ **9.** $y = 4x - 3$ **10.** $y = -2x + 2$

11. $y = -\frac{1}{2}x + 3 + \dfrac{\sqrt{2}}{2}$ **12.** $y = \sqrt{3}\,x + 5 + \sqrt{3}$

Chapter II, §4

1. $\sqrt{97}$ **2.** $\sqrt{2}$ **3.** $\sqrt{52}$ **4.** $\sqrt{13}$ **5.** $\sqrt{5/4}$ **6.** $(4, -3)$ **7.** 5 and 5

Chapter II, §7

5. $(x - 2)^2 + (y + 1)^2 = 25$　**6.** $x^2 + (y - 1)^2 = 9$

7. $(x + 1)^2 + y^2 = 3$　**8.** $y + \frac{25}{8} = 2(x + \frac{1}{4})^2$　**9.** $y - 1 = (x + 2)^2$

10. $y + 4 = (x - 1)^2$　**11.** $(x + 1)^2 + (y - 2)^2 = 2$

12. $(x - 2)^2 + (y - 1)^2 = 2$　**13.** $x + \frac{25}{8} = 2(y + \frac{1}{4})^2$

14. $x - 1 = (y + 2)^2$

Chapter III, §1

1. 4　**2.** -2　**3.** 2　**4.** $\frac{3}{4}$　**5.** $-\frac{1}{4}$　**6.** 0

Chapter III, §2

	Tangent line at $x = 2$
1. $2x$	$y = 4x - 3$
2. $3x^2$	$y = 12x - 16$
3. $6x^2$	$y = 24x - 32$
4. $6x$	$y = 12x - 12$
5. $2x$	$y = 4x - 9$
6. $4x + 1$	$y = 9x - 8$
7. $4x - 3$	$y = 5x - 8$
8. $\dfrac{3x^2}{2} + 2$	$y = 8x - 8$
9. $-\dfrac{1}{(x + 1)^2}$	$y = -\frac{1}{9}x + \frac{5}{9}$
10. $-\dfrac{2}{(x + 1)^2}$	$y = -\frac{2}{9}x + \frac{10}{9}$

11. The slopes are 4, 12, 24, 12, 4, 9, 5, 8, $-\frac{1}{9}$, $-\frac{2}{9}$. The tangent lines at the point $x = 2$ are indicated near the corresponding problem.

12. -1. Left derivative -1. No right derivative.

13. No. $f'(x)$ exists for all other values of x.

14. Left derivative 0. No right derivative. $f'(x) = 0$ if $x < 0$ and $f'(x) = 1$ if $x > 1$.

15. 0, 0, 0

Chapter III, §3

1. $4x + 3$　**2.** $-\dfrac{2}{(2x + 1)^2}$　**3.** $\dfrac{1}{(x + 1)^2}$　**4.** $2x + 1$　**5.** $-\dfrac{1}{(2x - 1)^2}$

6. $9x^2$　**7.** $4x^3$　**8.** $5x^4$　**9.** $6x^2$　**10.** $\dfrac{3x^2}{2} + 1$

Chapter III, §4

1. $x^4 + 4x^3h + 6x^2h^2 + 4xh^3 + h^4$　**2.** $4x^3$

3. (a) $\frac{2}{3}x^{-1/3}$　(b) $-\frac{3}{2}x^{-5/2}$　(c) $\frac{7}{6}x^{1/6}$　**4.** $y = 9x - 8$

5. $y = \frac{1}{3}x + \frac{4}{3}$, slope $\frac{1}{3}$ **6.** $y = \frac{-3}{2^9}x + \frac{7}{32}$, slope $\frac{-3}{2^9}$

7. $y = \frac{1}{2\sqrt{3}}x + \frac{\sqrt{3}}{2}$, slope $\frac{1}{2\sqrt{3}}$

8. (a) $\frac{1}{4}5^{-3/4}$ (b) $-\frac{1}{4}7^{-5/4}$ (c) $\sqrt{2}\,(10^{\sqrt{2}-1})$ (d) $\pi 7^{\pi-1}$

Chapter III, §5

1. $\frac{2}{3}x^{-2/3}$ **2.** $55x^{10}$ **3.** $-\frac{3}{8}x^{-7/4}$ **4.** $21x^2 + 8x$ **5.** $-25x^{-2} + 6x^{-1/2}$

6. $\frac{6}{5}x - 16x^7$ **7.** $(x^3 + x) + (3x^2 + 1)(x - 1)$

8. $(2x^2 - 1)4x^3 + 4x(x^4 + 1)$ **9.** $(x + 1)(2x + \frac{15}{2}x^{1/2}) + (x^2 + 5x^{3/2})$

10. $(2x - 5)(12x^3 + 5) + 2(3x^4 + 5x + 2)$

11. $(x^{-2/3} + x^2)\left(3x^2 - \frac{1}{x^2}\right) + (-\frac{2}{3}x^{-5/3} + 2x)\left(x^3 + \frac{1}{x}\right)$

12. $(2x + 3)(-2x^{-3} - x^{-2}) + 2(x^{-2} + x^{-1})$

13. $\frac{9}{(x + 5)^2}$ **14.** $\frac{(-2x^2 + 2)}{(x^2 + 3x + 1)^2}$

15. $\frac{(t + 1)(t - 1)(2t + 2) - (t^2 + 2t - 1)2t}{(t^2 - 1)^2}$

16. $\frac{(t^2 + t - 1)(-5/4)t^{-9/4} - t^{-5/4}(2t + 1)}{(t^2 + t - 1)^2}$

17. $\frac{5}{49}$. $y = \frac{5}{49}t + \frac{4}{49}$ **18.** $\frac{1}{2}$. $y = \frac{1}{2}t$

Chapter III, §6

1. $8(x + 1)^7$ **2.** $\frac{1}{2}(2x - 5)^{-1/2} \cdot 2$ **3.** $3(\sin x)^2 \cos x$ **4.** $5(\log x)^4 \frac{1}{x}$

5. $(\cos 2x)2$ **6.** $\frac{1}{x^2 + 1}2x$ **7.** $e^{\cos x}(-\sin x)$ **8.** $\frac{1}{e^x + \sin x}(e^x + \cos x)$

9. $\cos\left(\log x + \frac{1}{x}\right)\left(\frac{1}{x} - \frac{1}{x^2}\right)$ **10.** $\frac{\sin 2x - (x + 1)(\cos 2x)2}{(\sin 2x)^2}$

11. $3(2x^2 + 3)^2(4x)$ **12.** $-\sin(\sin 5x)(\cos 5x)5$ **13.** $\frac{1}{\cos 2x}(-\sin 2x)2$

14. $\cos((2x + 5)^2)2(2x + 5)2$ **15.** $\cos(\cos(x + 1))(-\sin(x + 1))$

16. $(\cos e^x)e^x$ **17.** $-\frac{1}{(3x - 1)^8}[4(3x - 1)^3] \cdot 3$ **18.** $-\frac{1}{(4x)^6} \cdot 3(4x)^2 \cdot 4$

19. $-\frac{1}{(\sin 2x)^4}2(\sin 2x)(\cos 2x) \cdot 2$ **20.** $-\frac{1}{(\cos 2x)^4}2(\cos 2x)(-\sin 2x)2$

21. $-\frac{1}{(\sin 3x)^2}\cos 3x \cdot 3$ **22.** $-\sin^2 x + \cos^2 x$ **23.** $(x^2 + 1)e^x + 2xe^x$

24. $(x^3 + 2x)\cos 3x \cdot 3 + (3x^2 + 2)\sin 3x$

25. $-\frac{1}{(\sin x + \cos x)^2}(\cos x - \sin x)$ **26.** $\frac{2e^x \cos 2x - (\sin 2x)e^x}{e^{2x}}$

27. $\dfrac{(x^2 + 3)/x - (\log x)(2x)}{(x^2 + 3)^2}$ **28.** $\dfrac{\cos 2x - (x + 1)(-\sin 2x) \cdot 2}{\cos^2 2x}$

29. $(2x - 3)(e^x + 1) + 2(e^x + x)$ **30.** $(x^3 - 1)(e^{3x} \cdot 3 + 5) + 3x^2(e^{3x} + 5x)$

31. $\dfrac{(x - 1)3x^2 - (x^3 + 1)}{(x - 1)^2}$ **32.** $\dfrac{(2x + 3)2x - (x^2 - 1)2}{(2x + 3)^2}$

33. $2(x^{4/3} - e^x) + (\frac{4}{3}x^{1/3} - e^x)(2x + 1)$

34. $(\sin 3x)\frac{1}{4}x^{-3/4} + 3(\cos 3x)(x^{1/4} - 1)$ **35.** $[\cos (x^2 + 5x)](2x + 5)$

36. $e^{3x^2+8}(6x)$ **37.** $\dfrac{-1}{[\log (x^4 + 1)]^2} \cdot \dfrac{1}{x^4 + 1} \cdot 4x^3$

38. $\dfrac{-1}{[\log (x^{1/2} + 2x)]^2} \dfrac{1}{(x^{1/2} + 2x)} (\frac{1}{2}x^{-1/2} + 2)$ **39.** $\dfrac{2e^x - 2xe^x}{e^{2x}}$

Chapter III, §7

1. $18x$ **2.** $5(x^2 + 1)^4 \cdot 2 + 20(x^2 + 1)^3 4x^2$ **3.** 0 **4.** 5040 **5.** 0 **6.** 6

7. $-\cos x$ **9.** $-\sin x$

Chapter III, §8

1. (a) 1/6 **2.** 0 **4.** 0 **5.** 240 in^3/sec **6.** 36π in^3/sec

7. $2\pi r, \dfrac{\pi d}{2}, \dfrac{c}{2\pi}$ **8.** $-3/16$ units/sec

Supplementary Exercises

Chapter III, Sums, Products, and Quotients

1. $9x^2 - 4$ **3.** $2x + 1$ **5.** $\frac{5}{2}x^{3/2} - \frac{5}{2}x^{-7/2}$ **7.** $x^2 - 1 + (x + 5)(2x)$

9. $(\frac{3}{2}x^{1/2} + 2x)(x^4 - 99) + (x^{3/2} + x^2)(4x^3)$

11. $(4x)\left(\dfrac{1}{x^2} + 4x + 8\right) + (2x^2 + 1)\left(\dfrac{-2}{x^3} + 4\right)$

13. $(x + 2)(x + 3) + (x + 1)(x + 3) + (x + 1)(x + 2)$

15. $3x^2(x^2 + 1)(x + 1) + x^3(2x)(x + 1) + (x^3)(x^2 + 1)$

17. $\dfrac{-2}{(2x + 3)^2}$ **19.** $\dfrac{5(3x^2 + 4x)}{(x^3 + 2x^2)^2}$ **21.** $\dfrac{-2(x + 1) + 2x}{(x + 1)^2}$

23. $\dfrac{(x + 1)(x - 1)3(\frac{1}{2}x^{-1/2}) - 3x^{1/2}[(x - 1) + (x + 1)]}{(x + 1)^2(x - 1)^2}$

25. $\dfrac{(x^2 + 1)(x + 7)(5x^4) - (x^5 + 1)((x^2 + 1) + (2x)(x + 7))}{(x^2 + 1)^2(x + 7)^2}$

27. $\dfrac{(1 - x^2)(3x^2) - x^3(-2x)}{(1 - x^2)^2}$ **29.** $\dfrac{(x^2 + 1)(2x - 1) - (x^2 - x)(2x)}{(x^2 + 1)^2}$

31. $\dfrac{(x^2 + x - 4)(2) - (2x + 1)(2x + 1)}{(x^2 + x - 4)^2}$

33. $\dfrac{(x^2 + 2)(4 - 3x^2) - (4x - x^3)(2x)}{(x^2 + 2)^2}$ **35.** $\dfrac{-5x - (1 - 5x)}{x^2}$

37. $\dfrac{(x + 1)(x - 2)(2x) - x^2((x - 2) + (x + 1))}{(x + 1)^2(x - 2)^2}$

39. $\dfrac{(4x^3 - x^5 + 1)(12x^3 + \frac{5}{4}x^{1/4}) - (3x^4 + x^{5/4})(12x^2 - 5x^4)}{(4x^3 - x^5 + 1)^2}$

41. $32y = 25x + 176$ **43.** $y = 19x - 12$ **45.** $y = 14x - 4$

47. $27y = -4x + 20$ **49.** $9y = -4x + 20$

51. Point of tangency: $(3, -3)$. Both curves intersect here and have the same slope.

53. Both curves have the same slope at this point.

55. $(-1, -13)$, $y = 16x + 3$; $(0, 7)$, $y = 16x + 7$; $(1, 19)$, $y = 16x + 3$

Chapter III, Chain rule

1. $2(2x + 1)2$ **3.** $7(5x + 3)^6 5$ **5.** $3(2x^2 + x - 5)^2(4x + 1)$

7. $\frac{1}{2}(3x + 1)^{-1/2}(3)$ **9.** $-2(x^2 + x - 1)^{-3}(2x + 1)$

11. $-\frac{5}{3}(x + 5)^{-8/3}$ **13.** $(x - 1)3(x - 5)^2 + (x - 5)^3$

15. $4(x^3 + x^2 - 2x - 1)^3(3x^2 + 2x - 2)$

17. $\dfrac{(x - 1)^{1/2}(\frac{3}{4})(x + 1)^{-1/4} - (x + 1)^{3/4}(\frac{1}{2})(x - 1)^{-1/2}}{x - 1}$

19. $\dfrac{(3x + 2)^9(\frac{5}{2})(2x^2 + x - 1)^{3/2}(4x + 1) - (2x^2 + x - 1)^{5/2}(9)(3x + 2)^8(3)}{(3x + 2)^{18}}$

21. $\frac{1}{2}(2x + 1)^{-1/2}(2)$ **23.** $\frac{1}{2}(x^2 + x + 5)^{-1/2}(2x + 1)$

25. $3x^2 \cos(x^3 + 1)$ **27.** $(e^{x^3+1})(3x^2)$ **29.** $(\cos(\cos x))(-\sin x)$

31. $(e^{\sin(x^3+1)})(3x^2 \cos(x^3 + 1))$

33. $[\cos((x + 1)(x^2 + 2))][(x + 1)(2x) + (x^2 + 2)]$

35. $(e^{(x+1)(x-3)})((x + 1) + (x - 3))$ **37.** $2 \cos(2x + 5)$

39. $\dfrac{2}{2x + 1}$ **41.** $\left(\cos\dfrac{x - 5}{2x + 4}\right)\left(\dfrac{(2x + 4) - (x - 5)2}{(2x + 4)^2}\right)$

43. $(e^{2x^2+3x+1})(4x + 3)$ **45.** $\dfrac{1}{2x + 1}\cos(\log(2x + 1))2$

47. $-(6x - 2)\sin(3x^2 - 2x + 1)$ **49.** $80(2x + 1)^{79}(2)$

51. $49(\log x)^{48}(x^{-1})$ **53.** $5(e^{2x+1} - x)^4(2e^{2x+1} - 1)$

55. $\frac{1}{2}(3 \log(x^2 + 1) - x^3)^{-1/2}\left(\dfrac{3}{x^2 + 1}(2x) - 3x^2\right)$

57. $\dfrac{2 \cos(3x)\cos(2x) - 3 \sin 2x (-\sin 3x)}{(\cos 3x)^2}$

59. $\dfrac{(\sin x^3)(1/2x^2)4x - (\log 2x^2)(\cos x^3)3x^2}{(\sin x^3)^2}$

61. $\dfrac{(\cos 2x)(4x^3 + 1) - 2(x^4 + x)(-\sin 2x)}{(\cos 2x)^2}$

63. $\dfrac{(\cos x)^3(4)(2x^2 + 1)^3(4x) - (2x^2 + 1)^4(3)(\cos x)^2(-\sin x)}{(\cos x)^6}$

65. $-3e^{-3x}$ **67.** $e^{-4x^2+x}(-8x + 1)$

69. $\dfrac{e^{-x}[2x/(x^2 + 2)] - (\log x^2 + 2)e^{-x}(-1)}{e^{-2x}}$

Chapter III, Rate of change

1. $(\tfrac{1}{2}, \tfrac{1}{4})$; $dx/dt = 3$, $dy/dt = 6$; $dx/dt = 1$, $dy/dt = 4$
3. 90 sq in/sec **5.** 0.15 ft/min **7.** $t = \tfrac{1}{4}$, acc $= 4$ **9.** $4/75\pi$ ft/min
11. $1/12\pi$ ft/min

Chapter IV, §1

1. $1/\sqrt{2}$ **2.** $\sqrt{3}/2$ **3.** $\dfrac{1}{2\sqrt{2}}(\sqrt{3} + 1)$ **4.** $\tfrac{1}{2}$ **5.** $-\sqrt{3}/2$ **6.** $-\tfrac{1}{2}$

7. $\sqrt{3}/2$ **8.** $-\dfrac{1}{\sqrt{2}}$ **9.** 1 **10.** $\sqrt{3}$ **11.** -1 **12.** -1

18. $\pi - a + 2\pi n$, where n is an integer.

Chapter IV, §3

1. $\dfrac{1}{2\sqrt{2}}(\sqrt{3} + 1)$ **3.** (a) $\dfrac{\sqrt{3} - 1}{2\sqrt{2}}$

Chapter IV, §4

1. $1 + \tan^2 x$ **2.** $\cos(3x) \cdot 3$ **3.** $-\sin(5x) \cdot 5$ **4.** $\cos(4x^2 + x)(8x + 1)$
5. $\sec^2(x^3 - 5)(3x^2)$ **6.** $\sec^2(x^4 - x^3)(4x^3 - 3x^2)$ **7.** $\sec^2(\sin x)\cos x$
8. $\cos(\tan x)(1 + \tan^2 x)$ **9.** $-\sin(\tan x)(1 + \tan^2 x)$ **10.** -1

11. -1 **12.** $\sqrt{3}/2$ **13.** $-\dfrac{2}{\sqrt{2}}$ **14.** 2 **15.** $-2\sqrt{3}$

16. (a) $y = 1$ (c) $y = 1$ (e) $y = 1$ (g) $2y = -4x + 2 + \pi$
  (i) $12y = 3\sqrt{3}\,x + 6 - \sqrt{3}\,\pi$ (k) $y = 1$ **18.** $12.5\pi\sqrt{3}$ ft/min

Chapter IV, §5

1. 2 **2.** 3 **3.** $\tfrac{1}{3}$ **4.** 1 **5.** 1 **6.** 0 **7.** 0 **8.** 1 **9.** 2 **10.** $\tfrac{1}{2}$ **11.** $\tfrac{2}{3}$

Chapter V, §1

1. 1 **2.** $\tfrac{3}{4}$ **3.** $\tfrac{1}{6}$ **4.** 1 **5.** $\tfrac{3}{4}$ **6.** 0 **7.** ± 1

8. $\dfrac{\pi}{4} + 2n\pi$ and $\dfrac{5\pi}{4} + 2n\pi$, $n =$ integer. **9.** $n\pi$, $n =$ integer

10. $\frac{\pi}{2} + n\pi$, $n =$ integer   **11.** Base $= \sqrt{C/3}$, height $= \sqrt{C/12}$

12. Radius $= \sqrt{C/3\pi}$, height $= \sqrt{C/3\pi}$

13. Base $= \sqrt{C/6}$, height $= \sqrt{C/6}$; Radius $= \sqrt{C/6\pi}$, height $= 2\sqrt{C/6\pi}$

Chapter V, §2

1. Maximum: 2; minimum: -1 **3.** maximum: -2; minimum: -1

5. No maximum; minimum: 2   **7.** Minimum at 1, maximum at 3

9. Minimum at $\frac{1}{3}$, maximum at 5

11. Relative and absolute maximum: $\pi/4$; relative and absolute minimum: $5\pi/4$

13. Relative and absolute maximum: $\pi/3$, $5\pi/3$; relative minima: 0, π, 2π; absolute minimum: π

15. Relative and absolute maxima: $\pi/6$, $5\pi/6$, $9\pi/6$; relative and absolute minima: $\pi/2$, $7\pi/6$, $11\pi/6$

17. Maximum at 0, π, 2π; minimum at $\pi/2$, $3\pi/2$ **19.** $\pi/2$

21. Minimum at 0, $\pi/2$; maximum at $\pi/3$

Chapter V, §3

1. $\left(\frac{13}{3}\right)^{1/2}$ **2.** 0   **3.** $\sqrt{7/3}$ **4.** 1

Chapter V, §4

1. Increasing for all x.

2. Increasing for $x \leq 2 - 1/\sqrt{3}$, and $x \geq 2 + 1/\sqrt{3}$.   Decreasing for $2 - 1/\sqrt{3} \leq x \leq 2 + 1/\sqrt{3}$.

3. Decreasing for $x \leq \frac{1}{2}$, increasing for $x \geq \frac{1}{2}$.

4. Decreasing for $\pi/4 \leq x \leq 5\pi/4$, increasing for $0 \leq x \leq \pi/4$ and $5\pi/4 \leq x \leq 2\pi$. In general, add $2n\pi$ to these intervals.

5. Decreasing for $\pi/4 \leq x \leq 3\pi/4$ and $5\pi/4 \leq x \leq 7\pi/4$, increasing for $0 \leq x \leq \pi/4$ and $3\pi/4 \leq x \leq 5\pi/4$ and $7\pi/4 \leq x \leq 2\pi$.

6. Decreasing $x \leq -\sqrt{3/2}$ and $0 \leq x \leq \sqrt{3/2}$. Increasing $-\sqrt{3/2} \leq x \leq 0$ and $\sqrt{3/2} \leq x$.

7. Increasing all x.

8. Decreasing $x \leq -\sqrt{2/3}$ and $x \geq \sqrt{2/3}$. Increasing $-\sqrt{2/3} \leq x \leq \sqrt{2/3}$.

9. Increasing all x.

10. Decreasing for $x \leq 0$. Increasing for $x \geq 0$.   **11.** All increasing.

13. (a) no maximum; minimum: 1   (b) minimum: 1; maximum: 4
(c) $x < 1$ decreasing; $x > 1$ increasing

15. (a) maximum: -2; no minimum   (b) maximum: -1; minimum: 4
(c) $x < -2$ increasing; $x > -2$ decreasing

17. (a) no maximum or minimum   (b) minimum: -1; maximum: -2, 1
(c) $x < -1$, $x > 1$ decreasing; $-1 < x < 1$ increasing

19. (a) no maximum; minima: ± 1 (b) maximum: -2; minima: ± 1
    (c) $x < -1, 0 < x < 1$ decreasing; $-1 < x < 0, x > 1$ increasing
21. (a) no maximum; minimum: 0 (b) maxima: ± 1; minimum: 0
    (c) $x < 0$ decreasing; $x > 0$ increasing

Supplementary Exercises, Chapter V

1. $r\sqrt{2}$ by $\frac{1}{2}r\sqrt{2}$ where r is the radius of the semicircle.   **5.** $8\sqrt{2}$ by $4\sqrt{2}$
7. Minimum: use $24\pi/(4 + \pi)$ inches for circle; $96/(4 + \pi)$ inches for square.
    Maximum: use whole wire for circle.
9. $(\sqrt{5}/2, \frac{1}{2}), (-\sqrt{5}/2, \frac{1}{2})$ **11.** $(5, 3), (-5, 3)$ **13.** $(-1, 0)$
15. $F = 2\sqrt{3}\, Q/9b^2$ **17.** $(2, 0)$ **19.** $13\sqrt{13}/2$ **21.** $4(1 + \sqrt[3]{4})^{3/2}$
25. $3y = -2x + 12$ **27.** $12.5\sqrt{2}$ **29.** $\pi/3$
31. $\dfrac{c}{1 + \sqrt[3]{a/b}}$ away from b **33.** radius $= 4$ ft; angle $= 2$ radians
35. $2(1 + \sqrt[3]{36})^{3/2}$

Chapter VI, §1

1. $0, 0$ **2.** $0, 0$ **3.** $0, 0$ **4.** $\dfrac{1}{\pi}, \dfrac{1}{\pi}$ **5.** $0, 0$ **6.** $\infty, -\infty$ **7.** $-\infty, \infty$
8. $-\frac{1}{2}, -\frac{1}{2}$ **9.** $-\infty, +\infty$ **10.** $0, 0$ **11.** $\infty, -\infty$ **12.** $-\infty, \infty$
13. ∞, ∞ **14.** $-\infty, -\infty$ **15.** $\infty, -\infty$ **16.** $-\infty, \infty$ **17.** ∞, ∞
18. $-\infty, -\infty$

19.

$x \to \infty$	$a_n > 0$	$a_n < 0$
n odd	∞	$-\infty$
n even	∞	$-\infty$

$x \to -\infty$	$a_n > 0$	$a_n < 0$
n odd	$-\infty$	∞
n even	∞	$-\infty$

Chapter VI, §2

	c.p.	Increasing	Decreasing
1.	$3 \pm \sqrt{11}$	$x \leq 3 - \sqrt{11}$ and $x \geq 3 + \sqrt{11}$	$3 - \sqrt{11} \leq x < 3$ and $3 < x \leq 3 + \sqrt{11}$
2.	$3 \pm \sqrt{10}$	$3 - \sqrt{10} \leq x \leq 3 + \sqrt{10}$	$3 + \sqrt{10} \leq x$ and $x \leq 3 - \sqrt{10}$
3.	$-1 \pm \sqrt{2}$	$-1 - \sqrt{2} \leq x \leq -1 + \sqrt{2}$	$x \leq -1 - \sqrt{2}$ and $x \geq -1 + \sqrt{2}$
4.	$n\pi/2$	$0 \leq x \leq \pi/2$ and add $n\pi$	$\pi/2 \leq x \leq \pi$ and add $n\pi$
5.	$n\pi/2$	$\pi/2 \leq x \leq \pi$ and add $n\pi$	$0 \leq x \leq \pi/2$ and add $n\pi$
6.	None	$x < 0$ and $x > 0$	Never
7.	$n\pi$	$0 \leq x < \pi/2$ and add $n\pi$	$-\pi/2 < x \leq 0$ and add $n\pi$
8.	$\frac{1}{2}$	$x \geq \frac{1}{2}$	$x \leq \frac{1}{2}$
9.	$0, \frac{3}{2}$	$x \geq \frac{3}{2}$	$x \leq \frac{3}{2}$

	c.p.	Increasing	Decreasing
10.	0	$x \leq 0$	$\sqrt{2} < x$ and $0 \leq x < \sqrt{2}$
11.	None	$x < -\frac{1}{3}$	$x > -\frac{1}{3}$
12.	-1	$x \geq -1$	$x \leq -1$
13.	None	All x	Never
14.	-1	$x \geq -1$	$x \leq -1$
15.	None	All x	Never
16.	$-(\frac{1}{8})^{1/7}$	$x \geq -(\frac{1}{8})^{1/7}$	$x \leq -(\frac{1}{8})^{1/7}$

17. (a), (e) 18. (c)

	Rel. Max.	Rel. Min.	Increasing	Decreasing
21.	2	-2	$-2 < x < 2$	$x < -2, x > 2$
23.	None	-2	$x > -2$	$x < -2$
25.	$-\sqrt{3}$	$\sqrt{3}$	$x < -\sqrt{3}, x > \sqrt{3}$	$-\sqrt{3} < x < 0, 0 < x < \sqrt{3}$
27.	$-1 - \sqrt{3}$	$-1 + \sqrt{3}$	$x < -1 - \sqrt{3}, x > \sqrt{3} - 1$	$-1 - \sqrt{3} < x < \sqrt{3} - 1$
29.	None	None	Nowhere	$x < 2, x > 2$
31.	None	None	Nowhere	$x < 5/3, x > 5/3$
33.	None	0	$x > 0$	$-1 < x < 0$
35.	None	None	Nowhere	$x < -\sqrt{5}, -\sqrt{5} < x < \sqrt{5},$ $x > \sqrt{5}$
37.	0	None	$x < -2, -2 < x < 0$	$0 < x < 2, x > 2$
39.	$\pm 3\sqrt{10}/5$	0	$-3 \leq x < -3\sqrt{10}/5$ $0 \leq x < 3\sqrt{10}/5$	$-3\sqrt{10}/5 < x \leq 0,$ $3\sqrt{10}/5 < x \leq 3$
41.	None	-1	$-1 \leq x \leq 7$	$-2 \leq x \leq -1$
43.	$(\pi/4) + 2n\pi$	$(5\pi/4) + 2n\pi$	$5\pi/4 < x < 9\pi/4$ and add $2n\pi$	$\pi/4 < x < 5\pi/4$ and add $2n\pi$
45.	$(\pi/12) + n\pi$	$(7\pi/12) + n\pi$	$7\pi/12 < x < 13\pi/12$ and add $n\pi$	$\pi/12 < x < 7\pi/12$ and add $n\pi$
47.	$(\pi/3) + 2n\pi$	$(5\pi/3) + 2n\pi$	$5\pi/3 < x < 7\pi/3$ and add $2n\pi$	$\pi/3 < x < 5\pi/3$ and add $2n\pi$

49. Relative maxima: $3\pi/2$, $\arcsin (\sqrt{3}/3)$, $\pi - \arcsin (\sqrt{3}/3)$ and add $2n\pi$. Relative minima: $\pi/2$, $\pi + \arcsin (\sqrt{3}/3)$, $2\pi - \arcsin (\sqrt{3}/3)$ and add $2n\pi$. Increasing and decreasing as expected, i.e. between each maximum and the next minimum it is decreasing and between each minimum and the next maximum it is increasing.

Chapter VI, §3

11. (a) Convex upward for $x > 0$. Convex downward for $x < 0$.
   (c) Convex upward for $x > 1$, $-1 < x \leq 0$. Downward for $x < -1$ and $0 \leq x < 1$.

Chapter VI, §4

3. (a) $(\sqrt{2}, \pi/4)$ (b) $(\sqrt{2}, 5\pi/4)$ (c) $(6, \pi/3)$ (d) $(1, \pi)$
32. $y = x(\tan 2), x \leq 0$ 34. $(y - 1)^2 + x^2 = 1$
36. $(x^2 + x + y^2)^2 = x^2 + y^2$ 38. $x = 1$ 40. $y^2 = 2x + 1$
42. $y = 0, x \leq 0$ 43. $y = x(\tan 3), x \leq 0$ 46. $y = x(\tan 0.3), x \geq 0$

Chapter VII, §1

1. Yes; all real numbers 3. Yes; all real numbers 5. Yes; for $y < 1$
7. Yes; for $y \geq 1$ 9. Yes; for $y \leq -1$ 11. Yes; for $y \geq 2$
13. Yes; for $-1 \leq y \leq 1$

Chapter VII, §2 (Alternative answers depend on the choice of intervals.)

1. $\frac{1}{3}$ 2. $\frac{1}{8}$ 3. $\frac{1}{3}$ or $-\frac{1}{3}$ 4. -1 or 1 5. 1 or -1

6. $-\frac{1}{2}$ or $-\frac{1}{10}$, or $\pm \dfrac{1}{2\sqrt{2}}$ 7. $\frac{1}{4}$ 8. -1 or $\frac{1}{2} \pm \frac{3}{10}\sqrt{5}$ 9. $\frac{1}{24}$

10. $\dfrac{1}{10\sqrt{2}}$ or $\dfrac{-1}{10\sqrt{2}}$

Chapter VII, §3

2. $-1/\sqrt{1-x^2}$ 3. $2/\sqrt{3}, \sqrt{2}, \pi/6, \pi/4$ 4. $-2/\sqrt{3}, -\sqrt{2}, \pi/3, \pi/4$

5. Let $y = \sec x$ on interval $0 < x < \pi/2$. Then $x = \operatorname{arcsec} y$ is defined

on $1 < y$, and $dx/dy = \dfrac{1}{y\sqrt{y^2 - 1}}$.

6. $-\pi/2$ 7. 0 8. $\pi/2$ 9. $\pi/2$ 10. $-\pi/4$

11. $\dfrac{2}{\sqrt{2-x^2}} \, (x \neq 0)$ 13. $\dfrac{-1}{(\arcsin x)^2 \sqrt{1-x^2}}$

Chapter VII, §4

1. $\pi/4, \pi/6, -\pi/4, \pi/3$ 2. $\frac{1}{2}, \frac{3}{4}, \frac{1}{2}, \frac{1}{4}$ 3. $1/(1+y^2)$

4. (a) $-\pi/4$ (b) 0 (c) $-\pi/6$ (d) $\pi/6$ 5. $\dfrac{3}{1+9x^2}$ 7. 0

9. $\dfrac{2\cos 2x}{1 + \sin^2 2x}$ 11. $\dfrac{(\cos x)(\arcsin x) - (\sin x)/\sqrt{1-x^2}}{(\arcsin x)^2}$

13. $\dfrac{-1}{1+x^2}$ 15. $\dfrac{9}{\sqrt{1-9x^2}}(1 + \arcsin 3x)^2$

17. $4y = 4\sqrt{2}\,x + \pi - 4$ 19. $12y = 6x + 4\pi - 3\sqrt{3}$

21. $6y = 4\sqrt{3}\,x + 2\sqrt{3} - \pi$ 23. 440 ft/sec 25. 0.02 rad/sec

27. $\dfrac{d\theta}{dt} = \frac{1}{6}\sin\theta\tan\theta$ 29. $\frac{1}{82}$ rad/sec

Chapter VIII, §1

1. (a) $y = \frac{1}{2}x + \log 2 - 1$ (b) $y = \frac{1}{5}x + \log 5 - 1$
(c) $y = 2x - \log 2 - 1$
2. (a) $y = -x + \log 2 - 1$ (b) $y = \frac{4}{5}x + \log 5 - \frac{8}{5}$
(c) $y = -\frac{3}{5}x + \log 10 - \frac{9}{5}$

‣ 3. (a) $\dfrac{\cos x}{\sin x}$ (b) $\cos\left(\log\left(2x+3\right)\right)\dfrac{1}{2x+3}\cdot 2$ (c) $\dfrac{1}{x^2+5}\cdot 2x$

(d) $\dfrac{(\sin x)1/x - (\log 2x)\cos x}{\sin^2 x}$

4. $y = \frac{1}{4}x + \log 4 - \frac{3}{4}$ 5. $y = \dfrac{2x}{3} + \log 3 - \frac{8}{3}$

11. $\dfrac{2}{2x+5}$ **13.** $\dfrac{1}{\sqrt{1-x^2}\arcsin x}$ **15.** $\dfrac{-1}{x(\log x)^2}$

17. $\frac{1}{3}(\log x)^{-2/3} + (\log x)^{1/3}$

Chapter VIII, §2

1. (a) $y = 2e^2x - e^2$ (b) $y = 2e^{-4}x + 5e^{-4}$ (c) $y = 2x + 1$

2. (a) $y = \frac{1}{2}e^{-2}x + 3e^{-2}$ (b) $y = \frac{1}{2}e^{1/2}x + \frac{1}{2}e^{1/2}$ (c) $y = \frac{1}{2}x + 1$

3. $y = 3e^2x - 4e^2$

4. (a) $e^{\sin 3x}(\cos 3x)3$ (b) $\dfrac{1}{e^x + \sin x}(e^x + \cos x)$ (c) $\cos(e^{x+2})e^{x+2}$

    (d) $4\cos(e^{4x-5})e^{4x-5}$

9. $y = \dfrac{x}{e}$ **11.** $y = (1 + \log 2)x - 2$ **13.** $y = \dfrac{-1}{e}x + 2$

15. $y = 2e^2x - e^2$ **17.** $y = 6e^5x - 25e^5$ **19.** $y = 1$

27. $0 \le x < 1$; defined by $y \ge 0$.

31. f is increasing in the interval; as x approaches 1, $f(x)$ approaches ∞, and as x approaches -1, $f(x)$ approaches $-\infty$.

Chapter VIII, §3

1. $10^x \log 10$, $7^x \log 7$ **2.** $3^x \log 3$, $\pi^x \log \pi$ **3.** $x^x(1 + \log x)$

4. $x^{(x^x)}[x^{x-1} + (\log x)x^x(1 + \log x)]$ **5.** e **6.** Yes   **8.** $y = x$

9. $y = (\log 10)x + 1$, $y = (\log 7)x + 1$

10. $y = (9 \log 3)x - 18 \log 3 + 9$ and $y = (\pi^2 \log \pi)x - 2\pi^2 \log \pi + \pi^2$

Chapter VIII, §4

13. 14. All derivatives are 0 at 0.

17. Limit is 0 in both cases.

Chapter VIII, §5

1. $-\log 25$ **2.** $5e^{-4}$ **3.** $e^{-(\log 10)10^{-6}t}$ **4.** $20/e$ **5.** $-(\log 2)/K$

6. $(\log 3)/4$ **7.** $12 \log 10/\log 2$ **8.** $\dfrac{-3 \log 2}{\log 9 - \log 10}$

Chapter IX, §1

1. $-(\cos 2x)/2$ **2.** $\dfrac{\sin 3x}{3}$ **3.** $\log(x + 1)$, $x > -1$

4. $\log(x + 2)$, $x > -2$

Chapter IX, §3

1. $\frac{624}{4}$ **2.** 2   **3.** 2   **4.** $\log 2$ **5.** $\log 3$ **6.** $\frac{2}{5}$ **7.** $e - 1$

Chapter X, §1

1. $\frac{63}{6}$ **2.** 0   **3.** 0   **4.** 0

Chapter X, §2

1. x^4 **2.** $3x^5/5 - x^6/6$ **3.** $-2\cos x + 3\sin x$ **4.** $\frac{9}{5}x^{5/3} + 5\sin x$
5. $5e^x + \log x$ **6.** 0   **7.** 0   **8.** $e^2 - e^{-1}$ **9.** $4 \cdot 28/3$ **11.** $\frac{1}{2}$ **12.** $\frac{1}{12}$
13. $70 - \frac{139}{2}$ **14.** $\frac{8}{3} + \frac{5}{12}$ **15.** $\sqrt{2} - 1$ **16.** $9/2$ **17.** $\frac{1}{3} - 1$ **18.** 0
19. $2 + \pi^2/2$ **20.** 4   **21.** 4   **22.** 1   **23.** 4   **24.** π^2 **25.** 4

Chapter X, §4

1. Yes   **2.** No   **3.** Yes   **4.** No   **5.** No   **6.** Yes
7. $-\frac{1}{2}e^{-2B} + \frac{1}{2}e^{-4}$. Yes, $\frac{1}{2}e^{-4}$.

Chapter XI, §1

1. $e^{x^2}/2$ **2.** $-\frac{1}{4}e^{-x^4}$ **3.** $\frac{1}{6}(1 + x^3)^2$ **4.** $(\log x)^2/2$

5. $\dfrac{(\log x)^{-n+1}}{1 - n}$ if $n \neq 1$, and $\log(\log x)$ if $n = 1$.   **6.** $\log(x^2 + x + 1)$

7. $x - \log(x + 1)$ **8.** $\dfrac{\sin^2 x}{2}$ **9.** $\dfrac{\sin^3 x}{3}$ **10.** 0   **11.** $\frac{2}{5}$

12. $-\arctan(\cos x)$ **13.** $\frac{1}{2}(\arctan x)^2$ **14.** $2/15$ **15.** $-\frac{1}{4}\cos(\pi^2/2) + \frac{1}{4}$
16. $-\frac{1}{2}e^{-B^2} + \frac{1}{2}$. Yes, $\frac{1}{2}$ **17.** $-\frac{1}{3}e^{-B^3} + \frac{1}{3}$. Yes, $\frac{1}{3}$
18. $2\sqrt{1 + e^x} - \log(\sqrt{1 + e^x} + 1) + \log(\sqrt{1 + e^x} - 1)$
19. $x - \log(1 + e^x)$ **20.** $\arctan(e^x)$
21. $-\log(\sqrt{1 + e^x} + 1) + \log(\sqrt{1 + e^x} - 1)$

Chapter XI, §2

1. $x\arcsin x + \sqrt{1 - x^2}$ **2.** $x\arctan x - \frac{1}{2}\log(x^2 + 1)$

3. $\dfrac{e^{2x}}{13}(2\sin 3x - 3\cos 3x)$ **4.** $\frac{1}{10}e^{-4x}\sin 2x - \frac{1}{5}e^{-4x}\cos 2x$

5. $x(\log x)^2 - 2x\log x + 2x$ **6.** $(\log x)^3 x - 3\int(\log x)^2\, dx$
7. $x^2 e^x - 2xe^x + 2e^x$ **8.** $-x^2 e^{-x} - 2xe^{-x} - 2e^{-x}$ **9.** $-x\cos x + \sin x$
10. $x\sin x + \cos x$ **11.** $-x^2\cos x + 2\int x\cos x\, dx$
12. $x^2\sin x - 2\int x\sin x\, dx$ **13.** $\frac{1}{2}[x^2\sin x^2 + \cos x^2]$

14. $-\frac{1}{3}x^4(1 - x^2)^{3/2} - \dfrac{4}{3 \cdot 5}x^2(1 - x^2)^{5/2} - \dfrac{8}{3 \cdot 5 \cdot 7}(1 - x^2)^{7/2}$

15. $\frac{1}{3}x^3\log x = \frac{1}{9}x^3$ **16.** $(\log x)\dfrac{x^4}{4} - \dfrac{x^4}{16}$ **17.** $(\log x)^2\dfrac{x^3}{3} - \dfrac{2}{3}\int x^2\log x\, dx$

18. $-\frac{1}{2}x^2 e^{-x^2} - \frac{1}{2}e^{-x^2}$ **19.** $\frac{1}{4}x^4\left(\dfrac{1}{1 - x^4}\right) + \frac{1}{4}\log(1 - x^4)$ **20.** -4π

21. $-Be^{-B} - e^{-B} + 1$. Yes, 1   **22.** Yes   **23.** Yes

24. $-\dfrac{1}{\log B} + \dfrac{1}{\log 2}$. Yes, $1/\log 2$.   **25.** Yes, $1/3(\log 3)^3$

Chapter XI, §3

1. $-\frac{1}{4}\sin^3 x \cos x - \frac{3}{8}\sin x \cos x + \frac{3}{8}x$ **2.** $\frac{1}{3}\cos^2 x \sin x + \frac{2}{3}\sin x$

3. $\dfrac{\sin^3 x}{3} - \dfrac{\sin^5 x}{5}$ **4.** 3π **5.** 8π **6.** πab (If $a, b > 0$).   **7.** πr^2

13. $-\log \cos x$ **14.** $\arcsin \dfrac{x}{3}$ **15.** $\arcsin \dfrac{x}{\sqrt{3}}$ **16.** $\frac{1}{2}\arcsin(\sqrt{2}\,x)$

17. $\dfrac{1}{b}\arcsin \dfrac{bx}{a}$

18. (a) $c_0 = a_n = 0$ all n, $b_n = -2/n$.
   (b) $c_0 = 4\pi^2/3$, $a_n = 4/n^2$, $b_n = 0$ all n.
   (c) $c_0 = \pi/2$, $a_n = 2(\cos n\pi - 1)/\pi n^2$, $b_n = 0$
19. (b) all a_n and $c_0 = 0$

Chapter XI, §4

1. $C_1 = -\frac{33}{100}$, $C_2 = -\frac{11}{100}$, $C_3 = -\frac{130}{100}$, $C_4 = -\frac{110}{100}$, $C_5 = \frac{11}{100}$

2. $\dfrac{x}{2(x^2+1)} + \frac{1}{2}\arctan x$

3. (a) $\frac{1}{5}[\log(x-3) - \log(x+2)]$ (b) $\log(x+1) - \log(x+2)$
4. $-\frac{1}{2}\log(x+1) + 2\log(x+2) - \frac{3}{2}\log(x+3)$

5. $-\log(x^2+x) + 3\log x$ **6.** $\log(x+1) + \dfrac{1}{x+1}$

7. $\dfrac{1}{2}\dfrac{-1}{x^2+9} + \dfrac{1}{18}\dfrac{x}{x^2+9} + \dfrac{1}{54}\arctan\dfrac{x}{3}$ **8.** $\dfrac{1}{8}\dfrac{x}{x^2+16} + \dfrac{1}{32}\arctan\dfrac{x}{4}$

9. $-\log(x+1) + \log(x+2) - \dfrac{2}{x+2}$

10. $\dfrac{1}{4}\dfrac{x}{(x^2+1)^2} + \dfrac{3}{8}\dfrac{x}{(x^2+1)} + \dfrac{3}{8}\arctan x$

11. $-\frac{1}{8}\log(x-1) + \frac{17}{8}\log(x+7)$

12. $\frac{1}{2}\log\dfrac{x^2}{x^2+x+1} - \dfrac{1}{\sqrt{3}}\arctan\dfrac{2x+1}{\sqrt{3}}$

13. $\frac{1}{4}\log\dfrac{(x+1)^2}{x^2+1} + \dfrac{1}{2}\arctan x$

14. $\dfrac{1}{2}\left(\arctan x + \dfrac{x}{x^2+1}\right)$

Supplementary Exercises

Chapter XI, Substitution

1. $\frac{1}{4}\log(x^4+2)$ **3.** $\dfrac{\sin^5 x}{5}$ **5.** $\sqrt{x^2-1}$ **7.** $\dfrac{-1}{6(3x^2+5)}$ **9.** $\dfrac{-1}{2\sin^2 x}$

11. $\frac{5}{51}(x^3+1)^{12/5}(x^3-\frac{5}{12})$ **13.** $\dfrac{-\cos 3x}{3}$ **15.** $-\cos e^x$ **17.** $\log(\log x)$

19. $\log (e^x + 1)$ **21.** $\frac{1}{4}$ **23.** $\frac{4\sqrt{2}}{3} - \frac{2}{3}$

25. $\frac{\pi}{4}$ **27.** $\frac{\pi^2}{72}$ **29.** $e - \frac{1}{e}$

31. $-2e^{-\sqrt{x}}(x^{3/2} + 3x + 6x^{1/2} + 6)$

Chapter XI, By parts

1. $\frac{1}{2}(x^2 \arctan x + \arctan x - x)$

3. $\frac{1}{4}(2x^2 \arccos x - \arccos x - x\sqrt{1 - x^2})$

5. $1 - \frac{\pi}{2}$ **7.** $\frac{\pi}{32}$ **9.** $\frac{2}{e}$

Chapter XI, Trigonometric integrals

1. $\log \sin x - \frac{\sin^2 x}{2}$ **3.** $-\cos e^x$ **5.** $\frac{\pi}{4}$ **7.** $\frac{\pi}{4}$ **9.** $\frac{\pi}{16}$

11. $\frac{1}{3} \log \frac{\sqrt{x^2 + 9} - 3}{x}$ **13.** $\frac{\pi}{2}$ **15.** $\frac{-1}{3} (x^2 + 32)(16 - x^2)^{1/2}$

17. $\frac{-1}{a} \log \left[\frac{a + \sqrt{a^2 - x^2}}{x} \right]$ **19.** $\frac{-1}{a} \log \left[\frac{a + \sqrt{a^2 + x^2}}{x} \right]$

21. $\frac{x}{\sqrt{x^2 + 1}}$ **23.** $\frac{x}{\sqrt{a^2 - x^2}} - \arcsin \frac{x}{a}$ **25.** $\frac{\pi + 2}{512}$

Miscellaneous Exercises

3. -1 **4.** $n!$ **5.** $-1/2$

Chapter XII, §1

2. (a) $4/e^2$ (b) $2^2 5^5 e^{-4}/3^3$

Chapter XIII, §1

2. $2\pi r$ **3.** $\sqrt{2}(e - 1)$ **4.** (a) $\frac{3}{4}$ (b) 3

5. $\sqrt{1 + e^2} - \sqrt{2} + \frac{1}{2} \log \frac{\sqrt{1 + e^2} - 1}{\sqrt{1 + e^2} + 1} + \frac{1}{2} \log \frac{\sqrt{2} + 1}{\sqrt{2} - 1}$

6. $\frac{1}{27}(31^{3/2} - 13^{3/2})$ **7.** $e - \frac{1}{e}$ **8.** 4

9. π **10.** $2\sqrt{3}$ **11.** 2π

13. $\sqrt{2}(e^2 - e)$ **14.** $\sqrt{2}(e^{\theta_2} - e^{\theta_1})$

Chapter XIII, §2

1. 6π **2.** a^2 (taking values of θ such that $\sin 2\theta \geq 0$)   **3.** πa^2 **4.** $\frac{\pi}{12}$

5. $3\pi/2$ **6.** $3\pi/2$ **7.** $9\pi/2$ **8.** $\pi/3$

Chapter XIII, §3

1. $\frac{4}{3}\pi r^3$ **2.** π **3.** $\dfrac{\pi^2}{8} - \dfrac{\pi}{4}$ **4.** $\dfrac{\pi^2}{8} + \dfrac{\pi}{4}$ **5.** $\dfrac{2 \cdot 5^4 \pi}{3}$ **6.** $\pi(e - 2)$ **7.** πe^2

8. $\pi[2(\log 2)^2 - 4\log 2 + 2]$ **9.** 12π **10.** $\dfrac{\pi}{2}\left[\dfrac{1}{e^2} - \dfrac{1}{e^{2B}}\right]$, yes, $\dfrac{\pi}{2e^2}$

11. $\pi r^2 h/3$

Chapter XIII, §6

1. $c = 1, x, 1/2$ **2.** $c = 2, x^2, 1/2$ **4.** $c = \pi/2, \frac{1}{2}(1 - \cos \pi x), 1/2$
7. $c = 1, ex - e^x + 1, (e/2) - e^{1/2} + 1$
8. $c = 1/4, F(\pi/2) - F(0) = 1/4.$

$$F(x) = \begin{cases} \frac{1}{4}|\sin x| & -\pi \le x \le -\pi/2 \\ \frac{1}{4}(2 + \sin x) & -\pi/2 \le x \le \pi/2 \\ \frac{1}{4}(4 - \sin x) & \pi/2 \le x \le \pi \end{cases}$$

12. $c = 1/\pi, \ F(x) = 0$ if $-\pi \le x \le 0$, and $F(x) = (1/\pi)(x - \sin x)$ if $0 \le x \le \pi$. $F(\pi/2) - F(0) = \frac{1}{2} - (1/\pi)$.

Supplementary Exercises

Chapter XIII, Length of curves

1. $\frac{8}{27}(10^{3/2} - 1)$

3. $\sqrt{e^4 + 1} + 2 - \sqrt{2} + \log(1 + \sqrt{2}) - \log(1 + \sqrt{e^4 + 1})$

5. $2\sqrt{5} + \log(\sqrt{5} + 2)$ **7.** $2\sqrt{3}$ **9.** $\log 7 - \frac{3}{4}$ **11.** $\log(2 + \sqrt{3})$

13. $4a$ **15.** $\dfrac{\sqrt{17}}{4}(e^{-4} - e^{-8})$ **17.** $2\sqrt{5} - \dfrac{\sqrt{17}}{2} + 2\log\left[\dfrac{8 + 2\sqrt{17}}{1 + \sqrt{5}}\right]$

19. 4

Chapter XIII, Area

1. 25π **3.** π **5.** $\dfrac{3\pi}{8}$ **7.** $2\pi + \dfrac{3\sqrt{3}}{2}$ **9.** $\dfrac{\pi}{4}$ **11.** $10\frac{2}{3}$ **13.** $\frac{4}{3}$ **15.** $\dfrac{5\sqrt{5}}{6}$

Chapter XIII, Volumes of revolution

1. $\dfrac{\pi r^2 h}{3}$ **3.** 12π **5.** $\frac{2}{3}\pi$ **7.** $\dfrac{\pi}{3}$ **9.** $\dfrac{\pi}{2}(e^{-2} - e^{-10})$ **11.** $\pi\left(\sqrt{3} - \dfrac{\pi}{3}\right)$

13. $\dfrac{\pi}{3}\left(1 - \dfrac{1}{B^3}\right)$; as B becomes very large, the volume approaches $\dfrac{\pi}{3}$.

15. $\pi \log\left(\dfrac{1}{a}\right)$; as a approaches 0, the volume increases without limit.

17. $\pi\left[\dfrac{\sqrt{2}}{2} - \cos a - \log(\sqrt{2} + 1) + \log(\csc a + \cot a)\right]$; as a approaches 0, the volume increases without limit.

Chapter XIII, Work

1. 5 lb/in; 80 in-lb   **3.** $c\left[\dfrac{1}{r_1} - \dfrac{1}{r}\right]$

5. $\dfrac{99c}{200}$ where c is the constant of proportionality   **7.** 1944 ft-lb

Chapter XIV, §3

1. $1 - \dfrac{x^2}{2!} + \dfrac{x^4}{4!}$ **2.** $|R_n| \leqq \dfrac{|x|^n}{n!}$ **3.** $1 - \dfrac{0.01}{2} = .995$ **4.** $|R_3| \leqq \frac{1}{6}10^{-3}$

5. $|R_4| \leqq \frac{2}{3}10^{-4}$ **6.** $\tan x = x + \dfrac{x^3}{3}$

7. $|R_4| \leqq 10^{-4}$ by crude estimates

8. $\sin\left(\dfrac{\pi}{6} + \dfrac{\pi}{180}\right) = \dfrac{1}{2} + \dfrac{\sqrt{3}}{2}\cdot\dfrac{\pi}{180} = 0.515$ **9.** $x^2 - \frac{1}{8}x^4$

10. $1 - \dfrac{3x^2}{2} + \dfrac{7}{8}x^4$ **11.** $1 + \dfrac{x^2}{2} + \dfrac{5}{24}x^4$ **12.** x^3

Chapter XIV, §4

1. $1 - x^2 + \dfrac{x^4}{2}$ **2.** $|R_3| \leqq 1/24$ **3.** $|R_4| \leqq 10^{-9}$ **4.** $|R_3| \leqq \frac{1}{3}10^{-6}$

5. $1 - x + \dfrac{x^2}{2!} - \dfrac{x^3}{3!} + \dfrac{x^4}{4!} - \dfrac{x^5}{5!}$

6. Use $|R_7| \leqq \frac{1}{5040}$ **7.** All equal to 0.

Chapter XIV, §5

1. (a) $\log 1.2 = 0.2 - \dfrac{0.04}{2} + \dfrac{0.008}{3}$ with an error R_3 such that

$$|R_3| \leqq 4 \times 10^{-4}.$$

(e) $\log(1 - \frac{1}{25}) = -\frac{1}{25}$ with an error R_2 such that $|R_2| \leqq 10^{-3}$.

Chapter XIV, §6

5. 1   **6.** 1   **7.** 1   **8.** 1   **9.** 1   **10.** 2   **11.** $\frac{1}{2}$ **12.** 0   **13.** $-\frac{1}{2}$ **14.** 1
15. 1   **16.** 1

Chapter XIV, §7

1. $5 + \frac{1}{75}$ **2.** $10 - \frac{3}{20} - \frac{9}{8000}$ **3.** $|R_2| \leqq 2 \times 10^{-2}$ **4.** $|R_2| \leqq 0.09$
5. $|R_2| \leqq 2 \times 10^{-5}$

Supplementary Exercises, Chapter XIV

1. $1 - x + x^2 - \frac{5}{6}x^3$ **3.** $1 + x^2$ **5.** $x + \dfrac{x^3}{3}$ **7.** $-1 + x + \dfrac{x^2}{2} - \dfrac{x^3}{6}$

9. $x + x^2 + \dfrac{x^3}{3}$ **11.** $2 + x^2$ **13.** $\dfrac{1}{2} - \dfrac{x^2}{4}$ **15.** (a) $x - \dfrac{2x^3}{3}$

To see this, note that up to terms of degree 4, we have

$$\sin x = x - \frac{x^3}{3!} + O(x^4)$$

$$\cos x = 1 - \frac{x^2}{2!} + O(x^4).$$

Thus

$$(\sin x)(\cos x) = \left(x - \frac{x^3}{6}\right)\left(1 - \frac{x^2}{2}\right) + O(x^4),$$

and in multiplying out the polynomial, we can leave off the term of degree 5.

(f) $1 - x - \dfrac{x^2}{2} + \dfrac{x^3}{2}$.

17. 0.1353   **19.** 2   **21.** 1   **23.** -1 **25.** 1
27. $-\frac{1}{6}$ **29.** $\frac{1}{2}$ **31.** $-\frac{1}{8}$ **33.** (a) 0   (b) 0   (c) 0
35. $-\frac{1}{2}$ **37.** $\dfrac{1}{5!}$ **39.** -1 **41.** $\dfrac{1}{4!}$ **43.** 0   **45.** -1

46. (a) For $0 \leq x \leq 1$, we have

$$\sin x = x - \frac{x^3}{3!} + \frac{x^5}{5!} + R_7(x),$$

where $|R_7(x)| \leq x^7/7!$ Hence

$$\frac{\sin x}{x} = 1 - \frac{x^2}{3!} + \frac{x^4}{5!} + R_7(x)/x,$$

and

$$\int_0^1 \frac{\sin x}{x}\, dx = \left[x - \frac{x^3}{3!3} + \frac{x^5}{5!5}\right]_0^1 + \int_0^1 R_7(x)/x\, dx$$

$$= 1 - \frac{1}{3!3} + \frac{1}{5!5} = 0.946$$

with an error bounded by

$$\int_0^1 \frac{x^6}{7!}\, dx \leq \frac{1}{7!7} \leq \frac{1}{35,000}$$

Chapter XV, §2

3. No   **4.** Yes   **5.** No   **6.** No   **7.** No   **8.** Yes   **9.** Yes

Chapter XV, §3

1. Yes   **3.** No   **5.** No   **7.** No   **9.** No   **11.** No   **13.** No   **15.** Yes
17. Yes

Chapter XV, §4

3. Yes **4.** Yes **5.** Yes **6.** Yes **7.** Yes **8.** Yes **9.** Yes **10.** Yes

Chapter XV, §5

1. Yes **2.** Yes **3.** Yes **4.** Yes **5.** Yes **6.** Yes **7.** Yes **8.** No
9. Yes **10.** Yes **11.** converges, but not absolutely
13. Does not converge; does not converge absolutely
15. Converges, but not absolutely **17.** Converges, but not absolutely
19. Converges, but not absolutely

Chapter XV, §6

1. 0 **3.** 1 **5.** 1 **7.** 1 **9.** 2 **11.** 1 **13.** $\frac{1}{2}$ **15.** $\frac{1}{4}$ **16.** $1/e$
17. 27 **18.** $4/e^2$ **19.** 0 **20.** 2 **21.** 2 **22.** 3 **23.** 1 **24.** ∞
25. 1 **26.** ∞ **27.** 1 **28.** ∞ **29.** e **30.** ∞

Chapter XVI, §1

1. (a) $-\dfrac{1}{10} - \dfrac{3}{10}i$ (b) 2 (c) $-1 + 3i$ (d) $-1 + 3i$

(e) $6\pi + (7 + \pi^2)i$ (f) $-2\pi + \pi i$ (g) $-3\sqrt{2} + \sqrt{2}\pi i$
(h) $-8 - 6i$

2. (a) $\dfrac{1}{2} - \dfrac{i}{2}$ (b) $\dfrac{3}{10} - \dfrac{i}{10}$ (c) $\dfrac{3}{5} + \dfrac{4}{5}i$ (d) $\dfrac{2}{5} + \dfrac{1}{5}i$

(e) $1 - i$ (f) $\dfrac{1}{2} + \dfrac{i}{2}$ (g) $-\dfrac{1}{5} + \dfrac{3}{5}i$ (h) $-\dfrac{1}{2} - \dfrac{i}{2}$

3. $1, \alpha$

Chapter XVI, §2

1. (a) $\sqrt{2}\,e^{i\pi/4}$ (b) $\sqrt{3}\,e^{i(\arctan \sqrt{2})}$ (c) $3e^{e^{i\pi}}$ (d) $4e^{i\pi/2}$
(e) $\sqrt{3}\,e^{-i(\arctan \sqrt{2})}$ (f) $5e^{-i\pi/2}$ (g) $7e^{i\pi}$ (h) $\sqrt{2}\,e^{i5\pi/4}$

2. (a) -1 (b) $-\dfrac{1}{2} + \dfrac{\sqrt{3}}{2}i$ (c) $\dfrac{3}{\sqrt{2}} + \dfrac{3}{\sqrt{2}}i$ (d) $\dfrac{\pi}{2} - \dfrac{\sqrt{3}}{2}\pi i$

(e) $\dfrac{1}{2} + \dfrac{\sqrt{3}}{2}i$ (f) $-i$ (g) -1 (h) $-\dfrac{1}{\sqrt{2}} + \dfrac{1}{\sqrt{2}}i$

4. If $\alpha = re^{i\theta}$, then the *n*-th roots are

$$r^{1/n}e^{i(\theta+2\pi k)/n}, \qquad 0 \leq k \leq n - 1$$

6. $\sqrt{\dfrac{a + \sqrt{a^2 + b^2}}{2}} + \sqrt{\dfrac{-a + \sqrt{a^2 + b^2}}{2}}\,i$

7. All u such that $u = z + 2n\pi i$, *n* integer
8. All $z = 2n\pi i$ **11.** (c) 0 **13.** (a) $1 - 3i$ (b) $-6 - 4i$ **14.** Yes

Second Course

I am much indebted to Mr. I. Schochetman and Mr. J. Hennefeld for the answers to the exercises.

Chapter I, §1

	$A + B$	$A - B$	$3A$	$-2B$
1.	$(1, 0)$	$(3, -2)$	$(6, -3)$	$(2, -2)$
2.	$(-1, 7)$	$(-1, -1)$	$(-3, 9)$	$(0, -8)$
3.	$(1, 0, 6)$	$(3, -2, 4)$	$(6, -3, 15)$	$(2, -2, -2)$
4.	$(-2, 1, -1)$	$(0, -5, 7)$	$(-3, -6, 9)$	$(2, -6, 8)$
5.	$3\pi, 0, 6)$	$(-\pi, 6, -8)$	$(3\pi, 9, -3)$	$(-4\pi, 6, -14)$
6.	$(15 + \pi, 1, 3)$	$(15 - \pi, -5, 5)$	$(45, -6, 12)$	$(-2\pi, -6, 2)$

Chapter I, §3

1. $5, 10, 30, 14, 10 + \pi^2, 245$ **2.** $-3, 12, 2, -17, 2\pi^2 - 16, 15\pi - 10$
4. (b) and (d)   **6.** $\frac{2}{3}, \frac{2}{5}, 0$

Chapter I, §4

1. $\sqrt{5}, \sqrt{10}, \sqrt{30}, \sqrt{14}, \sqrt{10 + \pi^2}, \sqrt{245}$
2. $\sqrt{2}, 4, \sqrt{3}, \sqrt{26}, \sqrt{4\pi^2 + 58}, \sqrt{\pi^2 + 10}$
3. $(\frac{3}{2}, -\frac{3}{2}), (0, 3), \frac{2}{3}(-1, 1, 1), \frac{17}{26}(1, -3, 4),$

$$\frac{\pi^2 - 8}{2\pi^2 + 29}(2\pi, -3, 7), \quad \frac{15\pi - 10}{\pi^2 + 10}(\pi, 3, -1)$$

4. $\frac{3}{5}(-2, 1), \frac{6}{5}(-1, 3), \frac{1}{5}(2, -1, 5), \frac{17}{14}(1, 2, -3),$

$$\frac{2\pi^2 - 16}{\pi^2 + 10}(\pi, 3, -1), \quad \frac{3\pi - 2}{49}(15, -2, 4)$$

5. $0, 0$ **6.** $\sqrt{\pi}, \sqrt{\pi}$ **7.** $\sqrt{2\pi}$ **8.** $\sqrt{2}$

Chapter I, §5

1. $X = (1, 1, -1) + t(3, 0, -4)$ **2.** $X = (-1, 5, 2) + t(-4, 9, 1)$
3. $y = x + 8$ **4.** $4y = 5x - 7$ **6.** (c) and (d)
7. (a) $x - y + 3z = -1$ (b) $3x + 2y - 4z = 2\pi + 26$
   (c) $x - 5z = -33$
8. (a) $2x + y + 2z = 7$ (b) $7x - 8y - 9z = -29$
   (c) $y + z = 1$
9. $(3, -9, -5), (1, 5, -7)$ (Others would be constant multiples of these.)
10. (a) $2(t^2 + 5)^{1/2}$ **11.** $(15t^2 + 26t + 21)^{1/2}, \sqrt{146/15}$
12. $(-2, 1, 5)$ **13.** $(11, 13, -7)$
14. (a) $X = (1, 0, -1) + t(-2, 1, 5)$ (b) $X = (1, 0, 0) + t(11, 13, -7)$
15. (a) $-\frac{1}{3}$ (b) $-2/\sqrt{42}$ (c) $4/\sqrt{66}$ (d) $-\sqrt{2}/3$
16. $t = \dfrac{P \cdot N - Q \cdot N}{N \cdot N}$ **17.** $(1, 3, -2)$ **18.** $2/\sqrt{3}$

19. $(-4, \frac{11}{2}, \frac{15}{2})$ **20.** $\dfrac{\sqrt{2240}}{35}$

21. (a) $\frac{1}{2}(-3, 8, 1)$ (b) $(-\frac{2}{3}, \frac{11}{3}, 0), (-\frac{7}{3}, \frac{13}{3}, 1)$ **22.** $\dfrac{P+Q}{2}$

Chapter I, §6

1. $(-4, -3, 1)$ **2.** $(-1, 1, -1)$ **3.** $(-9, 6, -1)$
4. 0 **5.** E_3, E_1, E_2 in that order.

Chapter II, §1

1. $(e^t, -\sin t, \cos t)$ **2.** $\left(2 \cos 2t, \dfrac{1}{1+t}, 1\right)$

3. $(-\sin t, \cos t)$ **4.** $(-3 \sin 3t, 3 \cos 3t)$
7. B **8.** $y = \sqrt{3}x$ and $y = 0$
9. $ex + y + 2z = e^2 + 3$ **10.** $x + y = 1$
11. $[(X(t) - Q) \cdot (X(t) - Q)]^{1/2}$ **12.** $\sqrt{2}$ **13.** $2\sqrt{13}$
16. (a) $\left(0, 1, \dfrac{\pi}{8}\right) + t(-4, 0, 1)$ (b) $(1, 2, 1) + t(1, 2, 2)$
     (c) $(e^3, e^{-3}, 3\sqrt{2}) + t(3e^3, -3e^{-3}, 3\sqrt{2})$ (d) $(1, 1, 1) + t(1, 3, 4)$
17. (a) $\dfrac{\pi\sqrt{17}}{8}$ (b) $\frac{3}{2}(\sqrt{41} - 1) + \dfrac{5}{4}\left(\log \dfrac{6 + \sqrt{41}}{5}\right)$ (c) $\frac{3}{2}e^2 - \frac{3}{2}e^{-2} + 6$
18. $\pi/2$ **19.** $(2, 0, 4)$ and $(18, 4, 12)$

Chapter II, §2

1. (a) $x + 4z = \pi/2$ (b) $y = 2x$ (c) $-x + e^6y + \sqrt{2}\, e^3z = 6e^3$
     (d) $2x - 2y + z = 1$
3. $r/(r^2 + c^2)$ **4.** (a) $\sqrt{266}/98$

9. $\frac{1}{2}(1 + 4x^2)^{3/2}$ **10.** $\dfrac{(a^2 \sin^2 t + b^2 \cos^2 t)^{3/2}}{ab}$

11. $\sqrt{t}$ **12.** πs

Chapter III, §2

	$\partial f/\partial x$	$\partial f/\partial y$	$\partial f/\partial z$
1.	y	x	1
2.	$2xy^5$	$5x^2y^4$	0
3.	$y \cos(xy)$	$x \cos(xy)$	$-\sin(z)$
4.	$-y \sin(xy)$	$-x \sin(xy)$	0
5.	$yz \cos(xyz)$	$xz \cos(xyz)$	$xy \cos(xyz)$
6.	yze^{xyz}	xze^{xyz}	xye^{xyz}
7.	$2x \sin(yz)$	$x^2z \cos(yz)$	$x^2y \cos(yz)$
8.	yz	xz	xz
9.	$z + y$	$z + x$	$x + y$
10.	$\cos(y - 3z)$ $+ \dfrac{y}{\sqrt{1 - x^2y^2}}$	$-x \sin(y - 3z)$ $+ \dfrac{x}{\sqrt{1 - x^2y^2}}$	$3x \sin(y - 3z)$

11. (1) $(2, 1, 1)$ (2) $(64, 80, 0)$ (6) $e^6(6, 3, 2)$ (8) $(6, 3, 2)$ (9) $(5, 4, 3)$
12. (4) $(0, 0, 0)$ (5) $\pi \cos (\pi^2)(\pi, 1, 1)$ (7) $(2 \sin \pi^2, \pi \cos \pi^2, \pi \cos \pi^2)$
13. $(-1, -2, 1)$ $\qquad\qquad\qquad$ **14.** $yx^{y-1}, x^y \log x$

Chapter III, §3

6. $\lim_{h \to 0} g(h, k) = -1, \quad \lim_{k \to 0} g(h, k) = 1, \quad \lim_{k \to 0} \lim_{h \to 0} g(h, k) = -1,$

$\lim_{h \to 0} \lim_{k \to 0} g(h, k) = 1$

Chapter IV, §1

1. $\dfrac{\partial z}{\partial r} = \dfrac{\partial f}{\partial x}\dfrac{\partial u}{\partial r} + \dfrac{\partial f}{\partial y}\dfrac{\partial v}{\partial r}$ $\quad$ and $\quad$ $\dfrac{\partial z}{\partial t} = \dfrac{\partial f}{\partial x}\dfrac{\partial u}{\partial t} + \dfrac{\partial f}{\partial y}\dfrac{\partial v}{\partial t}$

2. (a) $\dfrac{\partial f}{\partial x} = 3x^2 + 3yz, \quad \dfrac{\partial f}{\partial y} = 3xz - 2yz$

$\dfrac{\partial f}{\partial s} = 3x^2 + (3 + 2s)yz - 3xz + 6sxy - 2sy^2$

$\dfrac{\partial f}{\partial t} = 6x^2 + 8yz - 3xz + 6txy - 2ty^2$

(b) $\dfrac{\partial f}{\partial x} = \dfrac{y^2 + 1}{(1 - xy)^2}, \quad \dfrac{\partial f}{\partial y} = \dfrac{x^2 + 1}{(1 - xy)^2}$

$\dfrac{\partial f}{\partial s} = \dfrac{(x^2 + 1) \sin(3t - s)}{(1 - xy)^2}$

$\dfrac{\partial f}{\partial t} = \dfrac{2(y^2 + 1) \cos 2t - 3(x^2 + 1) \sin(3t - s)}{(1 - xy)^2}$

3. $\dfrac{\partial f}{\partial x} = \dfrac{x}{(x^2 + y^2 + z^2)^{1/2}}, \quad \dfrac{\partial f}{\partial y} = \dfrac{y}{(x^2 + y^2 + z^2)^{1/2}}$

4. $\dfrac{\partial r}{\partial x_i} = \dfrac{x_i}{r}$

9. (a) $-X/r^3$ (b) $2X$ (c) $-3X/r^5$ (d) $2e^{-r^2}X$ (e) $-X/r^2$
(f) $-4mX/r^{m+2}$

Chapter IV, §2

1.

	Plane	Line
(a)	$6x + 2y + 3z = 49$	$X = (6, 2, 3) + t(12, 4, 6)$
(b)	$x + y + 2z = 2$	$X = (1, 1, 0) + t(1, 1, 2)$
(c)	$13x + 15y + z = -15$	$X = (2, -3, 4) + t(13, 15, 1)$
(d)	$6x - 2y + 15z = 22$	$X = (1, 7, 2) + t(-6, 2, -15)$
(e)	$4x + y + z = 13$	$X = (2, 1, 4) + t(8, 2, 2)$
(f)	$z = 0$	$X = (1, \pi/2, 0) + t(0, 0, \pi/2 + 1)$

2. (a) $(3, 0, 1)$ (b) $X = (\log 3, 3\pi/2, -3) + t(3, 0, 1)$
(c) $3x + z = 3 \log 3 - 3$

3. (a) $X = (3, 2, -6) + t(2, -3, 0)$ (b) $X = (2, 1, -2) + t(-5, 4, -3)$
(c) $X = (3, 2, 2) + t(2, 3, 0)$

4. Distance $= \sqrt{[X(t) - Q]^2}$
5. (a) $6x + 8y - z = 25$ (b) $16x + 12y - 125z = -75$
6. $x - 2y + z = 1$

Chapter IV, §3

1. (a) $\frac{5}{3}$ (b) max $= \sqrt{10}$, min $= -\sqrt{10}$
2. (a) $3/2\sqrt{5}$ (b) $\frac{48}{13}$ (c) $\sqrt{580}$

3. Increasing $\left(-\dfrac{9\sqrt{3}}{2}, -\dfrac{3\sqrt{3}}{2}\right)$, decreasing $(9\sqrt{3}/2, 3\sqrt{3}/2)$

4. (a) $\left(\dfrac{3}{4 \cdot 6^{3/4}}, \dfrac{3}{2 \cdot 6^{7/4}}, \dfrac{-3}{6^{7/4}}\right)$ (b) $(1, 2, -1, 1)$

Chapter IV, §4

1. $\log \|X\|$ **2.** $-1/2r^2$

Chapter V, §1

1. ~~Yes~~ No   **2.** No   **3.** No   **4.** No
5. Yes   **6.** Yes

Chapter V, §3

1. No   **2.** No   **3.** No   **4.** No

5. (a) r (b) $\log r$ (c) $\dfrac{r^{n+2}}{n+2}$ if $n \neq -2$

6. $2x^2 y$ **7.** $x \sin xy$ **8.** $x^3 y^2$
9. $x^2 + y^4$ **10.** e^{xy} **11.** $g(r)$
12. Given the vector field $F = (f_1, \ldots, f_n)$ in n-space, defined on a rectangle, $[a_1, b_1] \times \cdots \times [a_n, b_n]$. Assume that

$$\frac{\partial f_i}{\partial x_j} = \frac{\partial f_j}{\partial x_i} \quad (\text{or} \quad D_j f_i = D_i f_j)$$

for all indices i, j. For $n = 3$, define $\varphi(x, y, z)$ to be

$$\int_{a_1}^{x} f_1(t, y, z)\, dt + \int_{a_2}^{y} f_2(a_1, t, z)\, dt + \int_{a_3}^{z} f_3(a_1, a_2, t)\, dt,$$

and similarly for n variables. Using the hypothesis and the fact that a partial derivative of parameters can be taken in and out of an integral, you will find easily that φ is a potential function for F.

Conversely, given a vector field $F = (f_1, \ldots, f_n)$ on an open set U, if there exists a potential function, and if the partial derivatives of the functions f_i exist and are continuous, then the relations

$$\frac{\partial f_i}{\partial x_j} = \frac{\partial f_j}{\partial x_i}$$

must be satisfied for all i, j, for the same reason as that given in the text for two variables. This generalizes Theorem 2.

Chapter V, §4

1. $-369/10$ **2.** $23/6$ **3.** 0 **4.** 0 **5.** 54
6. $\sqrt{3C/2}$ **7.** $4/3$ **8.** $-\pi - \frac{8}{3}$ **9.** $4/15$ **10.** 4π
11. $3\pi/4$ **12.** $-1/2$ **13.** -56

Chapter VI, §1

	$\partial^2 f/\partial x^2$	$\partial^2 f/\partial y^2$	$\partial^2 f/\partial x\,\partial y$
1.	$y^2 e^{xy}$	$x^2 e^{xy}$	$yxe^{xy} + e^{xy}$
2.	$-y^2 \sin xy$	$-x^2 \sin xy$	$-xy \sin xy + \cos xy$
3.	$2y^3$	$6x^2 y$	$6xy^2 + 3$
4.	0	2	2
5.	$2e^{x^2+y^2} + 4x^2 e^{x^2+y^2}$	$e^{x^2+y^2}(2 + 4y^2)$	$4xye^{x^2+y^2}$
6.	$2\cos(x^2 + y)$ $-4x^2 \sin(x^2 + y)$	$-\sin(x^2 + y)$	$-2x \sin(x^2 + y)$
7.	$-(3x^2 + y)^2 \cos(x^3 + xy)$ $-6x \sin(x^3 + xy)$	$-x^2 \cos(x^3 + xy)$	$-(3x^2 + y)x \cos(x^3 + xy)$ $-\sin(x^3 + xy)$

8.
$$\frac{\partial^2 f}{\partial x^2} = \frac{2(1 + (x^2 - 2xy)^2) - (2x - 2y)^2(x^2 - 2xy)}{(1 + (x^2 - 2xy)^2)^2}$$

$$\frac{\partial^2 f}{\partial y^2} = \frac{-(1 + (x^2 - 2xy)^2) - 2y(x^2 - 2xy)}{(1 + (x^2 - 2xy)^2)^2}$$

$$\frac{\partial^2 f}{\partial x\,\partial y} = \frac{-2(1 + (x^2 - 2xy)^2) - (2x - 2y)(x^2 - 2xy)(-2y)}{(1 + (x^2 - 2xy)^2)^2}$$

9. All three $= e^{x+y}$ **10.** All three $= -\sin(x + y)$
11. 1 **12.** $2x$ **13.** $e^{xyz}(1 + 3xyz + x^2 y^2 z^2)$
14. $(1 - x^2 y^2 z^2) \cos xyz - 3xyz \sin xyz$
15. $\sin(x + y + z)$ **16.** $-\cos(x + y + z)$

17. $-\dfrac{48xyz}{(x^2 + y^2 + z^2)^4}$ **18.** $6x^2 y$

Chapter VI, §2

1. $9D_1^2 + 12D_1 D_2 + 4D_2^2$
2. $D_1^2 + D_2^2 + D_3^2 + 2D_1 D_2 + 2D_2 D_3 + 2D_1 D_3$
3. $D_1^2 - D_2^2$ **4.** $D_1^2 + 2D_1 D_2 + D_2^2$
5. $D_1^3 + 3D_1^2 D_2 + 3D_1 D_2^2 + D_2^3$
6. $D_1^4 + 4D_1^3 D_2 + 6D_1^2 D_2^2 + 4D_1 D_2^3 + D_2^4$
7. $2D_1^2 - D_1 D_2 - 3D_2^2$ **8.** $D_1 D_2 - D_3 D_2 + 5D_1 D_3 - 5D_3^2$

9. $\left(\dfrac{\partial}{\partial x}\right)^3 + 12\left(\dfrac{\partial}{\partial x}\right)^2 \dfrac{\partial}{\partial y} + 48 \dfrac{\partial}{\partial x} \left(\dfrac{\partial}{\partial y}\right)^2 + 64\left(\dfrac{\partial}{\partial y}\right)^3$

10. $4\left(\dfrac{\partial}{\partial x}\right)^2 + 4\dfrac{\partial}{\partial x} \dfrac{\partial}{\partial y} + \left(\dfrac{\partial}{\partial y}\right)^2$

11. $h^2 \left(\dfrac{\partial}{\partial x}\right)^2 + 2hk \dfrac{\partial}{\partial x} \dfrac{\partial}{\partial y} + k^2 \left(\dfrac{\partial}{\partial y}\right)^2$

12. $h^3 \left(\dfrac{\partial}{\partial x} \right)^3 + 3h^2 k \left(\dfrac{\partial}{\partial x} \right)^2 \dfrac{\partial}{\partial y} + 3hk^2 \dfrac{\partial}{\partial x} \left(\dfrac{\partial}{\partial y} \right)^2 + k^3 \left(\dfrac{\partial}{\partial y} \right)^3$

13. 8   **14.** 4   **15.** 4   **16.** 1

Chapter VI, §3

1. xy **2.** 1   **3.** xy **4.** $x^2 + y^2$

5. $1 + x + y + \dfrac{x^2}{2} + xy + \dfrac{y^2}{2}$ **6.** $1 - \dfrac{y^2}{2}$ **7.** x

8. $y + xy$ **9.** $x + xy + 2y^2$ **10.** Yes, 0

11. (a) Yes, 0   (b) Yes, 1   **12.** Yes, 0   **13.** Yes, 0

14. $1 + x + \dfrac{x^2}{2} - \dfrac{y^2}{2} + \dfrac{x^3}{6} - \dfrac{xy^2}{2}$ **15.** 0

17. Terms up to degree 2 given in text. Term of degree 3 is $\tfrac{1}{3}(x + 2y)^3$.

20. (a) $X + t(Y - X), 0 \leq t \leq 1$

(b) By the mean value theorem applied to the function

$$g(t) = f(X + t(Y - X)),$$

we get

$$f(Y) - f(X) = (\operatorname{grad} f(Z)) \cdot (Y - X)$$

for some Z on the line segment. Now use the Schwarz inequality.

Chapter VI, §4

1. First observe that for each point X we have

$$f(X) - f(O) = \int_0^1 Df(tX)\, dt,$$

where $D = x_1 D_1 + \cdots + x_n D_n$. Assuming that $f(O) = 0$, and repeating the argument, assuming that $\nabla f(O) = 0$, we obtain

$$f(X) = \int_0^1 \int_0^1 t D^2 f(stX)\, ds\, dt.$$

Thus we find

$$f(X) = \sum_{i,j=1}^{n} h_{ij}(X) x_i x_j,$$

where

$$h_{ij}(X) = \int_0^1 \int_0^1 t D_i D_j f(stX)\, ds\, dt, \qquad \text{if } i \neq j,$$

$$h_{ij}(X) = \int_0^1 \int_0^1 \tfrac{1}{2} t D_i D_j f(stX)\, ds\, dt, \qquad \text{if } i = j.$$

We have $h_{ij} = h_{ji}$ because $D_i D_j = D_j D_i$.

Chapter VII, §1

1. (2, 1), neither max nor min

2. $((2n + 1)\pi, 1)$ and $(2n\pi, 1)$, neither max nor min

3. $(0, 0, 0)$, min, value 0

4. $(\sqrt{2}/2, \sqrt{2}/2)$, neither local max nor min. [*Hint:* Change variables, letting $u = x + y$ and $v = x - y$. Then the critical point is at $(\sqrt{2}, 0)$, and in the (u, v)-plane, near this point, the function increases in one direction, and decreases in the other.]

5. All points of form $(0, t, -t)$, neither max nor min.

6. All (x, y, z) with $x^2 + y^2 + z^2 = 2n\pi$ are local max, value 1.
All (x, y, z) with $x^2 + y^2 + z^2 = (2n + 1)\pi$ are local min, value -1.

7. All points $(x, 0)$ and $(0, y)$ are mins, value 0.

8. $(0, 0)$, min, value 0

9. (t, t), min, value 0

10. $(0, n\pi)$, neither max nor min

11. $(1/2, 0)$, neither max nor min

12. $(0, 0, 0)$, max, value 1

13. $(0, 0, 0)$, min, value 1

Chapter VII, §2

1. $x^2 + 4xy - y^2$

2. At $((2n + 1)\pi, 1)$, $-xy$. At $(2n\pi, 1)$, $+xy$.

3. $x^2 + y^2 + z^2$

4. $\dfrac{1}{\sqrt{2}} e^{-1/2} \left(\dfrac{x^2}{2} + 3xy + \dfrac{y^2}{2} \right)$

5. $xy + xz$

6. At (a, b, c) such that $a^2 + b^2 + c^2 = 2n\pi$, the form is

$$-2(a^2x^2 + b^2y^2 + c^2z^2) - 4(abxy + acxz + bcyz).$$

At the point (a, b, c) such that $a^2 + b^2 + c^2 = (2n + 1)\pi$, the form is

$$2(a^2x^2 + b^2y^2 + c^2z^2) + 4(abxy + acxz + bcyz).$$

7. At points $(a, 0)$ we get a^2y^2. At points $(0, b)$, we get x^2b^2.

8. y^2 **9.** 0   **10.** $\pm xy$ **11.** $x^2 + 2y^2$

12. $-x^2 - y^2 - z^2$ **13.** $x^2 + y^2 + z^2$

Chapter VII, §3

1. Min $= -2$ at $(-1, -1)$, max $= 2$ at $(1, 1)$

2. None

3. Max $\frac{1}{2}$ at $(\sqrt{2}/2, \sqrt{2}/2)$ and $(-\sqrt{2}/2, -\sqrt{2}/2)$

4. Max at $(\frac{1}{2}, \frac{1}{3})$, no min

5. Min 0 at $(0, 0)$, max $2/e$ at $(0, \pm 1)$, rel. max at $(\pm 1, 0)$

6. Max $= 1$ at $(1, 0)$, min $= 1/9$ at $(3, 0)$

7. (a) max (b) neither (c) neither (d) min

8. $t = (2n + 1)\pi$, so $(-1, 0, 1)$ and $(-1, 0, -1)$

Chapter VII, §4

1. $-1/\sqrt{2}$ **2.** $1 + 1/\sqrt{2}$ **3.** at $(\frac{5}{3}, \frac{2}{3}, \frac{1}{3})$ min $= 12$

4. $X = \frac{1}{3}(A + B + C)$, min value is $\frac{2}{3}(A^2 + B^2 + C^2 - AB - AC - BC)$

5. 45 at $\pm(\sqrt{3}, \sqrt{6})$ **6.** $(\frac{2}{3})^{3/2}$ at $\sqrt{\frac{2}{3}}(1, 1, 1)$ **7.** Min 0, max 0

8. Max at $(\pi/8, -\pi/8)$, value $2\cos^2(\pi/8)$; min at $(5\pi/8, 3\pi/8)$ value $\cos^2(5\pi/8) + \cos^2(3\pi/8)$

9. $(0, 0, \pm1)$ **10.** No min, max $= \frac{1}{4}$ at $(\frac{1}{2}, \frac{1}{2})$ **11.** 1

12. Max $= \sqrt{3}$ at $\sqrt{3}/3(1, 1, 1)$, min $= -\sqrt{3}$ at $-\sqrt{3}/3(1, 1, 1)$.

17. $25/52$ **18.** $d^2/(a^2 + b^2 + c^2)$

19. Closest: $(\pm\frac{1}{2}\sqrt{2}, \pm\frac{1}{2}\sqrt{2})$, farthest: $(\pm\sqrt{2}, \mp\sqrt{2})$

Chapter VIII, §2

2. (a) $A - B$, $(1, -1)$ (b) $\frac{1}{2}A + \frac{3}{2}B$, $(\frac{1}{2}, \frac{3}{2})$
   (c) $A + B$, $(1, 1)$ (d) $3A + 2B$, $(3, 2)$

3. (a) $(\frac{1}{3}, -\frac{1}{3}, \frac{1}{3})$ (b) $(1, 0, 1)$ (c) $(\frac{1}{3}, -\frac{1}{3}, -\frac{2}{3})$

7. $(3, 5)$ **8.** $(-5, 3)$

Chapter IX, §1

1. $A + B = \begin{pmatrix} 0 & 7 & 1 \\ 0 & 1 & 1 \end{pmatrix}$, $3B = \begin{pmatrix} -3 & 15 & -6 \\ 3 & 3 & -3 \end{pmatrix}$

$-2B = \begin{pmatrix} 2 & -10 & 4 \\ -2 & -2 & 2 \end{pmatrix}$, $A + 2B = \begin{pmatrix} -1 & 12 & -1 \\ 1 & 2 & 0 \end{pmatrix}$

$2A + B = \begin{pmatrix} 1 & 9 & 4 \\ -1 & 1 & 3 \end{pmatrix}$, $A - B = \begin{pmatrix} 2 & -3 & 5 \\ -2 & -1 & 3 \end{pmatrix}$

$A - 2B = \begin{pmatrix} 3 & -8 & 7 \\ -3 & -2 & 4 \end{pmatrix}$, $B - A = \begin{pmatrix} -2 & 3 & -5 \\ 2 & 1 & -3 \end{pmatrix}$

2. $A + B = \begin{pmatrix} 0 & 0 \\ 2 & -2 \end{pmatrix}$, $3B = \begin{pmatrix} -3 & 3 \\ 0 & -9 \end{pmatrix}$

$-2B = \begin{pmatrix} 2 & -2 \\ 0 & 6 \end{pmatrix}$, $A + 2B = \begin{pmatrix} -1 & 1 \\ 2 & -5 \end{pmatrix}$

$A - B = \begin{pmatrix} 2 & -2 \\ 2 & 4 \end{pmatrix}$, $B - A = \begin{pmatrix} -2 & 2 \\ -2 & -4 \end{pmatrix}$

Chapter IX, §2

3. ${}^tA = \begin{pmatrix} 1 & -1 \\ 2 & 0 \\ 3 & 2 \end{pmatrix}$, ${}^tB = \begin{pmatrix} -1 & 1 \\ 5 & 1 \\ -2 & -1 \end{pmatrix}$

4. ${}^tA = \begin{pmatrix} 1 & 2 \\ -1 & 1 \end{pmatrix}$, ${}^tB = \begin{pmatrix} -1 & 0 \\ 1 & -3 \end{pmatrix}$

7. Same   **8.** $\begin{pmatrix} 0 & 2 \\ 0 & -2 \end{pmatrix}$,   same

9. $A + {}^tA = \begin{pmatrix} 2 & 1 \\ 1 & 2 \end{pmatrix}$, $\qquad B + {}^tB = \begin{pmatrix} -2 & 1 \\ 1 & -6 \end{pmatrix}$

11. Rows of A: $(1, 2, 3)$, $(-1, 0, 2)$. Columns of A:

$$\begin{pmatrix} 1 \\ -1 \end{pmatrix}, \quad \begin{pmatrix} 2 \\ 0 \end{pmatrix}, \quad \begin{pmatrix} 3 \\ 2 \end{pmatrix}$$

Chapter IX, §3

1. mn; $\{E_{ij}\}$ where E_{ij} has component 1 at the (i, j) place and 0 otherwise

2. $n^2 - n$ $\qquad\qquad\qquad\qquad$ **3.** $n(n + 1)/2$

Chapter IX, §4

1. $IA = AI = A$ $\qquad\qquad\qquad$ **2.** 0

3. (a) $\begin{pmatrix} 3 & 2 \\ 4 & 1 \end{pmatrix}$ (b) $\begin{pmatrix} 1 & 0 \\ 1 & 4 \end{pmatrix}$ (c) $\begin{pmatrix} 3 & 3 & 37 \\ 1 & 1 & -18 \end{pmatrix}$

5. $AB = \begin{pmatrix} 4 & 2 \\ 5 & -1 \end{pmatrix}$, $\qquad BA = \begin{pmatrix} 2 & 4 \\ 4 & 1 \end{pmatrix}$

6. $AC = CA = \begin{pmatrix} 7 & 14 \\ 21 & -7 \end{pmatrix}$, $\qquad BC = CB = \begin{pmatrix} 14 & 0 \\ 7 & 7 \end{pmatrix}$.

$\quad$ If $C = xI$, where x is a number, then $AC = CA = xA$.

7. $(3, 1, 5)$, first row $\qquad\qquad$ **8.** Second row, third row, i-th row

11. $A^2 = \begin{pmatrix} 0 & 0 & 1 \\ 0 & 0 & 0 \\ 0 & 0 & 0 \end{pmatrix}$, $\quad A^3 = O$ matrix. $\quad$ If $B = \begin{pmatrix} 0 & 1 & 1 & 1 \\ 0 & 0 & 1 & 1 \\ 0 & 0 & 0 & 1 \\ 0 & 0 & 0 & 0 \end{pmatrix}$ then

$B^2 = \begin{pmatrix} 0 & 0 & 1 & 1 \\ 0 & 0 & 0 & 1 \\ 0 & 0 & 0 & 0 \\ 0 & 0 & 0 & 0 \end{pmatrix}$, $\quad B^3 = \begin{pmatrix} 0 & 0 & 0 & 1 \\ 0 & 0 & 0 & 0 \\ 0 & 0 & 0 & 0 \\ 0 & 0 & 0 & 0 \end{pmatrix}$ and $B^4 = O$.

12. (a) $\begin{pmatrix} 9 \\ 5 \end{pmatrix}$ (b) $\begin{pmatrix} 3 \\ 1 \end{pmatrix}$ (c) $\begin{pmatrix} x_2 \\ 0 \end{pmatrix}$ (d) $\begin{pmatrix} 0 \\ x_1 \end{pmatrix}$

13. (a) $\begin{pmatrix} 2 \\ 4 \end{pmatrix}$ (b) $\begin{pmatrix} 4 \\ 6 \end{pmatrix}$ (c) $\begin{pmatrix} 3 \\ 5 \end{pmatrix}$

14. (a) $\begin{pmatrix} 3 \\ 1 \\ 2 \end{pmatrix}$ (b) $\begin{pmatrix} 12 \\ 3 \\ 9 \end{pmatrix}$ (c) $\begin{pmatrix} 5 \\ 4 \\ 8 \end{pmatrix}$

15. Second column of A **16.** i-th column of A

Chapter X, §1

1. (a) $\cos x$ (b) e^x (c) $1/x$
2. (a) $e^x - 1$ (b) $\arctan x$ (c) $\sin x$
3. (a) 11 (b) 13 (c) 6
4. (a) $(e, 1)$ (b) $(1, 0)$ (c) $(1/e, -1)$
5. (a) $(e + 1, 3)$ (b) $(e^2 + 2, 6)$ (c) $(1, 0)$
6. (a) $(2, 0)$ (b) $(\pi e, \pi)$
7. (a) 1 (b) 11
8. Ellipse $9x^2 + 4y^2 = 36$ **9.** Line $x = 2y$
10. Circle $x^2 + y^2 = e^2$, circle $x^2 + y^2 = e^{2c}$
11. Cylinder, radius 1, z-axis = axis of cylinder
12. Circle $x^2 + y^2 = 1$

Chapter X, §2

1. All except (c), (g)
4. If u is one element such that $Tu = w$, then the set of all such elements is the set of elements $u + v$ where $Tv = 0$.
8. Only Ex. 8
9. If $F(A) = 0$, image = point $F(P)$.   If $F(A) \neq 0$, image is the line $F(P) + tF(A)$.
12. Parallelogram whose vertices are $B, 3A, 3A + B, 0$
13. Parallelogram whose vertices are $0, 2B, 5A, 5A + 2B$

Chapter X, §3

6. Constant functions
7. Ker D^2 = polynomials of deg ≤ 1, Ker D^n = polynomials of

$$\deg \leq n - 1$$

9. Constant multiples of e^x

10. Constant multiples of e^{ax}

Chapter XI, §1
1. (a) $(5, 3)$ (b) $(5, 0)$ (c) $(5, 1)$ (d) $(0, -3)$

Chapter XI, §2

1. (a) $\begin{pmatrix} 1 & 0 & 0 & 0 \\ 0 & 1 & 0 & 0 \end{pmatrix}$ (b) $\begin{pmatrix} 1 & 0 & 0 & 0 \\ 0 & 1 & 0 & 0 \\ 0 & 0 & 1 & 0 \end{pmatrix}$

(c) $3I$ (d) $7I$ (e) $-I$ (f) $\begin{pmatrix} 1 & 0 & 0 & 0 \\ 0 & 1 & 0 & 0 \\ 0 & 0 & 0 & 0 \\ 0 & 0 & 0 & 0 \end{pmatrix}$

2. (a) $\begin{pmatrix} 0 & -1 \\ 1 & 0 \end{pmatrix}$ (b) $\dfrac{1}{\sqrt 2}\begin{pmatrix} 1 & -1 \\ 1 & 1 \end{pmatrix}$ (c) $\begin{pmatrix} -1 & 0 \\ 0 & -1 \end{pmatrix}$ (d) $\begin{pmatrix} -1 & 0 \\ 0 & -1 \end{pmatrix}$

(e) $\dfrac{1}{2}\begin{pmatrix} 1 & \sqrt 3 \\ -\sqrt 3 & 1 \end{pmatrix}$ (f) $\dfrac{1}{2}\begin{pmatrix} \sqrt 3 & -1 \\ 1 & \sqrt 3 \end{pmatrix}$ (g) $\dfrac{1}{\sqrt 2}\begin{pmatrix} -1 & 1 \\ -1 & -1 \end{pmatrix}$

3. $\begin{pmatrix} \cos\theta & \sin\theta \\ -\sin\theta & \cos\theta \end{pmatrix}$ 4. $\dfrac{1}{\sqrt 2}(-1,3)$ 5. $(-3,-1)$

Chapter XII, §3

1. (a) $x = -\tfrac13, y = \tfrac23, z = -\tfrac13$
   (b) $x = \tfrac{5}{12}, y = -\tfrac{1}{12}, z = \tfrac{1}{12}$

Chapter XII, §4

1. (a) -20 (b) 5 (c) 4 (d) 5 (e) -76
2. (a) -18 (b) 45 (c) 0 (d) 0
3. $a_{11}a_{22}\cdots a_{nn}$ 4. 1
6. $a_{11}a_{22}\cdots a_{nn}$ 7. 1   8. $t^2 + 8t + 5$

Chapter XII, §5

1. (a) 1 (b) 1 (c) -1 (d) 1 (e) 1 (f) 1

2. (a) $\begin{bmatrix} 1 & 2 & 3 \\ 3 & 1 & 2 \end{bmatrix}$ (b) $\begin{bmatrix} 1 & 2 & 3 \\ 2 & 3 & 1 \end{bmatrix}$ (c) $\begin{bmatrix} 1 & 2 & 3 \\ 3 & 2 & 1 \end{bmatrix}$ (d) $\begin{bmatrix} 1 & 2 & 3 & 4 \\ 3 & 1 & 2 & 4 \end{bmatrix}$

(e) $\begin{bmatrix} 1 & 2 & 3 & 4 \\ 2 & 1 & 4 & 3 \end{bmatrix}$ (f) $\begin{bmatrix} 1 & 2 & 3 & 4 \\ 4 & 2 & 1 & 3 \end{bmatrix}$

Chapter XII, §9

1. (a) $-\dfrac{1}{20}\begin{pmatrix} 4 & 1 & -7 \\ -4 & -6 & 2 \\ 12 & 2 & 6 \end{pmatrix}$ (b) $\dfrac15\begin{pmatrix} 2 & 23 & -11 \\ 1 & 19 & -8 \\ 0 & -10 & 5 \end{pmatrix}$

(c) $\dfrac14\begin{pmatrix} 3 & 2 & -9 \\ 1 & 2 & -3 \\ -2 & -4 & 10 \end{pmatrix}$ (d) $\dfrac15\begin{pmatrix} 5 & -16 & 3 \\ 0 & 7 & -1 \\ 0 & -2 & 1 \end{pmatrix}$

(e) $-\dfrac{1}{76}\begin{pmatrix} 0 & -19 & 0 \\ -32 & -14 & 12 \\ 28 & 17 & -20 \end{pmatrix}$

3. $\dfrac{1}{ad-bc}\begin{pmatrix} d & -b \\ -c & a \end{pmatrix}$

Chapter XIII, §2

1. (a) $\begin{pmatrix} 1 & 1 \\ 2xy & x^2 \end{pmatrix}$　　(b) $\begin{pmatrix} \cos x & 0 \\ -y \sin xy & -x \sin xy \end{pmatrix}$　　(c) $\begin{pmatrix} ye^{xy} & xe^{xy} \\ 1/x & 0 \end{pmatrix}$

(d) $\begin{pmatrix} z & 0 & x \\ y & x & 0 \\ 0 & z & y \end{pmatrix}$　　(e) $\begin{pmatrix} yz & xz & xy \\ 2xz & 0 & x^2 \end{pmatrix}$

(f) $\begin{pmatrix} yz \cos xyz & xz \cos xyz & yx \cos xyz \\ z & 0 & x \end{pmatrix}$

2. (a) $\begin{pmatrix} 1 & 1 \\ 4 & 1 \end{pmatrix}$　　(b) $\begin{pmatrix} -1 & 0 \\ -\dfrac{\pi}{2} \sin \dfrac{\pi^2}{2} & -\pi \sin \dfrac{\pi^2}{2} \end{pmatrix}$　　(c) $\begin{pmatrix} 4e^4 & e^4 \\ 1 & 0 \end{pmatrix}$

(d) $\begin{pmatrix} -1 & 0 & 1 \\ 1 & 1 & 0 \\ 0 & -1 & 1 \end{pmatrix}$　　(e) $\begin{pmatrix} 1 & -2 & -2 \\ -4 & 0 & 4 \end{pmatrix}$　　(f) $\begin{pmatrix} 8 & 4\pi & 2\pi \\ 4 & 0 & \pi \end{pmatrix}$

5. $x = 0$, y arbitrary; also all points with $x = 2y$

7. $\begin{pmatrix} \cos \theta & -r \sin \theta \\ \sin \theta & r \cos \theta \end{pmatrix}$, r; determinant vanishes only for $r = 0$.

8. $\begin{pmatrix} \sin \varphi \cos \theta & -r \sin \varphi \sin \theta & r \cos \varphi \cos \theta \\ \cos \varphi & 0 & -r \sin \varphi \\ \sin \varphi \sin \theta & r \sin \varphi \cos \theta & r \cos \varphi \sin \theta \end{pmatrix}$

Determinant $r^2 \sin \varphi$

Chapter XIII, §4

1. Yes in all cases
5. Letting $y = \varphi(x)$, we have

$$\varphi''(x) = \frac{-1}{D_2 f(x,y)^2}\left[\begin{array}{l} D_2 f(x,y)(D_1^2 f(x,y) + D_2 D_1 f(x,y)\varphi'(x)) \\ -D_1 f(x,y)(D_1 D_2 f(x,y) + D_2^2 f(x,y)\varphi'(x)) \end{array} \right].$$

9. (a) We have $2x - y - xy' + 2yy' = 0$. This yields

$$\varphi'(1) = 0.$$

(e) $\varphi'(0) = -1$

10. (a) both -1 (c) both $\frac{1}{3}$

11. $3x^2 D_1\varphi(y, z) - 4y + 2z = 0$ so $D_1\varphi(1, 1) = \frac{1}{3}$

Chapter XIV, §2

1. (a) 12 (b) $\frac{11}{5}$ (c) $\frac{1}{10}$ (d) $2 + \pi^2/2$ (e) $\frac{5}{6}$ (f) $\pi/4$

3. (a) $-3\pi/2$ (b) $e - 1/e$ (c) $\pi^2 - \frac{40}{9}$ (d) $\frac{63}{32}$

4. $9\frac{3}{4} - \frac{28}{3}$

6. (a) $\frac{49}{20}$ (b) $e^{-3}/3 - e^{-2}/2 - e^3/3 + e^2/2$

(c) $1 - \cos 2$ (d) 0 (e) 1 (f) $\frac{1}{6}$

7. $3\pi/8$

8. (a) $\log 2$ (b) $\frac{1}{3}$ (c) π (d) $-\frac{1}{3}$ (e) $\log \frac{27}{16}$

Chapter XIV, §3

1. $(e - 1)\pi$ **2.** $3\pi/2$ **3.** $\pi(1 - e^{-a^2})$ **4.** π

5. $2ka^4/3$ **6.** $3k\pi a^4/2$ **7.** $k\pi/4$ **8.** πa^2

9. $\pi a^4/8$ **10.** $a^3\sqrt{2}/6$ **11.** $a^2(\pi + 8)/4$

12. $a^3(15\pi + 32)/24$ **13.** $2a^2$

14. $(3\pi + 20 - 16\sqrt{2})2\sqrt{2}\, a^3/9$

Chapter XIV, §5

1. π **2.** (a) $\frac{128}{3}$ (b) 128

3. (a) 42 (b) 120   **4.** 2   **6.** πab **7.** $\frac{99}{2}$

8. 1500π **9.** $15\pi ab$ **11.** πab^2 ⬭

Chapter XIV, §6

1. (a) $\begin{pmatrix} 1 & 0 & 0 \\ 0 & \rho\cos\varphi & \sin\varphi \\ 0 & -\rho\sin\varphi & \cos\varphi \end{pmatrix}$ and determinant is ρ.

(b) $\iiint_A f(G(\theta, \varphi, \rho))\rho \, d\rho \, d\varphi \, d\theta = \iiint_{G(A)} f(\theta, r, z) \, dz \, dr \, d\theta$

2. 0   **3.** $ka^4\pi$ **4.** $2\pi k(b^2 - a^2)$ **5.** $\pi ba^4/4$

6. $k\pi a^4/2$ **7.** $\pi/8$ **8.** $2\pi\left[-\frac{1}{3}(1 - r_0^2)^{3/2} + \frac{1}{3} - \frac{r_0^4}{4}\right]$

where $r_0^2 = \dfrac{-1 + \sqrt{5}}{2}$

9. $\frac{2}{9}a^3(3\pi - 4)$ **10.** πa^3

11. (a) $\pi/3$ (b) $2\pi\sqrt{2}/3$ (c) $\pi/2$ (d) $\pi/32$

12. (a) 25 (b) 15/2 (c) $7a^2b^3/3$

13. $4\pi/3$ **14.** $abck$ **15.** $\frac{4}{3}\pi abc$ **16.** $\frac{4}{3}\pi a^3 \cdot 14$

17. (a) $\frac{1}{3}$ (c) $\frac{2}{3}$ (d) $\frac{2}{3}$ **18.** (a) $\frac{7}{3}$ (b) 3

Chapter XV, §1

1. (a) -4 (b) 4 (c) 4π (d) π (e) 8 (f) πab
3. 2π

Chapter XVI, §2

1. dim 4

2. (a) $\dfrac{1}{\sqrt{3}}(1, 1, -1)$ and $\dfrac{1}{\sqrt{2}}(1, 0, 1)$

  (b) $\dfrac{1}{\sqrt{6}}(2, 1, 1)$, $\dfrac{1}{5\sqrt{3}}(-1, 7, -5)$

3. $\dfrac{1}{\sqrt{6}}(1, 2, 1, 0)$ and $\dfrac{1}{\sqrt{31}}(-1, -2, 5, 1)$

4. $\dfrac{1}{\sqrt{2}}(1, 1, 0, 0)$, $\tfrac{1}{2}(1, -1, 1, 1)$, $\dfrac{1}{\sqrt{18}}(-2, 2, 3, 4)$

5. $\sqrt{80}\,(t^2 - 3t/4)$, $\sqrt{3}\,t$
6. $\sqrt{80}\,(t^2 - 3t/4)$, $\sqrt{3}\,t$, $10t^2 - 12t + 3$

Chapter XVI, §3

1. (a) 2 (b) 2 (c) 2 (d) 1
3. n **4.** (a) 1 (b) 2 (c) 1 (d) 0
5. (a) 1 (b) 1 (c) 0 (d) 2   **6.** $n - 1$

Chapter XVI, §4

1. $\left(\displaystyle\int_{-\pi}^{\pi} (f(x) + g(x))^2\, dx\right)^{1/2} \leq \left(\displaystyle\int_{-\pi}^{\pi} f(x)^2\, dx\right)^{1/2} + \left(\displaystyle\int_{-\pi}^{\pi} g(x)^2\, dx\right)^{1/2}$

4. (a) $\dfrac{x}{2} = \sin x - \dfrac{\sin 2x}{2} + \cdots + (-1)^n\, \dfrac{\sin nx}{n} + \cdots$

  (b) $x^2 = \dfrac{\pi^2}{3} - 4\left(\cos x - \dfrac{\cos 2x}{2^2} + \cdots + (-1)^{n+1}\, \dfrac{\cos nx}{n^2} + \cdots\right)$

  (c) $x = \dfrac{\pi}{2} - \dfrac{4}{\pi}\left(\cos x + \dfrac{\cos 3x}{3^2} + \cdots + \dfrac{\cos (2n + 1)x}{(2n + 1)^2} + \cdots\right)$

  (f) $\cos x = \dfrac{4}{\pi}\left(\dfrac{1}{2} + \dfrac{\cos 2x}{3} + \cdots + (-1)^{n-1}\, \dfrac{\cos 2nx}{4n^2 - 1} + \cdots\right)$

  (g) $\sin^3 x = \tfrac{3}{4}\sin x - \tfrac{1}{4}\sin 3x$

Index

Index

II

ABCDE698